Study Guide with Selected Solutions

General, Organic, and Biological
Chemistry
Structures of Life

Second Edition

Karen C. Timberlake

Professor Emeritus,
Los Angeles Valley College

PEARSON

Prentice Hall

Upper Saddle River, NJ 07458

Acquisitions Editor: Jim Smith

Senior Editor: Kent Porter-Hamann

Editor-in-Chief: Nicole Folchetti

Project Editor: Katherine Brayton

Managing Editor: Corinne Benson

Assistant Editor: Jessica Neumann

Marketing Manager: Scott Dustan and Liz Averbeck

Production Supervisor: Mary O'Connell

Cover Designer: Jana Anderson

Manufacturing Coordinator: Stacy Wong

Cover Photographs: Getty, Laura Ronchi Collection, Bepi Ghiotti-Photographer

Cover Illustration: Imagineering Media Services, Inc.

© 2007 Pearson Education, Inc.
Pearson Prentice Hall
Pearson Education, Inc.
Upper Saddle River, NJ 07458

www.prenhall.com

Many of the designations used by manufacturers and sellers to distinguish their products are claimed as trademarks. Where those designations appear in this book, and the publisher was aware of a trademark claim, the designations have been printed in initial caps or all caps.

10 9 8 7 6 5 4

ISBN 0-8053-4883-2

This Study Guide is intended to accompany *General, Organic, and Biological Chemistry: Structures of Life,* Second Edition. The purpose of this Study Guide is to provide students with additional learning resources that increase their understanding of the concepts. Each section in the Study Guide is correlated with a chapter in the text. Within each section, there are Learning Exercises that focus on problem solving and promote an understanding of the chemical principles of that Learning Goal. A Checklist of learning goals and a multiple-choice Practice Test provide a review of the entire chapter content. Finally, the Answers and Solutions to Selected Text Problems give the odd-numbered solutions for problems at the end of each chapter in the text.

I hope that this Study Guide will help in the learning of chemistry. If you wish to make comments or corrections, or ask questions, you can send me an e-mail message at khemist@aol.com.

Karen C. Timberlake
Los Angeles Valley College
Valley Glen, CA

"One must learn by doing the thing;
though you think you know it, you
have no certainty until you try."
—*Sophocles*

Here you are in a chemistry class with your textbook in front of you. Perhaps you have already been assigned some reading or some problems to do in the book. Looking through the chapter, you may see words, terms, and pictures that are new to you. This may very well be your first experience with a science class like chemistry. At this point you may have some questions about what you can do to learn chemistry. This Study Guide is written with that consideration in mind.

Learning chemistry is similar to learning a new sport such as tennis or skiing or diving. If I asked you how you learn to play tennis or ski or drive a car, you would probably tell me that you need to practice often. It is the same with learning chemistry, where understanding the chemical ideas and successfully solving the problems depend on the time and effort you invest. If you practice every day, you will find that learning chemistry is an exciting experience and a way to understand the current issues of the environment, health, and medicine.

Manage Your Study Time

I often recommend a study system to students: read one section of the text and immediately practice the questions and problems that go with it. In this way, you concentrate on a small amount of information and actively use what you learned to answer questions. This helps you organize and review the information without being overwhelmed by the entire chapter. It is important to understand each section because they build like steps. Information presented in each chapter proceeds from the basic to the more complex. Perhaps you can only study three or four sections of the chapter. As long as you also practice doing some problems at the same time, the information will stay with you.

Form a Study Group

I highly recommend that you form a study group in the first week of your chemistry class. Working with your peers will help you use the language of chemistry. Scheduling a time to meet each week helps you study and prepare to discuss problems. You will be able to teach some things to the other students in the group, and sometimes they will help you understand a topic that puzzles you. You won't always understand a concept right away. Your group will help you see your way through it. Most of all, a study group creates a strong support system whereby students like you get together to help each other complete the class successfully.

Go to Office Hours

Try to go to your tutor's and/or professor's office hours. Your professor wants you to understand and enjoy learning this material and should have office hours. Often a tutor is assigned to a class or there are tutors available at your college. Don't be intimidated. Going to see a tutor or your professor is one of the best ways to clarify what you need to learn in chemistry.

Now you are ready to sit down and study chemistry. Let's go over some methods that can help you learn chemistry. This Study Guide is written specifically to help you understand and practice the chemical concepts that are presented in your class and in your text. Some of the exercises teach basic skills; others encourage you to extend your scientific curiosity. The following features are part of this Study Guide.

1. Study Goals

The Study Goals give you an overview of what the chapter is about and what you can expect to accomplish when you complete your study and learning of a chapter.

2. Think About It

Each chapter in the Study Guide has a group of questions that encourage you to think about some of the ideas and practical applications of the chemical concepts you are going to study. You may find that you already have knowledge of chemistry in some of the areas. That will be helpful to you. Other questions give you an overview of the chemistry ideas you will be learning.

3. Key Terms

Each chapter in the Study Guide introduces Key Terms. As you complete the description of the Key Terms, you will have an overview of the topics you will be studying in that chapter. Because many of the Key Terms may be new to you, this is an opportunity to review their meaning.

4. Chapter Sections

Each section of the chapter begins with the Key Concepts to illustrate the important ideas in that section. The summary of concepts is written to guide you through each of the learning activities. When you are ready to begin your study, read the matching section in the textbook and review the sample exercises in the text.

5. Learning Exercises

The Learning Exercises give you an opportunity to practice problem solving related to the chemical principles in the chapter. Each set of Exercises reviews one chemical principle. The answers are found immediately following each exercise. Check your answers right away. If they don't match the answer in the Study Guide, go back to the textbook and review the material for that section again. It is important to make corrections before you go on. In learning tennis, you hit the ball a lot from the baseline before you learn to volley or serve. Chemistry, too, involves a layering of skills such that each one is understood before the next one can be learned.

At various times, you will notice some essay questions that illustrate one of the concepts. I believe that writing out your ideas is a very important way of learning content.

6. Checklist

Use the Checklist to check your understanding of the Study Goals. This gives you an overview of the major topics in the section. If something does not sound familiar, go back and review. One aspect of being a strong problem-solver is the ability to check your knowledge and understanding as you study.

7. Practice Test

A Practice Test is found at the end of each chapter. When you have learned the material in a chapter, you can apply your understanding to the Practice Test. If the results of this test indicate that you know the material, you are ready to proceed to the next chapter. If, however, the results indicate further study is needed, you can repeat the learning Exercises in the sections you still need to work on. Answers for all of the questions are included at the end of the Practice Test.

Table of Contents

1

Measurements

Study Goals

- Describe the scientific method.
- Learn the units and abbreviations for the metric (SI) system.
- Distinguish between measured numbers and exact numbers.
- Determine the number of significant figures in a measurement.
- Use prefixes to change base units to larger or smaller units.
- Write conversion factors from the units in an equality.
- In problem solving, convert the initial unit of a measurement to another unit.
- Round off a calculator answer to report an answer with the correct number of significant figures.
- Calculate temperatures values in degrees Celsius and kelvins.

Think About It

1. What kind of device would you use to measure each of the following: your height, your weight, and the quantity of water to make soup?

2. How do you determine the amount of money in your wallet?

3. When you do a measurement, why should you write down a number and a unit?

4. Why does oil float on water?

Key Terms

Match each the following key terms with the correct definition.

    A. metric system   **B.** exact number   **C.** significant figures
    D. conversion factor   **E.** density   **F.** absolute zero

1. _____ all the numbers recorded in a measurement including the estimated digit

2. _____ a fraction that gives the equal quantities of a relationship in the numerator and denominator

3. _____ the relationship of the mass of an object to its volume, usually expressed as g/mL

4. _____ a number obtained by counting items or from a definition

5. _____ a decimal system of measurement used throughout the world

6. _____ the lowest temperature possible, which is 0 on the Kelvin scale

Answers   **1.** C   **2.** D   **3.** E   **4.** B   **5.** A   **6.** F

1.1 Scientific Method: Thinking Like a Scientist

- The scientific method is a process of making observations, writing a hypothesis, and testing the hypothesis with experiments.
- A theory develops when experiments that validate a hypothesis are repeated by many scientists with consistent results.

◆ Learning Exercise 1.1

Identify each of the following as observation (O), hypothesis (H), or experiment (E).

a. _____ Sunlight is necessary for the growth of plants.

b. _____ Plants in the shade were shorter than plants in the sun.

c. _____ Plant leaves are covered with aluminum foil and their growth measured.

d. _____ Fertilizer added to plants accelerates their growth.

e. _____ Ozone slows plant growth by interfering with photosynthesis.

f. _____ Ozone causes brown spots on plant leaves.

Answers   **a.** H   **b.** O   **c.** E   **d.** E   **e.** H   **f.** O

1.2 Units of Measurement and Scientific Notation

- In the sciences, physical quantities are described in units of the metric or International System (SI).
- Length or distance is measured in meters (m), volume in liters (L), mass in grams (g), and temperature in Celsius (°C) or kelvin (K).
- A number written in scientific notation has two parts: a coefficient between 1 and 10 followed by a power of 10.
- For numbers greater than 10, the decimal point is moved to the left to give a positive power of 10. For numbers less than 1, the decimal point is moved to the right to give a negative power of 10.

◆ Learning Exercise 1.2A

Indicate the type of measurement in each of the following:

1. length   **2.** mass   **3.** volume   **4.** temperature   **5.** time

a. _____ 45 g   **b.** _____ 8.2 m   **c.** _____ 215°C   **d.** _____ 50 s

e. _____ 45 L   **f.** _____ 825 K   **g.** _____ 8.8 kg   **h.** _____ 2.0 L

Answers   **a.** 2   **b.** 1   **c.** 4   **d.** 5   **e.** 3   **f.** 4   **g.** 2   **h.** 3

◆ Learning Exercise 1.2B

> **Study Note**
>
> **1.** The number 2.5×10^3 means that 2.5 is multiplied by 10^3 (1000).
>
> $$2. \times 1000 = 2500$$
>
> The number 8.2×10^{-2} means that 8.2 is multiplied by 10^{-2} (0.01).
>
> $$8.2 \times 0.01 = 0.082$$
>
> **2.** For a number greater than 10, the decimal point is moved to the left to give a number between 1 and 10 and a positive power of 10. For small numbers less than 1, the decimal point is moved to the right to give a number between 1 and 10 and a negative power of 10.

Write the following measurements in scientific notation:

a. 240 000 cm _____   **b.** 800 m _____   **c.** 230 000 kg _____

d. 50 000 years _____   **e.** 0.002 m _____   **f.** 0.000 0015 g _____

g. 0.08 kg _____   **h.** 0.0001 sec _____

2

Answers   **a.** 2.4×10^5 cm   **b.** 8×10^2 m   **c.** 2.3×10^5 kg   **d.** 5×10^4 years
e. 2×10^{-3} m   **f.** 1.5×10^{-6} g   **g.** 8×10^{-2} kg   **h.** 1×10^{-4} sec

◆ Learning Exercise 1.2C

Circle the larger number in each pair.

a. 2500 or 2.5×10^2 **b.** 0.04 or 4×10^{-3} **c.** 65 000 or 6.5×10^5

d. 0.000 35 or 3.5×10^{-3} **e.** 300 000 or 3×10^6 **f.** 0.002 or 2×10^{-4}

Answers   **a.** 2500   **b.** 0.04   **c.** 6.5×10^5 **d.** 3.5×10^{-3} **e.** 3×10^6 **f.** 0.002

◆ Learning Exercise 1.2D

Write each of the following in standard form:

Example: 2×10^2 m = 200 m and 3×10^{-4} g = 0.0003 g

a. 4×10^3 m _____   **b.** 5.2×10^4 g _____   **c.** 1.8×10^5 g _____

d. 8×10^{-3} L _____   **e.** 6×10^{-2} kg _____   **f.** 3.1×10^{-5} g _____

Answers   **a.** 4000 m   **b.** 52 000 g   **c.** 180 000 g   **d.** 0.008 L   **e.** 0.06 kg   **f.** 0.000 031 g

1.3   Measured Numbers and Significant Figures

- A measured number is obtained when you use a measuring device to determine an amount of some item.
- An exact number is obtained by counting items or from a definition that relates units in the same measuring system.
- There is uncertainty in every measured number, but not in exact numbers.
- Significant figures in a measured number are all the reported figures including the estimated digit.
- Zeros written in front of a nonzero number or zeros that are used as placeholders in a large number are not significant digits.

◆ Learning Exercise 1.3A

Are the numbers in each of the following statements measured (M) or exact (E)?

a. _____ There are 7 days in 1 week.   **b.** _____ A concert lasts for 73 minutes.

c. _____ There are 1000 g in 1 kg.   **d.** _____ The potatoes have a mass of 2.5 kg.

e. _____ A student has 26 CDs.   **f.** _____ The snake is 1.2 m long.

Answers   **a.** E (counted)   **b.** M (use a watch)   **c.** E (metric definition)
d. M (use a balance)   **e.** E (counted)   **f.** M (use a metric ruler)

◆ Learning Exercise 1.3B

Study Note
Significant figures are all the numbers reported in a measurement including the estimated digit. Zeros are significant unless they are placeholders appearing at the beginning of a decimal number or in a large number without a decimal point.
4.255 g (four sig figs)   0.0042 (two sig figs)   46 500 (three sig figs)

State the number of significant figures in the following measured numbers:

    a. 35.24 g _____   **b.** 0.000 080 m _____   **c.** 55 000 m _____   **d.** 805 mL _____

    e. 5.025 L _____   **f.** 0.006 kg _____   **g.** 268 200 mm _____   **h.** 25.0°C _____

Answers   **a.** 4   **b.** 2   **c.** 2   **d.** 3   **e.** 4   **f.** 1   **g.** 4   **h.** 3

1.4 Significant Figures in Calculations

- In a calculation with measured numbers, the number of significant digits given in the answer must match the number of significant figures in the measurement with the fewest significant figures.
- When evaluating a calculator answer, it is important to count the significant figures in the measurements and round off the calculator answer properly.
- Answers in chemical calculations rarely use all the numbers that appear in the calculator. Exact numbers are not included in the determination of the number of significant figures in an answer.

◆ Learning Exercise 1.4A

Study Note
1. To round off a number less than 5, keep the digits you need and drop all the digits that follow. Round 42.8254 to three significant figures → 42.8 (drop 254).
2. If the first number dropped is 5 or greater, keep the proper number of digits and increase the last retained digit by 1. Round 8.4882 to two significant figures → 8.5.
3. In large numbers, maintain the value of the answer by adding nonsignificant zeros. Round 356 835 to three significant figures → 357 000.

Round off each of the following to give **two** significant figures:

    a. 88.75 m _____   **b.** 0.002 923 g _____   **c.** 50.525 g _____

    d. 1.6726 m _____   **e.** 0.001 055 8 kg _____   **f.** 82.08 L _____

Answers   **a.** 89 m   **b.** 0.0029 g   **c.** 51 g   **d.** 1.7 m   **e.** 0.0011 kg   **f.** 82 L

◆ Learning Exercise 1.4B

Study Note

1. An answer from multiplying and dividing has the same number of significant figures as the initial measurement that has the smallest number of significant figures.
 	
    1.5   ×   32.546 = 48.819 → 49   *Answer rounded to two significant figures.*
  two sig figs   *five sig figs*

2. An answer from adding or subtracting has the same number of decimal places as the initial number with the fewest decimal places.   82.223 + 4.1 = 86.323 → 86.3   *Answer rounded to one decimal place.*

Solve each problem and give the answer with the correct number of significant figures:

    a. $1.3 \times 71.5 =$ **b.** $\dfrac{8.00}{4.00} =$

c. $\dfrac{0.082 \times 25.4}{0.116 \times 3.4} =$

d. $\dfrac{3.05 \times 1.86}{118.5} =$

e. $\dfrac{376}{0.0073} =$

f. $38.520 - 11.4 =$

g. $4.2 + 8.15 =$

h. $102.56 + 8.325 - 0.8825 =$

Answers   **a.** 93   **b.** 2.00   **c.** 5.3   **d.** 0.0479   **e.** 52 000   **f.** 27.1   **g.** 12.4   **h.** 110.00

1.5 Prefixes and Equalities

- In the metric system, larger and smaller units use prefixes to change the size of the unit by factors of 10. For example, a prefix such as *centi* or *milli* preceding the unit *meter* gives a smaller length than a meter. A prefix such as *kilo* added to gram gives a unit that measures a mass that is 1000 times greater than a gram.
- Some of the most common metric (SI) prefixes are shown below.

Prefix	Symbol	Meaning	Numerical Value	
mega	M	one million	1 000 000	10^6
kilo	k	one thousand	1000	10^3
deci	d	one-tenth	0.1	10^{-1}
centi	c	one-hundredth	0.01	10^{-2}
milli	m	one-thousandth	0.001	10^{-3}
micro	μ	one-millionth	0.000 001	10^{-6}
nano	n	one-billionth	0.000 000 001	10^{-9}

- An equality contains two units that measure the *same* length, volume, or mass.
- Some common metric equalities are the following: 1 m = 100 cm; 1 L = 1000 mL; 1 kg = 1000 g.
- Some useful metric–U.S. equalities are the following: 2.54 cm = 1 inch; 1 kg = 2.20 lb; 946 mL = 1 quart

◆ Learning Exercise 1.5A

Match the items in column A with those from column B.

	A		B
1. ____	kilo-	**a.**	millimeter
2. ____	one thousand liters	**b.**	0.1 L
3. ____	deciliter	**c.**	one-millionth of a liter
4. ____	milliliter	**d.**	kiloliter
5. ____	centimeter	**e.**	0.01 m
6. ____	one-tenth centimeter	**f.**	1000 g
7. ____	microliter	**g.**	one-thousandth of a liter
8. ____	kilogram	**h.**	one thousand times

Answers   **1. h**   **2. d**   **3. b**   **4. g**
              5. e   **6. a**   **7. c**   **8. f**

◆ **Learning Exercise 1.5B**

Place the following units in order from smallest to largest.

a. kilogram   milligram   gram   _____

b. centimeter   kilometer   millimeter _____

c. dL   mL   L   _____

d. kg   mg μg   _____

Answers   **a.** milligram, gram, kilogram   **b.** millimeter, centimeter, kilometer
                  c. mL, dL, L   **d.** μg, mg, kg

◆ **Learning Exercise 1.5C**

Complete the following metric relationships:

a. 1 L = _____mL   **b.** 1 L = _____dL   **c.** 1 m = _____cm

d. 1 dL = _____mL   **e.** 1 kg = _____g   **f.** 1 cm = _____mm

g. 1 mg = _____μg   **h.** 1 dL = _____L   **i.** 1 m = _____mm

j. 1 cm = _____m

Answers   **a.** 1000   **b.** 10   **c.** 100   **d.** 100   **e.** 1000
                f. 10   **g.** 1000   **h.** 0.1   **i.** 1000   **j.** 0.01

1.6   **Writing Conversion Factors**

- Conversion factors are used in a chemical calculation to change from one unit to another. Each factor represents an equality that is expressed in the form of a fraction.
- Two forms of a conversion factor can be written for any equality. For example, the metric–U.S. equality 2.54 cm = 1 inch can be written as follows:

$$\frac{2.54 \text{ cm}}{1 \text{ inch}} \quad \text{and} \quad \frac{1 \text{ inch}}{2.54 \text{ cm}}$$

◆ **Learning Exercise 1.6A**

Study Note
Metric conversion factors are obtained from metric prefixes. For example, the metric equality 1 m = 100 cm gives the factors $$\frac{1 \text{ m}}{100 \text{ cm}} \quad \text{and} \quad \frac{100 \text{ cm}}{1 \text{ m}}$$

Write two conversion factors for each of the following pairs of units:

     a. millimeters and meters   **b.** kilogram and grams

c. kilograms and pounds   **d.** inches and centimeters

e. centimeters and meters   **f.** milliliters and quarts

g. deciliters and liters   **h.** millimeters and centimeters

Answers   **a.** $\dfrac{1000 \text{ mm}}{1 \text{ m}}$ and $\dfrac{1 \text{ m}}{1000 \text{ mm}}$ **b.** $\dfrac{1000 \text{ g}}{1 \text{ kg}}$ and $\dfrac{1 \text{ kg}}{1000 \text{ g}}$ **c.** $\dfrac{2.20 \text{ lb}}{1 \text{ kg}}$ and $\dfrac{1 \text{ kg}}{2.20 \text{ lb}}$

d. $\dfrac{2.54 \text{ cm}}{1 \text{ in.}}$ and $\dfrac{1 \text{ in.}}{2.54 \text{ cm}}$ **e.** $\dfrac{100 \text{ cm}}{1 \text{ m}}$ and $\dfrac{1 \text{ m}}{100 \text{ cm}}$ **f.** $\dfrac{946 \text{ mL}}{1 \text{ qt}}$ and $\dfrac{1 \text{ qt}}{946 \text{ mL}}$

g. $\dfrac{10 \text{ dL}}{1 \text{ L}}$ and $\dfrac{1 \text{ L}}{10 \text{ dL}}$ **h.** $\dfrac{10 \text{ mm}}{1 \text{ cm}}$ and $\dfrac{1 \text{ cm}}{10 \text{ mm}}$

◆ Learning Exercise 1.6 B

Study Note

Sometimes a statement within a problem gives an equality that is only true for that problem. Then conversion factors can be written that are true only for that problem. For example, a problem states that there are 50 mg of vitamin B in a tablet. The conversion factors are

$$\frac{1 \text{ tablet}}{50 \text{ mg vitamin B}} \quad \text{and} \quad \frac{50 \text{ mg vitamin B}}{1 \text{ tablet}}$$

A problem may also state a percentage that is true for that problem only. Suppose that a problem states that a candy bar contains 45% by mass chocolate. This percentage equality can be written with factors using the same mass unit, such as grams.

$$\frac{45 \text{ g chocolate}}{100 \text{ g candy bar}} \quad \text{and} \quad \frac{100 \text{ g candy bar}}{45 \text{ g chocolate}}$$

Write two conversion factors for each of the following statements:

a. A cracker contains 55% fat by mass.   **b.** In the city, a car gets 14 miles to the gallon.

c. 125 g steak contains 45 g protein.   **d.** 18-karat pink gold contains 25% copper by mass.

Answers   **a.** $\dfrac{55 \text{ g fat}}{100 \text{ g cracker}}$ and $\dfrac{100 \text{ g cracker}}{55 \text{ g fat}}$ **b.** $\dfrac{14 \text{ mi}}{1 \text{ gal}}$ and $\dfrac{1 \text{ gal}}{14 \text{ mi}}$

             c. $\dfrac{45 \text{ g protein}}{125 \text{ g steak}}$ and $\dfrac{125 \text{ g steak}}{45 \text{ g protein}}$ **d.** $\dfrac{25 \text{ g copper}}{100 \text{ g pink gold}}$ and $\dfrac{100 \text{ g pink gold}}{25 \text{ g copper}}$

1.7   Problem Solving

- Conversion factors from metric and/or U.S. relationships and percent can be used to change a quantity expressed in one unit to a quantity expressed in another unit.

The process of solving a problem with units requires the change of the initial unit to one or more units until the final unit of the answer is obtained.

$$\text{Given unit} \xrightarrow{\text{Conversion Factors}} \text{Desired unit}$$

Guide to Problem Solving (GPS) Using Conversion Factors

STEP 1: Identify the given unit and the final unit needed for the answer.
STEP 2: Write a plan showing the sequence of units.
STEP 3: State the appropriate equalities and their conversion factors.
STEP 4: Set up the problem by arranging the factors to cancel units and provide the final unit.

Example: How many liters is 2850 mL?

     STEP 1:   **Given:** 2850 ml   **Need:** liters

     STEP 2:   **Plan:** milliliters $\xrightarrow{\text{Metric factors}}$ liters
     STEP 3:   **Equalities/Conversions Factors:**
                1 L = 1000 mL

                $\dfrac{1 \text{ L}}{1000 \text{ mL}}$ and $\dfrac{1000 \text{ mL}}{1 \text{ L}}$

     STEP 4:   **Set Up Problem:** $2850 \text{ mL} \times \dfrac{1\text{L}}{1000 \text{ mL}} = 2.85 \text{ L}$

◆ Learning Exercise 1.7A

Use metric–metric conversion factors to solve the following problems:

     a. 189 mL = _____L

     b. 2.7 cm = _____mm

     c. 0.0025 L = _____mL

d. 76 mg   = _____g

e. How many meters tall is a person whose height is 175 cm?

f. There are 285 mL in a cup of tea. How many liters is that?

g. An 18-karat ring contains 75% gold by mass. If the total mass of the ring is 13 500 mg, how many grams of gold does the ring contain?

h. You walked 1.5 km on the treadmill at the gym. How many meters did you walk?

Answers	**a.** 0.189 L	**b.** 27 mm	**c.** 2.5 mL	**d.** 0.076 g
	e. 1.75 m	**f.** 0.285 L	**g.** 10.1 g	**h.** 1500 m

◆ **Learning Exercise 1.7B**

Use metric–U.S. conversion factors to solve the following problems:

a. 18 inches = _____cm   **b.** 4.0 qt = _____L   **c.** 275 mL = _____qt

d. 1300 mg = _____lb   **e.** 150 lb = _____kg   **f.** 840 g = _____lb

g. 15 ft = _____cm   **h.** 8.50 oz = _____g

Answers	**a.** 46 cm	**b.** 3.8 L	**c.** 0.291 qt	**d.** 0.0029 lb
	e. 68 kg	**f.** 1.9 lb	**g.** 460 cm	**h.** 241 g

◆ **Learning Exercise 1.7c**

Study Note

1. For setups that require a series of conversion factors, it is helpful to write out the unit plan first. Work from the starting unit to the final unit. Then use a conversion factor for each unit change.

$$\text{Starting unit} \rightarrow \text{unit (1)} \rightarrow \text{unit (2)} = \text{final unit}$$

2. To convert from one unit to another, select conversion factors that cancel the given unit and provide a unit or the final unit for the problem. Several factors may be needed to work the units toward the final unit.

$$\cancel{\text{Starting unit}} \times \frac{\cancel{\text{unit (1)}}}{\cancel{\text{Starting unit}}} \times \frac{\text{unit (2)}}{\cancel{\text{unit (1)}}} = \text{final unit}$$

Use conversion factors to solve the following problems:

a. A piece of plastic tubing measures 120 mm. What is the length of the tubing in inches?

b. A statue weighs 240 pounds. What is the mass of the statue in kilograms?

c. Your friend has a height of 6 feet 3 inches. What is your friend's height in meters?

d. In a triple-bypass surgery, a patient requires 3.00 pints of whole blood. How many milliliters of blood were given if 1 quart = 2 pints?

e. A doctor orders 0.450 g of a sulfa drug. On hand are 150-mg tablets. How many tablets are needed?

f. A mouthwash contains 22% alcohol by volume. How many milliliters of alcohol are in a 1.05-pint bottle of mouthwash if there are 2 pints in 1 quart?

g. An 18-karat gold bracelet has a mass of 2.0 oz. If 18-karat gold contains 75% pure gold, how many grams of pure gold are in the bracelet?

Answers	**a.** 4.7 inches	**b.** 110 kg	**c.** 1.9 m	**d.** 1420 mL
	e. 3 tablets	**f.** 110 mL	**g.** 43 g	

1.8 Density

- The density of a substance is a ratio of its mass to its volume, usually in units of g/mL or g/cm^3 (1 mL is equal to 1 cm^3). For example, the density of sugar is 1.59 g/mL and silver is 10.5 g/mL.

$$\text{Density} = \frac{\text{mass of substance}}{\text{volume of substance}}$$

- Specific gravity (sp gr) is a unitless relationship of the density of a substance divided by the density of water, 1.00 g/mL. We can calculate the specific gravity of sugar as

$$\frac{1.59 \ \text{g/mL (density of sugar)}}{1.00 \ \text{g/mL (density of water)}} = 1.59 \text{ (sp gr of sugar)}$$

Study Note

Density can be used as a factor to convert between the mass (g) and volume (mL) of a substance. The density of silver is 10.5 g/mL. What is the mass of 6.0 mL of silver?

$$6.0 \ \text{mL silver} \times \frac{10.5 \text{ g silver}}{1 \ \text{mL silver}} = 63 \text{ g silver}$$

Density

What is the volume of 25 g of olive oil (D = 0.92 g/mL)?

$$25 \ \text{g olive oil} \times \frac{1 \text{ mL olive oil}}{0.92 \ \text{g olive oil}} = 27 \text{ mL olive oil}$$

◆ Learning Exercise 1.8

Calculate the density or specific gravity, or use density as a conversion factor to solve each of the following:

a. What is the density (g/mL) of glycerol if a 200.0-mL sample has a mass of 252 g?

b. A person with diabetes may produce 5 to 12 liters of urine per day. Calculate the specific gravity of a 100.0-mL sample that has a mass of 100.2 g.

c. A small solid has a mass of 5.5 oz. When placed in a graduated cylinder with a water level of 25.2 mL, the object causes the water level to rise to 43.8 mL. What is the density of the object in g/mL?

d. A sugar solution has a density of 1.20 g/mL. What is the mass in grams of 0.250 L of the solution?

e. A piece of pure gold weighs 0.26 pound. If gold has a density of 19.3 g/mL, what is the volume in milliliters of the piece of gold?

f. Diamond has a density of 3.52 g/mL. What is the specific gravity of diamond?

g. A salt solution has a specific gravity of 1.15 and a volume of 425 mL. What is the mass in grams of the solution?

h. A 50.0-g sample of a glucose solution has a density of 1.28 g/mL. What is the volume in liters of the sample?

Answers	**a.** 1.26 g/mL	**b.** 1.002	**c.** 8.4 g/mL	**d.** 300. g
	e. 6.1 mL	**f.** 3.52	**g.** 489 g	**h.** 0.0391 L

1.9 Temperature

- In the sciences, temperature is measured in Celsius units, °C, or kelvins, K. In the United States, the Fahrenheit scale, °F, is still in use.
- The equation °F = 1.8°C + 32 is used to convert a Celsius temperature to a Fahrenheit temperature. When rearranged for °C, the equation is used to convert from °F to °C.

$$°C = \frac{(°F - 32)}{1.8}$$

- The temperature on the Celsius scale is related to the Kelvin scale: K = °C + 273.

◆ Learning Exercise 1.9

Calculate the temperatures in the following problems:

a. To prepare yogurt, milk is warmed to 68°C. What Fahrenheit temperature is needed to prepare the yogurt?

b. On a cold day in Alaska, the temperature drops to −12°C. What is that temperature on a Fahrenheit thermometer?

c. A patient has a temperature of 39.5°C. What is that temperature in °F?

d. On a hot summer day, the temperature is 95°F. What is the temperature on the Celsius scale?

e. A pizza is cooked at a temperature of 425°F. What is the °C temperature?

f. A research experiment requires the use of liquid nitrogen to cool the reaction flask to −45°C. What temperature will this be on the Kelvin scale?

Answers: **a.** 154°F   **b.** 10°F   **c.** 103.1°F   **d.** 35°C   **e.** 218°C   **f.** 228 K

Checklist for Chapter 1

You are ready to take the self-test for chapter 1. Be sure that you have accomplished the following learning goals for this chapter. If you are not sure, review the section listed at the end of the goal. Then apply your new skills and understanding to the practice test. After studying chapter 1, I can successfully:

_____ Identify the steps in the scientific method (1.1).

_____ Write the names and abbreviations for the metric (SI) units of measurement (1.2).

_____ Write large or small numbers using scientific notation (1.2).

_____ Identify a number as a measured number or an exact number (1.3).

_____ Count the number of significant figures in measured numbers (1.3).

_____ Report an answer with the correct number of significant figures (1.4).

_____ Write a metric equality from the numerical values of metric prefixes (1.5).

_____ Write two forms of a conversion factor for an equality (1.6).

_____ Use conversion factors to change from one unit to another unit (1.7).

_____ Calculate the density of a substance, or use the density to calculate the mass or volume (1.8).

_____ Given a temperature, calculate a corresponding temperature on another scale (1.9).

Practice Test for Chapter 1

For questions 1–3, identify each statement as observation (O), hypothesis (H), or experiment (E):

1. _____ Hot water can dissolve more sugar than cold water.

2. _____ Place 20 g sugar each in a glass of cold water and a glass of hot water.

3. _____ Sugar is solid, white crystals.

4. Which of the following is a metric measurement of volume?
    A. kilogram   **B.** kilowatt   **C.** kiloliter   **D.** kilometer   **E.** kiloquart

5. The measurement 24 000 g written in scientific notation is
    A. 24 g   **B.** 24×10^3 g   **C.** 2.4×10^3 g   **D.** 2.4×10^{-3} g   **E.** 2.4×10^4 g

6. The measurement 0.005 m written in scientific notation is
    A. 5 m   **B.** 5×10^{-3} m   **C.** 5×10^{-2} m   **D.** 0.5×10^{-4} m   **E.** 5×10^3 m

7. The measured number in the following is
    A. 1 book   **B.** 2 cars   **C.** 4 flowers   **D.** 5 rings   **E.** 45 g

8. The number of significant figures in 105.4 m is
    A. 1   **B.** 2   **C.** 3   **D.** 4   **E.** 5

9. The number of significant figures in 0.000 82 g is
    A. 1   **B.** 2   **C.** 3   **D.** 4   **E.** 5

10. The calculator answer 5.780 52 rounded to two significant figures is
    A. 5   **B.** 5.7   **C.** 5.8   **D.** 5.78   **E.** 6.0

11. The calculator answer 3486.512 rounded to three significant figures is
    A. 4000   **B.** 3500   **C.** 349   **D.** 3487   **E.** 3490

12. The reported answer for the problem $16.0 \div 8.0$ is
    A. 2   **B.** 2.0   **C.** 2.00   **D.** 0.2   **E.** 5.0

13. The reported answer for the problem $58.5 + 9.158$ is
    A. 67   **B.** 67.6   **C.** 67.7   **D.** 67.66   **E.** 67.658

14. The reported answer for the problem $\dfrac{2.5 \times 3.12}{4.6}$ is
    A. 0.54   **B.** 7.8   **C.** 0.85   **D.** 1.7   **E.** 1.69

15. Which of these prefixes has the largest value?
    A. centi   **B.** deci   **C.** milli   **D.** kilo   **E.** micro

16. What is the decimal equivalent of the prefix *centi*?
    A. one-thousandth   **B.** one-hundredth   **C.** one-tenth
    D. ten   **E.** one hundred

17. Which of the following is the smallest unit of measurement?
    A. gram   **B.** milligram   **C.** kilogram   **D.** decigram   **E.** centigram

18. Which volume is the largest?
    A. mL   **B.** dL   **C.** cm^3 **D.** L   **E.** kL

19. Which of the following is a conversion factor?
    A. 12 inches   **B.** 3 feet   **C.** 20 meters   **D.** $\dfrac{1000 \text{ g}}{1 \text{ kg}}$ **E.** 2 cubic centimeters

20. Which is a conversion factor that relates milliliters to liters?
    A. $\dfrac{1000 \text{ mL}}{1 \text{ L}}$ **B.** $\dfrac{100 \text{ mL}}{1 \text{ L}}$ **C.** $\dfrac{10 \text{ mL}}{1 \text{ L}}$ **D.** $\dfrac{0.01 \text{ mL}}{1 \text{ L}}$ **E.** $\dfrac{0.001 \text{ mL}}{1 \text{ L}}$

21. Which is a conversion factor for millimeters and centimeters?
    A. $\dfrac{1 \text{ mm}}{1 \text{ cm}}$ **B.** $\dfrac{10 \text{ mm}}{1 \text{ cm}}$ **C.** $\dfrac{100 \text{ cm}}{1 \text{ mm}}$ **D.** $\dfrac{100 \text{ mm}}{1 \text{ cm}}$ **E.** $\dfrac{10 \text{ cm}}{1 \text{ mm}}$

22. 294 mm is equal to
    A. 2940 m   **B.** 29.4 m   **C.** 2.94 m   **D.** 0.294 m   **E.** 0.0294 m

23. The handle on a tennis racket measures 4.5 inches. What is that size in centimeters?
    A. 11 cm   **B.** 1.8 cm   **C.** 0.56 cm   **D.** 450 cm   **E.** 15 cm

24. What is the volume of 65 mL in liters?
  A. 650 L   **B.** 65 L   **C.** 6.5 L   **D.** 0.65 L   **E.** 0.065 L

25. What is the mass in kg of a 22-lb turkey?
  A. 10 kg   **B.** 48 kg   **C.** 10 000 kg   **D.** 0.048 kg   **E.** 22 000 kg

26. The number of milliliters in 2 deciliters is
  A. 20 mL   **B.** 200 mL   **C.** 2000 mL   **D.** 20 000 mL   **E.** 500 000 mL

27. A person who is 5 feet 4 inches tall would be
  A. 64 m   **B.** 25 m   **C.** 14 m   **D.** 1.6 m   **E.** 1.3 m

28. How many ounces are in 1500 grams? (1 lb = 16 oz)
  A. 94 oz   **B.** 53 oz   **C.** 24 000 oz   **D.** 33 oz   **E.** 3.3 oz

29. How many quarts of orange juice are in 255 mL of juice?
  A. 0.255 qt   **B.** 270 qt   **C.** 236 qt   **D.** 0.270 qt   **E.** 0.400 qt

30. An order for a patient calls for 0.020 grams of medication. On hand are 4-mg tablets. What dose is needed for the patient?
  A. 2 tablets   **B.** 4 tablets   **C.** 5 tablets   **D.** 8 tablets   **E.** 200 tablets

31. A doctor orders 1500 mg of a sulfa drug. Tablets in stock are 0.500 g. How many tablets are needed?
  A. 1 tablet   **B.** $1\frac{1}{2}$ tablet   **C.** $\frac{1}{3}$ tablets   **D.** $2\frac{1}{2}$ tablets   **E.** 3 tablets

32. What is the density of a bone with a mass of 192 g and a volume of 120 cm^3?
  A. 0.63 g/mL   **B.** 1.4 g/cm^3 **C.** 1.6 g/cm^3 **D.** 1.9 g/cm^3 **E.** 2.8 g/cm^3

33. How many milliliters of a salt solution with a density of 1.8 g/mL are needed to provide 400 g of salt solution?
  A. 220 mL   **B.** 22 mL   **C.** 720 mL   **D.** 400 mL   **E.** 4.5 mL

34. The density of a solution is 0.85 g/mL. Its specific gravity is
  A. 222 mL   **B.** 8.5   **C.** 0.85 mL   **D.** 1.2   **E.** 0.85

35. Three liquids have densities of 1.15 g/mL, 0.79 g/mL, and 0.95 g/mL. When the liquids, which do not mix, are poured into a graduated cylinder, the liquid at the top is the one with a density of
  A. 1.15 g/mL   **B.** 1.00 g/mL   **C.** 0.95 g/mL   **D.** 0.79 g/mL   **E.** 0.16 g/mL

36. A sample of oil has a mass of 65 g and a volume of 80.0 mL. What is the specific gravity of the oil?
  A. 1.5   **B.** 1.4   **C.** 1.2   **D.** 0.90   **E.** 0.81

37. What is the mass of a 10.0-mL sample of urine with a specific gravity of 1.04?
  A. 104 g   **B.** 10.4 g   **C.** 1.04 g   **D.** 1.40 g   **E.** 9.62 g

38. Ethyl alcohol has a density of 0.790 g/mL. What is the mass of 0.250 L of the alcohol?
  A. 198 g   **B.** 158 g   **C.** 3.95 g   **D.** 0.253 g   **E.** 0.160 g

39. 105°F = _____°C
  A. 73°C   **B.** 41°C   **C.** 58°C   **D.** 90°C   **E.** 189°C

40. The melting point of gold is 1064°C. The Fahrenheit temperature needed to melt gold would be
  A. 129°C   **B.** 623°F   **C.** 1031°F   **D.** 1913°F   **E.** 1947°F

41. The average daytime temperature on the planet Mercury is 683 K. What is this temperature on the Celsius scale?
  A. 956°C   **B.** 715°C   **C.** 680°C   **D.** 410°C   **E.** 303°C

Answers to the Practice Test

1. H	**2.** E	**3.** O	**4.** C	**5.** E	**6.** B	**7.** E
8. D	**9.** B	**10.** C	**11.** E	**12.** B	**13.** C	**14.** D
15. D	**16.** B	**17.** B	**18.** E	**19.** D	**20.** A	**21.** B
22. D	**23.** A	**24.** E	**25.** A	**26.** B	**27.** D	**28.** B
29. D	**30.** C	**31.** E	**32.** C	**33.** A	**34.** E	**35.** D
36. E	**37.** B	**38.** A	**39.** B	**40.** E	**41.** D	

Answers and Solutions to Selected Text Problems

1.1   **a.** A hypothesis proposes a possible explanation for a natural phenomenon.
   b. An experiment is a procedure that tests the validity of a hypothesis.
   c. A theory is a hypothesis that has been validated many times by many scientists.
   d. An observation is a description or measurement of a natural phenomenon.

1.3   **(1)** A change in number of sales is an observation.
   (2) Changing the menu to improve sales is a hypothesis.
   (3) A taste test is an experiment.
   (4) The ratings of the taste test are observations.
   (5) Improvement in sales is an observation.
   (6) Better sales by changing the menu is a theory.

1.5   **a.** meters (length)   **b.** grams (mass)   **c.** liters (volume)
   d. seconds (time)   **e.** Celsius degrees (temperature)

1.7   **a.** Move the decimal point left four decimal places to give 5.5×10^4 m.
   b. Move the decimal point left two decimal places to give 4.8×10^2 g.
   c. Move the decimal point right six decimal places to give 5×10^{-6} cm.
   d. Move the decimal point right four decimal places to give 1.4×10^{-4} s.
   e. Move the decimal point right three decimal places to give 7.85×10^{-3} L.
   f. Move the decimal point left six decimal places to 6.7×10^5 kg.

1.9   **a.** The value 7.2×10^3, which is also 72×10^2, is greater than 8.2×10^2.
   b. The value 3.2×10^{-2}, which is also 320×10^{-4}, is greater than 4.5×10^{-4}.
   c. The value 1×10^4 or 10 000 is greater than 1×10^{-4} or 0.0001.
   d. The value 6.8×10^{-2} or 0.068 is greater than 0.00052.

1.11   **a.** The standard number is 1.2 times the power of 10^4 or 10 000, which gives 12 000.
   b. The standard number is 8.25 times the power of 10^{-2} or 0.01, which gives 0.082 5.
   c. The standard number is 4 times the power of 10^6 or 1 000 000, which gives 4 000 000.
   d. The standard number is 5 times the power of 10^{-3} or 0.001, which gives 0.005.

1.13   Measured numbers are obtained using some kind of measuring tool. Exact numbers are numbers obtained by counting or from a definition in the metric or the U.S. measuring system.
   a. measured   **b.** exact   **c.** exact   **d.** measured

1.15   Measured numbers are obtained using some kind of measuring tool. Exact numbers are numbers obtained by counting or from a definition in the metric or the U.S. measuring system.
   a. The value 6 oz of meat is obtained by measurement, whereas 3 hamburgers is a counted/exact number.
   b. None; both 1 table and 4 chairs are counted/exact numbers.
   c. Both 0.75 lb and 350 g are obtained by measurements.
   d. None; the values in a definition are exact numbers.

1.17   **a.** Zeros preceding significant digits are *not significant.*
   b. Zeros between significant digits are *significant.*
   c. Zeros after significant digits in a decimal number are *significant.*
   d. Zeros in the coefficient of a number written in scientific notation are *significant.*
   e. Zeros in a number with no decimal point are considered placeholders only and *not significant.*

1.19   **a.** All five numbers are significant figures.
   b. Only the two nonzero numbers are significant; the preceding zeros are placeholders.
   c. Only the two nonzero numbers are significant; the zeros that follow are placeholders.
   d. All three numbers in the coefficient of a number written in scientific notation are significant.
   e. All four numbers including the last zero in a decimal number are significant.
   f. All three numbers including the zeros that follow a nonzero digit in a decimal number are significant.

1.21 Both measurements in c have two significant figures, and both measurements in d have four significant figures.

1.23 **a.** 5000 is the same as 5 × 1000, which is written in scientific notation as 5×10^3.
 b. 30 000 is the same as 3 × 10 000, which is written in scientific notation as 3×10^4.
 c. 100 000 is the same as 1 × 100 000, which is written in scientific notation as 1×10^5.
 d. 0.000 25 is the same as $2.5 \times \dfrac{1}{10\ 000}$, which is written in scientific notation as 2.5×10^{-4}.

1.25 Calculators carry out mathematical computations and display an answer without regard to significant figures. Our task is to round the calculator's answer to the number of significant figures allowed by the precision of the original data.

1.27 **a.** 1.85 **b.** 184 **c.** 0.004 74 (4.74×10^{-3})
 d. 8810 (8.81×10^3) **e.** 1.83

1.29 **a.** $45.7 \times 0.034 = 1.6$ **b.** $0.002\ 78 \times 5 = 0.01$
 c. $\dfrac{34.56}{1.25} = 27.6$ **d.** $\dfrac{(0.2465)(25)}{1.78} = 3.5$

1.31 **a.** 45.48 cm + 8.057 cm = 53.54 cm **b.** 23.45 g + 104.1 g + 0.025 g = 127.6 g
 c. 145.675 mL − 24.2 mL = 121.5 mL **d.** 1.08 L − 0.585 L = 0.50 L

1.33 The km/hr markings indicate how many kilometers (how much distance) will be traversed in 1 hour's time if the speed is held constant. The mph markings indicate the same distance traversed *but measured in miles* during the 1 hour of travel.

1.35 Because the prefix *kilo* means one thousand times, a *kilo*gram is equal to 1000 grams.

1.37 **a.** mg **b.** dL **c.** km **d.** kg **e.** μL

1.39 **a.** 0.01 **b.** 1000 **c.** 0.001 **d.** 0.1 **e.** 1 000 000

1.41 **a.** 100 cm **b.** 1000 m **c.** 0.001 m **d.** 1000 mL

1.43 **a.** kilogram **b.** milliliter **c.** km **d.** kL

1.45 Because a conversion factor is unchanged when inverted $\dfrac{1\ m}{100\ cm}$ and $\dfrac{100\ cm}{1\ m}$

1.47 1 kg = 1000 g

1.49 **a.** 1 yd = 3 ft $\dfrac{1\ yd}{3\ ft}$ and $\dfrac{3\ ft}{1\ yd}$

 b. 1 mi = 5280 ft $\dfrac{1\ mi}{5280\ ft}$ and $\dfrac{5280\ ft}{1\ mi}$

 c. 1 min = 60 s $\dfrac{1\ min}{60\ s}$ and $\dfrac{60\ s}{1\ min}$

 d. 1 gal = 27 mi. $\dfrac{1\ gal}{27\ mi}$ and $\dfrac{27\ mi}{1\ gal}$

 e. Using g as mass:
   100 g sterling = 93 g silver $\dfrac{93\ g\ silver}{100\ g\ sterling}$ and $\dfrac{100\ g\ sterling}{93\ g\ silver}$

1.51 Learning the relationships between the metric prefixes will help you write the following equalities and their resulting conversion factors.

a. 1 m = 100 cm $\qquad \dfrac{1\ m}{100\ cm}$ and $\dfrac{100\ cm}{1\ m}$

b. 1 g = 1000 mg $\qquad \dfrac{1\ g}{1000\ mg}$ and $\dfrac{1000\ mg}{1\ g}$

c. 1 L = 1000 mL $\qquad \dfrac{1\ L}{1000\ mL}$ and $\dfrac{1000\ mL}{1\ L}$

d. 1 dL = 100 mL $\qquad \dfrac{1\ dL}{100\ mL}$ and $\dfrac{100\ mL}{1\ dL}$

1.53 When using a conversion factor, you are trying to cancel existing units and arrive at a new (desired) unit. The conversion factor must be properly oriented so that unit cancellation (numerator to denominator) can be accomplished.

1.55 **a.** Plan: cm $\rightarrow$ m

$$175\ \cancel{cm} \times \dfrac{1\ m}{100\ \cancel{cm}} = 1.75\ m$$

b. Plan: mL $\rightarrow$ L

$$5500\ \cancel{mL} \times \dfrac{1\ L}{1000\ \cancel{mL}} = 5.5\ L$$

c. Plan: kg $\rightarrow$ g

$$0.0055\ \cancel{kg} \times \dfrac{1000\ g}{1\ \cancel{kg}} = 5.5\ g$$

1.57 **a.** Plan: qt $\rightarrow$ mL

$$0.750\ \cancel{qt} \times \dfrac{1\ \cancel{L}}{1.06\ \cancel{qt}} \times \dfrac{1000\ mL}{1\ \cancel{L}} = 710.\ mL$$

b. Plan: stones lb $\rightarrow$ kg

$$11.8\ \cancel{stones} \times \dfrac{14.0\ \cancel{lb}}{1\ \cancel{stone}} \times \dfrac{1\ kg}{2.20\ \cancel{lb}} = 75.1\ kg$$

c. Plan: in. $\rightarrow$ cm $\rightarrow$ mm

$$19.5\ \cancel{in.} \times \dfrac{2.54\ \cancel{cm}}{1\ \cancel{in.}} \times \dfrac{10\ mm}{1\ \cancel{cm}} = 495\ mm$$

d. Plan: μm $\rightarrow$ m $\rightarrow$ cm $\rightarrow$ in.

$$0.50\ \cancel{\mu m} \times \dfrac{1\ \cancel{m}}{10^6\ \cancel{\mu m}} \times \dfrac{100\ \cancel{cm}}{1\ \cancel{m}} \times \dfrac{1\ in.}{2.54\ \cancel{cm}} = 2.0 \times 10^{-5}\ in.$$

1.59 **a.** Plan: ft $\rightarrow$ in. $\rightarrow$ cm $\rightarrow$ m

$$78.0\ \cancel{ft} \times \dfrac{12\ \cancel{in.}}{1\ \cancel{ft}} \times \dfrac{2.54\ \cancel{cm}}{1\ \cancel{in.}} \times \dfrac{1\ m}{100\ \cancel{cm}} = 23.8\ m\ (length)$$

b. Plan: ft $\rightarrow$ in. $\rightarrow$ cm $\rightarrow$ m $\rightarrow$ m^2

$$27.0\ \cancel{ft} \times \dfrac{12\ \cancel{in.}}{1\ \cancel{ft}} \times \dfrac{2.54\ \cancel{cm}}{1\ \cancel{in.}} \times \dfrac{1\ m}{100\ \cancel{cm}} = 8.23\ m\ (width)$$

$$\text{Area} = 23.8\ m \times 8.23\ m = 196\ m^2$$

c. Plan: m → km → hr → min → s

$$23.8 \ \text{m} \times \frac{1 \ \text{km}}{1000 \ \text{m}} \times \frac{1 \ \text{hr}}{185 \ \text{km}} \times \frac{60 \ \text{min}}{1 \ \text{hr}} \times \frac{60 \ \text{s}}{1 \ \text{min}} = 0.463 \ \text{s}$$

1.61 **a.** Plan: L → qt → gal

$$250 \ \text{L} \times \frac{1.06 \ \text{qt}}{1 \ \text{L}} \times \frac{1 \ \text{gal}}{4 \ \text{qt}} = 66 \ \text{gal}$$

b. Plan: g → mg → tablet

$$0.024 \ \text{g} \times \frac{1000 \ \text{mg}}{1 \ \text{g}} \times \frac{1 \ \text{tablet}}{8 \ \text{mg}} = 3.0 \ \text{tablets}$$

c. Plan: lb → g → kg → mg ampicillin

$$34 \ \text{lb body weight} \times \frac{454 \ \text{g}}{1 \ \text{lb}} \times \frac{1 \ \text{kg}}{1000 \ \text{g}} \times \frac{115 \ \text{mg ampicillin}}{1 \ \text{kg body weight}} = 1.8 \times 10^3 \ \text{mg}$$

1.63 Each of the following requires a percent factor from the problem information.

a. Plan: g crust → g oxygen (percent equality: 100.0 g crust = 46.7 g oxygen)

$$325 \ \text{g crust} \times \frac{46.7 \ \text{g oxygen}}{100.0 \ \text{g crust}} = 152 \ \text{g oxygen}$$

b. Plan: g crust → g magnesium (percent equality: 100.0 g crust = 2.1 g magnesium)

$$125 \ \text{g crust} \times \frac{2.1 \ \text{g magnesium}}{100.0 \ \text{g crust}} = 0.026 \ \text{g magnesium}$$

c. Plan: oz → lb → g → g nitrogen (percent equality: 100.0 g fertilizer = 15 g nitrogen)

$$10.0 \ \text{oz fertilizer} \times \frac{1 \ \text{lb}}{16 \ \text{oz}} \times \frac{454 \ \text{g}}{1 \ \text{lb}} \times \frac{15 \ \text{g nitrogen}}{100.0 \ \text{g fertilizer}} = 43 \ \text{g nitrogen}$$

d. Plan: kg pecans → kg choc. bars → lb (percent equality: 100.0 kg bars = 22.0 kg pecans)

$$5.0 \ \text{kg pecans} \times \frac{100 \ \text{kg choc. bars}}{22.0 \ \text{kg pecans}} \times \frac{2.20 \ \text{lb}}{1 \ \text{kg}} = 50. \ \text{lb chocolate bars}$$

1.65 Because the density of aluminum is 2.70 g/cm³, silver is 10.5 g/cm³, and lead is 11.3 g/cm³, we can identify the unknown metal by calculating its density as follows:

$$\frac{217 \ \text{g metal}}{19.2 \ \text{cm}^3 \ \text{metal}} = 11.3 \ \text{g/cm}^3 \quad \text{The metal is lead.}$$

1.67 Density is the mass of a substance divided by its volume. The densities of solids and liquids are usually stated in g/ml or g/cm³.

$$\text{Density} = \frac{\text{mass (grams)}}{\text{Volume (mL)}}$$

a. $\dfrac{24.0 \ \text{g}}{20.0 \ \text{mL}} = 1.20 \ \text{g/mL}$

b. $\dfrac{0.250 \ \text{lb}}{130. \ \text{mL}} \times \dfrac{454 \ \text{g}}{1 \ \text{lb}} = \dfrac{0.873 \ \text{g}}{\text{mL}}$

c. volume of gem: 34.5 mL total − 20.0 mL water = 14.5 mL

density of gem: $\dfrac{45.0 \ \text{g}}{14.5 \ \text{mL}} = 3.10 \ \text{g/mL}$

d. $0.100 \text{ pint} \times \dfrac{1 \text{ qt}}{2 \text{ pints}} \times \dfrac{1 \text{ L}}{1.06 \text{ qt}} \times \dfrac{1000 \text{ mL}}{1 \text{ L}} = 47.3 \text{ mL}$

mass of syrup = $182.48 \text{ g} - 115.25 \text{ g} = 67.23 \text{ g}$

density of syrup = $\dfrac{67.23 \text{ g}}{47.3 \text{ mL}} = 1.42 \text{ g/mL}$

1.69 **a.** $1.5 \text{ kg alcohol} \times \dfrac{1000 \text{ g}}{1 \text{ kg alcohol}} \times \dfrac{1 \text{ mL}}{0.79 \text{ g}} \times \dfrac{1 \text{ L}}{1000 \text{ mL}} = 1.9 \text{ L}$

b. $6.5 \text{ mL} \times \dfrac{13.6 \text{ g}}{1 \text{ mL}} = 88 \text{ g}$

c. $225 \text{ mL} \times \dfrac{7.8 \text{ g}}{1 \text{ mL}} \times \dfrac{1 \text{ lb}}{454 \text{ g}} \times \dfrac{16 \text{ oz}}{1 \text{ lb}} = 62 \text{ oz}$

d. $12.0 \text{ gal} \times \dfrac{4 \text{ qt}}{\text{gal}} \times \dfrac{1000 \text{ mL}}{1.06 \text{ qt}} \times \dfrac{0.66 \text{ g}}{1 \text{ mL}} \times \dfrac{1 \text{ kg}}{1000 \text{ g}} = 30. \text{ kg}$

1.71 **a.** $\dfrac{1.030 \text{ g/mL}}{1.000 \text{ g/mL (H}_2\text{O)}} = 1.030$

b. $\dfrac{45.0 \text{ g}}{40.0 \text{ mL}} = 1.13 \text{ g/mL}$ $\qquad$ $\dfrac{1.13 \text{ g/mL}}{1.00 \text{ g/mL}} = 1.13$

c. 0.85 (sp gr of oil) $\times 1.00 \text{ g/mL (H}_2\text{O density)} = 0.85 \text{ g/mL density of oil}$

1.73 The Fahrenheit temperature scale is still used in the United States. A normal body temperature is 98.6°F on this scale. To convert her temperature to the equivalent reading on the Celsius scale, the following calculation must be performed:

$$\dfrac{(99.8°F - 32)}{1.8} = 37.7°C \text{ (32 is exact)}$$

Because a normal body temperature is 37.0 on the Celsius scale, her temperature of 37.7°C would be a mild fever.

1.75 **a.** $1.8 \, (37.0°C) + 32 = 66.6 + 32 = 98.6°F$

b. $\dfrac{(65.3°F - 32)}{1.8} = \dfrac{33.3}{1.8} = 18.5°C \text{ (1.8 is exact)}$

c. $-27°C + 273 = 246 \text{ K}$ $\qquad\qquad$ **d.** $62°C + 273 = 335 \text{ K}$

e. $\dfrac{(114°F - 32)}{1.8} = \dfrac{82}{1.8} = 46°C$ $\qquad$ **f.** $\dfrac{(72°F - 32)}{1.8} = \dfrac{40}{1.8} = 22°C; 22°C + 273 = 295 \text{ K}$

1.77 **a.** $\dfrac{(106°F - 32)}{1.8} = \dfrac{74}{1.8} = 41°C$ $\qquad\qquad$ **b.** $\dfrac{(103°F - 32)}{1.8} = \dfrac{71}{1.8} = 39°C$

No, there is no need to phone the doctor. The child's temperature is less than 40.0°C.

1.79 Sherlock Holmes's investigations used the scientific method: he made observations, formed a hypothesis, and tested and modified his hypothesis until one of the hypotheses was validated.

1.81 **a.** Exact $\qquad$ **b.** Measured $\qquad$ **c.** Exact $\qquad$ **d.** Measured

1.83 **a.** length 6.96 cm; width 4.75 cm
b. length 69.6 mm; width 47.5 mm
c. There are three significant figures in the length measurement.

d. There are three significant figures in the width measurement.
e. 33.3 cm^2
f. With three significant figures in both length and width, the area has three significant figures.

1.85 Mass of the object is 8.24 g; volume of the object is 23.1 ml $-$ 18.5 ml = 4.6 mL

$$\text{Density} = \frac{8.24 \text{ g}}{4.6 \text{ mL}} = 1.8 \text{ g/mL}$$

1.87 **a.** A hypothesis, which is a possible explanation for an observation, can be tested with experiments.

1.89 **b.** Another hypothesis needs to be written when experimental results do not support the previous hypothesis.
c. More experiments are needed for a new hypothesis.

1.91 **a.** Determination of a melting point with a thermometer is an observation.
b. Describing a reason for the extinction of dinosaurs is a hypothesis or theory.
c. Measuring the speed of a race is an observation.

1.93 This problem requires several conversion factors. Let's take a look first at a possible unit plan. When you write out the unit plan, be sure you know a conversion factor you can use for each step.

Plan: ft $\rightarrow$ in. $\rightarrow$ cm $\rightarrow$ m $\rightarrow$ min

$$7\,500 \text{ ft} \times \frac{12 \text{ in.}}{1 \text{ ft}} \times \frac{2.54 \text{ cm}}{1 \text{ in.}} \times \frac{1 \text{ m}}{100 \text{ cm}} \times \frac{1 \text{ min}}{55.0 \text{ m}} = 42 \text{ min}$$

1.95 Plan: lb $\rightarrow$ g $\rightarrow$ onions

$$4.0 \text{ lb onions} \times \frac{454 \text{ g}}{1 \text{ lb}} \times \frac{1 \text{ onion}}{115 \text{ g onion}} = 16 \text{ onions}$$

Because the number of onions is a counting number, the value obtained from calculation (15.8) is rounded to the whole number 16.

1.97 **a.** Plan: oz $\rightarrow$ crackers

$$8.0 \text{ oz} \times \frac{6 \text{ crackers}}{0.50 \text{ oz}} = 96 \text{ crackers}$$

b. Plan: crackers $\rightarrow$ servings $\rightarrow$ g $\rightarrow$ lb $\rightarrow$ oz

$$10 \text{ crackers} \times \frac{1 \text{ serving}}{6 \text{ crackers}} \times \frac{4 \text{ g fat}}{1 \text{ serving}} \times \frac{1 \text{ lb}}{454 \text{ g}} \times \frac{16 \text{ oz}}{1 \text{ lb}} = 0.2 \text{ oz fat}$$

c. Plan: boxes $\rightarrow$ oz $\rightarrow$ servings $\rightarrow$ mg $\rightarrow$ g

$$50 \text{ boxes} \times \frac{8.0 \text{ oz}}{1 \text{ box}} \times \frac{1 \text{ serving}}{0.50 \text{ oz}} \times \frac{140 \text{ mg sodium}}{1 \text{ serving}} \times \frac{1 \text{ g}}{1000 \text{ mg}} = 110 \text{ g sodium}$$

1.99 Plan: lb $\rightarrow$ kg $\rightarrow$ pesos $\rightarrow$ dollar $\rightarrow$ cents

$$0.45 \text{ lb} \times \frac{1 \text{ kg}}{2.20 \text{ lb}} \times \frac{48 \text{ pesos}}{1 \text{ kg}} \times \frac{1 \text{ dollar}}{10.8 \text{ pesos}} \times \frac{100 \text{ cents}}{1 \text{ dollar}} = 91 \text{ cents}$$

Because the calculation is for a counted number of cents, the value 90.7 is rounded to 91.

1.101 Plan: tubes $\rightarrow$ oz $\rightarrow$ lb $\rightarrow$ g sunscreen $\rightarrow$ kg sunscreen $\rightarrow$ kg benzyl salicylate

$$325 \text{ tubes} \times \frac{4.0 \text{ oz}}{1 \text{ tube}} \times \frac{1 \text{ lb}}{16 \text{ oz}} \times \frac{454 \text{ g}}{1 \text{ lb}} \times \frac{1 \text{ kg}}{1000 \text{ g}} \times \frac{2.50 \text{ kg benzyl salicylate}}{100 \text{ kg}} =$$

0.92 kg benzyl salicylate

1.103 This problem has two units. Convert g to mg, and convert L in the denominator to dL.

$$\frac{1.85 \; \cancel{g}}{1. \; \cancel{L}} \times \frac{1000 \; mg}{1 \; \cancel{g}} \times \frac{1 \; \cancel{L}}{10 \; dL} = 185 \; mg/dL$$

1.105 The difference between the initial volume of the water and its volume with the lead object will give us the volume of the lead object: 285 mL total − 215 mL water = 70 mL lead

Using the density of lead, we can convert mL to the mass in grams of the lead object.

$$70 \; \cancel{mL\;lead} \times \frac{11.3 \; g \; lead}{1 \; \cancel{mL\;lead}} = 790 \; g \; lead$$

1.107 Plan: L gas → mL gas → g gas → g oil → mL oil → cm³ oil

$$1.00 \; \cancel{L\;gas} \times \frac{1000 \; \cancel{mL\;gas}}{1 \; \cancel{L\;gas}} \times \frac{0.66 \; \cancel{g\;gas}}{1 \; \cancel{mL\;gas}} \times \frac{1 \; \cancel{g\;oil}}{1 \; \cancel{g\;gas}} \times \frac{1 \; \cancel{mL}\;oil}{0.92 \; \cancel{g\;oil}} \times \frac{1 \; cm^3}{1 \; \cancel{mL}} = 720 \; cm^3 \; oil$$

1.109 **a.** Plan: kg weight → kg fat → lb (percent equality: 100.0 kg weight = 3.0 kg fat)

$$45 \; \cancel{kg\;body\;weight} \times \frac{3.0 \; \cancel{kg}\;fat}{100.0 \; \cancel{kg\;body\;weight}} \times \frac{2.20 \; lb}{1 \; \cancel{kg}} = 3.0 \; lb \; fat$$

b. Plan: L fat → mL → g → lb

$$3.0 \; \cancel{L\;fat} \times \frac{1000 \; \cancel{mL}}{1 \; \cancel{L}} \times \frac{0.94 \; \cancel{g}\;fat}{1 \; \cancel{mL\;fat}} \times \frac{1 \; lb}{454 \; \cancel{g}} = 6.2 \; lb \; fat$$

1.111 Plan: cm³ → g → g silver → lb → oz (percent equality: 100 g sterling = 92.5 g silver)

$$27.0 \; \cancel{cm^3} \times \frac{10.3 \; \cancel{g}}{1 \; \cancel{cm^3}} \times \frac{92.5 \; \cancel{g}\;silver}{100 \; \cancel{g}} \times \frac{1 \; \cancel{lb}}{454 \; \cancel{g}} \times \frac{16 \; oz}{1 \; \cancel{lb}} = 9.07 \; oz \; of \; pure \; silver$$

1.113 $T_C = \dfrac{(T_F - 32°)}{1.8} = -26°C$

$K = -15°C + 273 = -247 \; K$

1.115 **a. (1)** observation
b. (2) hypothesis
c. (3) experiment
d. (2) hypothesis

1.117 You should record the mass as 34.075 g. Since your balance will weigh to the nearest 0.001 g, the mass values should be reported to 0.001 g.

1.119 $3.0 \; \cancel{hr} \times \dfrac{55 \; \cancel{mi}}{1 \; \cancel{hr}} \times \dfrac{1 \; \cancel{km}}{0.621 \; \cancel{mi}} \times \dfrac{1 \; \cancel{L}}{11 \; \cancel{km}} \times \dfrac{1.06 \; \cancel{qt}}{1 \; \cancel{L}} \times \dfrac{1 \; gal}{4 \; \cancel{qt}} = 6.4 \; gal$

1.121 Volume: $1.50 \; \cancel{g} \times \dfrac{1 \; cm^3}{2.33 \; \cancel{g}} = 0.644 \; cm^3$

Radius: $3.00 \; \cancel{in.} \times \frac{1}{2} \times \dfrac{2.54 \; cm}{1 \; \cancel{in.}} = 3.81 \; cm$

$$h = \frac{V}{\pi r^2} = \frac{0.644 \; cm^3}{3.14 \; (3.81 \; cm)^2} = 0.0141 \; \cancel{cm} \times \frac{10 \; mm}{1 \; \cancel{cm}} = 0.141 \; mm$$

2
Atoms and Elements

Study Goals

- Classify matter as a pure substance or a mixture.
- Classify a pure substance as an element or a compound.
- Write the name of an element from its symbol or its period and group number.
- Classify an element as a metal or nonmetal.
- Describe the three important particles in the atom and their locations, charges, and relative masses.
- Describe Rutherford's gold-foil experiment and how it led to the current model of the atom.
- Use atomic number and mass number of an atom to determine the number of protons, neutrons, and electrons in the atom.
- Understand the relationship of isotopes to the atomic mass of an element on the periodic table.
- Write the electron configurations for elements in the periodic table.
- Write the electron dot symbol for a representative element.
- Explain the relationship between electron arrangement, group number, and periodic law.
- Explain the trends in atomic size or ionization energy going across or down a period.

Think About It

1. Name some of the elements you have seen today.

2. How are the symbols of the elements related to their names?

3. What are some elements that are part of your vitamins?

4. On a dry day, you walk across a carpet and touch a doorknob. You feel a spark. What happened?

Key Terms

Match each the following key terms with the correct definition:

a. element   **b.** atom   **c.** atomic number
d. mass number   **e.** isotope

1. _____ the number of protons and neutrons in the nucleus of an atom

2. _____ the smallest particle of an element

3. _____ a primary substance that cannot be broken down into simpler substances

4. _____ an atom of an element that has a different number of neutrons than another atom of the same element

5. _____ the number of protons in an atom

Answers   **1.** d   **2.** b   **3.** a
                   4. e   **5.** c

2.1 Classification of Matter

- A pure substance, element or compound, has a definite composition.
- Elements are the simplest type of matter; compounds consist of a combination of two or more elements.
- Mixtures contain two or more substances that are physically, not chemically, combined.
- Mixtures are classified as homogeneous or heterogeneous.

◆ Learning Exercise 2.1A

Identify each of the following as an element (E) or compound (C):

1. _____ carbon
2. _____ carbon dioxide
3. _____ potassium iodide
4. _____ silver
5. _____ aluminum
6. _____ table salt (sodium chloride)

Answers   1. E   2. C   3. C
            4. E   5. E   6. C

◆ Learning Exercise 2.1B

Identify each of the following as a pure substance (P) or mixture (M):

1. _____ bananas and milk
2. _____ sulfur
3. _____ gold
4. _____ a bag of raisins and nuts
5. _____ water
6. _____ sand and water

Answers   1. M   2. P   3. P
            4. M   5. P   6. M

◆ Learning Exercise 2.1C

Identify each of the following mixtures as homogeneous (HO) or heterogeneous (HE):

1. _____ chocolate milk
2. _____ sand and water
3. _____ lemon soda
4. _____ a bag of raisins and nuts
5. _____ air
6. _____ vinegar

Answers   1. HO   2. HE   3. HO
            4. HE   5. HO   6. HO

2.2 Elements and Symbols

- Elements are the primary substances of matter.
- Chemical symbols are one- or two-letter abbreviations for the names of the elements.

◆ Learning Exercise 2.2A

Study Note
Now is the time to learn the names of the elements and their symbols. Practice saying and writing the names of the elements on the periodic table with atomic numbers 1–54 and Cs, Ba, Hg, Au, and Pb. Cover the symbols in the lists of elements and practice writing the symbols for the elemental names.

Write the symbols for each of the following elements:

1. carbon _____   2. iron _____   3. sodium _____

4. phosphorus _____   5. oxygen _____   6. nitrogen _____

7. iodine _____   8. sulfur _____   9. potassium _____

10. lead _____   11. calcium _____   12. gold _____

13. copper _____   14. neon _____   15. chlorine _____

Answers	1. C	2. Fe	3. Na	4. P	5. O
	6. N	7. I	8. S	9. K	10. Pb
	11. Ca	12. Au	13. Cu	14. Ne	15. Cl

◆ Learning Exercise 2.2B

Write the names of the elements represented by each of the following symbols:

1. Mg _____   2. K _____

3. Au _____   4. F _____

5. Cu _____   6. Be _____

7. Ag _____   8. Br _____

9. Zn _____   10. Al _____

11. Ba _____   12. Li _____

Answers	1. magnesium	2. potassium	3. gold
	4. fluorine	5. copper	6. beryllium
	7. silver	8. bromine	9. zinc
	10. aluminum	11. barium	12. lithium

2.3 The Periodic Table

- The periodic table is an arrangement of the elements by increasing atomic number.
- Each vertical column contains a *group* of elements that have similar properties.
- A horizontal row of elements is called a period.
- On the periodic table, the *metals* are located on the left of the heavy zigzag line, the nonmetals are to the right, and metalloids are next to the zigzag line.
- Main group or representative elements are 1A, 2A (1, 2) and 3A–8A (13–18). Transition elements are the B-group elements (3–13).

◆ Learning Exercise 2.3A

Study Note
1. The periodic table consists of horizontal rows called *periods* and vertical columns called *groups*.
2. Elements in Group 1A (1) are the *alkali metals*. Elements in Group 2A (2) are the *alkaline earth metals*, and Group 7A (17) contains the *halogens*. Elements in Group 8A (18) are the *Noble gases*.

Indicate whether the following elements are in a group (G), period (P), or neither (N):

a. Li, C, and O _____   **b.** Br, Cl, and F _____

c. Al, Si, and Cl _____   **d.** C, N, and O _____

    e. Mg, Ca, and Ba _____   **f.** C, S, and Br _____

    g. Li, Na, and K _____   **h.** K, Ca, and Br _____

Answers   **a.** P   **b.** G   **c.** P   **d.** P
                  e. G   **f.** N   **g.** G   **h.** P

◆ Learning Exercise 2.3B

Complete the list of elements, group numbers, and period numbers in the following table:

Element and Symbol	Group Number	Period Number
	2A (2)	3
Silicon, Si		
	5A (15)	2
Aluminum, Al		
	4A (14)	5
	1A (1)	6

Answers

Element Symbol	Group Number	Period Number
Magnesium, Mg	2A (2)	3
Silicon, Si	4A (14)	3
Nitrogen, N	5A (15)	2
Aluminum, Al	3A (13)	3
Tin, Sn	4A (14)	5
Cesium, Cs	1A (1)	6

◆ Learning Exercise 2.3C

Identify each of the following elements as a metal (M), nonmetal (NM), or metalloid (ML):

1. Cl ____   **2.** N ____   **3.** Fe ____   **4.** K ____   **5.** Sb ____

6. C ____   **7.** Ca ____   **8.** Ge ____   **9.** Ag ____   **10.** Mg ____

Answers   **1.** NM   **2.** NM   **3.** M   **4.** M
                  5. M   **6.** NM   **7.** M   **8.** M
                  9. M   **10.** M

◆ Learning Exercise 2.3D

Match the names of the chemical groups with the elements K, Cl, He, Fe, Mg, Ne, Li, Cu, and Br.

    1. Halogens   _____

    2. Noble gases   _____

3. Alkali metals _____

4. Alkaline earth metals _____

5. Transition elements _____

Answers   **1.** Cl, Br   **2.** He, Ne   **3.** K, Li
                  4. Mg   **5.** Fe, Cu

2.4 The Atom

- An atom is the smallest particle that retains the characteristics of an element.
- Atoms are composed of three subatomic particles. Protons have a positive charge (+), electrons carry a negative charge (−), and neutrons are electrically neutral.
- The protons and neutrons, each with a mass of about 1 amu, are found in the tiny, dense nucleus. The electrons are located outside the nucleus.

◆ Learning Exercise 2.4A

Indicate whether each of the following statements is consistent with atomic theory (true or false):

1. All matter is composed of atoms.

2. All atoms of an element are identical.

3. Atoms combine to form compounds.

4. Most of the mass of the atom is in the nucleus.

Answers   **1.** true   **2.** false   **3.** true   **4.** true

◆ Learning Exercise 2.4B

Match the following terms with the correct statements:

    a. proton   **b.** neutron   **c.** electron   **d.** nucleus

1. _____ found in the nucleus of an atom

2. _____ has a −1 charge

3. _____ found outside the nucleus

4. _____ has a mass of 1 amu

5. _____ the small, dense center of the atom

6. _____ is neutral

Answers   **1.** a and b   **2.** c   **3.** c
                  4. a and b   **5.** d   **6.** b

2.5 Atomic Number and Mass Number

- The *atomic number* is the number of protons in every atom of an element. In neutral atoms, the number of electrons is equal to the number of protons.
- The mass number is the total number of protons and neutrons in an atom.

◆ **Learning Exercise 2.5A**

Study Note
1. The *atomic number* is the number of protons in every atom of an element. In neutral atoms, the number of electrons equals the number of protons. 2. The *mass number* is the total number of neutrons and protons in the nucleus of an atom. 3. The number of neutrons is *mass number − atomic number.*

Give the number of protons in each of the following neutral atoms:

    a. an atom of carbon   _____

    b. an atom of the element with atomic number 15   _____

    c. an atom with a mass number of 40 and atomic number 19   _____

    d. an atom with 9 neutrons and a mass number of 19   _____

    e. a neutral atom that has 18 electrons   _____

Answers   **a.** 6   **b.** 15   **c.** 19   **d.** 10   **e.** 18

◆ **Learning Exercise 2.5B**

Find the number of neutrons in each of the following atoms:

    a. a mass number of 42 and atomic number 20   _____

    b. a mass number of 10 and 5 protons   _____

    c. $^{30}_{14}Si$ _____

    d. a mass number of 9 and atomic number 4   _____

    e. a mass number of 22 and 10 protons   _____

    f. a zinc atom with a mass number of 66   _____

Answers   **a.** 22   **b.** 5   **c.** 16   **d.** 5   **e.** 12   **f.** 36

◆ **Learning Exercise 2.5C**

Study Note
In the atomic symbol for a particular atom, the mass number appears in the upper left corner and the atomic number in the lower left corner.   Mass number → $^{32}_{16}S$ $^{27}_{13}Al$ Atomic number →

Complete the following table for neutral atoms:

Atomic Symbol	Atomic Number	Mass Number	Number of Protons	Number of Neutrons	Number of Electrons
	12			12	
			20	22	
		55		27	
	35			45	
		35	17		
$^{120}_{50}Sn$					

Answers

Atomic Symbol	Atomic Number	Mass Number	Number of Protons	Number of Neutrons	Number of Electrons
$^{24}_{12}Mg$	12	24	12	12	12
$^{42}_{20}Ca$	20	42	20	22	20
$^{55}_{26}Fe$	26	55	26	29	26
$^{80}_{35}Br$	35	80	35	45	35
$^{35}_{17}Cl$	17	35	17	18	17
$^{120}_{50}Sn$	50	120	50	70	50

2.6 Isotopes and Atomic Mass

- Atoms that have the same number of protons but different numbers of neutrons are called isotopes.
- The atomic mass of an element is the average mass of all the isotopes in a naturally occurring sample of that element.

◆ Learning Exercise 2.6A

Identify the sets of atoms that are isotopes.

A. $^{20}_{10}X$ **B.** $^{20}_{11}X$ **C.** $^{21}_{11}X$ **D.** $^{19}_{10}X$ **E.** $^{19}_{9}X$

Answer   Atoms A and D are isotopes (At. No. 10); atoms B and C are isotopes (At. No. 11).

◆ Learning Check 2.6B

Essay Copper has two naturally occurring isotopes, ^{63}Cu and ^{65}Cu. If that is the case, why is the atomic mass of copper listed as 63.35 on the periodic table?

Answer   Copper in nature consists of two isotopes with different atomic masses. The atomic mass is the average of the individual masses of the two isotopes and their percent abundance in the sample. The atomic mass does not represent the mass of any individual atom.

2.7 Electron Energy Levels

- Energy levels, which are indicated by the principal quantum number n, contain electrons of similar energies.
- Within each energy level, electrons with identical energy are grouped in *sublevels*: an s sublevel can accommodate 2 electrons, a p sublevel can accommodate 6 electrons, a d sublevel can accommodate 10 electrons, and a f sublevel can accommodate 14 electrons.
- An orbital is a region in an atom where there is the greatest probability of finding an electron of certain energy. An orbital can hold a maximum of two electrons, which have opposite spins.
- An s orbital is spherical, and p orbitals have two lobes along an axis. The d and f orbitals have more complex shapes.
- Each sublevel consists of a set of orbitals: an s sublevel consists of one orbital, a p sublevel consists of three orbitals, a d sublevel consists of five orbitals, and an f sublevel consists of seven orbitals.

◆ **Learning Exercise 2.7**

State the maximum number of electrons for each of the following:

a. $3p$ sublevel _____   b. $3d$ sublevel _____

c. $2s$ orbital _____   d. energy level 4 _____

e. $1s$ sublevel _____   f. $4p$ orbital _____

g. $5p$ sublevel _____   h. $4f$ sublevel _____

Answers   **a.** 6   **b.** 10   **c.** 2   **d.** 32
            e. 2   **f.** 2   **g.** 6   **h.** 14

2.8 Electron Configurations

- An orbital diagram represents the orbitals in an atom that contain electrons.
- The electron configuration shows the number of electrons in each sublevel in order of increasing energy.
- The abbreviated electron configuration uses the symbol of the previous noble gas and only shows the configuration of the electron in the higher energy levels.

◆ **Learning Exercise 2.8A**

Write the orbital diagram for each of the following elements:

a. beryllium _____   b. carbon _____

c. sodium _____   d. nitrogen _____

e. fluorine _____   f. magnesium _____

Answers   **a.**   **b.**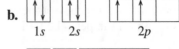

c. 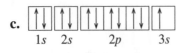   **d.**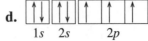

e. 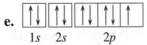   **f.**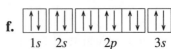

◆ **Learning Exercise 2.8B**

Write the electron configuration ($1s^2 2s^2 2p^6$, etc.) for each of the following elements:

a. carbon _____

b. magnesium _____

c. iron _____

d. silicon _____

e. chlorine _____

f. phosphorus _____

Answers   **a.** $1s^2 2s^2 2p^2$ **b.** $1s^2 2s^2 2p^6 3s^2$ **c.** $1s^2 2s^2 2p^6 3s^2 3p^6 4s^2 3d^6$
            d. $1s^2 2s^2 2p^6 3s^2 3p^2$ **e.** $1s^2 2s^2 2p^6 3s^2 3p^5$ **f.** $1s^2 2s^2 2p^6 3s^2 3p^3$

◆ Learning Exercise 2.8C

Write the abbreviated electron configuration for each of the elements in 2.8B:

a. carbon   _____

b. magnesium   _____

c. iron   _____

d. silicon   _____

e. chlorine   _____

f. phosphorus   _____

Answers   **a.** $[He]2p^2$ **b.** $[Ne]3s^2$ **c.** $[Ar]4s^2 3d^6$
                d. $[Ne]3s^2 3p^2$ **e.** $[Ne]3s^2 3p^5$ **f.** $[Ne]3s^2 3p^3$

◆ Learning Exercise 2.8D

Name the element with an electron configuration ending with each of the following notations:

a. $3p^5$ _____   **b.** $2s^1$ _____

c. $3d^8$ _____   **d.** $4p^1$ _____

e. $5p^5$ _____   **f.** $3p^2$ _____

g. $1s^1$ _____   **h.** $6s^2$ _____

Answers   **a.** chlorine   **b.** lithium   **c.** nickel   **d.** gallium
                e. iodine   **f.** silicon   **g.** hydrogen   **h.** barium

2.9 Periodic Trends

- The physical and chemical properties of elements change in a periodic manner going across each period and are repeated in each successive period.
- Representative elements in a group have similar behavior.
- The group number of an element gives the number of valence electrons.
- The electron dot symbol shows each valence electron as a dot placed around the atomic symbol.
- The atomic radius of representative elements generally increases going down a group and decreases going across a period.
- The ionization energy generally decreases going down a group and increases going across a period.

◆ Learning Exercise 2.9A

State the number of electrons in the outermost energy level, the group number of each element, and the electron dot symbol for the following elements:

Element	Valence Electrons	Group Number	Dot Symbol
a. sulfur	_____	_____	
b. oxygen	_____	_____	
c. magnesium	_____	_____	
d. hydrogen	_____	_____	
e. fluorine	_____	_____	
f. aluminum	_____	_____	

Answers

Element	Valence Electrons	Group Number	Dot Symbol
a. sulfur	6e⁻	Group 6A (16)	$\cdot\ddot{\underset{\cdot\cdot}{S}}:$
b. oxygen	6e⁻	Group 6A (16)	$\cdot\ddot{\underset{\cdot\cdot}{O}}:$
c. magnesium	2e⁻	Group 2A (2)	Mg·
d. hydrogen	1e⁻	Group 1A (1)	H·
e. fluorine	7e⁻	Group 7A (17)	$\cdot\ddot{\underset{\cdot\cdot}{F}}:$
f. aluminum	3e⁻	Group 3A (13)	· Al ·

◆ Learning Exercise 2.9B

Indicate the element that has the larger atomic radius.

a. _____ Mg or Ca   **b.** _____ Si or Cl

c. _____ Sr or Rb   **d.** _____ Br or Cl

e. _____ Li or Cs   **f.** _____ Li or N

g. _____ N or P   **h.** _____ As or Ca

Answers **a.** Ca **b.** Si **c.** Rb **d.** Br
e. Cs **f.** Li **g.** P **g.** Ca

◆ Learning Exercise 2.9C

Indicate the element that has the lower ionization energy.

a. _____ Mg or Na   **b.** _____ P or Cl

c. _____ K or Rb   **d.** _____ Br or F

e. _____ Li or O   **f.** _____ Sb or N

g. _____ K or Br   **h.** _____ S or Na

Answers **a.** Na **b.** P **c.** Rb **d.** Br
e. Li **f.** Sb **g.** K **g.** Na

Checklist for Chapter 2

You are ready to take the practice test for chapter 2. Be sure that you have accomplished the following learning goals for this chapter. If you are not sure, review the section listed at the end of the goal. Then apply your new skills and understanding to the practice test. Good luck.

After studying chapter 2, I can successfully:

_____ Write the correct symbol or name for an element (2.1).

_____ Use the periodic table to identify the group and period of an element, and describe it as a metal or nonmetal (2.2).

_____ State the electrical charge, mass, and location of the protons, neutrons, and electrons in an atom (2.3).

_____ Given the atomic number and mass number of an atom, state the number of protons, neutrons, and electrons (2.4).

_____ Identify an isotope and describe the atomic mass of an element (2.5).

_____ Explain the periodic law (2.6).

_____ State the maximum number of electrons in orbitals and subshells (2.7).

_____ Write the electron configuration for elements using subshell notation (2.8).

_____ Write the electron dot symbol for a representative element. (2.9).

_____ Determine which of two elements has a larger atomic size (2.9).

_____ Determine which of two elements has a higher ionization energy (2.9).

Practice Test for Chapter 2

Write or select the correct the correct answer for each of the following questions.

Write the correct symbol for each of the elements listed:

1. potassium _____   2. phosphorus _____

3. calcium _____   4. carbon _____

5. sodium _____

Write the correct name for each of the symbols listed below:

6. Fe _____   7. Cu _____

8. Cl _____   9. Pb _____

10. Ag _____

11. The elements C, N, and O are part of a
    A. period   **B.** family   **C.** neither

12. The elements Li, Na, and K are part of a
    A. period   **B.** family   **C.** neither

13. What is the classification of an atom with 15 protons and 17 neutrons?
    A. metal   **B.** nonmetal   **C.** transition element
    D. noble gas   **E.** halogen

14. What is the group number of the element with atomic number 3?
    A. 1   **B.** 2   **C.** 3   **D.** 7   **E.** 8

For questions 15–18, consider an atom with 12 protons and 13 neutrons.

15. This atom has an atomic number of
    A. 12   **B.** 13   **C.** 23   **D.** 24   **E.** 25

16. This atom has a mass number of
    A. 12   **B.** 13   **C.** 23   **D.** 24.3   **E.** 25

17. This is an atom of
    A. carbon   **B.** sodium   **C.** magnesium   **D.** aluminum   **E.** manganese

18. The number of electrons in this atom is
    A. 12   **B.** 13   **C.** 23   **D.** 24   **E.** 25

For questions 19–22, consider an atom of calcium with a mass number of 42.

19. This atom of calcium has an atomic number of
  A. 20   **B.** 22   **C.** 40   **D.** 41   **E.** 42

20. The number of protons in this atom of calcium is
  A. 20   **B.** 22   **C.** 40   **D.** 41   **E.** 42

21. The number of neutrons in this atom of calcium is
  A. 20   **B.** 22   **C.** 40   **D.** 41   **E.** 42

22. The number of electrons in this atom of calcium is
  A. 20   **B.** 22   **C.** 40   **D.** 41   **E.** 42

23. Platinum, ^{195}Pt, has
  A. $78p^+$, $78e^-$, $78n$ **B.** $195p^+$, $195e^-$, $195n$ **C.** $78p^+$, $78e^-$, $195n$
  D. $78p^+$, $78e^-$, $117n$ **E.** $78p^+$, $117e^-$, $117n$

For questions 24 and 25, use the following list of atoms:

  $^{14}_{7}V$ $^{16}_{8}W$ $^{19}_{9}X$ $^{16}_{7}Y$ $^{18}_{8}Z$

24. Which atom(s) are isotopes of an atom with 8 protons and 9 neutrons?
  A. W   **B.** W, Z   **C.** X, Y   **D.** X   **E.** Y

25. Which atom(s) are isotopes of an atom with 7 protons and 8 neutrons?
  A. V   **B.** W   **C.** V, Y   **D.** W, Z   **E.** none

26. Which element would you expect to have properties most like oxygen?
  A. Nitrogen   **B.** Carbon   **C.** Chlorine   **D.** Argon   **E.** Sulfur

27. Which of the following is an isotope of nitrogen?
  A. $^{14}_{8}N$ **B.** $^{7}_{3}N$ **C.** $^{10}_{5}N$ **D.** $^{4}_{2}He$ **E.** $^{15}_{7}N$

28. Except for helium, the number of electrons in the outer shells of the noble gases is
  A. 3   **B.** 5   **C.** 7   **D.** 8   **E.** 12

29. The electron configuration for an oxygen atom is
  A. $2s^2 2p^4$ **B.** $1s^2 2s^4 2p^4$ **C.** $1s^2 2s^6$ **D.** $1s^2 2s^2 2p^2 3s^2$ **E.** $1s^2 2s^2 2p^4$

30. The electron configuration for aluminum is
  A. $1s^2 2s^2 2p^9$ **B.** $1s^2 2s^2 2p^6 3p^5$ **C.** $1s^2 2s^2 2p^6 3s^2 3p^1$ **D.** $1s^2 2s^2 2p^8 3p^1$ **E.** $1s^2 2s^2 2p^6 3p^3$

For questions 31–35, match the final notation in the electron configuration with the following elements:
  A. As   **B.** Rb   **C.** Na   **D.** N   **E.** Xe

31. $4p^3$ _____   **32.** $5s^1$ _____

33. $3s^1$ _____   **34.** $6p^6$ _____

35. $2p^3$ _____

36. Which element has a larger atomic radius, Mg or P? _____

37. Which element has a larger atomic radius, Ar or Xe? _____

38. Which element has a higher ionization energy, N or F? _____

39. Which element has a higher ionization energy, Br or F? _____

Answers for the Practice Test

1. K	**2.** P	**3.** Ca	**4.** C	**5.** Na
6. iron	**7.** copper	**8.** chlorine	**9.** lead	**10.** silver
11. A	**12.** B	**13.** B	**14.** A	**15.** A
16. E	**17.** C	**18.** A	**19.** A	**20.** A
21. B	**22.** A	**23.** D	**24.** B	**25.** C
26. E	**27.** E	**28.** D	**29.** E	**30.** C
31. A	**32.** B	**33.** C	**34.** E	**35.** D
36. Mg	**37.** Xe	**38.** F	**39.** F	

Answers and Solutions to Selected Text Problems

2.1 A *pure substance* has a definite composition. A *mixture* has a variable composition.
  a. pure substance **b.** mixture **c.** pure substance **d.** pure substance

2.3 *Elements* are the simplest type of pure substance. *Compounds* contain two or more elements in the same ratio.
  a. element **b.** compound **c.** element **d.** compound

2.5 A *homogeneous mixture* has a uniform composition. A *heterogeneous mixture* does not have a uniform composition throughout the mixture.
  a. heterogeneous **b.** homogeneous **c.** homogeneous **d.** heterogeneous

2.7 **a.** Cu **b.** Si **c.** K **d.** N
  e. Fe **f.** Ba **g.** Pb **h.** Sr

2.9 **a.** carbon **b.** chlorine **c.** iodine **d.** mercury
  e. fluorine **f.** argon **g.** zinc **h.** nickel

2.11 **a.** sodium (Na) and chlorine (Cl)
  b. calcium (Ca), sulfur (S), and oxygen (O)
  c. carbon (C), hydrogen (H), chlorine (Cl), nitrogen (N), and oxygen (O)
  d. calcium (Ca), carbon (C), and oxygen (O)

2.13 **a.** C, N, and O are in Period 2.
  b. He is the element at the top of Group 8A (18).
  c. The alkali metals are the elements in Group 1A (1).
  d. Period 2 is the horizontal row of elements that ends with neon (Ne).

2.15 **a.** alkaline earth metal **b.** transition element
  c. noble gas **d.** alkali metal **e.** halogen

2.17 **a.** C **b.** He **c.** Na **d.** Ca **e.** Al

2.19 On the periodic table, *metals* are located to the left of the heavy zigzag line, *nonmetals* are elements to the right, and metalloids B, Si, Ge, As, Sb, Te, Po, and At are located along the line.
  a. metal **b.** nonmetal **c.** metal **d.** nonmetal
  e. nonmetal **f.** nonmetal **g.** metalloid **h.** metal

2.21 **a.** electron **b.** proton **c.** electron **d.** neutron

2.23 The two most massive subatomic particles, protons and neutrons, are located in a very small region of the atom, which is called the nucleus.

2.25 Selection b (a proton and an electron) is the only one with a pair of particles having opposite charges.

2.27 In the process of brushing hair, like charges on the hair and brush repel each other.

2.29 The atomic number is equal to the number of protons. The mass number is the sum of the protons and neutrons.

    a. atomic number   **b.** both   **c.** mass number   **d.** atomic number

2.31 **a.** lithium, Li   **b.** fluorine, F   **c.** calcium, Ca   **d.** zinc, Zn
        e. neon, Ne   **f.** silicon, Si   **g.** iodine, I   **h.** oxygen, O

2.33 **a.** 12   **b.** 30   **c.** 53   **d.** 19

2.35

Name of Element	Symbol	Atomic Number	Mass Number	Number of Protons	Number of Neutrons	Number of Electrons
Aluminum	Al	13	27	13	14	13
Magnesium	Mg	12	24	12	12	12
Potassium	K	19	39	19	20	19
Sulfur	S	16	31	16	15	16
Iron	Fe	26	56	26	30	26

2.37 **a.** Since the atomic number of aluminum is 13, every Al atom has 13 protons. An atom of aluminum (mass number 27) has 14 neutrons ($27 - 13 = 14$ n). Neutral atoms have the same number of protons and electrons. Therefore, 13 protons, 14 neutrons, 13 electrons.
    b. Since the atomic number of chromium is 24, every Cr atom has 24 protons. An atom of chromium (mass number 52) has 28 neutrons ($52 - 24 = 28$ n). Neutral atoms have the same number of protons and electrons. Therefore, 24 protons, 28 neutrons, 24 electrons.
    c. Since the atomic number of sulfur is 16, every S atom has 16 protons. An atom of sulfur (mass number 34) has 18 neutrons ($34 - 16 = 18$ n). Neutral atoms have the same number of protons and electrons. Therefore, 16 protons, 18 neutrons, 16 electrons.
    d. Since the atomic number of iron is 26, every Fe atom has 26 protons. An atom of iron (mass number 56) has 30 neutrons ($56 - 26 = 30$ n). Neutral atoms have the same number of protons and electrons. Therefore, 26 protons, 30 neutrons, 26 electrons.

2.39 **a.** $^{31}_{15}P$ **b.** $^{80}_{35}Br$ **c.** $^{27}_{13}Al$ **d.** $^{35}_{17}Cl$

2.41 **a.** $^{32}_{16}S$ $^{33}_{16}S$ $^{34}_{16}S$ $^{36}_{16}S$
    b. They all have the same atomic number (the same number of protons and electrons).
    c. They have different numbers of neutrons, which is reflected in their mass numbers.
    d. The atomic mass of sulfur on the periodic table is the average atomic mass of all the naturally occurring isotopes of sulfur.

2.43 Since the atomic mass of copper is closer to 63, there are more atoms of ^{63}Cu.

2.45 $68.93 \text{ amu} \times \dfrac{60.11}{100} + 70.92 \text{ amu} \times \dfrac{39.89}{100} = 69.72 \text{ amu}$

2.47 **a.** A $1s$ orbital is spherical.   **b.** A $2p$ orbital has two lobes.
    c. A $5s$ orbital is spherical.

2.49 **a.** All *s* orbitals are spherical.
    b. A 3*s* sublevel and a 3*p* sublevel are in the energy level *n* = 3.
    c. All *p* sublevels contain 3*p* orbitals.
    d. The 3*p* orbitals all have two lobes and are in energy level *n* = 3.

2.51 **a.** There are five orbitals in the 3*d* sublevel.
    b. There is one sublevel in the *n* = 1 principal energy level.
    c. There is one orbital in the 6*s* sublevel.
    d. There are nine orbitals in the *n* = 3 energy level: one 3*s* orbital, three 3*p* orbitals, and five 3*d* orbitals.

2.53 **a.** Any orbital has a maximum of two electrons. Thus, a 2*p* orbital has a maximum of two electrons.
    b. The 3*p* sublevel contains three *p* orbitals, each of which can hold a maximum of two electrons, which gives a maximum of six electrons in the 3*p* sublevel.
    c. Using $2n^2$, the calculation for the maximum number of electrons in the *n* = 4 energy level is $2(4)^2 = 2(16) = 32$ electrons.
    d. The 5*d* sublevel contains five *d* orbitals each of which can hold a maximum of two electrons, which gives a maximum of 10 electrons in the 5*d* sublevel.

2.55 **a.**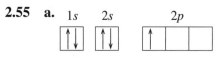

    b.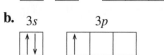

    c.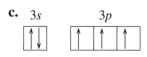

    d.

2.57 **a.** N $1s^22s^22p^3$ **b.** Na $1s^22s^22p^63s^1$
    c. S $1s^22s^22p^63s^23p^4$ **d.** As $1s^22s^22p^63s^23p^64s^23d^{10}4p^3$
    e. Fe $1s^22s^22p^63s^23p^64s^23d^6$

2.59 The abbreviated electron configuration consists of the symbol of the preceding noble gas followed by the electron configuration in the next period. [He] = $1s^2$ and [Ne] = $1s^22s^22p^6$.
    a. Mg [Ne]$3s^2$ **b.** S [Ne]$3s^23p^4$
    c. Al [Ne]$3s^23p^1$ **d.** Ti [Ar]$4s^23d^2$
    e. Ba [Xe]$6s^2$

2.61 **a.** S has two electrons in the 3*s* and four electrons in the 3*p* sublevels.
  b. Co (ends in 3d^7)
  c. Si has two electrons in the 3*s* and two electrons in the 3*p* sublevels.
  d. Br (ends in 4p^5)

2.63 **a.** Al has three electrons in the third energy level: $3s^2 3p^1$.
  b. C has two 2*p* electrons.
  c. Ar completes the 3*p* sublevel 3p^6.
  d. Zr has two 4*d* electrons.

2.65 **a.** Zn is the tenth element in the 3*d* block; it has ten 3*d* electrons.
  b. Na has an electron in the 3*s* block; the 2*p* block in Na is complete with six electrons.
  c. As is the third element in the 4*p* block; it has three 4*p* electrons.
  d. Rb is the first element in the 5*s* block; it has one 5*s* electron.

2.67 **a.** An element with two valence electrons is in Group 2A (2).
  b. An element with five valence electrons is in Group 5A (15).
  c. An element with six valence electrons is in Group 6A (16).

2.69 **a.** Aluminum in Group 3A (13) has three valence electrons.
  b. Any element in Group 5A (15) has five valence electrons.
  c. Each halogen in Group 7A (17) has seven valence electrons.

2.71 The number of dots is equal to the number of valence electrons as indicated by the group number.
  a. Sulfur has six valence electrons $\cdot \overset{\cdot\cdot}{\underset{\cdot}{S}} :$
  b. Nitrogen has five valence electrons $\cdot \overset{\cdot\cdot}{\underset{\cdot}{N}} \cdot$
  c. Calcium has two valence electrons $\overset{\cdot}{Ca} \cdot$
  d. Sodium has one valence electron $Na \cdot$
  e. Barium has two valence electrons $Ba \cdot$

2.73 **a.** M·
  b. ·M·

2.75 **a.** The atomic radius of representative elements decreases from Group 1A(1) to 8A(18): Mg, Al, Si.
  b. The atomic radius of representative elements increase going down a group: I, Br, Cl.
  c. The atomic radius of representative elements decrease from Group 1A(1) to 8A(18): Sr, Sb, I.

2.77 The atomic radius of representative elements decreases going across a period from Group 1A(1) to 8A(18) and increases going down a group.
  a. In Period 3, Na, which is on the left, is larger than Cl.
  b. In Group 1A(1), Rb, which is further down the group, is larger than Na.
  c. In Period 3, Na, which is on the left, is larger than Mg.

2.79 **a.** The ionization energy decreases going down a group: Br, Cl, F.
  b. Going across a period from left to right, the ionization energy generally increases: Na, Al, Cl.
  c. The ionization energy decreases going down a group: Cs, K, Na.

2.81 **a.** Br, which is above I in Group 7A(17), has a higher ionization energy than I.
  b. Ionization energy increases from Group 2A(2) to Group 6A(16), which gives S a higher ionization energy than Mg.
  c. Ionization energy increases from Group 4A(14) to Group 5A(15), which gives P a higher ionization energy than Si.

2.83 **a.** has two different types of atoms combined in the same ratio; it is a compound.
b. consists of two different types of atoms; it is a mixture.
c. has only one type of atom; it is an element.

2.85 **b** and **c** are not the same throughout the mixture, and **b** and **c** are heterogeneous.

2.87 **a.** element   **b.** compound   **c.** mixture
d. element   **e.** mixture

2.89 **a.** Mg, magnesium   **b.** Br, bromine   **c.** Al, aluminum   **d.** O, oxygen

2.91 **a.** False. A proton has a positive charge.
b. False. The neutron has about the same mass as a proton.
c. True
d. False. The nucleus is the tiny, dense central core of an atom.
e. True

2.93 **a.** 13 protons, 14 neutrons, 13 electrons
b. 24 protons, 28 neutrons, 24 electrons
c. 16 protons, 18 neutrons, 16 electrons
d. 26 protons, 30 neutrons, 26 electrons
e. 54 protons, 82 neutrons, 54 electrons

2.95

Name	Nuclear Symbol	Number of Protons	Number of Neutrons	Number of Electrons
sulfur	$^{34}_{16}S$	16	18	16
Zinc	$^{70}_{30}Zn$	30	40	30
magnesium	$^{26}_{12}Mg$	12	14	12
radon	$^{220}_{86}Rn$	86	134	86

2.97 **a.** On the periodic table, the $3p$ sublevel block follows the $3s$ sublevel block.
b. On the periodic table, the $5s$ sublevel block follows the $4p$ sublevel block.
c. On the periodic table, the $4p$ sublevel block follows the $3d$ sublevel block.
d. On the periodic table, the $4s$ sublevel block follows the $3p$ sublevel block.

2.99 **a.** Iron is the sixth element in the $3d$ block; iron has six $3d$ electrons.
b. Barium has a completely filled $5p$ sublevel, which is six $5p$ electrons.
c. Iodine has a completely filled $4d$ sublevel, which is ten $4d$ electrons.
d. Barium has a filled $6s$ sublevel or $6s$ block, which is two $6s$ electrons.

2.101 Ca, Sr, and Ba all have two valence electrons, ns^2, which places them in Group 2A (2).

2.103 **a.** Phosphorus in Group 5A(15) has an electron configuration that ends with $3s^23p^3$.
b. Lithium is the alkali metal that is highest in Group 1A (1) and has the smallest atomic radius.
[H in Group 1A (1) is a nonmetal.]
c. Cadmium in Period 5 has a complete $4d$ sublevel with 10 electrons.
d. Nitrogen at the top of Group 5A(15) has the highest ionization energy in that group.
e. Sodium, the first element in Period 3, has the largest atomic radius of that period.

2.105 Calcium has a greater net nuclear charge than K. The least tightly bound electron in Ca is further from the nucleus than in Mg and needs less energy to remove.

2.107 **a.** Na is on the far left of the heavy zigzag line. Na is a metal.
b. Na, at the beginning of Group 3, has the largest atomic radius.
c. F, at the top of Group 7A(17) and to the far right in Period 2, has the highest ionization energy.
d. Na has the lowest ionization energy and loses an electron most easily.
e. Cl is found in Period 3 in Group 7A (17).

2.109 **a.** homogeneous **b.** heterogeneous **c.** heterogeneous
d. homogeneous **e.** homogeneous

2.111 **a.** 26 protons, 30 neutrons, 26 electrons
b. $^{51}_{26}Fe$ **c.** $^{51}_{24}Cr$

2.113 $1 \text{ in.} \times \dfrac{2.54 \text{ cm}}{1 \text{ in.}} \times \dfrac{1 \text{ atom}}{3.14 \times 10^{-8} \text{ cm}} = 8.09 \times 10^7 \text{ atoms}$

2.115 $0.0140 (203.97) + 0.2410 (205.97) + 0.2210 (206.98) + 0.5240 (207.98) = 207.22$

2.117 **a.** X is a metal; Y and Z are nonmetals.
b. X has the largest atomic radius.
c. Y and Z have six valence electrons and are in Group 6A (16).
d. Y has the highest ionization energy.
e. Y has the smallest atomic radius.

2.119 **a.** X and Y are metals, and Z is a nonmetal. **b.** Z
c. X and Y are both metals. **d.** Z **e.** X

Study Goals

- Identify the types of radiation as alpha particles, beta particles, or gamma radiation.
- Describe the methods required for proper shielding for each type of radiation.
- Write an equation for an atom that undergoes radioactive decay.
- Identify some radioisotopes used in nuclear medicine.
- Calculate the amount of radioisotope that remains after a given number of half-lives.
- Describe nuclear fission and fusion.

Think About It

1. What is nuclear radiation?

2. Why do you receive more radiation if you live in the mountains or travel on an airplane?

3. In nuclear medicine, iodine-125 is used for detecting a tumor in the thyroid. What does the number 125 indicate?

4. How are living cells damaged by radiation?

5. How does nuclear fission differ from nuclear fusion?

6. Why is there a concern about radon in our homes?

Key Terms

Match each the following key terms with the correct definition.

    a. radioactive nucleus   **b.** half-life   **c.** curie

    d. nuclear fission   **e.** alpha particle

1. _____ a particle identical to a helium nucleus produced in a radioactive nucleus

2. _____ the time required for one-half of a radioactive sample to undergo radioactive decay

3. _____ a unit of radiation measurement equal to 3.7×10^{10} disintegrations per second

4. _____ a process in which large nuclei split into smaller nuclei with the release of energy

5. _____ a nucleus that spontaneously emits radiation

Answers   **1.** e   **2.** b   **3.** c
              4. d   **5.** a

3.1 Natural Radioactivity

- Radioactive isotopes have unstable nuclei that break down (decay) spontaneously, emitting alpha (α), beta (β), and gamma (γ) radiation.
- An alpha particle is the same as a helium nucleus; it contains two protons and two neutrons. A beta particle is a high-energy electron, and a gamma ray is high-energy radiation.
- Because radiation can damage the cells in the body, proper protection must be used: shielding, time limitation, and distance.

◆ **Learning Exercise 3.1A**

Study Note
It is important to learn the symbols for the radiation particles in order to describe the different types of radiation:

$_{1}^{1}H$ or $_{1}^{1}p$	$_{0}^{1}n$	$_{-1}^{0}\beta$ or $_{-1}^{0}e$	$_{2}^{4}He$ or $_{2}^{4}\alpha$	$_{+1}^{0}\beta$ or $_{+1}^{0}e$
proton	*neutron*	*electron*	*alpha particle*	*positron*

Match the description in column B with the terms in column A:

	A		**B**
1. _____	$_{8}^{18}O$	**a.**	symbol for a beta particle
2. _____	γ	**b.**	symbol for an alpha particle
3. _____	radioactive isotope	**c.**	an atom that emits radiation
4. _____	$_{2}^{4}He$	**d.**	symbol for an atom of oxygen
5. _____	β	**e.**	symbol for gamma radiation

Answers   **1.** d   **2.** e   **3.** c
            4. b   **5.** a

◆ **Learning Exercise 3.1B**

Discuss some things you can do to minimize the amount of radiation received if you work with a radioactive substance. Describe how each method helps to limit the amount of radiation you would receive.

Answer

Three ways to minimize exposure to radiation are: (1) use shielding, (2) keep time short in the radioactive area, and (3) keep as much distance as possible from the radioactive materials. Shielding such as clothing and gloves stops alpha and beta particles from reaching your skin, whereas lead or concrete will absorb gamma rays. Limiting the time spent near radioactive samples reduces exposure time. Increasing the distance from a radioactive source reduces the intensity of radiation. Wearing a film badge will monitor the amount of radiation you receive.

◆ **Learning Exercise 3.1C**

What type(s) of radiation (alpha, beta, and/or gamma) would each of the following shielding materials protect you from?

a. clothing _____   **b.** skin _____

c. paper _____   **d.** concrete _____

e. lead wall _____

Answers   **a.** alpha, beta   **b.** alpha   **c.** alpha, beta
               d. alpha, beta, gamma   **e.** alpha, beta, gamma

3.2 Nuclear Equations

- A balanced nuclear equation is used to represent the changes that take place in the nuclei of the reactants and products.
- The new isotopes and the type of radiation emitted can be determined from the symbols that show the mass numbers and atomic numbers of the isotopes in the nuclear reaction.

Radioactive nucleus $\longrightarrow$ new nucleus + radiation

Total of the mass numbers are equal

$$^{11}_{6}C \longrightarrow {}^{7}_{4}Be + {}^{4}_{2}He$$

Total of the atomic numbers are equal

◆ **Learning Exercise 3.2**

Study Note
When balancing nuclear equations for radioactive decay, be sure that
1. the mass number of the reactant equals the sum of the mass numbers of the products.   **2.** the atomic number of the reactant equals the sum of the atomic numbers of the products.

Write a nuclear symbol that completes each of the following nuclear equations:

a. $^{66}_{29}Cu \rightarrow {}^{66}_{30}Zn + ?$ **a.** _____

b. $^{127}_{53}I \rightarrow {}^{1}_{0}n + ?$ **b.** _____

c. $^{238}_{92}U \rightarrow {}^{4}_{2}He + ?$ **c.** _____

d. $^{24}_{11}N \rightarrow {}^{0}_{-1}e + ?$ **d.** _____

e. $? \rightarrow {}^{30}_{14}Si + {}^{0}_{-1}e$ **e.** _____

Answers   **a.** ${}^{0}_{-1}e$ **b.** ${}^{126}_{53}I$ **c.** ${}^{234}_{90}Th$
           d. ${}^{24}_{12}Mg$ **e.** ${}^{30}_{13}Al$

3.3 Radiation Measurement

- A Geiger counter is used to detect radiation. When radiation passes through the gas in the counter tube, some atoms of gas are ionized, producing an electrical current.
- The activity of a radioactive sample measures the number of nuclear transformations per second. The curie (Ci) is equal to 3.7×10^{10} disintegrations in 1 second. The becquerel (Bq) is equal to 1 disintegration per second.
- The radiation dose absorbed by a gram of material such as body tissue is measured in units of rad and gray.
- The biological damage of different types of radiation on the body is measured in radiation units of rem and sievert.

◆ Learning Exercise 3.3

Match each type of measurement unit with the radiation process measured.

   a. curie   **b.** becquerel   **c.** rad   **d.** gray   **e.** rem

1. _____ An activity of one disintegration per second.

2. _____ The amount of radiation absorbed by one gram of material.

3. _____ An activity of 3.7×10^{10} disintegrations per second.

4. _____ The biological damage caused by different kinds of radiation.

5. _____ A unit of absorbed dose equal to 100 rads.

Answers   **1.** b   **2.** c   **3.** a
                4. e   **5.** d

3.4 Half-Life of a Radioisotope

- The half-life of a radioactive sample is the time required for one half of the sample to decay (emit radiation).
- Most radioisotopes used in medicine, such as Tc-99m and I-131, have short half-lives. By comparison, many naturally occurring radioisotopes, such as C-14, Ra-226, and U-238, have long half-lives. For example, potassium-42 has a half-life of 12 hr, whereas potassium-40 takes 1.3×10^9 years for one-half of the radioactive sample to decay.

◆ Learning Exercise 3.4

   a. Suppose you have an 80-mg sample of iodine-125. If iodine-125 has a half-life of 60 days, how many milligrams are radioactive

   (1) after one half-life?

   (2) after two half-lives?

   (3) after 240 days?

b. ^{99m}Tc has a half-life of 6 hours. If a technician picked up a 16-mg sample at 8 AM, how much of the radioactive sample remained at 8 PM that same day?

c. Phosphorus-32 has a half-life of 14 days. How much of a 240-μg sample will be radioactive after 56 days?

d. Iodine-131 has a half-life of 8 days. How many days will it take for 80 mg of I-131 to decay to 5 mg?

e. Suppose a group of archaeologists digs up some pieces of a wooden boat at an ancient site. When a sample of the wood is analyzed for C-14, scientists determine that 12.5% or 1/8 of the original amount of C-14 remains. If the half-life of carbon-14 is 5730 years, how long ago was the boat made?

Answers   **a.** (1) 40 mg (2) 20 mg (3) 5 mg   **b.** 4.0 mg   **c.** 15 μg
d. 32 days   **e.** 17 200 years ago

3.5 Medical Applications Using Radioactivity

- In nuclear medicine, radioactive isotopes are given that go to specific sites in the body.
- For diagnostic work, radioisotopes are used that emit gamma rays and produce nonradioactive products.
- By detecting the radiation emitted by medical radioisotopes, evaluations can be made about the location and extent of an injury, disease, or tumor, blood flow, or level of function of a particular organ.

◆ Learning Exercise 3.5

Write the nuclear symbol for each of the following radioactive isotopes:

a. _____ Iodine-131 used to study thyroid gland activity.

b. _____ Phosphorus-32 used to locate brain tumors.

c. _____ Sodium-24 used to determine blood flow and locate a blood clot or embolism.

d. _____ Nitrogen-13 used in positron emission tomography.

Answers   **a.** $^{131}_{53}$I   **b.** $^{32}_{15}$P   **c.** $^{24}_{11}$Na   **d.** $^{13}_{7}$N

3.6 Nuclear Fission and Fusion

- In fission, a large nucleus breaks apart into smaller pieces, releasing one or more types of radiation and a great amount of energy.
- In fusion, small nuclei combine to form a larger nucleus, which releases great amounts of energy.

◆ **Learning Exercise 3.6**

Discuss the nuclear processes of fission and fusion for the production of energy.

Answer   *Nuclear fission* is a splitting of the atom into two or more nuclei accompanied by the release of large amounts of energy and radiation. In the process of *nuclear fusion*, two or more nuclei combine to form a heavier nucleus and release a large amount of energy. However, fusion requires a considerable amount of energy to initiate the process.

Checklist for Chapter 3

You are ready to take the practice test for chapter 3. Be sure that you have accomplished the following learning goals for this chapter. If you are not sure, review the section listed at the end of the goal. Then apply your new skills and understanding to the practice test. Good luck.

After studying chapter 3, I can successfully:

_____   Describe alpha, beta, and gamma radiation (3.1).

_____   Write a nuclear equation showing mass numbers and atomic number for radioactive decay (3.2).

_____   Describe the detection and measurement of radiation (3.3).

_____   Given a half-life, calculate the amount of radioisotope remaining after one or more half-lives (3.4).

_____   Describe the use of radioisotopes in medicine (3.5).

_____   Describe the processes of nuclear fission and fusion (3.6).

Practice Test for Chapter 3

1. The correctly written symbol for an atom of sulfur would be

    A. $^{30}_{16}Su$ **B.** $^{14}_{30}Si$ **C.** $^{30}_{16}S$ **D.** $^{30}_{16}Si$ **E.** $^{16}_{30}S$

2. Alpha particles are composed of

    A. protons   **B.** neutrons   **C.** electrons

    D. protons and electrons   **E.** protons and neutrons

3. Gamma radiation is a type of radiation that

    A. originates in the electron shells

    B. is most dangerous

    C. is least dangerous

    D. is the heaviest

    E. goes the shortest distance

4. The charge on an alpha particle is

    A. -1 **B.** $+1$ **C.** -2 **D.** $+2$ **E.** $+4$

5. Beta particles formed in a radioactive nucleus are
  A. protons   **B.** neutrons   **C.** electrons
  D. protons and electrons   **E.** protons and neutrons

For questions 6 through 10, select from the following:

  A. $_{-1}^{0}X$ **B.** $_{2}^{4}X$ **C.** $_{1}^{1}X$ **D.** $_{0}^{1}X$ **E.** $_{0}^{0}X$

6. An alpha particle

7. A beta particle

8. A gamma ray

9. A proton

10. A neutron

---

11. Shielding from gamma rays is provided by
  A. skin   **B.** paper   **C.** clothing   **D.** lead   **E.** air

12. The skin will provide shielding from
  A. alpha particles   **B.** beta particles   **C.** gamma rays
  D. ultraviolet rays   **E.** X rays

13. The radioisotope iodine-131 is used as a radioactive tracer for studying thyroid gland activity. The symbol for iodine-131 is
  A. I   **B.** $_{131}I$ **C.** $_{53}^{131}I$
  D. $_{131}^{53}I$ **E.** $_{53}^{78}I$

14. When an atom emits an alpha particle, its atomic mass will
  A. increase by 1   **B.** increase by 2   **C.** increase by 4
  D. decrease by 4   **E.** not change

15. When a nucleus emits a beta particle, the atomic number of the new nucleus
  A. increases by 1   **B.** increases by 2   **C.** decreases by 1
  D. decreases by 2   **E.** will not change

16. When a nucleus emits a gamma ray, the atomic number of the new nucleus
  A. increases by 1   **B.** increases by 2   **C.** decreases by 1
  D. decreases by 2   **E.** will not change

For questions 17–20, select the particle that completes each of the equations.
  A. neutron   **B.** alpha particle   **C.** beta particle
  D. gamma ray

17. $_{50}^{126}Sn \rightarrow {}_{51}^{126}Sb \ + \ ?$

18. $_{30}^{69}Zn \rightarrow {}_{31}^{69}Ga \ + \ ?$

19. $_{43}^{99m}Tc \rightarrow {}_{43}^{99}Tc \ + \ ?$

20. $_{62}^{149}Sm \rightarrow {}_{60}^{145}Nd \ + \ ?$

---

21. What symbol completes the following reaction?
  $_{7}^{14}N \ + \ _{0}^{1}n \rightarrow ? \ + \ _{1}^{1}H$

  A. $_{8}^{15}O$ **B.** $_{6}^{15}C$ **C.** $_{8}^{14}O$

  D. $_{6}^{14}C$ **E.** $_{7}^{15}N$

22. To complete this nuclear equation, you need to write

$${}^{54}_{26}\text{Fe} + ? \rightarrow {}^{57}_{28}\text{Ni} + {}^{1}_{0}\text{n}$$

   A. an alpha particle   **B.** a beta particle   **C.** gamma
   D. neutron   **E.** proton

23. The name of the unit used to measure the number of disintegrations per second is
   A. curie   **B.** rad   **C.** rem
   D. RBE   **E.** MRI

24. The rem and the sievert are units used to measure
   A. activity of a radioactive sample
   B. biological damage of different types of radiation
   C. radiation absorbed
   D. background radiation

25. Radiation can cause
   A. nausea   **B.** a lower white cell count   **C.** fatigue
   D. hair loss   **E.** all of these

26. Radioisotopes used in medical diagnosis
   A. have short half-lives   **B.** emit only gamma rays   **C.** locate in specific organs
   D. produce nonradioactive nuclei   **E.** all of these

27. The imaging technique that uses the energy emitted by exciting the nuclei of hydrogen atoms is
   A. computerized tomography (CT)
   B. positron emission tomography (PET)
   C. radioactive tracer
   D. magnetic resonance imaging (MRI)
   E. radiation

28. The imaging technique that detects the absorption of X rays by the body tissues is
   A. computerized tomography (CT)
   B. positron emission tomography (PET)
   C. radioactive tracer
   D. magnetic resonance imaging (MRI)
   E. radiation

29. The time required for a radioisotope to decay is measured by its
   A. half-life   **B.** protons   **C.** activity   **D.** fusion   **E.** radioisotope

30. Oxygen-15 used in PET imaging has a half-life of 2 minutes. How many half-lives have occurred in the 10 minutes it takes to prepare the sample?
   A. 2   **B.** 3   **C.** 4   **D.** 5   **E.** 6

31. Iodine-131 has a half-life of 8 days. How long will it take for a 160-mg sample to decay to 10 mg?
   A. 8 days   **B.** 16 days   **C.** 32 days   **D.** 40 days   **E.** 48 days

32. Phosphorus-32 has a half-life of 14 days. After 28 days, how many milligrams of a 100-mg sample will still be radioactive?
   A. 75 mg   **B.** 50 mg   **C.** 40 mg   **D.** 25 mg   **E.** 12.5 mg

33. The "splitting" of a large nucleus to form smaller particles accompanied by a release of energy is called
   A. radioisotope   **B.** fission   **C.** fusion   **D.** rem   **E.** half-life

34. The process of combining small nuclei to form larger nuclei is
   A. radioisotope   **B.** fission   **C.** fusion   **D.** rem   **E.** half-life

35. The fusion reaction
   A. occurs in the sun   **B.** forms larger nuclei from smaller nuclei
   C. requires extremely high temperatures   **D.** releases a large amount of energy
   E. all of these

Answers to the Practice Test

1. C	**2.** E	**3.** B	**4.** D	**5.** C
6. B	**7.** A	**8.** E	**9.** C	**10.** D
11. D	**12.** A	**13.** C	**14.** D	**15.** A
16. E	**17.** C	**18.** C	**19.** D	**20.** B
21. D	**22.** A	**23.** A	**24.** B	**25.** E
26. E	**27.** D	**28.** A	**29.** A	**30.** D
31. C	**32.** D	**33.** B	**34.** C	**35.** E

Answers and Solutions to Selected Problems

3.1 **a.** An α-particle and a helium nucleus both contain two protons and two neutrons. However, an α-particle has no electrons and carries a $2+$ charge. Alpha particles are emitted from unstable nuclei during radioactive decay.

   b. α, $_2^4\text{He}$

3.3 **a.** $_{19}^{39}\text{K}$, $_{19}^{40}\text{K}$, $_{19}^{41}\text{K}$

   b. Each isotope has 19 protons and 19 electrons, but they differ in the number of neutrons present. Potassium-39 has 20 neutrons, potassium-40 has 21 neutrons, and potassium-41 has 22 neutrons.

3.5

Medical Use	Nuclear Symbol	Mass Number	Number of Protons	Number of Neutrons
Heart imaging	$_{81}^{201}\text{Tl}$	201	81	120
Radiation therapy	$_{27}^{60}\text{Co}$	60	27	33
Abdominal scan	$_{31}^{67}\text{Ga}$	67	31	36
Hyperthyroidism	$_{53}^{131}\text{I}$	131	53	78
Leukemia treatment	$_{15}^{32}\text{P}$	32	15	17

3.7 **a.** α, $_2^4\text{He}$ **b.** $_0^1\text{n}$ **c.** β, $_{-1}^{0}\text{e}$ **d.** $_7^{15}\text{N}$ **e.** $_{53}^{125}\text{I}$

3.9 **a.** β (or e^-)   **b.** α (or He)   **c.** n   **d.** Na   **e.** C

3.11 **a.** Because β-particles move faster than α-particles, they can penetrate further into tissue.

   b. Ionizing radiation breaks bonds and forms reactive species that cause undesirable reactions in the cells.

   c. X-ray technicians leave the room to increase their distance from the radiation source. A thick wall or one that contains lead also shields them.

   d. Wearing gloves shields the skin from α and β radiation.

3.13 The mass number of the radioactive atom is reduced by 4 when an alpha particle is emitted. The unknown product will have an atomic number that is 2 less than the atomic number of the radioactive atom.

   a. $_{84}^{208}\text{Po} \rightarrow _{82}^{204}\text{Pb} + _2^4\text{He}$ **b.** $_{90}^{232}\text{Th} \rightarrow _{88}^{228}\text{Ra} + _2^4\text{He}$

   c. $_{102}^{251}\text{No} \rightarrow _{100}^{247}\text{Fm} + _2^4\text{He}$ **d.** $_{86}^{220}\text{Rn} \rightarrow _{86}^{216}\text{Po} + _2^4\text{He}$

3.15 **a.** $_{11}^{25}\text{Na} \rightarrow _{12}^{25}\text{Mg} + _{-1}^{0}\text{e}$ **b.** $_8^{20}\text{O} \rightarrow _9^{20}\text{F} + _{-1}^{0}\text{e}$

   c. $_{38}^{92}\text{Sr} \rightarrow _{39}^{92}\text{Y} + _{-1}^{0}\text{e}$ **d.** $_{19}^{42}\text{K} \rightarrow _{20}^{42}\text{Ca} + _{-1}^{0}\text{e}$

3.17 a. $^{26}_{14}\text{Si} \rightarrow \, ^{26}_{13}\text{Al} + \, ^{0}_{+1}\text{e}$ **b.** $^{54}_{27}\text{Co} \rightarrow \, ^{54}_{26}\text{Fe} + \, ^{0}_{+1}\text{e}$

c. $^{77}_{37}\text{Rb} \rightarrow \, ^{77}_{36}\text{Kr} + \, ^{0}_{+1}\text{e}$ **d.** $^{93}_{45}\text{Rh} \rightarrow \, ^{93}_{44}\text{Ru} + \, ^{0}_{+1}\text{e}$

3.19 a. $^{28}_{13}\text{Al} \rightarrow \, ^{28}_{14}\text{Si} + \, ^{0}_{-1}\text{e}$ **b.** $^{87}_{36}\text{Kr} \rightarrow \, ^{86}_{36}\text{Kr} + \, ^{1}_{0}\text{n}$ **c.** $^{66}_{29}\text{Cu} \rightarrow \, ^{66}_{30}\text{Zn} + \, ^{0}_{-1}\text{e}$

d. $^{238}_{92}\text{U} \rightarrow \, ^{4}_{2}\text{He} + \, ^{234}_{90}\text{Th}$ **e.** $^{188}_{80}\text{Hg} \rightarrow \, ^{188}_{79}\text{Au} + \, ^{0}_{+1}\text{e}$

3.21 a. $^{9}_{4}\text{Be} + \, ^{1}_{0}\text{n} \rightarrow \, ^{10}_{4}\text{Be}$ **b.** $^{32}_{16}\text{S} + \, ^{0}_{-1}\text{e} \rightarrow \, ^{32}_{15}\text{P}$ **c.** $^{27}_{13}\text{Al} + \, ^{1}_{0}\text{n} \rightarrow \, ^{24}_{11}\text{Na} + \, ^{4}_{2}\text{He}$

d. To balance the mass numbers, the unknown product must have a mass of 1. Balancing the number of protons gives an atomic number of 1. The unknown product is a proton.

$$^{27}_{13}\text{Al} + \, ^{4}_{2}\text{He} \rightarrow \, ^{30}_{14}\text{Si} + \, ^{1}_{1}\text{H}$$

3.23 a. When radiation enters the Geiger counter, it ionizes a gas in the detection tube. The ions created in the tube move toward an electrode of opposite charge. This flow of charge produces an electric current, which is detected by the instrument.

b. The becquerel (Bq) is the SI unit for activity. The curie (Ci) is the original unit for activity of radioactive samples.

c. The SI unit for absorbed dose is the gray (Gy). The rad (radiation absorbed dose) is a unit of radiation absorbed per gram of sample. It is the older unit.

d. A kilogray is 1000 gray, which is equivalent to 100 000 rads.

3.25 $70.0 \, \cancel{\text{kg}} \times \dfrac{4.20 \, \mu\text{Ci}}{1 \, \cancel{\text{kg}}} = 294 \, \mu\text{Ci}$

3.27 While flying a plane, a pilot is exposed to higher levels of background radiation because there is less atmosphere to act as a shield against cosmic radiation.

3.29 Half-life is the time required for one-half of a radioactive sample to decay.

3.31 a. After one half-life, one-half of the sample would be radioactive: $80.0 \text{ mg} \times \frac{1}{2} = 40.0 \text{ mg}$

b. After two half-lives, one-fourth of the sample would still be radioactive:

$80.0 \text{ mg} \times \frac{1}{2} \times \frac{1}{2} = 80.0 \text{ mg} \times \frac{1}{4} = 20.0 \text{ mg}.$

c. $18 \, \cancel{\text{hr}} \times \dfrac{1 \text{ half-life}}{6.0 \, \cancel{\text{hr}}} = 3.0 \text{ half-lives}$

$80.0 \text{ mg} \times \frac{1}{2} \times \frac{1}{2} \times \frac{1}{2} = 80.0 \text{ mg} \times \frac{1}{8} = 10.0 \text{ mg}$

d. $24 \, \cancel{\text{hr}} \times \dfrac{1 \text{ half-life}}{6.0 \, \cancel{\text{hr}}} = 4.0 \text{ half-lives}$

$80.0 \text{ mg} \times \frac{1}{2} \times \frac{1}{2} \times \frac{1}{2} \times \frac{1}{2} = 80.0 \text{ mg} \times 1/16 = 5.00 \text{ mg}$

3.33 The radiation level in a radioactive sample is cut in half with each half-life. We must first determine the number of half-lives.

$\frac{1}{4} = \frac{1}{2} \times \frac{1}{2} = 2 \text{ half-lives}$

Because each half-life is 64 days, it will take 128 days for the radiation level of strontium-85 to fall to one fourth of its original value: $2 \, \cancel{\text{half-lives}} \times 64 \text{ days}/\cancel{\text{half-life}} = 128 \text{ days}$.

To determine the amount of time for the strontium-85 to drop to one-eighth its original activity, we calculate the number of half-lives: $1/8 = \frac{1}{2} \times \frac{1}{2} \times \frac{1}{2} = 3 \text{ half-lives}$.

Because each half-life is 64 days, it will take 192 days for the radiation level of strontium-85 to fall to one-eighth of its original value: $3 \, \cancel{\text{half-lives}} \times 64 \text{ days}/\cancel{\text{half-life}} = 192 \text{ days}$.

3.35 **a.** Because the elements calcium and phosphorus are part of bone, any calcium and/or phosphorus atom, regardless of isotope, will be carried to and become part of the bony structures in the body. Once there, the radiation emitted by the radioisotope can be used for diagnosis or treatment of bone diseases.

b. Strontium is chemically similar to calcium, so it too will be carried to the bones. Once in the bone, the radiation emitted can destroy healthy bone and bony structures.

3.37 $4.0 \text{ mL} \times \dfrac{45 \ \mu\text{Ci}}{1 \text{ mL}} = 180 \ \mu\text{Ci}$

3.39 Nuclear fission is the splitting of a large atom into smaller fragments with a simultaneous release of large amounts of energy.

3.41 $^{235}_{92}\text{U} + ^{1}_{0}\text{n} \rightarrow ^{131}_{50}\text{Sn} + ^{103}_{42}\text{Mo} + 2^{1}_{0}\text{n}$

3.43 **a.** fission **b.** fusion **c.** fission **d.** fusion

3.45 **a.** $^{11}_{6}\text{C}$

b.

3.47

3.49 Half of a radioactive sample decays with each half-life:

$\frac{1}{2}$ lives

$\begin{array}{cccccc} & (1) & & (2) & & (3) \\ & 5740 \ y & & 5740 \ y & & 5740 \ y \\ 6.4 \ \mu\text{Ci} & \longrightarrow & 3.2 \ \mu\text{Ci} & \longrightarrow & 1.6 \ \mu\text{Ci} & \longrightarrow & 0.80 \ \mu\text{Ci} \end{array}$

Therefore, the activity of carbon-14 drops to 0.80 μCi in three half-lives or 3 × 5740 years, which makes the age of the painting 17 200 years.

3.51 Both carbon-12 and carbon-14 contain six protons and six electrons, but there are only six neutrons in a carbon-12 nucleus, whereas a carbon-14 nucleus has eight. Carbon-12 is a stable isotope, but carbon-14 is radioactive and will emit radiation.

3.53 **a.** Alpha (α) and beta (β) radiation consist of particles emitted from an unstable nucleus, whereas gamma (γ) rays are radiation emitted as pure energy.

b. Alpha radiation is abbreviated as α, $^{4}_{2}\alpha$, and $^{4}_{2}\text{He}$. Beta radiation is abbreviated as β, β^{-}, $^{0}_{-1}\beta$, and $^{0}_{-1}\text{e}$. Gamma radiation is abbreviated as γ and $^{0}_{0}\gamma$.

c. Alpha particles cannot penetrate skin, beta particles penetrate 4 to 5 mm into body tissue, and gamma radiation easily passes through body tissues.

d. Lightweight clothing or a piece of paper will shield against alpha particles, heavy clothing and gloves will shield against beta particles, and thick concrete and lead will shield against gamma rays.

3.55 **a.** $^{225}_{90}\text{Th} \rightarrow ^{221}_{88}\text{Ra} + ^{4}_{2}\text{He}$ **b.** $^{210}_{83}\text{Bi} \rightarrow ^{206}_{81}\text{Tl} + ^{4}_{2}\text{He}$

 c. $^{137}_{55}\text{Cs} \rightarrow ^{137}_{56}\text{Ba} + ^{0}_{-1}\text{e}$ **d.** $^{126}_{50}\text{Sn} \rightarrow ^{126}_{51}\text{Sb} + ^{0}_{-1}\text{e}$

3.57 **a.** $^{14}_{7}\text{N} + ^{4}_{2}\text{He} \rightarrow ^{17}_{8}\text{O} + ^{1}_{1}\text{H}$

b. $^{27}_{13}\text{Al} + ^{4}_{2}\text{He} \rightarrow ^{30}_{14}\text{Si} + ^{1}_{1}\text{H}$

c. $^{235}_{92}\text{U} + ^{1}_{0}\text{n} \rightarrow ^{90}_{38}\text{Sr} + 3^{1}_{0}\text{n} + ^{143}_{54}\text{Xe}$

3.59 **a.** $^{16}_{8}\text{O} + ^{16}_{8}\text{O} \rightarrow ^{4}_{2}\text{He} + ^{28}_{14}\text{Si}$

b. $^{249}_{98}\text{Cf} + ^{18}_{8}\text{O} \rightarrow ^{263}_{106}\text{Sg} + 4^{1}_{0}\text{n}$

c. $^{222}_{86}\text{Rn} \rightarrow ^{4}_{2}\text{He} + ^{218}_{84}\text{Po}$

Then polonium-218 decays as follows:

$^{218}_{84}\text{Po} \rightarrow ^{4}_{2}\text{He} + ^{214}_{82}\text{Pb}$

3.61 Half of a radioactive sample decays with each half-life:

$\frac{1}{2}$ lives   (1)   (2)
1.2 g $\longrightarrow$ 0.60 g $\longrightarrow$ 0.30 g

Therefore, the amount of phosphorus-32 will drop to 0.30 g in two half-lives, which is 28 days. One half-life is 14 days: 28 days/2 half-lives = 14 days/half-life.

3.63 **a.** $^{131}_{53}\text{I} \rightarrow ^{0}_{-1}\text{e} + ^{131}_{47}\text{Xe}$
b. First we must determine the number of half-lives.

$$40 \text{ days} \times \frac{1 \text{ half-life}}{8.0 \text{ days}} = 5.0 \text{ half-lives}$$

Now we can calculate the number of grams of iodine-131 remaining:

$$2.0 \text{ g} \times (\tfrac{1}{2} \times \tfrac{1}{2} \times \tfrac{1}{2} \times \tfrac{1}{2} \times \tfrac{1}{2}) = 12.0 \text{ g} \times 1/32 = 0.375 \text{ g}$$

c. One-half of a radioactive sample decays with each half-life:

$\frac{1}{2}$ lives (1)   (2)   (3)   (4)
48 g $\longrightarrow$ 24 g $\longrightarrow$ 12 g $\longrightarrow$ 6.0 g $\longrightarrow$ 3.0 g

When 3.0 g remains, four half-lives must have passed. Because each half-life is 8.0 days, we can calculate the number of days that the sample required to decay to 3.0 g.

$$4 \text{ half-lives} \times \frac{8.0 \text{ days}}{1 \text{ half-life}} = 32 \text{ days}$$

3.65 First, calculate the number of half-lives that have passed since the nurse was exposed:

$$36 \text{ hrs} \times \frac{1 \text{ half-life}}{12 \text{ hrs}} = 3.0 \text{ half-lives}$$

Because the activity of a radioactive sample is cut in half with each half-life, the activity must have been double its present value before each half-life. For 3.0 half-lives, we need to double the value three times: $2.0 \ \mu\text{Ci} \times (2 \times 2 \times 2) = 16 \ \mu\text{Ci}$.

3.67 First, calculate the number of half-lives:

$$24 \text{ hrs} \times \frac{1 \text{ half-life}}{6.0 \text{ hrs}} = 4.0 \text{ half-lives}$$

And now calculate the amount of technetium-99^{m} that remains after four half-lives have passed:

$$120 \text{ mg} \times (\tfrac{1}{2} \times \tfrac{1}{2} \times \tfrac{1}{2} \times \tfrac{1}{2}) = 120 \text{ mg} \times 1/16 = 7.5 \text{ mg}$$

3.69 Irradiating foods kills bacteria that are responsible for food-borne illnesses and food spoilage. As a result, shelf life of the food is extended.

3.71 Nuclear fission is the splitting of a large atom into smaller fragments with a simultaneous release of large amounts of energy. Nuclear fusion occurs when two (or more) nuclei combine (fuse) to form a larger species, with a simultaneous release of large amounts of energy.

3.73 Fusion reactions naturally occur in stars, such as our sun.

3.75 **a.** gamma radiation **b.** positron emission
c. beta decay **d.** alpha decay

3.77 $\frac{1}{2}$ life $= 4.5$ days ^{47}Ca 4.0 μCi after 18 days

$$18 \text{ days} \times \frac{1 \text{ half-life}}{4.5 \text{ days}} = 4 \text{ half-lives}$$

$$64 \ \mu\text{Ci} \rightarrow 32 \ \mu\text{Ci} \rightarrow 16 \ \mu\text{Ci} \rightarrow 8.0 \ \mu\text{Ci} \rightarrow 4.0 \ \mu\text{Ci}$$

3.79 **a.** $^{180}_{80}\text{Hg} \rightarrow \ ^{176}_{78}\text{Pt} + \ ^{4}_{2}\text{He}$

b. $^{126}_{50}\text{Sn} \rightarrow \ ^{126}_{51}\text{Sb} + \ ^{0}_{-1}\text{e}$

c. $^{49}_{25}\text{Mn} \rightarrow \ ^{49}_{24}\text{Cr} + \ ^{0}_{-1}\text{e}$

Compounds and Their Bonds

Study Goals

- Use the octet rule to determine the ionic charge of ions for representative elements.
- Use charge balance to write an ionic formula.
- Draw the electron dot structure for covalent compounds.
- Write the correct names for ionic and covalent compounds.
- Use electronegativity values to identify polar and nonpolar covalent bonds.
- Write ionic formulas and names of compound with polyatomic ions.
- Use VSEPR theory to determine the shape and bond angles of a molecule.
- Identify a covalent compound as polar or nonpolar.

Think About It

1. What is the octet rule?

2. How does a compound differ from an element?

3. What are some compounds listed on the labels of your vitamins, toothpaste, and foods?

4. What makes salt an ionic compound?

5. How can you predict the bond angles in a molecule of a covalent compound?

Key Terms

Match each the following key terms with the correct definition.

A. valence electrons	**B.** cation	**C.** ionic bond
D. covalent bond	**E.** octet	**F.** anion

1. _____ a sharing of valence electrons by two atoms

2. _____ an arrangement of eight electrons in the outer electron energy level

3. _____ the attraction between positively and negatively charged particles

4. _____ the electrons that make up the outmost energy level (shell) of an atom

5. _____ an atom or group of atoms with a positive charge

6. _____ an atom or group of atoms with a negative charge

Answers   **1.** D   **2.** E   **3.** C   **4.** A   **5.** B   **6.** F

4.1 Octet Rule and Ions

- The stability of the noble gases is associated with an electron configuration of eight electrons (s^2p^6), an octet, in their outer energy level. Helium is stable, with two electrons in the outer energy level.

  He $1s^2$ Ne $1s^2 2s^2 2p^6$
  Ar $1s^2 2s^2 2p^6 3s^2 3p^6$ Kr $1s^2 2s^2 2p^6 3s^2 3p^6 4s^2 3d^{10} 4p^6$

  Atoms of elements other than the noble gases achieve stability by losing, gaining, or sharing their valence electrons with other atoms in the formation of compounds.

- A metal of the representative elements in Groups 1, 2, and 3 achieves a noble gas electron arrangement by losing its valence electrons to form a positively charged cation 1+, 2+, or 3+.
- When a nonmetal forms ions, electrons add to give an octet and form a negatively charged anion with a charge of 3−, 2−, or 1−.

◆ Learning Exercise 4.1A

Study Note

When an atom loses or gains electrons, it acquires the electron configuration of its nearest noble gas. For example, sodium loses one electron, which gives the Na^+ ion a configuration like neon. Oxygen gains two electrons to give an oxide ion O^{2-} a configuration like neon.

The following elements lose electrons when they form ions. Indicate the group number, the number of electrons lost, and the ion (symbol and charge) for each of the following:

Group Number	Element	Electrons Lost	Ion Formed
	Magnesium		
	Sodium		
	Calcium		
	Potassium		
	Aluminum		

Answers

Group Number	Element	Electrons Lost	Ion Formed
2A (2)	Magnesium	2	Mg^{2+}
1A (1)	Sodium	1	Na^+
2A (2)	Calcium	2	Ca^{2+}
1A (1)	Potassium	1	K^+
3A (13)	Aluminum	3	Al^{3+}

◆ Learning Exercise 4.1B

Study Note

The valence electrons are the electrons in the outermost energy level of an atom. For representative elements, you can determine the number of valence electrons by looking at the group number.

The following elements gain electrons when they form ions. Indicate the group number, the number of electrons gained, and the ion (symbol and charge) for each of the following:

Element	Group Number	Electrons Gained	Ion Formed
Chlorine			
Oxygen			
Nitrogen			
Fluorine			
Sulfur			

Answers

Element	Group Number	Electrons Gained	Ion Formed
Chlorine	7A (17)	1	Cl^-
Oxygen	6A (16)	2	O^{2-}
Nitrogen	5A (15)	3	N^{3-}
Fluorine	7A (17)	1	F^-
Sulfur	6A (16)	2	S^{2-}

4.2 Ionic Compounds

- In the formulas of ionic compounds, the total positive charge is equal to the total negative charge. For example, the compound magnesium chloride, $MgCl_2$, contains Mg^{2+} and $2\,Cl^-$. The sum of the charges is zero: $(2+) + 2(-) = 0$.
- When two or more ions are needed for charge balance, that number is indicated by subscripts in the formula.

◆ Learning Exercise 4.2A

For this exercise, you may want to cut pieces of paper that represent typical positive and negative ions as shown below. To determine an ionic formula, place the pieces together (positive ion first). Add more positive or negative ions to complete a geometric shape. Write the number of positive ions and negative ions as the subscripts for the formula.

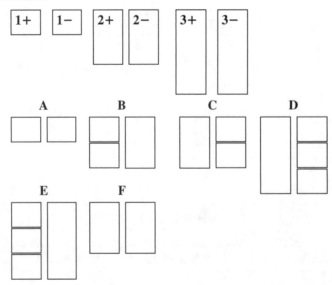

Give the letter (A, B, C, etc.) that matches the arrangement of ions in the following compounds:

Compound	Combination	Compound	Combination
1. $MgCl_2$	_____	2. Na_2S	_____
3. LiCl	_____	4. CaO	_____
5. K_3N	_____	6. $AlBr_3$	_____
7. MgS	_____	8. $BaCl_2$	_____

Answers   1. C   2. B   3. A   4. F
5. E   6. D   7. F   8. C

◆ **Learning Exercise 4.2B**

Study Note
You can check that the formula you write is electrically neutral by multiplying each of the ionic charges by their subscripts. When added together, their sum should equal zero. For example, the formula Na_2O gives $2(1+) + 1(2-) = (2+) + (2-) = 0$.

Write the correct ionic formula for the compound formed from the following pairs of ions:

1. Na^+ and Cl^- _____

2. K^+ and S^{2-} _____

3. Al^{3+} and O^{2-} _____

4. Mg^{2+} and Cl^- _____

5. Ca^{2+} and S^{2-} _____

6. Al^{3+} and Cl^- _____

7. Li^+ and N^{3-} _____

8. Ba^{2+} and P^{3-} _____

Answers   1. NaCl   2. K_2S 3. Al_2O_3 4. $MgCl_2$
5. CaS   6. $AlCl_3$ 7. Li_3N 8. Ba_3P_2

4.3 Naming and Writing Ionic Compounds

- In naming ionic compounds, the positive ion is named first, followed by the name of the negative ion. The name of a representative metal ion (Group 1A, 2A, or 3A) is the same as its elemental name. The name of a nonmetal ion is obtained by replacing the end of its element name with *ide*.
- Most transition metals form cations with two or more ionic charges. Then the ionic charge must be written as a Roman numeral after the name of the metal. For example, the cations of iron Fe^{2+} and Fe^{3+} are named iron(II) and iron(III). The ions of copper are Cu^+, copper(I) and Cu^{2+}, copper(II).
- The only transition elements with fixed charges are zinc, Zn^{2+}, silver, Ag^+, and cadmium, Cd^{2+}.

◆ **Learning Exercise 4.3A**

Many of the transition metals form two or more ions with positive charge. Complete the table:

Name of Ion	Symbol of Ion	Name of Ion	Symbol of Ion
1. iron(III)	_____	2. _____	Cu^{2+}
3. zinc	_____	4. _____	Fe^{2+}
5. copper(I)	_____	6. _____	Ag^+
7. tin(IV)	_____	8. _____	Cr^{2+}

Answers **1.** Fe^{3+} **2.** copper(II)   **3.** Zn^{2+}
4. iron(II)   **5.** Cu^+ **6.** silver
7. Sn^{4+} **8.** chromium(II)

◆ Learning Exercise 4.3B

Write the ions and the correct ionic formula for the following ionic compounds:

Compound	Positive Ion	Negative Ion	Formula of Compound
Aluminum sulfide			
Copper(II) chloride			
Magnesium oxide			
Iron(II) bromide			
Silver oxide			

Answers

Compound	Positive Ion	Negative Ion	Formula of Compound
Aluminum sulfide	Al^{3+}	S^{2-}	Al_2S_3
Copper(I) chloride	Cu^{2+}	Cl^-	$CuCl_2$
Magnesium oxide	Mg^{2+}	O^{2-}	MgO
Iron(II) bromide	Fe^{2+}	Br^-	$FeBr_2$
Silver oxide	Ag^+	O^{2-}	Ag_2O

◆ Learning Exercise 4.3C

Write the names of each of the following ions:

1. Cl^- _____   **2.** Fe^{2+} _____

3. Cu^+ _____   **4.** Ag^+ _____

5. O^{2-} _____   **6.** Ca^{2+} _____

7. S^{2-} _____   **8.** Al^{3+} _____

9. Fe^{3+} _____   **10.** Ba^{2+} _____

11. Cu^{2+} _____   **12.** N^{3-} _____

Answers   **1.** chloride   **2.** iron(II)
3. copper(I)   **4.** silver
5. oxide   **6.** calcium
7. sulfide   **8.** aluminum
9. iron(III)   **10.** barium
11. copper(II)   **12.** nitride

◆ Learning Exercise 4.3D

Study Note
The ionic charge of a metal that forms more than one positive ion is determined from the total negative charge in the formula. For example, in $FeCl_3$, the $3\ Cl^- = 3(-)$. Therefore, the iron ion has an ionic charge of $3+$ or Fe^{3+}, which is named iron(III).

Write the ions and a correct name for each of the following ionic compounds:

Formula	Ions		Name
1. $BaCl_2$	_____	_____	_____
2. $FeBr_3$	_____	_____	_____
3. Na_3P	_____	_____	_____
4. Al_2O_3	_____	_____	_____
5. CuO	_____	_____	_____
6. Mg_3N_2	_____	_____	_____

Answers
1. Ba^{2+}, Cl^-, barium chloride
2. Fe^{3+}, Br^-, iron(III) bromide
3. Na^+, P^{3-}, sodium phosphide
4. Al^{3+}, O^{2-}, aluminum oxide
5. Cu^{2+}, O^{2-}, copper(II) oxide
6. Mg^{2+}, N^{3-}, magnesium nitride

4.4 Polyatomic Ions

- A polyatomic ion is a group of nonmetal atoms that carries an electrical charge, usually negative, $1-$, $2-$, or $3-$.
- Polyatomic ions cannot exist alone but are combined with an ion of the opposite charge.
- Ionic compounds containing three elements (polyatomic ions) end with *-ate* or *-ite*.

Study Note

Learn the most common polyatomic ions: nitrate NO_3^{2-}, carbonate CO_3^{2-}, sulfate SO_4^{2-}, and phosphate PO_4^{3-}. From these, you can derive the related polyatomic ions. For example, the nitrite ion, NO_2^-, has one oxygen atom less than the nitrate.

◆ Learning Exercise 4.4

Write the polyatomic ion (symbol and charge) for each of the following:

1. sulfate ion _____   2. hydroxide ion _____

3. carbonate ion _____   4. sulfite ion _____

5. ammonium ion _____   6. phosphate ion _____

7. nitrate ion _____   8. nitrite ion _____

Answers
1. SO_4^{2-} 2. OH^- 3. CO_3^{2-} 4. SO_3^{2-}
5. NH_4^+ 6. PO_4^{3-} 7. NO_3^- 8. NO_2^-

4.5 Covalent Compounds

- In a covalent bond, atoms of nonmetals share electrons to achieve an octet. For example, oxygen with six valence electrons shares electrons with two hydrogen atoms to form the covalent compound water (H_2O).

$$H\!:\!\ddot{\underset{\displaystyle H}{O}}\!:$$

- In a double bond, two pairs of electrons are shared between the same two atoms. In a triple bond, three pairs of electrons are shared.
- Covalent compounds are composed of nonmetals bonded together to give discrete units called molecules.

- The formula of a covalent compound is written using the symbol of the nonmetals in the name followed by subscripts given by the prefixes.

◆ Learning Exercise 4.5A

List the number of bonds typically formed by the following atoms in covalent compounds:

a. N ____   b. S ____   c. P ____   d. C ____

e. Cl ____   f. O ____   g. H ____   h. F ____

Answers   **a.** 3   **b.** 2   **c.** 3   **d.** 4
             e. 1   **f.** 2   **g.** 1   **h.** 1

◆ Learning Exercise 4.5B

Write the electron dot structures for the following covalent compounds (the central atom is underlined):

H_2 $\underline{N}Cl_3$ HCl

Cl_2 $H_2\underline{S}$ $\underline{C}Cl_4$

Answers

H:H   :Cl:N:Cl: H:Cl: :Cl:Cl: H:S: :Cl:C:Cl:
            :Cl: H   :Cl:

(with :Cl: above the central C in CCl_4)

◆ Learning Exercise 4.5C

Study Note
Two nonmetals can form two or more different covalent compounds. In their names, prefixes are used to indicate the subscript in the formula. Some typical prefixes are mono (1), di (2), tri (3), tetra (4), and penta (5). The ending of the second nonmetal is changed to *-ide*.

Use the appropriate prefixes in naming the following covalent compounds:

1. CS_2 _____   **2.** CCl_4 _____

3. CO _____   **4.** SO_2 _____

5. N_2O_4 _____   **6.** PCl_3 _____

Answers   **1.** carbon disulfide   **2.** carbon tetrachloride   **3.** carbon monoxide
             4. sulfur dioxide   **5.** dinitrogen tetroxide   **6.** phosphorus trichloride

◆ Learning Exercise 4.5D

Write the formula of each of the following covalent compounds:

1. dinitrogen oxide _____   **2.** silicon tetrabromide _____

3. nitrogen trichloride _____ **4.** carbon dioxide _____

5. sulfur hexafluoride _____ **6.** oxygen diflouride _____

Answers **1.** N_2O **2.** $SiBr_4$ **3.** NCl_3
 4. CO_2 **5.** SF_6 **6.** OF_2

Summary of Writing Formulas and Names

- In both ionic and covalent compounds containing *two* different elements, the name of the element written first is named as the element. The ending of the name of the second element is replaced by "ide." For example, $BaCl_2$ is named *barium chloride*. If the metal is variable and forms two or more positive ions, a Roman numeral is added to its name to indicate the ionic charge in the compound. For example, $FeCl_3$ is named *iron(III) chloride*.
- In naming covalent compounds, a prefix before the name of an element indicates the numerical value of a subscript. For example, N_2O_3 is named *dinitrogen trioxide*.
- In ionic compounds with three or more elements, a group of atoms is named as a polyatomic ion. The names of negative polyatomic ions end in "ate" or "ite," except for hydroxide. For example, Na_2SO_4 is named *sodium sulfate*.
- When a polyatomic ion occurs two or three times in a formula, its formula is placed inside parenthesis and the number of ions are shown as a subscript after the parenthesis: $Ca(NO_3)_2$.

◆ Learning Exercise 4.5E

Write the formula of each ion or polyatomic ion and the correct formula for the following compounds:

Compound	Positive Ion	Negative Ion	Formula
Sodium phosphate			
Iron(II) hydroxide			
Ammonium carbonate			
Silver bicarbonate			
Iron(III) sulfate			
Ferrous nitrate			
Potassium sulfite			
Barium phosphate			

Answers

Compound	Positive Ion	Negative Ion	Formula
Sodium phosphate	Na^+	PO_4^{3-}	Na_3PO_4
Iron(II) hydroxide	Fe^{2+}	OH^-	$Fe(OH)_2$
Ammonium carbonate	NH_4^+	CO_3^{2-}	$(NH_4)_2CO_3$
Silver bicarbonate	Ag^+	HCO_3^-	$AgHCO_3$
Iron(III) sulfate	Fe^{3+}	SO_4^{2-}	$Fe_2(SO_4)_3$
Iron(II) nitrate	Fe^{2+}	NO_3^-	$Fe(NO_3)_2$
Potassium sulfite	K^+	SO_3^{2-}	K_2SO_3
Barium phosphate	Ba^{2+}	PO_4^{3-}	$Ba_3(PO_4)_2$

◆ Learning Exercise 4.5F

Indicate the type of compound (ionic or covalent) formed from each pair of elements. If it is ionic, write the ions; if covalent, write the structure of the molecule. Then give a formula and name for each.

Components	Ionic or Covalent	Ions or Structure of Molecule	Formula	Name
Mg and Cl				
N and Cl				
K and SO_4				
Li and O				
C and Cl				
Na and PO_4				
H and S				
Ca and HCO_3				

Answers

Mg and Cl	ionic	Mg^{2+}, Cl^-	$MgCl_2$	magnesium chloride
N and Cl	covalent	Cl—N—Cl $\quad$ Cl	NCl_3	nitrogen trichloride
K and SO_4	ionic	K^+, SO_4^{2-}	K_2SO_4	potassium sulfate
Li and O	ionic	Li^+, O^{2-}	Li_2O	lithium oxide
C and Cl	covalent	Cl—C—Cl with Cl above and Cl below	CCl_4	carbon tetrachloride
Na and PO_4	Ionic	Na^+, PO_4^{3-}	Na_3PO_4	sodium phosphate
H and S	covalent	H—S—H	H_2S	dihydrogen sulfide
Ca and HCO_3	Ionic	Ca^{2+}, HCO_3^-	$Ca(HCO_3)_2$	calcium hydrogen carbonate (bicarbonate)

4.6 Electronegativity and Bond Polarity

- Electronegativity values indicate the ability of an atom to attract electrons. In general, metals have low electronegativity values and nonmetals have high values.
- When atoms sharing electrons have the same or almost the same electronegativity values (usually atoms of the same element), the pair is shared equally and the bond is nonpolar covalent. The electronegativity difference is 0 to 0.4.
- Electrons are shared unequally in polar covalent bonds because they are attracted to the more electronegative atom. Then electronegativity difference is between 0.4 and about 1.6. Above 1.6, the bond is considered to be ionic.

◆ Learning Exercise 4.6

Identify the bonding between the following pairs of elements as ionic (I), polar covalent (P), nonpolar covalent (C), or none.

1. H and N _____   2. P and O _____   3. Mg and O_____

4. Li and F _____   5. H and Cl _____   6. Cl and Cl_____

7. S and F _____   8. He and He _____

Answers   1. P   2. P   3. I   4. I
              5. P   6. C   7. P   8. none

4.7 Shapes and Polarities of Molecules

- Valence-shell electron-pair repulsion (VSEPR) theory predicts the geometry of a molecule by placing the electron pairs around a central atom as far apart as possible.
- A central atom with two electron groups has a linear structure (180°); three electron groups give a trigonal planar structure (120°); and four electron pairs give a tetrahedral structure (109°).
- The number of bonded atoms determines the shape of a molecule. A linear molecule has a central atom bonded to two atoms and no lone pairs. A trigonal planar molecule has a central atom bonded to three atoms and no lone pairs. A bent molecule at 120° has a central atom bonded to two atoms and one lone pair.
- A tetrahedral molecule has a central atom bonded to four atoms and no lone pairs. In a pyramidal molecule (109°), a central atom is bonded to three atoms and one lone pair. In a bent molecule at 109°, a central atom is bonded to two atoms and two lone pairs.
- A polar bond with its charge separation is called a dipole; the positive end is marked as δ^+ and the negative end as δ^-.
- Nonpolar molecules can have polar bonds when the dipoles are in a symmetrical arrangement that cancels.
- In polar molecules, the dipoles do not cancel each other.

Study Note

Guidelines for predicting the shaping of molecules:

1. Write the electron dot structure.
2. Use VSEPR theory to predict the arrangement of the electron groups around the central atom.
3. Identify the shape of the molecule or ion from the number of atoms bonded to the central atom.

◆ Learning Exercise 4.7A

Match the shape of a molecule with the following descriptions of the electron groups around the central atoms and the number of bonded atoms.

A. linear   B. trigonal planar   C. tetrahedral
D. pyramidal   E. bent (120°)   F. bent (109°)

1. three electron groups with three bonded atoms _____

2. two electron groups with two bonded atoms _____

3. four electron groups with three bonded atoms _____

4. three electron groups with two bonded atoms _____

5. four electron groups with four bonded atoms _____

6. four electron groups with two bonded atoms _____

Answers   1. B   2. A   3. D
4. E   5. C   6. F

◆ **Learning Exercise 4.7B**

For each of the following, write the electron dot structure, state the number of electron groups and bonded atoms, and predict the shape and angles of the molecule or ion:

Molecule or Ion	Electron Dot Structure	Number of Electron Groups	Number of Bonded Atoms	Shape and Angle
CH_4				
PCl_3				
SO_3				
H_2S				

Answers

Molecule or Ion	Electron Dot Structure	Number of Electron Groups	Number of Bonded Atoms	Shape and Angle
CH_4	H H:C:H H	4	4	Tetrahedral, 109°
PCl_3	:Cl:P:Cl: :Cl:	4	3	Pyramidal, 109°
SO_3	:O:S::O: :O:	3	3	Trigonal planar, 120°
H_2S	H:S: H	4	2	Bent, 109°

◆ **Learning Exercise 4.7C**

Write the symbols δ^+ and δ^- over the atoms in polar bonds.

1. H—O   2. N—H   3. C—Cl

4. O—F   5. N—F   6. P—Cl

Answers

1. $\overset{\delta^+}{H}—\overset{\delta^-}{O}$ 2. $\overset{\delta^-}{N}—\overset{\delta^+}{H}$ 3. $\overset{\delta^+}{C}—\overset{\delta^-}{Cl}$

4. $\overset{\delta^+}{O}—\overset{\delta^-}{F}$ 5. $\overset{\delta^+}{N}—\overset{\delta^-}{F}$ 6. $\overset{\delta^+}{P}—\overset{\delta^-}{Cl}$

◆ **Learning Exercise 4.7D**

Indicate the dipoles in each of the following and determine whether the molecule is polar or nonpolar.

1. CF_4 2. HCl

3. NH_3 4. OF_2

Answers   **1.** CF_4

$$F \leftarrow C \rightarrow F \quad \text{dipoles cancel, nonpolar}$$

with F above (arrow up into C) and F below (arrow down from C)

2. HCl $\overset{\delta^+}{H} \rightarrow \overset{\delta^-}{Cl} \longleftrightarrow$ dipoles do not cancel, polar

3. NH_3 $H \rightarrow \ddot{N} \leftarrow N \uparrow$ dipoles do not cancel, polar

with H below N (arrow up)

4. OF_2 $:\!\ddot{O} \rightarrow F$ dipoles do not cancel, polar

with F below O (arrow down)

Checklist for Chapter 4

You are ready to take the self-test for chapter 4. Be sure that you have accomplished the following learning goals for this chapter. If you are not sure, review the section listed at the end of the goal. Then apply your new skills and understanding to the self-test. Good luck.

After studying chapter 4, I can successfully:

_____ Illustrate the octet rule for the formation of ions (4.1).

_____ Write the formulas of compounds containing the ions of metals and nonmetals of representative elements (4.2).

_____ Use charge balance to write an ionic formula (4.3).

_____ Write the name of an ionic compound (4.3).

_____ Write the formula of a compound containing a polyatomic ion (4.4).

_____ Write the electron dot structure of a covalent compound (4.5).

_____ Write the name and formula of a covalent compound (4.5).

_____ Classify a bond as nonpolar covalent, polar covalent, or ionic (4.6).

_____ Predict the shape and bond angles for a molecule (4.7).

_____ Classify a molecule as a polar or nonpolar (4.7).

Practice Test for Chapter 4

For questions 1–4, consider an atom of phosphorus.

1. It is in group
   A. 2A(2)   **B.** 3A(13)   **C.** 5A(15)   **D.** 7A(17)   **E.** 8A(18)

2. How many outer level electrons does it have?
   A. 2   **B.** 3   **C.** 5   **D.** 8   **E.** 15

3. To achieve an octet, the phosphorus atom will
   A. lose one electron   **B.** lose two electrons   **C.** lose five electrons
   D. gain two electrons   **E.** gain three electrons

4. As an ion, it has an ionic charge (valence) of
   A. 1+   B. 2+   C. 5+   D. 2−   E. 3−

5. To achieve an octet, a calcium atom
   A. loses one electron   B. loses two electrons   C. loses three electrons
   D. gains one electron   E. gains two electrons

6. To achieve an octet, a chlorine atom
   A. loses one electron   B. loses two electrons   C. loses three electrons
   D. gains one electron   E. gains two electrons

7. Another name for a positive ion is
   A. anion   B. cation   C. proton   D. positron   E. sodium

8. The correct ionic charge (valence) for calcium ion is
   A. 1+   B. 2+   C. 1−   D. 2−   E. 3−

9. The silver ion has a charge of
   A. 1+   B. 2+   C. 1−   D. 2−   E. 3−

10. The correct ionic charge (valence) for phosphate ion is
    A. 1+   B. 2+   C. 1−   D. 2−   E. 3−

11. The correct ionic charge (valence) for fluoride is
    A. 1+   B. 2+   C. 1−   D. 2−   E. 3−

12. The correct ionic charge (valence) for sulfate ion is
    A. 1+   B. 2+   C. 1−   D. 2−   E. 3−

13. When the elements magnesium and sulfur are mixed
    A. an ionic compound forms
    B. a covalent compound forms
    C. no reaction occurs
    D. the two repel each other and will not combine
    E. None of the above.

14. An ionic bond typically occurs between
    A. two different nonmetals
    B. two of the same type of nonmetals
    C. two noble gases
    D. two different metals
    E. a metal and a nonmetal

15. A nonpolar covalent bond typically occurs between
    A. two different nonmetals
    B. two of the same type of nonmetals
    C. two noble gases
    D. two different metals.
    E. a metal and a nonmetal

16. A polar covalent bond typically occurs between
    A. two different nonmetals
    B. two of the same type of nonmetals
    C. two noble gases
    D. two different metals
    E. a metal and a nonmetal

17. The formula for a compound between carbon and chlorine is
    A. Cl B. CCl_2 C. C_4Cl D. CCl_4 E. C_4Cl_2

18. The formula for a compound between sodium and sulfur is
    A. SoS B. NaS C. Na_2S D. NaS_2 E. Na_2SO_4

19. The formula for a compound between aluminum and oxygen is
    A. AlO   **B.** Al_2O **C.** AlO_3 **D.** Al_2O_3 **E.** Al_3O_2

20. The formula for a compound between barium and sulfur is
    A. BaS   **B.** Ba_2S **C.** BaS_2 **D.** Ba_2S_2 **E.** $BaSO_4$

21. The correct formula for iron(III) chloride is
    A. FeCl   **B.** $FeCl_2$ **C.** Fe_2Cl **D.** Fe_3Cl **E.** $FeCl_3$

22. The correct formula for ammonium sulfate is
    A. AmS   **B.** $AmSO_4$ **C.** $(NH_4)_2S$ **D.** NH_4SO_4 **E.** $(NH_4)_2SO_4$

23. The correct formula for copper(II) chloride is
    A. CoCl   **B.** CuCl   **C.** $CoCl_2$ **D.** $CuCl_2$ **E.** Cu_2Cl

24. The correct formula for lithium phosphate is
    A. $LiPO_4$ **B.** Li_2PO_4 **C.** Li_3PO_4 **D.** $Li_2(PO_4)_3$ **E.** $Li_3(PO_4)_2$

25. The correct formula for silver oxide is
    A. AgO   **B.** Ag_2O **C.** AgO_2 **D.** Ag_3O_2 **E.** Ag_3O

26. The correct formula for magnesium carbonate is
    A. $MgCO_3$ **B.** Mg_2CO_3 **C.** $Mg(CO_3)_2$ **D.** MgCO   **E.** $Mg_2(CO_3)_3$

27. The correct formula for copper(I) sulfate is
    A. $CuSO_3$ **B.** $CuSO_4$ **C.** Cu_2SO_3 **D.** $Cu(SO_4)_2$ **E.** Cu_2SO_4

28. The name of $AlPO_4$ is
    A. aluminum phosphide   **B.** alum phosphate   **C.** aluminum phosphate
    D. aluminum phosphorus oxide   **E.** aluminum phosphite

29. The name of CuS is
    A. copper sulfide   **B.** copper(I) sulfate   **C.** copper(I) sulfide
    D. copper(II) sulfate   **E.** copper(II) sulfide

30. The name of $FeCl_2$ is
    A. iron chloride   **B.** iron(II) chlorine   **C.** iron(II) chloride
    D. iron chlorine   **E.** iron(III) chloride

31. The name of $ZnCO_3$ is
    A. zinc(III) carbonate   **B.** zinc(II) carbonate   **C.** zinc bicarbonate
    D. zinc carbon trioxide   **E.** zinc carbonate

32. The name of Al_2O_3 is
    A. aluminum oxide   **B.** aluminum(II) oxide   **C.** aluminum trioxide
    D. dialuminum trioxide   **E.** aluminum oxygenate

33. The name of NCl_3 is
    A. nitrogen chloride   **B.** nitrogen trichloride   **C.** trinitrogen chloride
    D. nitrogen chlorine three   **E.** nitrogen chloride (III)

34. The name of CO is
    A. carbon monoxide   **B.** carbonic oxide   **C.** cobalt
    D. carbonious oxide   **E.** carboxide

For questions 35–40, indicate the type of bonding expected between the following elements:
    A. ionic   **B.** nonpolar covalent   **C.** polar covalent   **D.** none

35. _____ silicon and oxygen   **36.** _____ barium and chlorine

37. _____ aluminum and chlorine   **38.** _____ chlorine and chlorine

39. _____sulfur and oxygen   **40.** _____neon and oxygen

Determine the shape and angles of each of the following molecules as:

  A. linear, 180°   **B.** trigonal planar, 120°   **C.** bent, 120°
  D. tetrahedral, 109°   **E.** pyramidal, 109°   **F.** bent, 109°

41. PCl_3 **42.** CBr_4 **43.** H_2S

44. BCl_3 **45.** $BeBr_2$

Answers to the Practice Test

1. C	**2.** C	**3.** E	**4.** E	**5.** B
6. D	**7.** B	**8.** B	**9.** A	**10.** E
11. C	**12.** D	**13.** A	**14.** E	**15.** B
16. A	**17.** D	**18.** C	**19.** D	**20.** A
21. E	**22.** E	**23.** D	**24.** C	**25.** B
26. A	**27.** E	**28.** C	**29.** E	**30.** C
31. E	**32.** A	**33.** B	**34.** A	**35.** C
36. A	**37.** A	**38.** B	**39.** C	**40.** D
41. E	**42.** D	**43.** F	**44.** B	**45.** A

Answers and Solutions to Selected Text Problems

4.1 **a.** If a sodium atom loses its valence electron, its second energy level has a complete octet.

  b. A neon atom has the same electronic arrangement as a sodium ion.

  c. Group 1A (1) and Group 2A (2) elements do not have a stable octet until each has lost one or two electrons, respectively. Electrically charged ions are formed when electrons are lost, and these positively charged ions are attracted to negatively charged ions, resulting in the formation of compounds. Group 8A (18) elements have stable octets that remain electrically neutral and have no tendency to form compounds.

4.3 Atoms with one, two, or three valence electrons will lose those electrons.

  a. one   **b.** two   **c.** three   **d.** one   **e.** two

4.5 **a.** Li^+ **b.** F^- **c.** Mg^{2+} **d.** Fe^{3+} **e.** Zn^{2+}

4.7 **a.** Cl^- **b.** K^+ **c.** O^{2-} **d.** Al^{3+}

4.9 **a.** (Li and Cl)   and   **c.** (K and O) will form ionic compounds

4.11 **a.** Na_2O **b.** $AlBr_3$ **c.** BaO **d.** $MgCl_2$ **e.** Al_2S_3

4.13 **a.** Na_2S **b.** K_3N **c.** AlI_3 **d.** Li_2O

4.15 **a.** aluminum oxide   **b.** calcium chloride   **c.** sodium oxide
  d. magnesium nitride   **e.** potassium iodide

4.17 The Roman numeral is used to specify the positive charge on the transition metal in the compound. It is necessary for most transition metal compounds because many transition metals can exist as more than one cation; transition metals have variable ionic charges.

4.19 **a.** iron(II)   **b.** copper(II)   **c.** zinc   **d.** lead(IV)   **e.** chromium(III)

4.21 **a.** tin(II) chloride   **b.** iron(II) oxide   **c.** copper(I) sulfide
  d. copper(II) sulfide   **e.** chromium(III) bromide

4.23 **a.** Au^{3+} **b.** Fe^{3+} **c.** Pb^{4+} **d.** Sn^{2+}

4.25 **a.** $MgCl_2$ **b.** Na_2S **c.** Cu_2O
   d. Zn_3P_2 **e.** AuN **f.** $CrCl_2$

4.27 **a.** HCO_3^- **b.** NH_4^+ **c.** PO_4^{3-} **d.** HSO_4^-

4.29 **a.** sulfate   **b.** carbonate   **c.** phosphate   **d.** nitrate

4.31

	OH^-	NO_2^-	CO_3^{2-}	HSO_4^-	PO_4^{3-}
Li^+	LiOH	$LiNO_2$	Li_2CO_3	$LiHSO_4$	Li_3PO_4
Cu^{2+}	$Cu(OH)_2$	$Cu(NO_2)_2$	$CuCO_3$	$Cu(HSO_4)_2$	$Cu_3(PO_4)_2$
Ba^{2+}	$Ba(OH)_2$	$Ba(NO_2)_2$	$BaCO_3$	$Ba(HSO_4)_2$	$Ba_3(PO_4)_2$

4.33 **a.** CO_3^{2-}, sodium carbonate   **b.** NH_4^+, ammonium chloride
   c. PO_4^{3-}, lithium phosphate   **d.** NO_2^-, copper(I) nitrite
   e. SO_3^{2-}, iron(II) sulfite

4.35 **a.** $Ba(OH)_2$ **b.** Na_2SO_4 **c.** $Fe(NO_3)_2$ **d.** $Zn_3(PO_4)_2$ **e.** $Fe_2(CO_3)_3$

4.37 The nonmetallic elements that are not noble gases are likely to form covalent bonds.

4.39 **a.** When two H atoms share, each has two valence electrons. In H_2, there is one bonding pair and no (0) lone pairs.
   b. The Br atom achieves an octet by sharing a valence electron with one H atom to give eight valence electrons, one bonding pair, and three lone pairs on the Br atom.
   c. Each Br atom achieves an octet by sharing one valence electron to give a total of 14 valence electrons, one bonding pair between the Br atoms, and six lone pairs (three lone pairs for each Br atom).

4.41 **a.** HF ($8e^-$) $H\!:\!\ddot{\underset{..}{F}}\!:$ or $H\!-\!\ddot{\underset{..}{F}}\!:$

   b. SF_2 (20 e^-) $:\!\ddot{\underset{..}{F}}\!:\!\ddot{\underset{..}{S}}\!:\!\ddot{\underset{..}{F}}\!:$ or $:\!\ddot{\underset{..}{F}}\!-\!\ddot{\underset{..}{S}}\!-\!\ddot{\underset{..}{F}}\!:$

   c. NBr_3 (26 e^-) $:\!\ddot{\underset{..}{B}r}\!:\!N\!:\!\ddot{\underset{..}{B}r}\!:$ or $:\!\ddot{\underset{..}{B}r}\!-\!N\!-\!\ddot{\underset{..}{B}r}\!:$ (with $:\ddot{Br}:$ above)

   d. CH_3OH (14 e^-) $H\!:\!\ddot{\underset{..}{C}}\!:\!\ddot{\underset{..}{O}}\!:\!H$ or $H\!-\!C\!-\!\ddot{\underset{..}{O}}\!-\!H$ (with H above and below C)

   e. N_2H_4 (14 e^-) $H\!:\!\ddot{\underset{..}{N}}\!:\!\ddot{\underset{..}{N}}\!:\!H$ or $H\!-\!N\!-\!N\!-\!H$ (with H above each N)

4.43 When using all the valence electrons does not give complete octets, it is necessary to write multiple bonds.

4.45 Resonance occurs when we can write two or more formulas for the same molecule or ion.

4.47 **a.** CO (10 e$^-$) :C:::O: or :C≡C:

b. H_2CCH_2 (12 e$^-$) 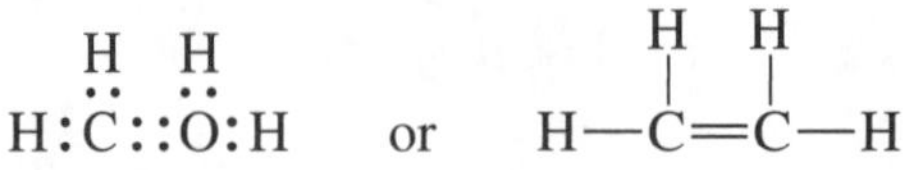

c. H_2CO (12 e$^-$) 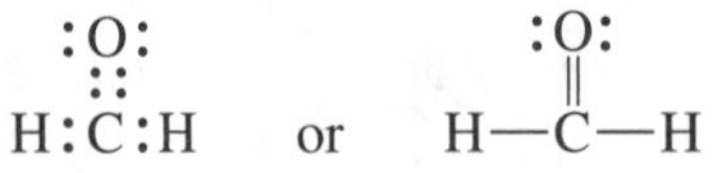

4.49 $ClNO_2$ 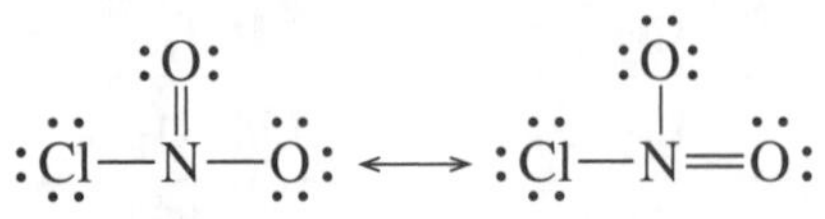

4.51 **a.** phosphorus tribromide
b. carbon tetrabromide
c. silicon dioxide
d. dinitrogen trioxide
e. silicon tetrabromide
f. phosphorus pentachloride

4.53 **a.** CCl_4
b. CO
c. PCl_3
d. N_2O_4
e. BF_3
f. SF_6

4.55 **a.** This is an ionic compound with Al^{3+} ion and the sulfate SO_4^{2-} polyatomic ion. The correct name is aluminum sulfate.
b. This is an ionic compound with Ca^{2+} ion and the carbonate CO_3^{2-} polyatomic ion. The correct name is calcium carbonate.
c. This is a covalent compound because it contains two nonmetals. Using prefixes, it is named dinitrogen monoxide.
d. This is an ionic compound with sodium ion Na^+ and the PO_4^{3-} polyatomic ion. The correct name is sodium phosphate.
e. This ionic compound contains two polyatomic ions, ammonium NH_4^+ and sulfate SO_4^{2-}. It is named ammonium sulfate.
f. This is an ionic compound containing the variable metal ion Fe^{3+} and oxide ion O^{2-}. It is named using the Roman numeral as iron(III) oxide.

4.57 The electronegativity increases going across a period.

4.58 The electronegativity values decrease going down a group.

4.59 A nonpolar covalent bond would have an electronegativity difference of 0.0 to 0.4.

4.61 **a.** Electronegativity increases going up a group: K, Na, Li.
b. Electronegativity increases going across a period: Na, P, Cl.
c. Electronegativity increases going across a period and at the top of a group: Ca, Br, O.

4.63 **a.** Si—Br electronegavity difference 1.0, polar covalent
b. Li—F electronegavity difference 3.0, ionic
c. Br—F electronegavity difference 1.2, polar covalent
d. Br—Br electronegavity difference 0, nonpolar covalent
e. N—P electronegavity difference 0.9, polar covalent
f. C—P electronegavity difference 0.4, nonpolar covalent

4.65 **a.** $\overset{\delta^+ \quad \delta^-}{\text{N—F}}$ **b.** $\overset{\delta^+ \quad \delta^-}{\text{Si—Br}}$ **c.** $\overset{\delta^+ \quad \delta^-}{\text{C—O}}$

d. $\overset{\delta^+ \quad \delta^-}{\text{P—Br}}$ **e.** $\overset{\delta^+ \quad \delta^-}{\text{B—Cl}}$

4.67 Tetrahedral. Four atoms bonded to the central atom with four electron pairs forms a tetrahedron.

4.69 The four electron groups in PCl_3 have a tetrahedral arrangement, but three bonded.

4.71 In the electron dot formulas of PH_3, the central atom P has three bonded atoms and one lone pair, which give PH_3 a pyramidal shape with angles of 109°. In the molecule NH_3, the central atom N is also bonded to three atoms and one lone pair. Thus, NH_3 also has a pyramidal shape with angles of 109°.

4.73 **a.** The central oxygen atom has four electron pairs with two bonded to fluorine atoms. Its shape is bent with 109° angles.
b. The central atom C has four electron pairs bonded to four chlorine atoms; CCl_4 has a tetrahedral shape.
c. The central carbon atom has two bonded atoms and no lone pairs. The shape is linear.
d. The central Se atom has two bonded atoms and one lone pair. Its shape is bent with 109° angles.

4.75 Cl_2 is a nonpolar molecule because there is a nonpolar covalent bond between Cl atoms, which have identical electronegativity values. In HCl, the bond is a polar bond, which is a dipole, and makes HCl a polar molecule.

4.77 **a.** polar **b.** dipoles do not cancel; polar
c. four dipoles cancel; nonpolar **d.** three dipoles cancel; nonpolar

4.79 **A.** P^{3-} **B.** O atom **C.** Zn^{2+} **D.** Fe^{3+} **E.** Li^+ **F.** N^{3-}

4.81 **a.** 2– pyramidal, polar **b.** 1– bent, polar **c.** 3– tetrahedral, nonpolar

4.83 **a.** Chlorine in Group 7A (17) gains one electron to form chloride ion Cl^-.
b. Potassium in Group 1A (1) loses one electron to form potassium ion K^+.
c. Oxygen in Group 6A (16) gains two electrons to form oxide ion O^{2-}.
d. Aluminum in Group 1A (1) loses three electrons to form aluminum ion Al^{3+}.

4.85 **a.** potassium ion **b.** sulfide ion **c.** calcium ion **d.** nitride ion

4.87 **a.** Ions: Au^{3+} and $Cl^- \rightarrow AuCl_3$
b. Ions: Pb^{4+} and $O^{2-} \rightarrow PbO_2$
c. Ions: Ag^+ and $Cl^- \rightarrow AgCl$
d. Ions: Ca^{2+} and $N^{3-} \rightarrow Ca_3N_2$
e. Ions: Cu^+ and $P^{3-} \rightarrow Cu_3P$
f. Ions: Cr^{2+} and $Cl^- \rightarrow CrCl_2$

4.89 **a.** Cl_2O (20 e$^-$) $:\!\overset{..}{\underset{..}{Cl}}\!:\!\overset{..}{\underset{..}{O}}\!:\!\overset{..}{\underset{..}{Cl}}\!:$ or $:\!\overset{..}{\underset{..}{Cl}}\!-\!\overset{..}{\underset{..}{O}}\!-\!\overset{..}{\underset{..}{Cl}}\!:$

b. CF_4 (32 e$^-$) $:\!\overset{..}{\underset{..}{F}}\!:\!\overset{:F:}{\underset{:F:}{C}}\!:\!\overset{..}{\underset{..}{F}}\!:$ or $:\!\overset{..}{\underset{..}{F}}\!-\!\overset{\overset{..}{F}}{\underset{\underset{..}{F}}{C}}\!-\!\overset{..}{\underset{..}{F}}\!:$

c. H_2NOH (14 e$^-$)   H:N:O:H   or   H—N—O—H

(with H above N, and lone pairs shown on N and O)

d. H_2CCCl_2 (24 e$^-$)   H:C::C:Cl: or   H—C=C—Cl:

(with H and Cl above, Cl on right with lone pairs)

4.91 **a.** 1 N and 3 Cl → nitrogen trichloride
   b. 1 S and 2 Cl → sulfur dichloride
   c. 2 N and 1 O → dinitrogen oxide
   d. 2 F → fluorine (named as the element)
   e. 1 P and 5 Cl → phosphorus pentachloride
   f. 2 P and 5 O → diphosphorus pentoxide

4.93 **a.** 1 C and 1 O → CO
   b. di(2) and penta (5) → P_2O_5
   c. di(2) and 1 S → H_2S
   d. 1 S and di(2) Cl → SCl_2

4.95 **a.** ionic, iron(III) chloride
   b. ionic, sodium sulfate
   c. covalent, 2 N and 1 O → dinitrogen oxide
   d. covalent, nitrogen (named as the element)
   e. covalent, 1 P and 5 Cl → phosphorus pentachloride
   f. covalent, 1 C and 4 F → carbon tetrafluoride

4.97 **a.** Tin(II) is Sn^{2+}; carbonate is CO_3^{2-}. With charges balanced, the formula is $SnCO_3$.
   b. Lithium is Li^+; phosphide is P^{3-}. Using three Li^+ for charge balance, the formula is Li_3P.
   c. Silicon has four valence electrons to share with four chlorine atoms to give $SiCl_4$.
   d. Iron(III) is Fe^{3+}; sulfide is S^{2-}. Charge is balanced with two Fe^{3+} and three S^{2-} to give the formula Fe_2S_3.
   e. Carbon has four valence electrons to form two double bonds with two oxygen atoms to give the formula CO_2.
   f. Calcium is Ca^{2+}; bromide is Br^-. With charges balanced, the formula is $CaBr_2$.

4.99 Determine the difference in electronegativity values:
   a. C—O (1.0)   C—N is less (0.5)
   b. N—F (1.0)   N—Br is less (0.2)
   c. S—Cl (0.5)   Br—Cl is less (0.2)
   d. Br—I (0.3)   Br—Cl is less (0.2)
   e. C—O (1.0)   C—S is less (0)

4.101 A dipole arrow points from the atom with the lower electronegativity value (more positive) to the atom in the bond that has the higher electronegativity value (more negative).
   a. Si has the lower electronegativity value of 1.8, making Si the positive end of the dipole. The Cl atom has a higher electronegativity value of 3.0.

   Si—Cl
   ⊢——→

   b. C has the lower electronegativity value of 2.5, making C the positive end of the dipole. The N atom has a higher electronegativity value of 3.0.

   C—N
   ⊢——→

c. Cl has the lower electronegativity value of 3.0, making Cl the positive end of the dipole. The F atom has a higher electronegativity value of 4.0.

F—Cl
←—+

d. C has the lower electronegativity value of 2.5, making C the positive end of the dipole. The F atom has a higher electronegativity value of 4.0.

C—F
+—→

e. N has the lower electronegativity value of 3.0, making N the positive end of the dipole. The F atom has a higher electronegativity value of 4.0.

N—F
+—→

4.103 a. polar covalent (Cl $3.0 - $ Si $1.8 = 1.2$)
b. nonpolar covalent (C $2.5 - $ C $2.5 = 0.0$)
c. ionic (Cl $3.0 - $ Na $0.9 = 2.1$)
d. nonpolar covalent (C $2.5 - $ H $2.1 = 0.4$)
e. nonpolar covalent (F $4.0 - $ F $4.0 = 0.0$)

4.105 a. In a molecule that has a trigonal planar shape, the dipoles cancel, making the molecule nonpolar.
b. In a molecule with a bent shape and one lone pair, the dipoles do not cancel, making the molecule polar.
c. In a linear molecule with identical atoms, any dipoles cancel, making the molecule nonpolar.
d. Tetrahedral; dipoles do not cancel, making the molecule polar.

4.107 a. NF_3 :F—N—F: trigonal pyramidal
                          |
                         :F:

b. $SiBr_4$:Br:
                    |
          :Br—Si—Br: tetrahedral
                    |
                   :Br:

c. $BeCl_2$:Cl—Be—Cl: linear

d. SO_2 (:O=S—O:) ⟷ (:O—S=O:)   bent (120°)

4.109 a. bent, dipoles do not cancel, polar
b. pyramidal, dipoles do not cancel, polar
c. pyramidal, dipoles do not cancel, polar
d. tetrahedral; dipoles do not cancel; polar
e. tetrahedral; dipoles cancel; nonpolar

4.111 a. X is in Group 1A (1); Y is in Group 6A(16)   **b.** ionic
c. X^+, Y^{2-} **d.** X_2Y **e.** XCl   **f.** YCl_2

4.113 a. Sn^{4+} **b.** 50 protons, 46 electrons   **c.** SnO_2 **d.** $Sn_3(PO_4)_4$

4.115 a. iron(II) chloride   **b.** dichlorine heptoxide
c. nitrogen   **d.** calcium phosphate
e. phosphorus trichloride   **f.** aluminum nitrate
g. lead(IV) chloride   **h.** magnesium carbonate
i. nitrogen dioxide   **j.** tin(II) sulfate
k. barium nitrate   **l.** copper(II) sulfide

Chemical Reactions and Quantities

Study Goals

- Classify a change in matter as a chemical change or a physical change.
- Show that a balanced equation has an equal number of atoms of each element on the reactant side and the product side.
- Write a balanced equation for a chemical reaction when given the formulas of the reactants and products.
- Classify an equation as a combination, decomposition, replacement, and/or combustion reaction.
- Describe the features of oxidation and reduction in an oxidation-reduction reaction.
- Determine the molar mass of a compound from its formula.
- Use the molar mass to convert between the grams of a substance and the number of moles.
- Using a given number of moles and a mole-mole conversion factor, determine the corresponding number of moles for a reactant or a product.
- Using a given mass of a substance in a reaction and the appropriate mole factor and molar masses, calculate the mass of a reactant or a product.
- Given the actual yield of a product, calculate the percent yield.
- Determine the limiting reactant and calculate the amount of product formed.

Think About It

1. What causes a slice of apple or an avocado to turn brown?

2. How is a recipe like a chemical equation?

3. Why is the digestion of food a series of chemical reactions?

Key Terms

Match the following terms with the statements below:

a. chemical change	**b.** chemical equation	**c.** combination reaction
d. mole	**e.** molar mass	**f.** physical change

1. _____ the amount of a substance that contains 6.02×10^{23} particles of that substance

2. _____ a change that alters the composition of a substance, producing a new substance with new properties

3. _____ the mass in grams of an element or compound that is equal numerically to its atomic or sum of atomic masses

4. _____ the type of reaction in which reactants combine to form a single product

5. _____ a shorthand method of writing a chemical, with the formulas of the reactants written on the left side of an arrow and the formulas of the products on the right side

Answers   **1.** d   **2.** a   **3.** e   **4.** c   **5.** b

5.1 Chemical Changes

- A chemical change occurs when the atoms of the initial substances rearrange to form new substances.
- Chemical change is indicated by a change in properties of the reactants. For example, a rusting nail, souring milk, and a burning match are all chemical changes.
- When new substances form, a chemical reaction has taken place.

◆ Learning Exercise 5.1

Identify each of the following as a chemical (C) or a physical (P) change:

1. _____ tearing a piece of paper   **2.** _____ burning paper

3. _____ rusting iron   **4.** _____ digestion of food

5. _____ dissolving salt in water   **6.** _____ boiling water

7. _____ chewing gum   **8.** _____ removing tarnish with silver polish

Answers   **1.** P   **2.** C   **3.** C   **4.** C
                 5. P   **6.** P   **7.** P   **8.** C

5.2 Chemical Equations

- A chemical equation shows the formulas of the reactants on the left side of the arrow and the formulas of the products on the right side.
- In a balanced equation, *coefficients* in front of the formulas provide the same number of atoms for each kind of element on the reactant and product sides.
- A chemical equation is balanced by placing coefficients in front of the symbols or formulas in the equation.

Example: Balance the following equation:

$$N_2(g) + H_2(g) \rightarrow NH_3(g)$$

1. Count the atoms of N and H on the reactant side and on the product side.

$$N_2(g) + H_2(g) \rightarrow NH_3(g)$$
$$\text{2N, 2H} \qquad\qquad \text{1N, 3H}$$

2. Balance the N atoms by placing a coefficient of 2 in front of NH_3. (This increases the H atoms, too.) Recheck the number of N atoms and the number of H atoms.

$$N_2(g) + H_2(g) \rightarrow \mathbf{2}NH_3(g)$$

3. Balance the H atoms by placing a coefficient of 3 in front of H_2. Recheck the number of N atoms and the number of H atoms.

$$N_2(g) + \mathbf{3}H_2(g) \rightarrow \mathbf{2}NH_3(g)$$
$$\text{2N, 6H} \qquad\qquad \text{2N, 6H} \qquad\qquad \textit{The equation is balanced.}$$

◆ Learning Exercise 5.2A

State the number of atoms of each element on the reactant side and on the product side for each of the following balanced equations:

a. $CaCO_3(s) \rightarrow CaO(g) + CO_2(g)$

Element	Atoms on Reactant Side	Atoms on Product Side
Ca		
C		
O		

b. $2Na(s) + H_2O(l) \rightarrow Na_2O(s) + H_2(g)$

Element	Atoms on Reactant Side	Atoms on Product Side
Na		
H		
O		

c. $C_5H_{12}(g) + 8O_2(g) \rightarrow 5CO_2(g) + 6H_2O(g)$

Element	Atoms on Reactant Side	Atoms on Product Side
C		
H		
O		

d. $2AgNO_3(aq) + K_2S(aq) \rightarrow 2KNO_3(aq) + Ag_2S(s)$

Element	Atoms on Reactant Side	Atoms on Product Side
Ag		
N		
O		
K		
S		

e. $2Al(OH)_3(aq) + 3H_2SO_4(aq) \rightarrow Al_2(SO_4)_3(s) + 6H_2O(l)$

Element	Atoms on Reactant Side	Atoms on Product Side
Al		
O		
H		
S		

Answers

a. $CaCO_3(s) \rightarrow CaO(g) + CO_2(g)$

Element	Atoms on Reactant Side	Atoms on Product Side
Ca	1	1
C	1	1
O	3	3

b. $2Na(s) + H_2O(l) \rightarrow Na_2O(s) + H_2(g)$

Element	Atoms on Reactant Side	Atoms on Product Side
Na	2	2
H	2	2
O	1	1

c. $C_5H_{12}(g) + 8O_2(g) \rightarrow 5CO_2(g) + 6H_2O(g)$

Element	Atoms on Reactant Side	Atoms on Product Side
C	5	5
H	12	12
O	16	16

d. $2AgNO_3(aq) + K_2S(aq) \rightarrow 2KNO_3(aq) + Ag_2S(s)$

Element	Atoms on Reactant Side	Atoms on Product Side
Ag	2	2
N	2	2
O	6	6
K	2	2
S	1	1

e. $2Al(OH)_3(aq) + 3H_2SO_4(aq) \rightarrow Al_2(SO_4)_3(s) + 6H_2O(l)$

Element	Atoms on Reactant Side	Atoms on Product Side
Al	2	2
O	18	18
H	12	12
S	3	3

◆ **Learning Exercise 5.2B**

Balance each of the following equations by placing appropriate coefficients in front of the formulas as needed:

a. _____ $MgO(s) \rightarrow$ _____ $Mg(s) +$ _____ $O_2(g)$

b. _____ $Zn(s) +$ _____ $HCl(aq) \rightarrow$ _____ $ZnCl_2(aq) +$ _____ $H_2(g)$

c. _____ $Al(s) +$ _____ $CuSO_4(aq) \rightarrow$ _____ $Cu(s) +$ _____ $Al_2(SO_4)_3(aq)$

d. _____ $Al_2S_3(s) +$ _____ $H_2O(l) \rightarrow$ _____ $Al(OH)_3(aq) +$ _____ $H_2S(g)$

e. _____ $BaCl_2(aq) +$ _____ $Na_2SO_4(aq) \rightarrow$ _____ $BaSO_4(s) +$ _____ $NaCl(g)$

f. _____ $CO(g) +$ _____ $Fe_2O_3(s) \rightarrow$ _____ $Fe(s) +$ _____ $CO_2(g)$

g. _____ $K(s) +$ _____ $H_2O(l) \rightarrow$ _____ $K_2O(s) +$ _____ $H_2(g)$

h. _____ $Fe(OH)_3 \rightarrow$ _____ $Fe_2O_3(s) +$ _____ $H_2O(l)$

Answers   **a.** $2MgO(s) \rightarrow 2Mg(s) + O_2(g)$
            b. $Zn(s) + 2HCl(aq) \rightarrow ZnCl_2(aq) + H_2(g)$
            c. $2Al(s) + 3CuSO_4(aq) \rightarrow 3Cu(s) + Al_2(SO_4)_3(aq)$
            d. $Al_2S_3(s) + 6H_2O(l) \rightarrow 2Al(OH)_3 + 3H_2S(g)$
            e. $BaCl_2(aq) + Na_2SO_4 \rightarrow BaSO_4(s) + 2NaCl(aq)$
            f. $3CO(g) + Fe_2O_3(s) \rightarrow 2Fe(s) + 3CO_2(g)$
            g. $2K(s) + H_2O(l) \rightarrow K_2O(s) + H_2(g)$
            h. $2Fe(OH)_3(a) \rightarrow Fe_2O_3(s) + 3H_2O(l)$

5.3 Types of Reactions

- Reactions are classified as combination, decomposition, replacement, and combustion.
- In a *combination* reaction, reactants are combined. In a *decomposition* reaction, a reactant splits into simpler products.
- In *single* (or *double*) *replacement* reactions, one (or two) elements in the reacting compounds are replaced with the element(s) from the other reactant(s).

Study Note

Combination reactions combine reactants. *Decomposition* splits compounds into simpler products. In *replacement*, elements in the reacting compounds are replaced with the element(s) from the other reactant(s).

◆ **Learning Exercise 5.3A**

Match each of the following reactions with the type of reaction:

   a. combination   **b.** decomposition   **c.** single replacement   **d.** double replacement

1. _____ $N_2(g) + 3H_2(g) \rightarrow 2\,NH_3(g)$

2. _____ $BaCl_2(aq) + K_2CO_3(aq) \rightarrow BaCO_3(s) + 2\,KCl(aq)$

3. _____ $2H_2O_2(aq) \rightarrow 2H_2O(l) + O_2(g)$

4. _____ $CuO(s) + H_2(g) \rightarrow Cu(s) + H_2O(l)$

5. _____ $N_2(g) + 2O_2(g) \rightarrow 2NO_2(g)$

6. _____ $2NaHCO_3(s) \rightarrow Na_2O(s) + 2CO_2(g) + H_2O(l)$

7. _____ $PbCO_3(s) \rightarrow PbO + CO_2(g)$

8. _____ $Al(s) + Fe_2O_3(s) \rightarrow Fe(s) + Al_2O_3(s)$

Answers **1.** a **2.** d **3.** b **4.** c **5.** a **6.** b **7.** b **8.** c

◆ Learning Exercise 5.3B

1. One way to remove tarnish from silver is to place the silver object on a piece of aluminum foil and add boiling water and some baking soda. The unbalanced equation is the following:

$$Al(s) + Ag_2S(s) \rightarrow Ag(s) + Al_2S_3(s)$$

  a. What is the balanced equation?

  b. What type of reaction takes place?

2. Octane, C_8H_{18}, a compound in gasoline, burns in oxygen to produce carbon dioxide and water.

  a. What is the balanced equation for the reaction?

  b. What type of reaction takes place?

Answers **1a.** $2Al(s) + 3Ag_2S(s) \rightarrow 6Ag(s) + Al_2S_3(s)$ **1b.** single replacement
2a. $2C_8H_{18}(l) + 25O_2(g) \rightarrow 16CO_2(g) + 18H_2O(l)$ **2b.** combustion

5.4 Oxidation-Reduction Reactions

- An oxidation-reduction reaction consists of a loss and gain of electrons. In an oxidation, electrons are lost. In a reduction, there is a gain of electrons.
- An oxidation must always be accompanied by a reduction. The number of electrons lost in the oxidation reaction and gained in the reduction reaction are equal.
- In biological systems, the term *oxidation* describes the gain of oxygen or the loss of hydrogen. The term *reduction* is used to describe a loss of oxygen or a gain of hydrogen.

◆ Learning Exercise 5.4

For each of the following reactions, indicate whether the underlined element is *oxidized* or *reduced*.

  a. $4\underline{Al}(s) + 3O_2(g) \rightarrow 2Al_2O_3(s)$ Al is _____
  b. $\underline{Fe}^{3+}(aq) + 1e^- \rightarrow Fe^{2+}(aq)$ Fe^{3+} is _____
  c. $\underline{Cu}O(s) + H_2(g) \rightarrow Cu(s) + H_2O(l)$ Cu^{2+} is _____
  d. $2\underline{Cl}^-(aq) \rightarrow Cl_2(g) + 2e^-$ Cl^- is _____
  e. $2H\underline{Br}(aq) + Cl_2(g) \rightarrow 2HCl(aq) + Br_2(g)$ Br^- is _____
  f. $2\underline{Na}(s) + Cl_2(g) \rightarrow 2NaCl(s)$ Na is _____
  g. $\underline{Cu}Cl_2(aq) + Zn(g) \rightarrow ZnCl_2(aq) + Cu(g)$ Cu^{2+} is _____

Answers **a.** Al is oxidized to Al^{3+}; loss of electrons (addition of O)
b. Fe^{3+} is reduced to Fe^{2+}; gain of electrons
c. Cu^{2+} is reduced to Cu; gain of electrons (loss of O)

    d. $2Cl^-$ is oxidized to Cl_2; loss of electrons
    e. $2 Br^-$ is oxidized to Br_2; loss of electrons
    f. Na is oxidized to Na^+; loss of electrons
    g. Cu^{2+} is reduced to Cu; gain of electrons

5.5 The Mole

- A mole of any element contains Avogadro's number, 6.02×10^{23}, of atoms; a mole of any compound contains 6.02×10^{23} molecules or formula units.
- The subscripts in a formula indicate the number of moles of each element in one mole of the compound.

◆ Learning Exercise 5.5A

Calculate each of the following:

    a. number of P atoms in 1.50 moles P

    b. number of H_2S molecules in 0.0750 mole H_2S

    c. moles of Ag in 5.4×10^{24} atoms Ag

    d. moles of C_3H_8 in 8.25×10^{24} molecules C_3H_8

Answers   **a.** 9.03×10^{23} P atom   **b.** 4.52×10^{22} H_2S molecules
                      c. 0.90 mole Ag   **d.** 13.7 moles C_3H_8

◆ Learning Exercise 5.5B

Consider the formula for vitamin C (ascorbic acid), $C_6H_8O_6$.

    a. How many moles of carbon are in 2.0 moles of vitamin C?

    b. How many moles of hydrogen are in 5.0 moles of vitamin C?

    c. How many moles of oxygen are in 1.5 moles of vitamin C?

Answers   **a.** 12 moles of carbon (C)   **b.** 30 moles of hydrogen (H)
             c. 9 moles of oxygen (O)

◆ **Learning Exercise 5.5C**

For the compound ibuprofen used in Advil™ and Motrin™ ($C_{13}H_{18}O_2$), determine the moles of each of the following:

   a. moles of carbon (C) atoms in 2.20 moles of ibuprofen

   b. moles of hydrogen (H) in 0.5 moles of ibuprofen

   c. moles of oxygen (O) in 0.75 mole of ibuprofen

   d. moles of ibuprofen that contain 36 moles of hydrogen (H)

Answers   **a.** 28.6 moles of C   **b.** 9 moles of H
             c. 1.5 moles of O   **d.** 2 moles of ibuprofen

5.6 Molar Mass

- The molar mass (g/mole) of an element is numerically equal to its atomic mass in grams.
- The molar mass (g/mole) of a compound is the mass in grams equal numerically to the sum of the mass for each element in the formula. $MgCl_2$ has a molar mass that is the sum of the mass of 1 mole of Mg (24.3 g) and 2 moles of Cl (2 × 35.5 g) = 95.3 g/mole.
- The molar mass is useful as a conversion factor to change a given quantity in moles to grams.

$$\text{moles of substance} \times \frac{\text{number of grams}}{1 \text{ mole of substance}} = \text{grams}$$

Study Note

The molar mass of an element or compound is determined as follows:
   1. Determine the moles of each element (from subscripts) in the compound.
   2. Calculate the total mass contributed by each element.
   3. Total the masses of all the elements.
   Example: What is the molar mass of silver nitrate, $AgNO_3$?

1 mole Ag	×	107.9 g/mole	=	107.9 g
1 mole N	×	14.0 g/mole	=	14.0 g
3 moles O	×	16.0 g/mole	=	48.0 g
		molar mass $AgNO_3$	=	169.9 g

◆ Learning Exercise 5.6A

Determine the molar mass for each of the following:

    a. K_2O **b.** $AlCl_3$

    c. $C_{13}H_{18}O_2$ ibuprofen   **d.** C_4H_{10}

    e. $Ca(NO_3)_2$ **f.** Mg_3N_2

    g. $FeCO_3$ **h.** $(NH_4)_3PO_4$

Answers   **a.** 94.2 g   **b.** 133.5 g   **c.** 206.0 g   **d.** 58.0 g
                     e. 164.1 g   **f.** 100.9 g   **g.** 115.9 g   **h.** 149.0 g

---

Study Note

Use the molar mass as a conversion factor to change the number of moles of a substance to its mass in grams. Find the mass in grams of 0.25 mole Na_2CO_3.

$$\text{Grams} \xleftrightarrow{\ \textit{Molar mass}\ } \text{Moles}$$

Example: $0.25 \text{ mole Na}_2\text{CO}_3 \times \dfrac{106.0 \text{ g Na}_2\text{CO}_3}{1 \text{ mole Na}_2\text{CO}_3} = 27 \text{ g Na}_2\text{CO}_3$

◆ Learning Exercise 5.6B

Find the number of grams in each of the following quantities:

    a. 0.100 mole SO_2 **b.** 0.100 mole H_2SO_4

    c. 2.50 moles NH_3 **d.** 1.25 moles O_2

e. 0.500 mole Mg   **f.** 5.00 moles H_2

g. 10.0 moles PCl_3 **h.** 0.400 mole S

Answers   **a.** 6.41 g   **b.** 9.81 g   **c.** 42.5 g   **d.** 40.0 g
              e. 12.2 g   **f.** 10.0 g   **g.** 1380 g   **h.** 12.8 g

---

Study Note

When the grams of a substance are given, the molar mass is used to calculate the number of moles of substance present.

$$\text{grams of substance} \times \frac{1 \text{ mole}}{\text{grams of substance}} = \text{moles}$$

Example: How many moles of NaOH are in 4.0 g NaOH?

$$4.0 \text{ g NaOH} \times \frac{1 \text{ mole NaOH}}{40.0 \text{ g NaOH}} = 0.10 \text{ mole NaOH}$$

Molar Mass (inverted)

◆ Learning Exercise 5.6C

Calculate the number of moles in each of the following quantities:

a. 32.0 g CH_4 **b.** 391 g K

c. 8.00 g C_3H_8 **d.** 25.0 g Cl_2

e. 0.220 g CO_2 **f.** 5.00 g Al_2O_3

    g. The methane burned in a gas heater has a formula of CH_4. If 725 grams methane are used in 1 month, how many moles of methane were burned?

    h. There are 18 mg of iron in a vitamin tablet. If there are 100 tablets in a bottle, how many moles of iron are contained in the vitamins in the bottle?

Answers   **a.** 2.00 moles   **b.** 10.0 moles   **c.** 0.182 mole
              d. 0.352 mole   **e.** 0.005 00 mole   **f.** 0.0490 mole
              g. 45.3 moles   **h.** 0.032 mole

5.7 Mole Relationships in Chemical Equations

- The coefficients in a balanced chemical equation describe the moles of reactants and products in the reactions.
- Using the coefficients, mole-mole conversion factors are written for any two substances in the equation.
- For the reaction of oxygen forming ozone, $3O_2(g) \rightarrow 2O_3(g)$, the mole-mole conversion factors are the following:

$$\frac{3 \text{ moles } O_2}{2 \text{ moles } O_3} \quad \text{and} \quad \frac{2 \text{ moles } O_3}{3 \text{ moles } O_2}$$

◆ Learning Exercise 5.7A

Write the conversion factors that are possible from the following equation: $N_2(g) + O_2(g) \rightarrow 2NO(g)$

Answers $\dfrac{1 \text{ mole } N_2}{1 \text{ mole } O_3}$ and $\dfrac{1 \text{ mole } O_2}{1 \text{ mole } N_2}$; $\dfrac{1 \text{ mole } N_2}{2 \text{ moles } NO}$ and $\dfrac{2 \text{ moles } NO}{1 \text{ mole } N_2}$

              $\dfrac{1 \text{ mole } O_2}{2 \text{ moles } NO}$ and $\dfrac{2 \text{ moles } NO}{1 \text{ mole } O_2}$

Study Note

The appropriate mole factor is used to change the number of moles of the given to moles of a product. *Example:* Using the equation $N_2(g) + O_2(g) \rightarrow 2NO(g)$, calculate the moles of NO obtained from 3 moles N_2.

$$3 \text{ moles } N_2 \times \frac{2 \text{ moles NO}}{1 \text{ mole } N_2} = 6 \text{ moles NO}$$

Mole–mole factor

◆ Learning Exercise 5.7B

Use the equation below to answer the following questions:

$$C_3H_8(g) + 5O_2(g) \rightarrow 3CO_2(g) + 4 H_2O(g)$$

a. How many moles of O_2 are needed to react with 2.00 moles C_3H_8?

b. How many moles of CO_2 are produced when 4.00 moles O_2 react?

c. How many moles of C_3H_8 react with 3.00 moles O_2?

d. How many moles of H_2O are produced from 0.50 mole C_3H_8?

Answers **a.** 10.0 moles O_2 **b.** 2.4 moles CO_2
c. 0.600 mole C_3H_8 **d.** 2.0 moles H_2O

5.8 Mass Calculations for Reactions

* The grams or moles of a substance in an equation are converted to another using molar masses and mole-mole factors.
* Suppose that a problem asks for the number of grams of O_3 (ozone) produced from 8.0 g O_2. The equation is $3O_2 \rightarrow 2O_3$.

Step 1 Use molar mass of O_2	*Step 2* Use mole factor from coefficients	*Step 3* Use molar mass of O_3

$$8.0 \text{ g } O_2 \longrightarrow \text{moles } O_2 \longrightarrow \text{moles } O_3 \longrightarrow \text{g } O_3$$

$$8.0 \text{ g } O_2 \times \frac{1 \text{ mole } O_2}{32.0 \text{ g } O_2} \times \frac{2 \text{ moles } O_3}{3 \text{ moles } O_2} \times \frac{48.0 \text{ g } O_3}{1 \text{ mole } O_3} = 8.0 \text{ g } O_3$$

◆ Learning Exercise 5.8

Consider the equation for the following questions:

$$2C_2H_6(g) + 7O_2(g) \rightarrow 4CO_2(g) + 6H_2O(g)$$

a. How many grams of oxygen (O_2) are needed to react with 4.00 moles C_2H_6?

b. How many grams of C_2H_6 are needed to react with 115 g O_2?

c. How many grams of C_2H_6 react if 2.00 L CO_2 gas are produced at STP?

d. How many grams of CO_2 are produced when 2.00 moles C_2H_6 react with sufficient oxygen?

e. How many grams of water are produced when 82.5 g O_2 react with sufficient C_2H_6?

Answers   **a.** 448 g O_2 **b.** 30.8 g C_2H_6 **c.** 1.34 g C_2H_6
                  d. 176 g of CO_2 **e.** 39.8 g H_2O

5.9 Percent Yield and Limiting Reactants

- Theoretical yield is the maximum amount of product calculated for a given amount of a reactant.
- Percent yield is the ratio of the actual amount (yield) of product obtained to the theoretical yield.
- In a limiting reactant problem, the availability of one of the reactants limits the amount of product.
- The reactant that is used up is the limiting reactant; the reactant that remains is the excess reactant.
- The limiting reactant produces the smallest number of moles of product.

Study Note

The percent yield is the ratio of the actual yield obtained to the theoretical yield, which is calculated for a given amount of starting reactant. If we calculate that the reaction of 35.5 g N_2 can theoretically produce 43.1 g NH_3, but the actual yield is 26.0 g NH_3, the percent yield is

$$\frac{26.0 \, NH_3 \, (\text{actual})}{43.1 \, g \, NH_3 \, (\text{theoretical})} \times 100 = 60.3\% \text{ Percent yield}$$

◆ Learning Exercise 5.9A

Consider the following reaction: $2H_2S(g) + 3O_2(g) \rightarrow 2SO_2(g) + 2H_2O(g)$

a. If 60.0 g H_2S reacts with sufficient oxygen and produces 45.5 g SO_2, what is the percent yield for SO_2?

b. If 25.0 g O_2 reacts with H_2S and produces 18.6 g SO_2, what is the percent yield for SO_2?

Consider the following reaction: $2C_2H_6(g) + 7O_2(g) \rightarrow 4CO_2(g) + 6H_2O(g)$
                                                    ethane

c. If 125 g C_2H_6 reacts with sufficient oxygen and produces 175 g CO_2, what is the percent yield for CO_2?

d. When 35.0 g O_2 reacts with sufficient ethane to produce 12.5 g H_2O, what is the percent yield of water?

Answers   **a.** 40.3%   **b.** 55.7%   **c.** 47.8%   **d.** 74.0%

Study Note

The amount of product possible from a mixture of two reactants is determined by calculating the moles of product each will produce. The limiting reactant produces the smallest amount of product.

In the reaction $S(l) + 3F_2(g) \rightarrow SF_6(g)$, how many grams of SF_6 are possible when 5.00 moles S are mixed with 12.0 moles F_2?

Find the limiting reactant:

$$5.00 \text{ moles S} \times \frac{1 \text{ mole } SF_6}{1 \text{ mole S}} = 5.00 \text{ moles } SF_6$$

$$12.0 \text{ moles } F_2 \times \frac{1 \text{ mole } SF_6}{3 \text{ moles } F_2} = 4.00 \text{ moles } SF_6 \quad \text{limiting reactant (smallest number of moles)}$$

Calculate the grams of 4.0 moles SF_6 produced by the limiting reactant:

$$4.00 \text{ moles } SF_6 \times \frac{146.1 \text{ g } SF_6}{1 \text{ mole } SF_6} = 584 \text{ g } SF_6$$

◆ **Learning Exercise 5.9B**

a. How many grams of Co_2S_3 can be produced from the reaction of 2.20 moles CO and 3.60 moles S?

$$2Co(s) + 3S(s) \rightarrow Co_2S_3(s)$$

b. How many grams of NO_2 can be produced from the reaction of 32.0 g NO and 24.0 g O_2?

$$2NO(g) + O_2(g) \rightarrow 2NO_2(g)$$

Answers   **a.** 235 g   **b.** 49.1 g

Checklist for Chapter 5

You are ready to take the practice test for Chapter 5. Be sure that you have accomplished the following learning goals for this chapter. If you are not sure, review the section listed at the end of the goal. Then apply your new skills and understanding to the practice test.

After studying Chapter 5, I can successfully:

_____ Identify a chemical and physical change (5.1).

_____ State a chemical equation in words and calculate the total atoms of each element in the reactants and products (5.2).

_____ Write a balanced equation for a chemical reaction from the formulas of the reactants and products (5.2).

_____ Identify a reaction as a combination, decomposition, and single or double replacement (5.3).

_____ Identify an oxidation and reduction reaction (5.4).

_____ Calculate the number of particles in a mole of a substance (5.5).

_____ Calculate the molar mass given the formula of a substance (5.6).

_____ Convert the grams of a substance to moles; convert moles to grams (5.6).

_____ Use mole-mole factors for the mole relationships in an equation to calculate the moles of another substance in an equation for a chemical reaction (5.7).

_____ Calculate the mass of a substance in an equation using mole factors and molar masses (5.8).

_____ Given the actual yield of a product, calculate the percent yield (5.9).

_____ Given the mass of reactants, find the limiting reactant and calculate the amount of product formed (5.9).

Practice Test for Chapter 5

Indicate whether each change is a physical change (A) or a chemical change (B):

1. _____ a melting ice cube
2. _____ breaking glass

3. _____ bleaching a stain
4. _____ a burning candle

5. _____ milk turning sour

For each of the *unbalanced equations* in questions 6–10, balance and indicate the correct coefficient for the component in the equation written in **boldface type.**

    A. 1   **B.** 2   **C.** 3   **D.** 4   **E.** 5

6. _____ $Sn(s) + \mathbf{Cl_2}(g) \rightarrow SnCl_4(s)$

7. _____ $Al(s) + H_2O(l) \rightarrow Al_2O_3(s) + \mathbf{H_2}(g)$

8. _____ $C_3H_8(g) + \mathbf{O_2}(g) \rightarrow CO_2(g) + H_2O(g)$

9. _____ $\mathbf{NH_3}(g) + O_2(g) \rightarrow N_2(g) + H_2O(g)$

10. _____ $N_2O(g) \rightarrow N_2(g) + \mathbf{O_2}(g)$

For questions 11–15, classify each reaction as one of the following:

    A. combination   **B.** decomposition

    C. single replacement   **D.** double replacement

11. _____ $S(s) + O_2(g) \rightarrow SO_2(g)$

12. _____ $Fe_2O_3(s) + 3C(s) \rightarrow 2Fe(s) + 3CO(g)$

13. _____ $CaCO_3(s) \rightarrow CaO + CO_2(g)$

14. _____ $Mg(s) + 2AgNO_3(aq) \rightarrow Mg(NO_3)_2(aq) + 2Ag(s)$

15. _____ $Na_2S(aq) + Pb(NO_3)_2(aq) \rightarrow PbS(s) + 2NaNO_3(aq)$

For questions 16–20, identify as an oxidation (A) or a reduction (B).

16. $Ca \rightarrow Ca^{2+} + 2e^-$ _____

17. $Fe^{3+} + 3e^- \rightarrow Fe$ _____

18. $Al^{3+} + 3e^- \rightarrow Al$ _____

19. $Br_2 + 2e^- \rightarrow 2Br^-$ _____

20. $Sn^{2+} \rightarrow Sn^{4+} + 2e^-$ _____

21. The moles of oxygen (O) in 2.0 moles $Al(OH)_3$ is
   A. 1   **B.** 2   **C.** 3   **D.** 4   **E.** 6

22. What is the molar mass of Li_2SO_4?
   A. 55.1 g   **B.** 62.1 g   **C.** 100.1 g   **D.** 109.9 g   **E.** 103.1 g

23. What is the molar mass of $NaNO_3$?
   A. 34.0 g   **B.** 37.0 g   **C.** 53.0 g   **D.** 75.0 g   **E.** 85.0 g

24. The number of grams in 0.600 mole Cl_2 is
   A. 71.0 g   **B.** 118 g   **C.** 42.6 g   **D.** 84.5 g   **E.** 4.30 g

25. How many grams are in 4.00 moles NH_3?
   A. 4.00 g   **B.** 17.0 g   **C.** 34.0 g   **D.** 68.0 g   **E.** 0.240 g

26. How many moles is 8.0 g NaOH?
   A. 0.10 mole   **B.** 0.20 mole   **C.** 0.40 mole   **D.** 2.0 moles   **E.** 4.0 moles

27. The number of moles of aluminum in 54 g Al is
   A. 0.50 mole   **B.** 1.0 mole   **C.** 2.0 moles   **D.** 3.0 moles   **E.** 4.0 moles

28. The number of moles of water in 36 g H_2O is
   A. 0.50 mole   **B.** 1.0 mole   **C.** 2.0 moles   **D.** 3.0 moles   **E.** 4.0 moles

29. What is the number of moles in 2.2 g CO_2?
   A. 2.0 moles   **B.** 1.0 mole   **C.** 0.20 mole   **D.** 0.050 mole   **E.** 0.010 mole

30. $0.20\,g\,H_2 = $ _____ mole H_2
   A. 0.10 mole   **B.** 0.20 mole   **C.** 0.40 mole   **D.** 0.040 mole   **E.** 0.010 mole

For questions 31–35, use the reaction $C_2H_5OH + 3O_2 \rightarrow 2CO_2 + 3H_2O$
Ethanol

31. How many grams of oxygen are needed to react with 1.0 mole of ethanol?
   A. 8.0 g   **B.** 16 g   **C.** 32 g   **D.** 64 g   **E.** 96 g

32. How many moles of water are produced when 12 moles of oxygen react?
   A. 3.0 moles   **B.** 6.0 moles   **C.** 8.0 moles   **D.** 12.0 moles   **E.** 36.0 moles

33. How many grams of carbon dioxide are produced when 92 g ethanol react?
   A. 22 g   **B.** 44 g   **C.** 88 g   **D.** 92 g   **E.** 176 g

34. How many moles of oxygen would be needed to produce 44 g CO_2?
   A. 0.67 mole   **B.** 1.0 mole   **C.** 1.5 moles   **D.** 2.0 moles   **E.** 3.0 moles

35. How many grams of water will be produced if 23 g ethanol react?
   A. 54 g   **B.** 27 g   **C.** 18 g   **D.** 9.0 g   **E.** 6.0 g

36. When 25.0 g N_2 is reacted, the actual yield of NH_3 is 20.8 g. The percent yield of NH_3 is

   $N_2(g) + 3H_2(g) \rightarrow 2NH_3(g)$

   A. 68.5%   **B.** 20.8%   **C.** 25.0%   **D.** 82.5%   **E.** 100%

For questions 37–38, use the following reaction: $C_3H_8(g) + 5O_2(g) \rightarrow 3CO_2(g) + 4H_2O(g)$

37. If 50.0 g C_3H_8 and 150. g O_2 react, the limiting reactant is
   A. C_3H_8 **B.** O_2 **C.** both   **D.** neither   **E.** CO_2

38. If 50.0 g C_3H_8 and 150. g O_2 react, the mass of CO_2 formed is
    A. 150. g   **B.** 206 g   **C.** 200. g   **D.** 124 g   **E.** 132 g

Answers to the Practice Test

1. A	**2.** A	**3.** B	**4.** B	**5.** B	**6.** B
7. C	**8.** E	**9.** D	**10.** A	**11.** A	**12.** C
13. B	**14.** C	**15.** D	**16.** A	**17.** B	**18.** B
19. B	**20.** A	**21.** E	**22.** D	**23.** E	**24.** C
25. D	**26.** B	**27.** C	**28.** C	**29.** D	**30.** A
31. E	**32.** D	**33.** E	**34.** C	**35.** B	**36.** A
37. B	**38.** D				

Answers and Solutions to Selected Text Problems

5.1 A chemical change occurs when the atoms of the initial substances rearrange to form new substances. Chemical change is indicated by a change in properties of the reactants. For example, a rusting nail, souring milk, and a burning match are all chemical changes.
    a. physical: the shape changes but not the substance
    b. chemical: new substances form
    c. physical: water evaporates, forming gaseous water
    d. chemical: the composition of the substances changes to give new substances
    e. physical: water freezes

5.3 An equation is balanced when there are equal numbers of atoms of each element on the reactant and on the product sides.
    a. not balanced   **b.** balanced   **c.** not balanced   **d.** balanced

5.5 Place coefficients in front of formulas until you make the atoms of each element equal on each side of the equation. Try starting with the formula that has subscripts.
    a. $N_2(g) + O_2(g) \rightarrow 2NO(g)$ **b.** $2HgO(s) \rightarrow 2Hg(l) + O_2(g)$
    c. $4Fe(s) + 3O_2(g) \rightarrow 2Fe_2O_3(s)$ **d.** $2Na(s) + Cl_2(g) \rightarrow 2NaCl(s)$

5.7   **a.** There are 2 NO_3 in the product. Balance by placing a 2 before $AgNO_3$.
        $Mg(s) + 2AgNO_3(aq) \rightarrow Mg(NO_3)_2(aq) + 2Ag(s)$
    b. Start with the formula $Al_2(SO_4)_3$. Balance the Al by writing 2 Al, and balance the SO_4 by writing 3 $CuSO_4$.
        $2Al(s) + 3CuSO_4(aq) \rightarrow 3Cu(s) + Al_2(SO_4)_3(aq)$
    c. $Pb(NO_3)_2(aq) + 2NaCl(aq) \rightarrow PbCl_2(s) + 2NaNO_3(aq)$
    d. $2Al(s) + 6HCl(aq) \rightarrow 2AlCl_3(aq) + 3H_2(g)$

5.9   **a.** This is a decomposition reaction because a single reactant splits into two simpler substances.
    b. This is a single replacement reaction because I_2 in BaI_2 is replaced by Br_2.

5.11   **a.** combination   **b.** single replacement   **c.** decomposition
     d. double replacement   **e.** double replacement

5.13   **a.** Zinc(Zn) is oxidized because it loses electrons to form Zn^{2+}; chlorine (Cl_2) is reduced.
    b. Bromide ion $2Br^-$ is oxidized to Br_2^0; chlorine (Cl_2) is reduced to $2Cl^-$ (gains electrons).
    c. Oxide ion (O^{2-}) is oxidized to O_2^0 (loses electrons); lead(II) ion Pb^{2+} is reduced.
    d. Sn^{2+} ion is oxidized to Sn^{4+} (loses electrons); Fe^{3+} ion is reduced to Fe^{2+} (gains electrons).

5.15   **a.** $Fe^{3+} + e^- \rightarrow Fe^{2+}$ is a reduction.   **b.** $Fe^{2+} \rightarrow Fe^{3+} + e^-$ is an oxidation.

5.17 A mole is the amount of a substance that contains 6.02×10^{23} items. For example, one mole of water contains 6.02×10^{23} molecules of water.

5.19 The subscripts indicate the moles of each element in one mole of that compound.

    a. $1.0 \text{ mole quinine} \times \dfrac{24 \text{ moles H}}{1 \text{ mole quinine}} = 24 \text{ moles H}$

    b. $5.0 \text{ moles quinine} \times \dfrac{20 \text{ moles C}}{1 \text{ mole quinine}} = 100 \text{ moles C}$

    c. $0.020 \text{ mole quinine} \times \dfrac{2 \text{ moles N atoms}}{1 \text{ mole quinine}} = 0.040 \text{ mole N atoms}$

5.21 **a.** $0.500 \text{ mole C} \times \dfrac{6.02 \times 10^{23} \text{ atoms C}}{1 \text{ mole C}} = 3.01 \times 10^{23} \text{ C atoms}$

    b. $1.28 \text{ moles SO}_2 \times \dfrac{6.02 \times 10^{23} \text{ molecules SO}_2}{1 \text{ mole SO}_2} = 7.71 \times 10^{23} \text{ SO}_2 \text{ molecules}$

    c. $5.22 \times 10^{22} \text{ atoms Fe} \times \dfrac{1 \text{ mole Fe}}{6.02 \times 10^{23} \text{ atoms Fe}} = 0.0867 \text{ mole Fe}$

    d. $8.50 \times 10^{24} \text{ molecules C}_2\text{H}_5\text{OH} \times \dfrac{1 \text{ mole C}_2\text{H}_5\text{OH}}{6.02 \times 10^{23} \text{ molecules C}_2\text{H}_5\text{OH}} = 14.1 \text{ mole C}_2\text{H}_5\text{OH}$

5.23 1 mole H_3PO_4 molecules contains 3 moles H atoms, 1 mole P atoms, and 4 moles O atoms.

    a. $2.00 \text{ moles H}_3\text{PO}_4 \times \dfrac{3 \text{ moles H}}{1 \text{ mole H}_3\text{PO}_4} = 6.00 \text{ moles H}$

    b. $2.00 \text{ moles H}_3\text{PO}_4 \times \dfrac{4 \text{ moles O}}{1 \text{ mole H}_3\text{PO}_4} = 8.00 \text{ moles O}$

    c. $2.00 \text{ moles H}_3\text{PO}_4 \times \dfrac{1 \text{ mole P}}{1 \text{ mole H}_3\text{PO}_4} \times \dfrac{6.02 \times 10^{23} \text{ atoms P}}{1 \text{ mole P}} = 1.20 \times 10^{24} \text{ P atoms}$

    d. $2.00 \text{ moles H}_3\text{PO}_4 \times \dfrac{4 \text{ moles O}}{1 \text{ mole H}_3\text{PO}_4} \times \dfrac{6.02 \times 10^{23} \text{ atoms O}}{1 \text{ mole O}} = 4.82 \times 10^{24} \text{ O atoms}$

5.25 **a.** 1 mole Na and 1 mole Cl:
       $23.0 \text{ g} + 35.5 \text{ g} = 58.5 \text{ g/mole NaCl}$
    b. 2 moles of Fe and 3 moles of O:
       $111.8 \text{ g} + 48.0 \text{ g} = 159.8 \text{ g/mole Fe}_2\text{O}_3$
    c. 2 moles Li and 1 mole C and 3 moles O:
       $13.8 \text{ g} + 12.0 \text{ g} + 48.0 \text{ g} = 73.8 \text{ g/mole Li}_2\text{CO}_3$
    d. 2 moles of Al and 3 moles S and 12 moles O:
       $54.0 \text{ g} + 96.3 \text{ g} + 192.0 \text{ g} = 342.3 \text{ g/mole Al}_2(\text{SO}_4)_3$
    e. 1 mole Mg and 2 moles O and 2 moles H:
       $24.3 \text{ g} + 32.0 \text{ g} + 2.0 \text{ g} = 58.3 \text{ g/mole Mg(OH)}_2$
    f. 16 moles C and 19 moles H and 3 moles N and 5 moles O and 1 mole S:
       $192.0 \text{ g} + 19.0 \text{ g} + 42.0 \text{ g} + 80.0 \text{ g} + 32.1 \text{ g} = 365.1 \text{ g/mole C}_{16}\text{H}_{19}\text{N}_3\text{O}_5\text{S}$

5.27 **a.** $2.00 \text{ moles Na} \times \dfrac{23.0 \text{ g Na}}{1 \text{ mole Na}} = 46.0 \text{ g Na}$

    b. $2.80 \text{ moles Ca} \times \dfrac{40.1 \text{ g Ca}}{1 \text{ mole Ca}} = 112 \text{ g Ca}$

    c. $0.125 \text{ mole Sn} \times \dfrac{118.7 \text{ g Sn}}{1 \text{ mole Sn}} = 14.8 \text{ g Sn}$

5.29 **a.** $0.500 \text{ mole NaCl} \times \dfrac{58.5 \text{ g NaCl}}{1 \text{ mole NaCl}} = 29.3 \text{ g NaCl}$

b. $1.75 \text{ moles Na}_2\text{O} \times \dfrac{62.0 \text{ g Na}_2\text{O}}{1 \text{ mole Na}_2\text{O}} = 109 \text{ g Na}_2\text{O}$

c. $0.225 \text{ mole H}_2\text{O} \times \dfrac{18.0 \text{ g H}_2\text{O}}{1 \text{ mole H}_2\text{O}} = 4.05 \text{ g H}_2\text{O}$

5.31 **a.** $5.00 \text{ moles MgSO}_4 \times \dfrac{120.4 \text{ g MgSO}_4}{1 \text{ mole MgSO}_4} = 602 \text{ g MgSO}_4$

b. $0.25 \text{ mole CO}_2 \times \dfrac{44.0 \text{ g CO}_2}{1 \text{ mole CO}_2} = 11 \text{ g CO}_2$

5.33 **a.** $50.0 \text{ g Ag} \times \dfrac{1 \text{ mole Ag}}{107.9 \text{ g Ag}} = 0.463 \text{ mole Ag}$

b. $0.200 \text{ g C} \times \dfrac{1 \text{ mole C}}{12.0 \text{ g C}} = 0.0167 \text{ mole C}$

c. $15.0 \text{ g NH}_3 \times \dfrac{1 \text{ mole NH}_3}{17.0 \text{ g NH}_3} = 0.882 \text{ mole NH}_3$

d. $75.0 \text{ g SO}_2 \times \dfrac{1 \text{ mole SO}_2}{64.1 \text{ g SO}_2} = 0.623 \text{ mole SO}_2$

5.35 $480 \text{ g NaOH} \times \dfrac{1 \text{ mole NaOH}}{40.0 \text{ g NaOH}} = 12 \text{ moles NaOH}$

5.37 **a.** $25 \text{ g S} \times \dfrac{1 \text{ mole S}}{32.1 \text{ g S}} = 0.78 \text{ mole of S}$

b. $125 \text{ g SO}_2 \times \dfrac{1 \text{ mole SO}_2}{64.1 \text{ g SO}_2} \times \dfrac{1 \text{ mole S}}{1 \text{ mole SO}_2} = 1.95 \text{ moles of S}$

c. $2.0 \text{ moles AL}_2\text{S}_3 \times \dfrac{3 \text{ moles S}}{1 \text{ mole Al}_2\text{S}_3} = 6.0 \text{ moles S}$

5.39 **a.** $40.0 \text{ g N} \times \dfrac{1 \text{ mole N}}{14.0 \text{ g N}} \times \dfrac{6.02 \times 10^{23} \text{ atoms of N}}{1 \text{ mole N}} = 1.72 \times 10^{24} \text{ atoms N}$

b. $1.5 \text{ moles N}_2\text{O}_4 \times \dfrac{2 \text{ moles N}}{1 \text{ mole N}_2\text{O}_4} \times \dfrac{6.02 \times 10^{23} \text{ atoms of N}}{1 \text{ mole N}} = 1.8 \times 10^{24} \text{ atoms N}$

c. $2.0 \text{ moles N}_2 \times \dfrac{2 \text{ moles N}}{1 \text{ moles N}_2} \times \dfrac{6.02 \times 10^{23} \text{ atoms N}}{1 \text{ mole N}} = 2.4 \times 10^{24} \text{ atoms N}$

5.41 **a.** $\dfrac{2 \text{ moles SO}_2}{1 \text{ mole O}_2}$ and $\dfrac{1 \text{ mole O}_2}{2 \text{ moles SO}_2}$

$\dfrac{2 \text{ moles SO}_3}{2 \text{ moles SO}_2}$ and $\dfrac{2 \text{ moles SO}_2}{2 \text{ moles SO}_3}$

$\dfrac{1 \text{ mole O}_2}{2 \text{ moles SO}_3}$ and $\dfrac{2 \text{ moles SO}_3}{1 \text{ mole O}_2}$

b. $\dfrac{4 \text{ moles P}}{5 \text{ moles O}_2}$ and $\dfrac{5 \text{ moles O}_2}{4 \text{ moles P}}$

$\dfrac{2 \text{ moles P}_2\text{O}_5}{4 \text{ moles P}}$ and $\dfrac{4 \text{ moles P}}{2 \text{ moles P}_2\text{O}_5}$

$\dfrac{5 \text{ moles O}_2}{2 \text{ moles P}_2\text{O}_5}$ and $\dfrac{2 \text{ moles P}_2\text{O}_5}{5 \text{ moles O}_2}$

5.43 a. $2.0 \text{ moles H}_2 \times \dfrac{1 \text{ mole O}_2}{2 \text{ moles H}_2} = 1.0 \text{ mole O}_2$

b. $5.0 \text{ moles O}_2 \times \dfrac{2 \text{ moles H}_2}{1 \text{ mole O}_2} = 10. \text{ moles H}_2$

c. $2.5 \text{ moles O}_2 \times \dfrac{2 \text{ moles H}_2\text{O}}{1 \text{ mole O}_2} = 5.0 \text{ moles H}_2\text{O}$

5.45 a. $0.500 \text{ mole SO}_2 \times \dfrac{5 \text{ moles C}}{2 \text{ moles SO}_2} = 1.25 \text{ moles C}$

b. $1.2 \text{ moles C} \times \dfrac{4 \text{ moles CO}}{5 \text{ moles C}} = 0.96 \text{ mole CO}$

c. $0.50 \text{ mole CS}_2 \times \dfrac{2 \text{ moles SO}_2}{1 \text{ mole CS}_2} = 1.0 \text{ mole SO}_2$

5.47 a. $2.50 \text{ moles Na} \times \dfrac{2 \text{ moles Na}_2\text{O}}{4 \text{ moles Na}} \times \dfrac{62.0 \text{ g Na}_2\text{O}}{1 \text{ mole Na}_2\text{O}} = 77.5 \text{ g Na}_2\text{O}$

b. $18.0 \text{ g Na} \times \dfrac{1 \text{ mole Na}}{23.0 \text{ g Na}} \times \dfrac{1 \text{ mole O}_2}{4 \text{ moles Na}} \times \dfrac{32.0 \text{ g O}_2}{1 \text{ mole O}_2} = 6.26 \text{ g O}_2$

c. $75.0 \text{ g Na}_2\text{O} \times \dfrac{1 \text{ mole Na}_2\text{O}}{62.0 \text{ g Na}_2\text{O}} \times \dfrac{1 \text{ mole O}_2}{2 \text{ moles Na}_2\text{O}} \times \dfrac{32.0 \text{ g O}_2}{1 \text{ mole O}_2} = 19.4 \text{ g O}_2$

5.49 a. $8.00 \text{ moles NH}_3 \times \dfrac{3 \text{ moles O}_2}{4 \text{ moles NH}_3} \times \dfrac{32.0 \text{ g O}_2}{1 \text{ mole O}_2} = 192 \text{ g O}_2$

b. $6.50 \text{ g O}_2 \times \dfrac{1 \text{ mole O}_2}{32.0 \text{ g O}_2} \times \dfrac{2 \text{ moles Na}_2}{3 \text{ moles O}_2} \times \dfrac{28.0 \text{ g N}_2}{1 \text{ mole N}_2} = 3.79 \text{ g N}_2$

c. $34.0 \text{ g NH}_3 \times \dfrac{1 \text{ mole NH}_3}{17.0 \text{ g NH}_3} \times \dfrac{6 \text{ moles H}_2\text{O}}{4 \text{ moles NH}_3} \times \dfrac{18.0 \text{ g H}_2\text{O}}{1 \text{ mole H}_2\text{O}} = 54.0 \text{ g H}_2\text{O}$

5.51 a. $28.0 \text{ g NO}_2 \times \dfrac{1 \text{ mole NO}_2}{46.0 \text{ g NO}_2} \times \dfrac{1 \text{ mole H}_2\text{O}}{3 \text{ moles NO}_2} \times \dfrac{18.0 \text{ g H}_2\text{O}}{1 \text{ mole H}_2\text{O}} = 3.65 \text{ g H}_2\text{O}$

b. $15.8 \text{ g NO}_2 \times \dfrac{1 \text{ mole NO}_2}{46.0 \text{ g NO}_2} \times \dfrac{1 \text{ mole NO}}{3 \text{ moles NO}_2} \times \dfrac{30.0 \text{ g NO}}{1 \text{ mole NO}} = 3.43 \text{ g NO}$

c. $8.25 \text{ g NO}_2 \times \dfrac{1 \text{ mole NO}_2}{46.0 \text{ g NO}_2} \times \dfrac{2 \text{ moles HNO}_3}{3 \text{ moles NO}_2} \times \dfrac{63.0 \text{ g HNO}_3}{1 \text{ mole HNO}_3} = 7.53 \text{ g NO}$

5.53 a. $2\text{PbS}(s) + 3\text{O}_2(g) \rightarrow 2\text{PbO}(s) + 2\text{SO}_2(g)$

b. $0.125 \text{ mole PbS} \times \dfrac{3 \text{ moles O}_2}{2 \text{ moles PbS}} \times \dfrac{32.0 \text{ g O}_2}{1 \text{ mole O}_2} = 6.00 \text{ g O}_2$

c. $65.0 \text{ g PbS} \times \dfrac{1 \text{ mole PbS}}{239.3 \text{ g PbS}} \times \dfrac{2 \text{ moles SO}_2}{2 \text{ moles PbS}} \times \dfrac{64.1 \text{ g SO}_2}{1 \text{ mole SO}_2} = 17.4 \text{ g SO}_2$

d. $128 \text{ g PbO} \times \dfrac{1 \text{ mole PbO}}{223.2 \text{ g PbO}} \times \dfrac{2 \text{ moles PbS}}{2 \text{ moles PbO}} \times \dfrac{239.3 \text{ g PbS}}{1 \text{ mole PbS}} = 137 \text{ g PbS}$

5.55 a. $40.0 \text{ g C} \times \dfrac{1 \text{ mole C}}{12.0 \text{ g C}} \times \dfrac{1 \text{ mole CS}_2}{5 \text{ moles C}} \times \dfrac{76.2 \text{ g CS}_2}{1 \text{ mole CS}_2} = 50.8 \text{ g CS}_2$

$\dfrac{36.0 \text{ g CS}_2 \text{ (actual)}}{50.8 \text{ g CS}_2 \text{ (theoretical)}} \times 100 = 70.9\%$

b. $32.0 \text{ g SO}_2 \times \dfrac{1 \text{ mole SO}_2}{64.1 \text{ g SO}_2} \times \dfrac{1 \text{ mole CS}_2}{2 \text{ moles SO}_2} \times \dfrac{76.2 \text{ g CS}_2}{1 \text{ mole CS}_2} = 19.0 \text{ g CS}_2$

$\dfrac{12.0 \text{ g CS}_2 \text{ (actual)}}{19.0 \text{ g CS}_2 \text{ (theoretical)}} \times 100 = 63.1\%$

5.57 $50.0 \text{ g Al} \times \dfrac{1 \text{ mole Al}}{27.0 \text{ g Al}} \times \dfrac{2 \text{ moles Al}_2\text{O}_3}{4 \text{ moles Al}} \times \dfrac{102.0 \text{ g Al}_2\text{O}_3}{1 \text{ mole Al}_2\text{O}_3} = 94.4 \text{ Al}_2\text{O}_3$

Use the percent yield to convert theoretical to actual:

$94.4 \text{ g Al}_2\text{O}_3 \times \dfrac{75.0 \text{ g Al}_2\text{O}_3}{100 \text{ g Al}_2\text{O}_3} = 70.8 \text{ g Al}_2\text{O}_3 \text{ (actual)}$

5.59 $30.0 \text{ g C} \times \dfrac{1 \text{ mole C}}{12.0 \text{ g C}} \times \dfrac{2 \text{ moles CO}}{3 \text{ moles C}} \times \dfrac{28.0 \text{ g CO}}{1 \text{ mole CO}} = 46.6 \text{ g CO}$

$\dfrac{28.8 \text{ g CO (actual)}}{46.6 \text{ g CO (theoretical)}} \times 100 = 60.6\%$

5.61 a. With 8 drivers available, only 8 taxis can be used to pick up passengers.
b. Seven taxis are in working condition to be driven.

5.63 a. $3.0 \text{ moles N}_2 \times \dfrac{2 \text{ moles NH}_3}{1 \text{ mole N}_2} = 6.0 \text{ moles NH}_3$

$5.0 \text{ moles H}_2 \times \dfrac{2 \text{ moles NH}_3}{3 \text{ moles H}_2} = 3.3 \text{ moles NH}_3 \text{ (smallest)}$

The limiting reactant is 5.0 moles H_2.

b. $8.0 \text{ moles N}_2 \times \dfrac{2 \text{ moles NH}_3}{1 \text{ mole N}_2} = 16 \text{ moles NH}_3$

$4.0 \text{ moles H}_2 \times \dfrac{2 \text{ moles NH}_3}{3 \text{ moles H}_2} = 2.7 \text{ moles NH}_3 \text{ (smallest moles of product)}$

The limiting reactant is 4.0 moles H_2.

c. $3.0 \text{ moles N}_2 \times \dfrac{2 \text{ moles NH}_3}{1 \text{ mole N}_2} = 6.0 \text{ moles NH}_3 \text{ (smallest)}$

$12.0 \text{ moles H}_2 \times \dfrac{2 \text{ moles NH}_3}{3 \text{ moles H}_2} = 8.0 \text{ moles NH}_3$

The limiting reactant is 3.0 moles N_2.

5.65 **a.** $2.00 \text{ moles SO}_2 \times \dfrac{2 \text{ moles SO}_3}{2 \text{ moles SO}_2} = 2.00 \text{ moles SO}_3$ (smallest moles of product)

$2.00 \text{ moles O}_2 \times \dfrac{2 \text{ moles SO}_3}{1 \text{ mole O}_2} = 4.00 \text{ moles SO}_3$

b. $2.00 \text{ moles Fe} \times \dfrac{1 \text{ mole Fe}_3\text{O}_4}{3 \text{ moles Fe}} = 0.667 \text{ mole Fe}_3\text{O}_4$

$2.00 \text{ moles H}_2\text{O} \times \dfrac{1 \text{ mole Fe}_3\text{O}_4}{4 \text{ moles H}_2\text{O}} = 0.500 \text{ mole Fe}_3\text{O}_4$ (smallest moles of product)

c. $2.00 \text{ moles C}_7\text{H}_{16} \times \dfrac{7 \text{ moles CO}_2}{1 \text{ mole C}_7\text{H}_{16}} = 14.0 \text{ moles CO}_2$

$2.00 \text{ moles O}_2 \times \dfrac{7 \text{ moles CO}_2}{11 \text{ moles O}_2} = 1.27 \text{ moles CO}_2$ (smallest moles of product)

$3.00 \text{ moles H}_2\text{O} \times \dfrac{3 \text{ moles H}_2\text{S}}{3 \text{ moles H}_2\text{O}} = 3.00 \text{ moles H}_2\text{S}$ (smallest moles of product)

5.67 **a.** $20.0 \text{ g Al} \times \dfrac{1 \text{ mole Al}}{27.0 \text{ g Al}} \times \dfrac{2 \text{ moles AlCl}_3}{2 \text{ moles Al}} = 0.741 \text{ mole AlCl}_3$

$20.0 \text{ g Cl}_2 \times \dfrac{1 \text{ mole Cl}_2}{70.9 \text{ g Cl}_2} \times \dfrac{2 \text{ moles AlCl}_3}{3 \text{ moles Cl}_2} = 0.188 \text{ mole AlCl}_3$ (smallest)

b. $20.0 \text{ g NH}_3 \times \dfrac{1 \text{ mole NH}_3}{17.0 \text{ g NH}_3} \times \dfrac{6 \text{ moles H}_2\text{O}}{4 \text{ moles NH}_3} = 1.76 \text{ moles H}_2\text{O}$

$20.0 \text{ g O}_2 \times \dfrac{1 \text{ mole O}_2}{32.0 \text{ g O}_2} \times \dfrac{6 \text{ moles H}_2\text{O}}{5 \text{ moles O}_2} = 0.750 \text{ mole AlCl}_3$ (smallest)

c. $20.0 \text{ g CS}_2 \times \dfrac{1 \text{ mole CS}_2}{76.1 \text{ g CS}_2} \times \dfrac{2 \text{ moles SO}_2}{1 \text{ mole CS}_2} = 0.526 \text{ mole SO}_2$

$20.0 \text{ g O}_2 \times \dfrac{1 \text{ mole O}_2}{32.0 \text{ g O}_2} \times \dfrac{2 \text{ moles SO}_2}{3 \text{ moles O}_2} = 0.417 \text{ mole SO}_2$ (smallest)

5.69 Physical: solid candle wax melts (changes state), candle height is shorter, melted wax turns solid (changes state), shape of the wax changes, the wick becomes shorter.

Chemical: wax burns in oxygen, heat and light are emitted, wick burns in the presence of oxygen.

5.71 **a.** 1, 1, 2 combination reaction   **b.** 2, 2, 1 decomposition reaction
   c. 1, 1, 1, 1 double replacement reaction   **d.** 1, 4, 2 combination reaction

5.73 **a.** $37.6 \text{ g Cu} \times \dfrac{1 \text{ mole Cu}}{63.6 \text{ g Cu}} \times \dfrac{2 \text{ moles CuO}}{2 \text{ moles Cu}} \times \dfrac{79.6 \text{ g CuO}}{1 \text{ mole CuO}} = 47.1 \text{ g CuO}$

b. $37.6 \text{ g Cu} \times \dfrac{1 \text{ mole Cu}}{63.6 \text{ g Cu}} \times \dfrac{1 \text{ mole O}_2-}{2 \text{ moles Cu}} = 0.296 \text{ mole O}_2$

5.75 **a.** $NH_3(g) + HCl(g) \rightarrow NH_4Cl(s)$ combination
   b. $Fe_3O_4(s) + 4H_2(g) \rightarrow 3\,Fe(s) + 4H_2O(g)$ single replacement
   c. $2\,Sb(s) + 3Cl_2(g) \rightarrow 2\,SbCl_3(s)$ combination
   d. $2\,NI_3(s) \rightarrow N_2(g) + 3\,I_2(g)$ decomposition
   e. $2\,KBr(aq) + Cl_2(aq) \rightarrow 2\,KCl(aq) + Br_2(l)$ single replacement
   f. $Al_2(SO_4)_3(aq) + 6\,NaOH(aq) \rightarrow 3\,Na_2SO_4(aq) + 2\,Al(OH)_3(s)$ double replacement

5.77 **a.** $Zn^{2+} + 2e^- \rightarrow Zn$ reduction   **b.** $Al \rightarrow Al^{3+} + 3e^-$ oxidation
　　c. $Pb \rightarrow Pb^{2+} + 2e^-$ oxidation   **d.** $Cl_2 + 2e^- \rightarrow 2Cl^-$ reduction

5.79 **a.** $3 \times C\,(12.0) + 6 \times H\,(1.01) + 3 \times O\,(16.0) = 90.1 \text{ g/mole}$

b. $0.500 \text{ mole } C_3H_6O_3 \times \dfrac{6.02 \times 10^{23} \text{ molecules}}{1 \text{ mole } C_3H_6O_3} = 3.01 \times 10^{23} \text{ molecules}$

c. $1.50 \text{ moles } C_3H_6O_3 \times \dfrac{3 \text{ moles C}}{1 \text{ mole } C_3H_6O_3} \times \dfrac{6.02 \times 10^{23} \text{ atoms}}{1 \text{ mole C}} = 2.71 \times 10^{24} \text{ C atoms}$

d. $4.5 \times 10^{24} \text{ O atoms} \times \dfrac{1 \text{ mole O}}{6.02 \times 10^{23} \text{ O atoms}} \times \dfrac{1 \text{ mole } C_3H_6O_3}{3 \text{ moles O}} = 2.5 \text{ moles } C_3H_6O_3$

5.81 **a.** $1 \text{ mole Fe} \times \dfrac{55.9 \text{ g}}{1 \text{ mole Fe}} = 55.9 \text{ g}$

$1 \text{ mole S} \times \dfrac{32.1 \text{ g}}{1 \text{ mole S}} = 32.1 \text{ g}$

$4 \text{ moles O} \times \dfrac{16.0 \text{ g}}{1 \text{ mole O}} = \dfrac{64.0 \text{ g}}{152.0 \text{ g}}$

b. $1 \text{ mole Ca} \times \dfrac{40.1 \text{ g}}{1 \text{ mole Ca}} = 40.1 \text{ g}$

$2 \text{ moles I} \times \dfrac{126.9 \text{ g}}{1 \text{ mole I}} = 253.8 \text{ g}$

$6 \text{ moles O} \times \dfrac{16.0 \text{ g}}{1 \text{ mole O}} = \dfrac{96.0 \text{ g}}{389.9 \text{ g}}$

c. $5 \text{ moles C} \times \dfrac{12.0 \text{ g}}{1 \text{ mole C}} = 60.0 \text{ g}$

$8 \text{ moles H} \times \dfrac{1.01 \text{ g}}{1 \text{ mole H}} = 8.08 \text{ g}$

$1 \text{ mole N} \times \dfrac{14.0 \text{ g}}{1 \text{ mole N}} = 14.0 \text{ g}$

$1 \text{ mole Na} \times \dfrac{23.0 \text{ g}}{1 \text{ mole Na}} = 23.0 \text{ g}$

$4 \text{ moles O} \times \dfrac{16.0 \text{ g}}{1 \text{ mole O}} = \dfrac{64.0 \text{ g}}{169.1 \text{ g}}$

5.83 **a.** $0.150 \text{ mole K} \times \dfrac{39.1 \text{ g K}}{1 \text{ mole K}} = 5.87 \text{ g K}$

b. $0.150 \text{ mole } Cl_2 \times \dfrac{71.0 \text{ g } Cl_2}{1 \text{ mole } Cl_2} = 10.7 \text{ g } Cl_2$

c. $0.150 \text{ mole } Na_2CO_3 \times \dfrac{106.0 \text{ g } Na_2CO_3}{1 \text{ mole } Na_2CO_3} = 15.9 \text{ g } Na_2CO_3$

5.85 **a.** $25.0 \text{ g } CO_2 \times \dfrac{1 \text{ mole } CO_2}{44.0 \text{ g } CO_2} = 0.568 \text{ mole } CO_2$

b. $25.0 \text{ g Al(OH)}_3 \times \dfrac{1 \text{ mole Al(OH)}_3}{78.0 \text{ g Al(OH)}_3} = 0.321 \text{ mole Al(OH)}_3$

c. $25.0 \text{ g MgCl}_2 \times \dfrac{1 \text{ mole MgCl}_2}{95.3 \text{ g Mg Cl}_2} = 0.262 \text{ mole MgCl}_2$

5.87 a. $124 \text{ g C}_2\text{H}_6\text{O} \times \dfrac{1 \text{ mole C}_2\text{H}_6\text{O}}{46.0 \text{ g C}_2\text{H}_6\text{O}} \times \dfrac{1 \text{ mole C}_6\text{H}_{12}\text{O}_6}{2 \text{ moles C}_2\text{H}_6\text{O}} = 1.35 \text{ moles C}_6\text{H}_{12}\text{O}_6$

b. $0.240 \text{ kg C}_6\text{H}_{12}\text{O}_6 \times \dfrac{1000 \text{ g}}{1 \text{ kg}} \times \dfrac{1 \text{ mole C}_6\text{H}_{12}\text{O}_6}{180.0 \text{ g C}_6\text{H}_{12}\text{O}_6} \times \dfrac{2 \text{ moles C}_2\text{H}_6\text{O}}{1 \text{ mole C}_6\text{H}_{12}\text{O}_6} \times \dfrac{46.0 \text{ g C}_2\text{H}_6\text{O}}{1 \text{ mole C}_2\text{H}_6\text{O}}$

$\qquad = 123 \text{ g C}_2\text{H}_6\text{O}$

5.89 $2\text{NH}_3(g) + 5\text{F}_2(g) \rightarrow \text{N}_2\text{F}_4(g) + 6\text{HF}(g)$

a. $4.00 \text{ moles HF} \times \dfrac{2 \text{ moles NH}_3}{6 \text{ moles HF}} = 1.33 \text{ moles NH}_3$

$\qquad 4.00 \text{ moles HF} \times \dfrac{5 \text{ moles F}_2}{6 \text{ moles HF}} = 3.33 \text{ moles F}_2$

b. $1.50 \text{ moles NH}_3 \times \dfrac{5 \text{ moles F}_2}{2 \text{ moles NH}_3} \times \dfrac{38.0 \text{ g F}_2}{1 \text{ mole F}_2} = 143 \text{ g F}_2$

c. $3.40 \text{ g NH}_3 \times \dfrac{1 \text{ mole NH}_3}{17.0 \text{ g NH}_3} \times \dfrac{1 \text{ mole N}_2\text{F}_4}{2 \text{ moles NH}_3} \times \dfrac{104.0 \text{ g N}_2\text{F}_4}{1 \text{ mole N}_2\text{F}_4} = 10.4 \text{ g N}_2\text{F}_4$

5.91 a. $1.60 \text{ moles C}_2\text{Cl}_6 \times \dfrac{6 \text{ moles Cl}_2}{1 \text{ mole C}_2\text{Cl}_6} \times \dfrac{71.0 \text{ g Cl}_2}{1 \text{ mole Cl}_2} = 682 \text{ g Cl}_2$

b. $50.0 \text{ g C}_2\text{H}_6 \times \dfrac{1 \text{ mole C}_2\text{H}_6}{30.0 \text{ g C}_2\text{H}_6} \times \dfrac{6 \text{ moles HCl}}{1 \text{ mole C}_2\text{H}_6} \times \dfrac{36.5 \text{ g HCl}}{1 \text{ mole HCl}} = 365 \text{ g HCl}$

5.93 $2\text{C}_2\text{H}_2(g) + 5\text{O}_2(g) \rightarrow 4\text{CO}_2(g) + 2\text{H}_2\text{O}(g)$

$\qquad 22.5 \text{ g C}_2\text{H}_2 \times \dfrac{1 \text{ mole C}_2\text{H}_2}{26.0 \text{ g C}_2\text{H}_2} \times \dfrac{4 \text{ moles CO}_2}{2 \text{ moles C}_2\text{H}_2} \times \dfrac{44.0 \text{ g CO}_2}{1 \text{ mole CO}_2} = 76.2 \text{ g CO}_2 \text{ (theoretical)}$

$\qquad \dfrac{62.0 \text{ g (actual)}}{76.2 \text{ g (theoretical)}} \times 100 = 81.4\% \text{ (percent yield)}$

5.95 a. $4.0 \text{ moles H}_2\text{O} \times \dfrac{1 \text{ mole C}_5\text{H}_{12}}{6 \text{ moles H}_2\text{O}} \times \dfrac{72.2 \text{ g C}_5\text{H}_{12}}{1 \text{ mole C}_5\text{H}_{12}} = 48 \text{ g C}_5\text{H}_{12}$

b. $32.0 \text{ g O}_2 \times \dfrac{1 \text{ mole O}_2}{32.0 \text{ g O}_2} \times \dfrac{5 \text{ moles CO}_2}{8 \text{ moles O}_2} \times \dfrac{44.0 \text{ g CO}_2}{1 \text{ mole CO}_2} = 27.5 \text{ g CO}_2$

c. $44.5 \text{ g C}_5\text{H}_{12} \times \dfrac{1 \text{ mole C}_5\text{H}_{12}}{72.0 \text{ g C}_5\text{H}_{12}} \times \dfrac{5 \text{ moles CO}_2}{1 \text{ mole C}_5\text{H}_{12}} = 3.09 \text{ moles CO}_2$

$\qquad 108 \text{ g O}_2 \times \dfrac{1 \text{ mole O}_2}{32.0 \text{ g O}_2} \times \dfrac{5 \text{ moles CO}_2}{8 \text{ moles O}_2} = 2.11 \text{ moles CO}_2 \text{ (smallest moles of product)}$

$\qquad 2.11 \text{ moles CO}_2 \times \dfrac{44.0 \text{ g CO}_2}{1 \text{ mole CO}_2} = 92.8 \text{ g CO}_2$

5.97 $12.8 \text{ g Na} \times \dfrac{1 \text{ mole Na}}{23.0 \text{ g Na}} \times \dfrac{2 \text{ moles NaCl}}{2 \text{ moles Na}} = 0.557 \text{ mole NaCl}$

$10.2 \text{ g Cl}_2 \times \dfrac{1 \text{ mole Cl}_2}{70.9 \text{ g Cl}_2} \times \dfrac{2 \text{ moles NaCl}}{1 \text{ mole Cl}_2} = 0.288 \text{ mole NaCl (smallest moles of product)}$

$0.288 \text{ mole NaCl} \times \dfrac{58.5 \text{ g NaCl}}{1 \text{ mole NaCl}} = 16.8 \text{ g NaCl}$

5.99   **a.** $3Pb(NO_3)_2(aq) + 2Na_3PO_4(aq) \rightarrow Pb_3(PO_4)_2(s) + 6NaNO_3(aq)$ double replacement
   b. $4Ga(s) + 3O_2(g) \rightarrow 2Ga_2O_3(s)$ combination
   c. $2NaNO_3(s) \rightarrow 2NaNO_2(s) + O_2(g)$ decomposition
   d. $Bi_2O_3(s) + 3C(s) \rightarrow 2Bi(s) + 3CO(g)$ single replacement

5.101 **a.** 5.00 g gold
   b. 1.53×10^{22} Au atoms
   c. 0.038 mole oxygen
   d. Au_2O_3

5.103 **a.** $22.0 \text{ g C}_2\text{H}_2 \times \dfrac{1 \text{ mole C}_2\text{H}_2}{26.0 \text{ g C}_2\text{H}_2} \times \dfrac{5 \text{ moles O}_2}{2 \text{ moles C}_2\text{H}_2} \times \dfrac{6.02 \times 10^{23} \text{ molecules O}_2}{1 \text{ mole O}_2}$

$= 1.27 \times 10^{24} \text{ molecules O}_2$

   b. $22.0 \text{ g C}_2\text{H}_2 \times \dfrac{1 \text{ mole C}_2\text{H}_2}{26.0 \text{ g C}_2\text{H}_2} \times \dfrac{4 \text{ moles CO}_2}{2 \text{ moles C}_2\text{H}_2} \times \dfrac{44.0 \text{ g CO}_2}{1 \text{ mole CO}_2} = 74.4 \text{ g CO}_2 \text{ (theoretical)}$

   c. $\dfrac{64.0 \text{ g (actual)}}{74.4 \text{ g (theoretical)}} \times 100 = 86.0\% \text{ (percent yield)}$

5.105 **a.** $4Al(s) + 3O_2(g) \rightarrow 2Al_2O_3(s)$ **b.** This is a combination reaction.
   c. 3.38 moles oxygen.   **d.** 94.9 g aluminum oxide
   e. 17.0 g aluminum oxide   **f.** 59.6 g aluminum oxide

Study Goals

- Describe potential and kinetic energy.
- Given the heat of reaction, describe a reaction as an exothermic reactions or endothermic reaction.
- Calculate the calories lost or gained by a specific amount of a substance for a specific temperature change.
- Determine the kilocalories for food samples.
- Identify the states of matter.
- Describe the types of forces that hold particles together in liquids and solids.
- Determine the energy lost or gained during a change of state at the melting or boiling point.
- Identify the states of matter and changes of state on a heating or cooling curve.

Think About It

1. What kinds of activities did you do today that used *kinetic* energy?

2. What are some of the forms of energy you use in your home?

3. Why is the energy in your breakfast cereal *potential* energy?

4. Why is the high specific heat of water important to our survival?

5. How does perspiring during a workout help to keep you cool?

6. During a rain or snowfall, temperature rises. Why?

7. Why is a steam burn much more damaging to skin than a hot-water burn?

Key Terms

Match the following terms with the statements below:

    a. change of state   **b.** kinetic energy   **c.** potential energy
    d. Calorie   **e.** kilojoule

1. _____ the amount of heat needed to raise the temperature of 1 g water by 1°C

2. _____ water boiling at 100°C

3. _____ the energy of motion

4. _____ stored energy

5. _____ the amount of energy equal to 1000 joules

Answers   **1.** d   **2.** a   **3.** b   **4.** c   **5.** e

6.1 Energy

- Energy is the ability to do work.
- Potential energy is stored energy; kinetic energy is the energy of motion.
- Some forms of energy include heat, mechanical, radiant, solar, electrical, chemical, and nuclear.

◆ Learning Exercise 6.1A

Match the words in column A with the descriptions in column B.

A	**B**
1. _____ kinetic energy	**a.** inactive or stored energy
2. _____ potential energy	**b.** the ability to do work
3. _____ chemical energy	**c.** the energy of motion
4. _____ energy	**d.** the energy available in the bonds of chemical compounds

Answers   **1.** c   **2.** a   **3.** d   **4.** b

◆ Learning Exercise 6.1B

State whether the following statements describe potential (P) or kinetic (K) energy:

1. _____ a potted plant sitting on a ledge   2. _____ your breakfast cereal

3. _____ logs sitting in a fireplace   4. _____ a piece of candy

5. _____ an arrow shot from a bow   6. _____ a ski jumper at the top of the ski jump

7. _____ a jogger running   8. _____ a sky diver waiting to jump

9. _____ water flowing down a stream   10. _____ a bowling ball striking the pins

Answers   **1.** P   **2.** P   **3.** P   **4.** P   **5.** K
             6. P   **7.** K   **8.** P   **9.** K   **10.** K

◆ Learning Exercise 6.1C

Match the words in column A with the descriptions in column B.

A	**B**
1. _____ calorie	**a.** 1000 calories
2. _____ joule	**b.** the heat needed to raise 1 g water by 1°C
3. _____ kilocalorie	**c.** a unit of heat equal to 0.0239 cal

Answers   **1.** b   **2.** c   **3.** a

6.2 Energy in Chemical Reactions

- In a reaction, molecules (or atoms) must collide with energy equal to or greater than the energy of activation.
- The heat of reaction is the energy difference between the energy of the reactants and the products.

- In exothermic reactions, the heat of reaction is the energy released. In endothermic reactions, the heat of reaction is the energy absorbed.
- The rate of a reaction (the speed at which products form) can be increased by adding more reacting molecules, raising the temperature of the reaction, or adding a catalyst.

◆ Learning Exercise 6.2A

Indicate whether each of the following is an endothermic or exothermic reaction:

1. $2H_2(g) + O_2(g) \rightarrow 2H_2O(g) + 582$ kJ _____

2. $C_2H_4(g) + 42.1$ kcal $\rightarrow H_2(g) + C_2H_2(g)$ _____

3. $2C(s) + O_2(g) \rightarrow 2CO(g) + 53$ kcal _____

4. $\underset{glucose}{C_6H_{12}O_6(s)} + 6O_2(g) \rightarrow 6CO_2(g) + 6H_2O(l) + 1350$ kcal _____

5. $C_2H_4(g) + H_2O(g) \rightarrow C_2H_5OH(l) + 21$ kcal _____

Answers   **1.** exothermic   **2.** endothermic   **3.** exothermic
                     4. exothermic   **5.** exothermic

◆ Learning Exercise 6.2B

For the following reaction, how much heat (in kJ) is produced when 50.0 g CO_2 is formed?

$$C_6H_{12}O_6(s) + 6O_2(g) \rightarrow 6CO_2(g) + 6H_2O(l) + 1350 \text{ kcal}$$

Answer   **1070 kJ**

6.3 Specific Heat

- Specific heat is the amount of energy required to raise the temperature of 1 g of a substance by 1°C.
- The specific heat for liquid water is 1.00 calorie/g°C or 4.184 joules/g°C.

Study Note

The heat lost or gained by a substance is calculated from the mass, temperature change, and specific heat of the substance.

     Heat (calories) = **mass** (g) $\times$ **temperature change** (ΔT) $\times$ **specific heat** (cal/g°C)
     There are 4.184 joules in one calorie.
     Number of calories $\times$ 4.184 = number of joules

◆ Learning Exercise 6.3

Calculate the calories (cal) gained or released during the following:

1. heating 20. g water from 22°C to 77°C

2. heating 10. g water from 12°C to 97°C

3. cooling 4.00 kg water from 80.0°C to 35.0°C

4. cooling 125 g water from 45.0°C to 72.0°C

Answers   **1.** 1100 cal   **2.** 850 cal
                   3. 180 000 cal   **4.** 3380 cal

6.4 Energy and Nutrition

- A nutritional calorie is the same amount of energy as 1 kcal or 1000 calories.
- When a substance is burned in a calorimeter, the water that surrounds the reaction chamber absorbs the heat given off. The calories absorbed by the water are calculated and the caloric value (energy per gram) is determined for the substance.

◆ Learning Exercise 6.4A

State the caloric value in kcal/g associated with the following:

   a. amino acid _____   **b.** protein _____

   c. sugar _____   **d.** sucrose _____

   e. oil _____   **f.** fat _____

   g. starch _____   **h.** lipid _____

   i. glucose _____   **j.** lard _____

Answers   **a.** 4 kcal/g   **b.** 4 kcal/g   **c.** 4 kcal/g   **d.** 4 kcal/g   **e.** 9 kcal/g
                 f. 9 kcal/g   **g.** 4 kcal/g   **h.** 9 kcal/g   **i.** 4 kcal/g   **j.** 9 kcal/g

---

Study Note

The caloric content of a food is the sum of calories from carbohydrate, fat, and protein. It is calculated by using their number of grams in a food and the caloric values of 4 kcal/g for carbohydrate and protein and 9 kcal/g for fat.

◆ **Learning Exercise 6.4B**

Calculate the kcal for the following foods using the following data:

Food	Carbohydrate	Fat	Protein	kcal
a. Peas, green, cooked	19 g	1 g	9 g	____
b. Potato chips, 10 chips	10 g	8 g	1 g	____
c. Cream cheese, 8 oz	5 g	86 g	18 g	____
d. Hamburger, lean, 3 oz	0	10 g	23 g	____
e. Salmon, canned	0	5 g	17 g	____
f. Snap beans, 1 cup	7 g	2 g	30 g	____
g. Banana, 1	26 g	0	1 g	____

Answers   **a.** 120 kcal   **b.** 120 kcal   **c.** 870 kcal   **d.** 180 kcal
                    e. 110 kcal   **f.** 170 kcal   **g.** 110 kcal

◆ **Learning Exercise 6.4C**

Using caloric values, give answers with two significant figures for each of the following problems:

1. How many kcal are in a single serving of pudding that contains 4 g protein, 31 g carbohydrate, and 5 g fat?

2. A can of tuna has a caloric value of 200 kcal. If there are 2 g fat and no carbohydrate, how many grams of protein are contained in the can of tuna?

3. A serving of breakfast cereal provides 220 kcal. In this serving, there are 8 g protein and 6 g fat. How many grams of carbohydrates are in the cereal?

4. Complete the following table listing ingredients for a peanut butter sandwich.

	Protein	Carbohydrate	Fat	kcal
2 slices bread	4 g	30 g	0	____
2 Tbsp peanut butter	8 g	6 g	____	170 kcal
2 tsp jelly	0	____	0	40 kcal
1 tsp margarine	0	0	5 g	____
			Total kcal in sandwich	____

Answers
1. protein 16 kcal + carbohydrate 124 kcal + fat 45 kcal = 190 kcal
2. fat 18 kcal; 200 kcal − 18 = protein 182 kcal; 46 g protein
3. protein 32 kcal + fat 54 kcal = 86 kcal protein and fat; 220 kcal − 86 kcal = 134 kcal due to carbohydrate; 134 kcal/4 kcal/g = 34 g carbohydrate
4. bread, 136 kcal; peanut butter, 13 g fat; jelly, 10 g carbohydrate; margarine, 45 kcal; total = 400 kcal (4.0×10^2 kcal)

6.5 States of Matter

- Matter is anything that has mass and occupies space.
- The three states of matter are solid, liquid, and gas.
- Ionic solids have high melting points due to strong ionic interactions between positive and negative ions.
- In polar substances, dipole–dipole attractions occur between the positive end of one molecule and the negative end of another.
- Hydrogen bonding, a type of dipole–dipole interaction, occurs between partially positive hydrogen atoms and strongly electronegative atoms of F, O, or N.
- Dispersion forces occur when temporary dipoles form within the nonpolar molecules, causing attractions to other nonpolar molecules.

◆ Learning Exercise 6.5A

State whether the following statements describe a gas (G), a liquid (L), or a solid (S).

1. _____ There are no attractions among the molecules.

2. _____ Particles are held close together in a definite pattern.

3. _____ The substance has a definite volume but no definite shape.

4. _____ The particles are moving extremely fast.

5. _____ This substance has no definite shape and no definite volume.

6. _____ The particles are very far apart.

7. _____ This material has its own volume but takes the shape of its container.

8. _____ The particles of this material bombard the sides of the container with great force.

9. _____ The particles in this substance are moving very, very slowly.

10. _____ This substance has a definite volume and a definite shape.

Answers
| **1.** G | **2.** S | **3.** L | **4.** G | **5.** G |
| **6.** G | **7.** L | **8.** G | **9.** S | **10.** S |

◆ Learning Exercise 6.5B

Indicate the major type of interactive force that occurs in each of the following substances:

A. ionic   **B.** dipole–dipole   **C.** hydrogen bond
D. dispersion forces

1. _____ KCl   **5.** _____ HF

2. _____ NCl_3 **6.** _____ H_2O

3. _____ SBr_2 **7.** _____ C_4H_{10}

4. _____ Cl   **8.** _____ Na_2O

Answers   **1.** A   **2.** B   **3.** B   **4.** D
             5. C   **6.** C   **7.** D   **8.** A

◆ Learning Exercise 6.5C

Identify the substance that would have the higher boiling point in each pair:

1. NaCl or HCl_____   **4.** C_2H_6 or CO_2_____

2. Br_2 or HBr_____   **5.** $MgCl_2$ or OCl_2_____

3. H_2O or H_2S_____   **6.** NH_3 or PH_3_____

Answers   **1.** NaCl (ionic)   **2.** HBr (dipole–dipole)
             3. H_2O(hydrogen bonding)   **4.** CO_2 (dipole–dipole)
             5. $MgCl_2$ (ionic)   **6.** NH_3 (hydrogen bonding)

6.6 Changes of State

- A substance undergoes a physical change when its shape, size, or state changes, but the type of substance itself does not change.
- A substance melts and freezes at its melting (freezing) point.
- As long as a substance is changing state during boiling, or condensation, the temperature remains constant.
- The *heat of fusion* is the heat energy required to change 1 g of solid to liquid. For water to freeze at 0°C, the heat of fusion is 80. calories. This is also the amount of heat lost when 1 g water freezes at 0°C.
- Sublimation is the change of state from a solid directly to a gas.
- When water boils at 100°C, 540 calories, the heat of vaporization, is required to change 1 g of liquid to gas (steam); it is also the amount of heat released when 1 g water vapor condenses at 100°C.
- A heating or cooling curve illustrates the changes in temperature and states as heat is added to or removed from a substance.

◆ Learning Exercise 6.6A

Identify each of the following as

   1. melting   **2.** freezing   **3.** sublimation.

a. _____ A liquid changes to a solid.

b. _____ Ice forms on the surface of a lake in winter.

c. _____ Dry ice in an ice cream cart changes to a gas.

d. _____ Butter in a hot pan turns to liquid.

Answers   **a.** 2   **b.** 2   **c.** 3   **d.** 1

Study Note

The amount of heat needed or released during melting or freezing can be calculated using the heat of fusion:

$$\text{Heat (cal)} = \text{mass (g)} \times \text{heat of fusion}$$

◆ **Learning Exercise 6.6B**

Calculate the energy required or released when the following substances melt or freeze:

a. How many calories are needed to melt 15 g ice at 0°C?

b. How much heat in kilocalories is released when 325 g water freezes at 0°C?

c. How many grams of ice would melt when 4000 calories of heat was absorbed?

Answers   **a.** 1200 cal   **b.** 26 kcal   **c.** 50 g

◆ **Learning Exercise 6.6C**

Calculate the energy required or released for the following substances undergoing boiling or condensation:

a. How many calories are needed to completely change 10. g water to vapor at 100°C?

b. How many kilocalories are released when 515 grams of steam at 100°C condense to form liquid water at 100°C?

c. How many grams of water can be converted to steam at 100°C when 272 kcal of energy is absorbed?

Answers   **a.** 5400 cal   **b.** 278 kcal   **c.** 504 g

◆ Learning Exercise 6.6D

On each heating or cooling curve, indicate the portion that corresponds to a solid, liquid, or gas and the changes in state.

1. Draw a heating curve for water that begins at −20°C and ends at 120°C. Water has a melting point of 0°C and a boiling point of 100°C.

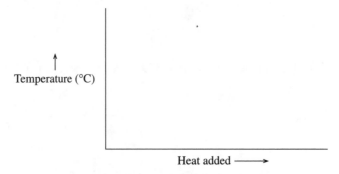

2. Draw a heating curve for bromine from −25° to 75°C. Bromine has a melting point of −7°C and a boiling point of 59°C.

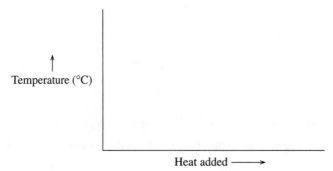

3. Draw a cooling curve for sodium from 1000°C to 0°C. Sodium has a freezing point of 98°C and a boiling (condensation) point of 883°C.

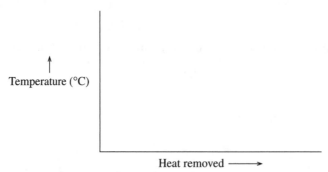

Answers   **1.**

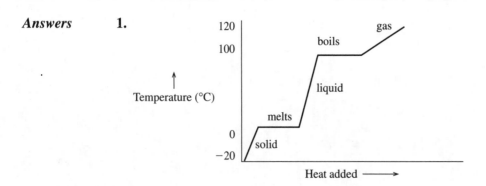

2.

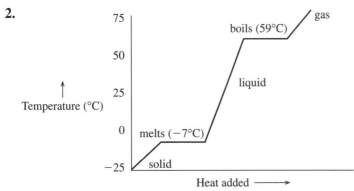

3.

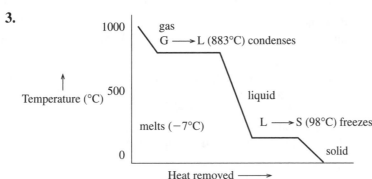

Checklist for Chapter 6

You are ready to take the practice test for Chapter 6. Be sure that you have accomplished the following learning goals for this chapter. If you are not sure, review the section listed at the end of the goal. Then apply your new skills and understanding to the practice test.

After studying Chapter 6, I can successfully:

_____ Describe some forms of energy (6.1).

_____ Determine if a reaction is exothermic or endothermic (6.2).

_____ Calculate the cal or joules given off or taken in by a chemical reaction (6.2).

_____ Given the mass of a sample, specific heats, and the temperature change, calculate the heat lost or gained (6.3).

_____ Calculate the energy of a food sample (6.4).

_____ Identify the physical state of a substance as a solid, liquid, or gas (6.5).

_____ Describe the attractive forces in molecules (6.5).

_____ Calculate the heat change for the melting or boiling of a specific amount of a substance (6.6).

_____ Draw heating and cooling curves using the melting and boiling points of a substance (6.6).

Practice Test for Chapter 6

1. Which of the following would be described as potential energy?
    A. a car going around a racetrack   **B.** a rabbit hopping   **C.** oil in an oil well
    D. a moving merry-go-round   **E.** a bouncing ball

2. Which of the following would be described as kinetic energy?
    A. a car battery   **B.** a can of tennis balls   **C.** gasoline in a car fuel tank
    D. a box of matches   **E.** a tennis ball crossing over the net

3. The number of calories needed to raise the temperature of 5.0 g water from 25°C to 55°C is
    A. 5 cal   **B.** 30 cal   **C.** 5 cal   **D.** 80 cal   **E.** 150 cal

4. The number of calories (kcal) released when 150 g water cools from 58°C to 22°C is
    A. 1.1 kcal   **B.** 4.2 kcal   **C.** 5.4 kcal   **D.** 6.9 kcal   **E.** 8.7 kcal

For questions 5–8, consider a cup of milk with a caloric value of 165 kcal. In the cup of milk, there are 9 g fat, 12 g carbohydrate, and some protein.

5. The number of kcal provided by the carbohydrate is
    A. 4 kcal   **B.** 9 kcal   **C.** 36 kcal   **D.** 48 kcal   **E.** 81 kcal

6. The number of kcal provided by the fat is
    A. 4 kcal   **B.** 9 kcal   **C.** 36 kcal   **D.** 48 kcal   **E.** 81 kcal

7. The number of kcal provided by the protein is
    A. 4 kcal   **B.** 9 kcal   **C.** 36 kcal   **D.** 48 kcal   **E.** 81 kcal

8. Which of the following describes a liquid?
    A. a substance that has no definite shape and no definite volume
    B. a substance with particles that are far apart
    C. a substance with a definite shape and a definite volume
    D. a substance containing particles that are moving very fast
    E. a substance that has a definite volume but takes the shape of its container

Identify the statements in questions 9–12 as:
    A. evaporation   **B.** heat of fusion
    C. heat of vaporization   **D.** boiling

9. _____ the energy required to convert a gram of solid to liquid

10. _____ the heat needed to boil a liquid

11. _____ the conversion of liquid molecules to gas at the surface of a liquid

12. _____ the formation of a gas within the liquid as well as on the surface

13. Ice cools down a drink because
    A. The ice is colder than the drink and heat flows into the ice cubes.
    B. Heat is absorbed from the drink to melt the ice cubes.
    C. The heat of fusion of the ice is higher than the heat of fusion for water.
    D. both A and B.
    E. none of the above

14. The number of kilocalories needed to convert 400 g ice to liquid at 0°C is
    A. 400 kcal   **B.** 320 kcal   **C.** 80 kcal   **D.** 40 kcal   **E.** 32 kcal

For questions 15–18, consider the heating curve below for *p*-toluidine. Answer the following questions when heat is added to *p*-toluidine at 20°C where toluidine is below its melting point.

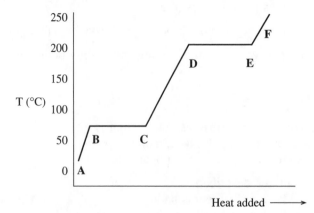

15. On the heating curve, segment BC indicates
    A. solid   **B.** melting   **C.** liquid   **D.** boiling   **E.** gas

16. On the heating curve, segment CD shows toluidine as
    A. solid   **B.** melting   **C.** liquid   **D.** boiling   **E.** gas

17. The boiling point of toluidine would be
    A. 20°C   **B.** 45°C   **C.** 100°C   **D.** 200°C   **E.** 250°C

18. On the heating curve, segment EF shows toluidine as
    A. solid   **B.** melting   **C.** a liquid   **D.** boiling   **E.** a gas

For questions 19–20, indicate the major type of interactive force that occurs in each:
    A. ionic   **B.** dipole–dipole   **C.** hydrogen bond   **D.** dispersion forces   **E.** none

19. HF

20. CH_4

Answers to the Practice Test

1. C	**2.** E	**3.** E	**4.** C	**5.** D
6. E	**7.** C	**8.** E	**9.** B	**10.** C
11. A	**12.** D	**13.** D	**14.** E	**15.** B
16. C	**17.** D	**18.** E	**19.** C	**20.** D

Answers and Solutions to Selected Text Problems

6.1   As the car climbs the hill, kinetic energy is converted to potential until, at the top of the hill, all of the energy is in the form of potential energy. As it descends down the hill, potential energy is being converted into kinetic energy. When the car reaches the bottom, all of its energy is in the form of motion (kinetic energy).

6.3   **a.** potential   **b.** kinetic   **c.** potential   **d.** potential

6.5   **a.** $3500 \text{ cal} \times \dfrac{1 \text{ kcal}}{1000 \text{ cal}} = 3.5 \text{ kcal}$

        b. $415 \text{ J} \times \dfrac{1 \text{ cal}}{4.184 \text{ J}} = 99.2 \text{ cal}$

        c. $28 \text{ cal} \times \dfrac{4.184 \text{ J}}{1 \text{ cal}} = 120 \text{ J}$

        d. $4.5 \text{ kJ} \times \dfrac{1000 \text{ J}}{1 \text{ kJ}} \times \dfrac{1 \text{ cal}}{4.184 \text{ J}} = 1100 \text{ cal}$

6.7   **a.** The energy of activation is the energy required to break the bonds in the reacting molecules.
        b. In exothermic reactions, the energy of the products is lower than the reactants.
        c.

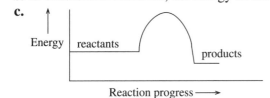

6.9   **a.** exothermic; heat loss   **b.** endothermic; heat gain
        c. exothermic; heat loss

6.11   **a.** Heat is released, which makes the reaction exothermic with $\Delta H = -210$ kcal.
       b. Heat is absorbed, which makes the reaction endothermic with $\Delta H = 65.3$ kJ.
       c. Heat is released, which makes the reaction exothermic with $\Delta H = -205$ kcal.

6.13 $125 \text{ g Cl}_2 \times \dfrac{1 \text{ moles Cl}_2}{70.9 \text{ g Cl}_2} \times \dfrac{157 \text{ kcal}}{2 \text{ moles Cl}_2} = 138$ kcal released

6.15   Copper has the lowest specific heat of the samples and will reach the highest temperature.

6.17   **a.** $\Delta T = 25°C - 15°C = 10.°C \quad 25 \text{ g} \times \dfrac{1.00 \text{ cal}}{\text{g}°C} \times 10.°C = 250$ cal

       b. $150 \text{ g} \times \dfrac{1.00 \text{ cal}}{\text{g}°C} \times 75°C = 11\,000$ cal

       c. $150 \text{ g} \times \dfrac{1.00 \text{ cal}}{\text{g}°C} \times 62°C \times \dfrac{1 \text{ kcal}}{1000 \text{ cal}} = 9.3$ kcal

6.19   The heat required is given by the following relationship: heat = m $\times \Delta T \times SH$.
       a. Heat = m $\times \Delta T \times SH = 25.0 \text{ g} \times (25.7°C - 12.5°C) \times 4.184$ J/g°C

          $= 25.0 \text{ g} \times 13.2°C \times 4.184 \text{ J/g}°C = 1380 \text{ J}$ and $1380 \text{ J} \times \dfrac{1 \text{ cal}}{4.184 \text{ J}} = 330.$ cal

       b. Heat = m $\times \Delta T \times SH = 38.0 \text{ g} \times (246°C - 122°C) \times 0.385$ J/g°C

          $= 38.0 \text{ g} \times 124°C \times 0.385 \text{ J/g}°C = 1810 \text{ J} \quad 1810 \text{ J} \times \dfrac{1 \text{ cal}}{4.184 \text{ J}} = 434$ cal

       c. Heat = m $\times \Delta T \times SH = 15.0 \text{ g} \times (65°C - 42.0°C) \times 2.46$ J/g°C

          $= 15.0 \text{ g} \times 107°C \times 2.46 \text{ J/g}°C = 3780 \text{ J} \quad 3780 \text{ J} \times \dfrac{1 \text{ cal}}{4.184 \text{ J}} = 904$ cal

       d. Heat = m $\times \Delta T \times SH = 125 \text{ g} \times (118°C - 55°C) \times 0.450$ J/g°C

          $= 112 \text{ g} \times 63°C \times 0.452 \text{ J/g}°C = 3200 \text{ J} \ (3.2 \times 10^3 \text{ J}) \ 3200 \text{ J} \times \dfrac{1 \text{ cal}}{4.184 \text{ J}} = 760$ cal

6.21   **a.** $505 \text{ g} \times \dfrac{100 \text{ cal}}{\text{g}°C} \times 10.5°C \times \dfrac{1 \text{ kcal}}{1000 \text{ cal}} = 5.30$ kcal

       b. $4980 \text{ g} \times \dfrac{1.00 \text{ cal}}{\text{g}°C} \times 42°C \times \dfrac{1 \text{ kcal}}{1000 \text{ cal}} = 208$ kcal

6.23   **a.** Because the orange juice contains both carbohydrate and protein, two calculations will be needed.

       $26 \text{ g carbohydrate} \times \dfrac{4 \text{ kcal}}{\text{g carbohydrate}} \times \dfrac{1 \text{ Cal}}{1 \text{ kcal}} = 100$ Cal

       $2 \text{ g protein} \times \dfrac{4 \text{ kcal}}{\text{g protein}} \times \dfrac{1 \text{ Cal}}{1 \text{ kcal}} = 8$ Cal

       Total: 100 Cal + 8 Cal = 108 Cal = 110 Cal (rounded)
       b. With only carbohydrate present, a single calculation is all that is required.

       $72 \text{ kcal} \times \dfrac{1 \text{ g carbohydrate}}{4 \text{ kcal}} = 18$ g carbohydrate

       c. With only fat present, a single calculation is all that is required.

       $14 \text{ g fat} \times \dfrac{9 \text{ kcal}}{\text{g fat}} \times \dfrac{1 \text{ Cal}}{1 \text{ kcal}} = 130$ Cal

d. Three calculations are needed:

$$30 \; \cancel{\text{g carbohydrate}} \times \frac{4 \; \cancel{\text{kcal}}}{\cancel{\text{g carbohydrate}}} \times \frac{1 \; \text{Cal}}{\cancel{1 \; \text{kcal}}} = 120 \; \text{Cal}$$

$$15 \; \cancel{\text{g fat}} \times \frac{9 \; \cancel{\text{kcal}}}{\cancel{\text{g fat}}} \times \frac{1 \; \text{Cal}}{\cancel{1 \; \text{kcal}}} = 140 \; \text{Cal}$$

$$5 \; \cancel{\text{g protein}} \times \frac{4 \; \cancel{\text{kcal}}}{\cancel{\text{g protein}}} \times \frac{1 \; \text{Cal}}{\cancel{1 \; \text{kcal}}} = 20 \; \text{Cal}$$

Total: 120 Cal + 140 Cal + 20 Cal = 280 Cal

6.25 Three calculations are needed:

$$9 \; \cancel{\text{g protein}} \times \frac{4 \; \text{kcal}}{\cancel{\text{g protein}}} = 40 \; \text{kcal}$$

$$12 \; \cancel{\text{g fat}} \times \frac{9 \; \text{kcal}}{\cancel{\text{g fat}}} = 110 \; \text{kcal}$$

$$16 \; \cancel{\text{g carbohydrate}} \times \frac{4 \; \text{kcal}}{\cancel{\text{g carbohydrate}}} = 64 \; \text{kcal}$$

6.27 **a.** A gas takes the shape and volume of its container. Thus, a gas has no definite volume or shape.
b. The particles in a gas have little attraction between them and do not interact.
c. A solid has a definite volume or shape.

6.29 **a.** An attraction between the positive end of one polar molecule and the negative end of another polar molecule is called dipole–dipole attraction.
b. An ionic bond is an attraction between a positive and negative ion.
c. The weak attractions that occurs between temporary dipoles in nonpolar CCl_4 molecules are dispersion forces.
d. The attraction between H and F, O, or N in a dipole is a hydrogen bond.
e. The weak attractions that occurs between temporary dipoles in nonpolar Cl_2 molecules are dispersion forces.

6.31 **a.** Hydrogen bonding occurs between dipoles containing H and F, O, or N.
b. Dispersion forces occur between temporary dipoles in nonpolar molecules.
c. Dipole–dipole interactions occurs between dipoles in polar molecules.
d. Dispersion forces occur between temporary dipoles in nonpolar molecules.
e. Dispersion forces occur between temporary dipoles in nonpolar molecules.

6.33 **a.** HF; hydrogen bonds are stronger than dipole–dipole interactions of HBr.
b. NaF; ionic bonds are stronger than the hydrogen bonds in HF.
c. $MgBr_2$; ionic bonds are stronger than the dipoles–dipole interactions in PBr_3.
d. CH_3OH can form hydrogen bonds and has a higher boiling point than CH_4.

6.35 **a.** melting   **b.** sublimation   **c.** freezing

6.37 **a.** $65 \; \cancel{\text{g ice}} \times \dfrac{80. \; \text{cal}}{1 \; \cancel{\text{g ice}}} = 5200 \; \text{cal absorbed}$

b. $17 \; \cancel{\text{g ice}} \times \dfrac{80. \; \text{cal}}{1 \; \cancel{\text{g ice}}} = 1400 \; \text{cal absorbed}$

c. $225 \; \cancel{\text{g water}} \times \dfrac{80. \; \text{cal}}{1 \; \cancel{\text{g water}}} \times \dfrac{1 \; \text{kcal}}{1000 \; \cancel{\text{cal}}} = 18 \; \text{kcal released}$

6.39   **a.** condensation   **b.** evaporation   **c.** boiling   **d.** condensation

6.41   **a.** The liquid water in perspiration absorbs heat and evaporates (changes to vapor). The heat needed for the change is removed from the skin.

       b. On a hot day, there are more liquid water molecules in the damp clothing that have sufficient energy to become water vapor. Thus, water evaporates from the clothes more readily on a hot day.

6.43   **a.** $10.0 \ \cancel{g \ water} \times \dfrac{540 \ cal}{1 \ \cancel{g \ water}} = 5400 \ cal$ absorbed

       b. $50.0 \ \cancel{g \ water} \times \dfrac{540 \ \cancel{cal}}{1 \ \cancel{g \ water}} \times \dfrac{1 \ kcal}{1000 \ \cancel{cal}} = 27 \ kcal$ absorbed

       c. $8.0 \ \cancel{kg \ steam} \times \dfrac{1000 \ \cancel{g}}{1 \ \cancel{kg}} \times \dfrac{540 \ \cancel{cal}}{1 \ \cancel{g \ steam}} \times \dfrac{1 \ kcal}{1000 \ \cancel{cal}} = 4300 \ kcal$ released

6.45

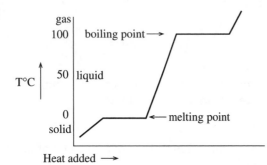

6.47   **a.** $20.0 \ \cancel{g} \times \dfrac{1.00 \ cal}{\cancel{g} \cancel{°C}} \times 57 \ \cancel{°C} = 1100 \ cal$

       b. Two calculations are needed:

         $50.0 \ \cancel{g \ ice} \times \dfrac{80. \ cal}{1 \ \cancel{g \ ice}} = 4000 \ cal$ (2 sig figs)

         $50.0 \ \cancel{g} \times \dfrac{1.00 \ cal}{\cancel{g} \cancel{°C}} \times 65 \ \cancel{°C} = 3300 \ cal$

       Total: $4000 \ cal + 3300 \ cal = 7300 \ cal$

       c. Two calculations are needed:

         $15 \ \cancel{g \ steam} \times \dfrac{540 \ \cancel{cal}}{1 \ \cancel{g \ steam}} \times \dfrac{4.18 \ \cancel{J}}{1 \ \cancel{cal}} \times \dfrac{1 \ kJ}{1000 \ \cancel{J}} = 34 \ kJ$

         $15 \ \cancel{g} \times \dfrac{4.18 \ \cancel{J}}{\cancel{g} \cancel{°C}} \times 100 \ \cancel{°C} \times \dfrac{1 \ kJ}{1000 \ \cancel{J}} = 6.3 \ kJ$

       Total: $34 \ kJ + 6.3 \ kJ = 40. \ kJ$

       d. Three calculations are needed:

         $24 \ \cancel{g \ ice} \times \dfrac{80. \ \cancel{cal}}{1 \ \cancel{g \ ice}} \times \dfrac{1 \ kcal}{1000 \ \cancel{cal}} = 1.9 \ kcal$

         $24 \ \cancel{g} \times \dfrac{1.00 \ \cancel{cal}}{\cancel{g} \cancel{°C}} \times 100 \ \cancel{°C} \times \dfrac{1 \ kcal}{1000 \ \cancel{cal}} = 2.4 \ kcal$

         $24 \ \cancel{g \ water} \times \dfrac{540 \ \cancel{cal}}{1 \ \cancel{g \ water}} \times \dfrac{1 \ kcal}{1000 \ \cancel{cal}} = 13 \ kcal$

       Total: $1.9 \ kcal + 2.4 \ kcal + 13 \ kcal = 17 \ kcal$

6.49 gold 250 J or 59 cal; aluminum 240 J or 58 cal; silver 250 J or 59 cal
The heat needed for 10.0-cm^3 samples of the metals are almost the same.

6.51 **a.** $-60°C$
   b. $60°C$
   c. A represents the solid state. B represents the change from solid to liquid or melting of the substance. C represents the liquid state as temperature increases. D represents the change from liquid to gas or boiling of the liquid. E represents a gas.
   d. At $-80°C$, solid; at $-40°C$, liquid; at $25°C$, liquid; at $80°C$, gas.

6.53 Liquid water has a higher specific heat (1.00 cal/g°C) than sand, which means that a large amount of energy is required to cause a significant temperature change. Sand, on the other hand, has a low specific heat (0.19 cal/g°C). Even a small amount of energy will cause a significant temperature change in the sand.

6.55 Both water condensation (formation of rain) and deposition (formation of snow) from the gaseous moisture in the air are exothermic processes (heat is released). The heat released in either of these processes warms the surrounding air, and so the air temperature is in fact raised.

6.57 $883 \ \cancel{g} \times \dfrac{4.184 \ \cancel{J}}{\cancel{g°C}} \times 23°\cancel{C} \times \dfrac{1 \ kJ}{1000 \ \cancel{J}} = 85 \ kJ$

6.59 **a.** $3.00 \ \cancel{g \ NO} \times \dfrac{1 \ \cancel{mole \ NO}}{30.0 \ \cancel{g \ NO}} \times \dfrac{21.6 \ kcal}{2 \ \cancel{moles \ NO}} = 1.08 \ kcal \ needed$

   b. $2 \ NO(g) \rightarrow N_2(g) + O_2(g) + 21.6 \ kcal$

   c. $5.00 \ \cancel{g \ NO} \times \dfrac{1 \ \cancel{mole \ NO}}{30.0 \ \cancel{g \ NO}} \times \dfrac{21.6 \ kcal}{2 \ \cancel{moles \ NO}} = 1.80 \ kcal \ released$

6.61 **a.** For 15% of one's total calories (kcal) to be supplied by protein, a conversion factor of 15 kcal from protein/100 kcal total in the daily diet will be used in the calculation. Similar factors will be used for the carbohydrate (carbs) and fat calculations.

$1200 \ \cancel{kcal \ (total)} \times \dfrac{15 \ \cancel{kcal \ (protein)}}{100 \ \cancel{kcal \ (total)}} \times \dfrac{1 \ g \ protein}{4 \ \cancel{kcal \ (protein)}} = 45 \ g \ protein$

$1200 \ \cancel{kcal \ (total)} \times \dfrac{45 \ \cancel{kcal \ (carbs)}}{100 \ \cancel{kcal \ (total)}} \times \dfrac{1 \ g \ carbs}{4 \ \cancel{kcal \ (carbs)}} = 140 \ g \ carbohydrate$

$1200 \ \cancel{kcal \ (total)} \times \dfrac{40. \ \cancel{kcal \ (fat)}}{100 \ \cancel{kcal \ (total)}} \times \dfrac{1 \ g \ fat}{9 \ \cancel{kcal \ (fat)}} = 53 \ g \ fat$

   b. The calculations for part **b** differ from part **a** only in the total kcal per day.

$1900 \ \cancel{kcal \ (total)} \times \dfrac{15 \ \cancel{kcal \ (protein)}}{100 \ \cancel{kcal \ (total)}} \times \dfrac{1 \ g \ protein}{4 \ \cancel{kcal \ (protein)}} = 71 \ g \ protein$

$1900 \ \cancel{kcal \ (total)} \times \dfrac{45 \ \cancel{kcal \ (carbs)}}{100 \ \cancel{kcal \ (total)}} \times \dfrac{1 \ g \ carbs}{4 \ \cancel{kcal \ (carbs)}} = 210 \ g \ carbohydrate$

$1900 \ \cancel{kcal \ (total)} \times \dfrac{40. \ \cancel{kcal \ (fat)}}{100 \ \cancel{kcal \ (total)}} \times \dfrac{1 \ g \ fat}{9 \ \cancel{kcal \ (fat)}} = 84 \ g \ fat$

c. The calculations for part **c** again differ only in the total kcal per day.

$$2600 \text{ kcal (total)} \times \frac{15 \text{ kcal (protein)}}{100 \text{ kcal (total)}} \times \frac{1 \text{ g protein}}{4 \text{ kcal (protein)}} = 98 \text{ g protein}$$

$$2600 \text{ kcal (total)} \times \frac{45 \text{ kcal (carbs)}}{100 \text{ kcal (total)}} \times \frac{1 \text{ g carbs}}{4 \text{ kcal (carbs)}} = 290 \text{ g carbohydrate}$$

$$2600 \text{ kcal (total)} \times \frac{40. \text{ kcal (fat)}}{100 \text{ kcal (total)}} \times \frac{1 \text{ g fat}}{9 \text{ kcal (fat)}} = 120 \text{ g fat}$$

6.63 Because each gram of body fat contains 15% water, a person actually loses 85 grams of fat per hundred grams of body fat. (We considered 1 lb of fat as exactly 1 lb.)

$$1 \text{ lb body fat} \times \frac{454 \text{ g}}{1 \text{ lb}} \times \frac{85 \text{ g fat}}{100 \text{ g body fat}} \times \frac{9 \text{ kcal}}{1 \text{ g fat}} = 3500 \text{ kcal}$$

6.65 $\quad 725 \text{ g} \times \dfrac{1 \text{ cal}}{\text{g} {}^\circ C} \times 28 {}^\circ C \times \dfrac{1 \text{ kcal}}{1000 \text{ cal}} = 20. \text{ kcal}$

6.67 **a.** hydrogen bond (3)   **b.** hydrogen bond (3)   **c.** dispersion (4)
      d. dipole–dipole (2)   **e.** hydrogen bond (3)   **f.** ionic (1)

6.69 53 kcal

6.71 $\quad 50. \text{ g} \times 12 {}^\circ C \times \dfrac{1.00 \text{ cal}}{\text{g} {}^\circ C} = 600 \text{ cal} \ (6.0 \times 10^2 \text{ cal})$

$\quad\quad$ specific heat $= \dfrac{600 \text{ cal}}{(25 \text{ g})(71 {}^\circ C)} = 0.34 \text{ cal/g} {}^\circ C$

6.73 condense steam: $75 \text{ g} \times 540 \text{ cal/g} = 40\,500 \text{ cal}$
$\quad\quad$ temperature change: $75 \text{ g} \times 100 {}^\circ C \times 1.00 \text{ cal/g} {}^\circ C = 7500 \text{ cal}$
$\quad\quad$ freeze water: $75 \text{ g} \times 80. \text{ cal/g} = 6000 \text{ cal}$
$\quad\quad 40\,500 \text{ cal} + 7500 \text{ cal} + 6000 \text{ cal} = 54\,000 \text{ cal} = 54 \text{ kcal}$

6.75 220 kJ

6.77 **a.** heat $= m \times \Delta T \times SH \quad m = \dfrac{\text{heat}}{\Delta T \times SH} = \dfrac{8250 \text{ J}}{(92.6 - 18.3 {}^\circ C)(4.184 \text{ J/g} {}^\circ C)} = 2.65 \text{ g}$

$\quad\quad$ **b.** heat $= m \times \Delta T \times SH \quad m = \dfrac{\text{heat}}{\Delta T \times SH} = \dfrac{225 \text{ J}}{(47.0 - 15.0 {}^\circ C)(4.184 \text{ J/g} {}^\circ C)} = 1.68 \text{ g}$

$\quad\quad$ **c.** heat $= m \times \Delta T \times SH \quad \Delta T = \dfrac{\text{heat}}{m \times SH} = \dfrac{1580 \text{ J}}{(20.0 \text{ g})(0.450 \text{ J/g} {}^\circ C)} = 176 {}^\circ C$

$\quad\quad$ **d.** heat $= m \times \Delta T \times SH \quad SH = \dfrac{\text{heat}}{m \times \Delta T} = \dfrac{28 \text{ cal}}{(8.50 \text{ g})(12 {}^\circ C)} = 0.27 \text{ cal/g} {}^\circ C$

6.79 $\quad 3.0 \text{ kg} \times \dfrac{1000 \text{ g}}{1 \text{ kg}} \times \dfrac{0.13 \text{ J}}{\text{g} {}^\circ C} \times 300. {}^\circ C = 117\,000 \text{ J}$ (not rounded) available to melt ice

$\quad\quad$ Since 334 J will melt 1 gram of ice, we can calculate the number of grams of ice that can melt.

$\quad\quad 117\,000 \text{ J} \times \dfrac{1 \text{ g}}{334 \text{ J}} = 350 \text{ g}$ (rounded) of ice will be melted

Study Goals

- Describe the kinetic theory of gases.
- Use the gas laws to determine the new pressure, volume, or temperature of a specific amount of gas.
- Describe the relationship between the amount of a gas and its volume.
- Use the ideal gas law to solve for pressure, volume, temperature, or moles of gas when three of the four variables are given.
- Use partial pressure to calculate the total pressure of a gas mixture.

Think About It

1. How does a barometer work?

2. What happens to the pressure on a person who is scuba diving?

3. Why are airplanes pressurized?

4. Why does a bag of chips expand when you take it to a higher altitude?

Key Terms

Match the key terms with the statements shown below.

    a. kinetic theory   **b.** pressure   **c.** Boyle's law
    d. Charles' law   **e.** partial pressure

1. _____ The volume of a gas varies directly with the Kelvin temperature when pressure and amount of gas remain constant.

2. _____ force exerted by gas particles that collide with the sides of a container

3. _____ the pressure exerted by the individual gases in a gas mixture

4. _____ The volume of a gas varies inversely with the pressure of a gas when temperature and amount of gas are constant.

5. _____ a model that explains the behavior of gaseous particles

Answers   **1.** d   **2.** b   **3.** e   **4.** c   **5.** a

7.1 Properties of Gases

- In a gas, particles are so far apart and moving so fast that they are not attracted to each other.
- A gas is described by the physical properties of pressure (P), volume (V), temperature (T), and amount in moles (n).

◆ Learning Exercise 7.1

True or false:

a. _____ Gases are composed of small particles.

b. _____ Gas molecules are usually close together.

c. _____ Gas molecules move rapidly because they are strongly attracted.

d. _____ The distances between gas molecules are great.

e. _____ Gas molecules travel in straight lines until they collide.

Answers   **a.** T   **b.** F   **c.** F   **d.** T   **e.** T

7.2 Gas Pressure

• A gas exerts pressure, which is the force of the gas particles on the surface of a container.
• Units of gas pressure include torr, mm Hg, and atmosphere.

◆ Learning Exercise 7.2

Complete the following:

a. 1.50 atm   =   _____ mm Hg

b. 550 mm Hg   =   _____ atm

c. 725 mm Hg   =   _____ torr

d. 1520 mm Hg   =   _____ atm

e. 30.5 psi   =   _____ mm Hg

f. During the weather report on TV, the pressure was given as 98.7 kilopascals. What is this pressure in mm Hg? In atm?

Answers   **a.** 1140 mm Hg   **b.** 0.72 atm   **c.** 725 torr
              d. 2.00 atm   **e.** 1570 mm Hg   **f.** 740. mm Hg; 0.974 atm

7.3 Pressure and Volume (Boyle's law)

• According to Boyle's law, pressure increases if volume decreases; pressure decreases if volume increases.
• The volume (V) of a gas changes inversely with the pressure (P) of the gas when T and n are held constant: $P_1V_1 = P_2V_2$.

◆ Learning Exercise 7.3A

Complete with *increases* or *decreases*:

1. Gas pressure increases (T constant) when volume _____.

2. Gas volume increases at constant T when pressure _____.

Answers   **1.** decreases   **2.** decreases

◆ Learning Exercise 7.3B

Calculate the variable in each of the following gas problems using Boyle's law.

a. Four (4.0) L helium gas have a pressure of 800. mm Hg. What will be the new pressure if the volume is reduced to 1.0 L (*n* and *T* constant)?

b. A gas occupies a volume of 360 mL at 750 mm Hg. What volume (mL) does it occupy at a pressure of (1) 1500 mm Hg? (2) 375 mm Hg? (*n* and *T* constant)

c. A gas sample at a pressure of 5.0 atm has a volume of 3.00 L. If the gas pressure is changed to 760 mm Hg, what volume will the gas occupy (*n* and *T* constant)?

d. A sample of 250. mL nitrogen is initially at a pressure of 2.50 atm. If the pressure changes to 825 mm Hg, what is the new volume in mL?

Answers **a.** 3200 mm Hg   **b.** (1) 180 mL (2) 720 mL
          c. 15 L   **d.** 576 mL

7.4 Temperature and Volume (Charles' law)

*   The volume (*V*) of a gas is directly related to its Kelvin temperature (*T*) when there is no change in the pressure of the gas:

$$\frac{V_1}{T_1} = \frac{V_2}{T_2}$$

*   According to Charles' law, temperature increases if the volume of the gas increases; temperature decreases if volume decreases.

◆ Learning Exercise 7.4A

Complete with *increases* or *decreases*:

a. When the temperature of a gas increases at constant pressure, its volume _____.

b. When the volume of a gas decreases at constant pressure, its temperature _____.

Answers   **a.** increases   **b.** decreases

◆ **Learning Exercise 7.4B**

Use Charles' law to solve the following gas problems.

    a. A large balloon has a volume of 2.5 L at a temperature of 0°C. What is the new volume of the balloon when the temperature rises to 120°C and the pressure remains constant?

    b. Consider a balloon filled with helium to a volume of 6600 L at a temperature of 223°C. To what temperature must the gas be cooled to decrease the volume to 4800 L (P constant)?

    c. A sample of 750 mL neon is heated from 120°C to 350°C. If pressure is kept constant, what is the new volume?

    d. What is the final temperature of 350 mL oxygen gas at 22°C if its volume increases to 0.80 L?

Answers   **a.** 3.6 L   **b.** 88°C   **c.** 1200 mL   **d.** 401°C

7.5 Temperature and Pressure (Gay-Lussac's law)

•   The pressure (P) of a gas is directly related to its Kelvin temperature (T).

$$\frac{P_1}{T_1} = \frac{P_2}{T_2}$$

    This means that an increase in temperature increases the pressure of a gas, or a decrease in temperature decreases the pressure, as long as the volume stays constant.

•   Vapor pressure is the pressure of the gas that forms when a liquid evaporates. At the boiling point of a liquid, the vapor pressure equals the atmospheric pressure.

◆ **Learning Exercise 7.5A**

Solve the following gas law problems using Gay-Lussac's law.

    a. A sample of helium gas has a pressure of 860 mm Hg at a temperature of 225 K. At what pressure (mm Hg) will the helium sample reach a temperature of 675 K (V constant)?

b. A balloon contains a gas with a pressure of 580 mm Hg and a temperature of 227°C. What is the new pressure (mm Hg) of the gas when the temperature drops to 27°C (*V* constant)?

c. A spray can contains a gas with a pressure of 3.0 atm at a temperature 17°C. What is the pressure (atm) in the container if the temperature inside the can rises to 110°C (*V* constant)?

d. A gas has a pressure of 1200 mm Hg at 300°C. What will the temperature (°C) be when the pressure falls to 1.10 atm (*V* constant)?

Answers   **a.** 2580 mm Hg   **b.** 348 mm Hg
              c. 4.0 atm   **d.** 126°C

◆ Learning Exercise 7.5B

Explain how a liquid can have a boiling point of 80°C at sea level and a boiling point of 74°C at an altitude of 1000 m.

Answers   The vapor pressure required for boiling is lower at higher altitude because the atmospheric pressure is lower. As a result, the substance boils at a lower temperature.

7.6 The Combined Gas Law

- The gas laws can be combined into a relationship of pressure (*P*), volume (*V*), and temperature (*T*).

$$\frac{P_1V_1}{T_1} = \frac{P_2V_2}{T_2}$$

This expression is used to determine the effect of changes in two of the variables on the third.

◆ **Learning Exercise 7.6**

Solve the following using the combined gas laws:

a. A 5.0-L sample of nitrogen gas has a pressure of 1200 mm Hg at 220 K. What is the pressure of the sample when the volume increases to 20.0 L at 440 K?

b. A 10.0-L sample of gas is emitted from a volcano with a pressure of 1.20 atm and a temperature of 150.0°C. What is the volume of the gas when its pressure is 0.900 atm and the temperature is −40.0°C?

c. A 25.0-mL bubble forms at the ocean depths where the pressure is 10.0 atm and the temperature is 5.0°C. What is the volume of that bubble at the ocean surface where the pressure is 760.0 mm Hg and the temperature is 25°C?

d. A 35.0-mL sample of argon gas has a pressure of 1.0 atm and a temperature of 15°C. What is the final volume if the pressure goes to 2.0 atm and the temperature to 45°C?

e. A 315-L weather balloon is launched at the Earth's surface where the temperature is 12°C and the pressure is 0.93 atm. What is the volume of the balloon in the upper atmosphere, where the pressure is 116 mm Hg and the temperature is −35°C?

Answers   **a.** 600 mm Hg   **b.** 7.34 L   **c.** 268 mL   **d.** 19 mL   **e.** 1600 L

7.7 Volume and Moles (Avogadro's law)

- Avogadro's law states that equal volumes of gases at the same temperature and pressure contain the same number of moles. The volume (V) of a gas is directly related to the number of moles of the gas when the pressure and temperature of the gas do not change.

$$\frac{V_1}{n_1} = \frac{V_2}{n_2}$$

- If the moles of gas increase, the volume must increase; if the moles of gas decrease, the volume decreases.
- At STP conditions, standard pressure (1 atm) and temperature (0°C), one mole of a gas occupies a volume of 22.4 L.

Study Note

AT STP, the molar volume factor 22.4 L/1 mole converts between moles of a gas and volume. *Example:* How many liters would 2.00 moles N_2 occupy at STP?

Solution: $\quad\quad\quad\quad\quad\quad 2.00 \text{ moles } N_2 \times \dfrac{22.4 \text{ L (STP)}}{1 \text{ mole } N_2} = 44.8 \text{ L (STP)}$

◆ **Learning Exercise 7.7**

Use Avogadro's law to solve the following gas problems:

a. A gas containing 0.50 mole helium has a volume of 4.00 L. What is the new volume when 1.0 mole nitrogen is added to the container when pressure and temperature remain constant?

b. A balloon containing 1.00 mole oxygen has a volume of 15 L. What is the new volume of the balloon when 2.00 moles helium are added (*T* and *P* constant)?

c. What is the volume occupied by 28.0 g nitrogen (N_2) at STP?

d. What is the volume (L) of a container that holds 6.40 g O_2 at STP?

Answers   **a.** 12 L   **b.** 45 L   **c.** 22.4 L   **d.** 4.48 L

7.8 The Ideal Gas Law

- The ideal gas law $PV = nRT$ gives the relationship between the following four variables: pressure, volume, moles, and temperature. When any three variables are given, the fourth can be calculated.
- *R* is the universal gas constant: 0.0821 L atm/mole K *or* 62.4 L mm Hg/mole K.

Study Note

Identify the three known variables for the ideal gas law, and arrange the equation to solve for the unknown variable. *Example:* Solve the ideal gas law for *P*.

$$PV = nRT \quad\quad\quad P = \frac{nRT}{V}$$

◆ Learning Exercise 7.8

Use the Ideal Gas Law to solve for the unknown variable in each of the following:

a. What volume (L) is occupied by 0.25 mole nitrogen gas (N_2) at 0°C and 1.50 atm?

b. What is the temperature (°C) of 0.500 mole helium that occupies a volume of 15.0 L at a pressure of 1200 mm Hg?

c. What is the pressure in atm of 1.0 mole neon in a 5.0-L steel container at a temperature of 18°C?

d. What is the pressure in atm of 8.0 g oxygen (O_2) that has a volume of 245 mL at a temperature of 22°C?

Answers   **a.** 3.7 L   **b.** 304°C   **c.** 4.8 atm   **d.** 25 atm

7.9 Partial Pressures (Dalton's law)

- In a mixture of two or more gases, the total pressure is the sum of the partial pressures of the individual gases.

$$P_{total} = P_1 + P_2 + P_3 + \dots$$

- The partial pressure of a gas in a mixture is the pressure it would exert if it were the only gas in the container.

◆ Learning Exercise 7.9A

Use Dalton's law to solve the following problems about gas mixtures:

a. What is the pressure in mm Hg of a sample of gases containing oxygen at 0.500 atm, nitrogen (N_2) at 132 torr, and helium at 224 mm Hg?

b. What is the pressure (atm) of a gas sample containing helium at 285 mm Hg and oxygen (O_2) at 1.20 atm?

c. A gas sample containing nitrogen (N_2) and oxygen (O_2) has a pressure of 1500. mm Hg. If the partial pressure of the nitrogen is 0.900 atm, what is the partial pressure (mm Hg) of the oxygen gas in the mixture?

Answers   **a.** 736 mm Hg   **b.** 1.58 atm   **c.** 816 mm Hg

◆ Learning Exercise 7.9B

Fill in the blanks by writing *I (increases)* or *D (decreases)* for a gas in a closed container.

Pressure	Volume	Moles	Temperature
a. _____	increases	constant	constant
b. increases	constant	_____	constant
c. constant	decreases	_____	constant
d. _____	constant	constant	increases
e. constant	_____	constant	decreases
f. _____	constant	increases	constant

Answers   **a.** D   **b.** I   **c.** D
              d. I   **e.** D   **f.** I

◆ Learning Exercise 7.9C

Complete the table for typical blood gas values for partial pressures.

Gas	Alveoli	Oxygenated blood	Deoxygenated blood	Tissues
CO_2	_____	_____	_____	_____
O_2	_____	_____	_____	_____

Answers

CO_2	40 mm Hg	40 mm Hg	50 mm Hg or greater	50 mm Hg or greater
O_2	100 mm Hg	100 mm Hg	30 mm Hg or less	30 mm Hg or less

Checklist for Chapter 7

You are ready to take the practice test for chapter 7. Be sure that you have accomplished the following learning goals for this chapter. If you are not sure, review the section listed at the end of the goal. Then apply your new skills and understanding to the practice test. Good luck.

After studying chapter 7, I can successfully:

_____ Describe the kinetic theory of gases (7.1).

_____ Change the units of pressure from one to another (7.2).

_____ Use the pressure-volume relationship (Boyle's law) to determine the new pressure or volume of a fixed amount of gas at constant temperature (7.3).

_____ Use the temperature-volume relationship (Charles' law) to determine the new temperature or volume of a fixed amount of gas at a constant pressure (7.4).

_____ Use the temperature-pressure relationship (Gay-Lussac's law) to determine the new temperature or pressure of a certain amount of gas at a constant volume (7.5).

_____ Use the combined gas law to find the new pressure, volume, or temperature of a gas when changes in two of these properties are given (7.6).

_____ Describe the relationship between the amount of a gas and its volume and use this relationship in calculations (7.7).

_____ Use the ideal gas law to solve for pressure, volume, temperature, or amount of a gas (7.8).

_____ Calculate the total pressure of a gas mixture from the partial pressures (7.9).

Practice Test for Chapter 7

Answer questions 1–5 using T (true) or F (false):

1. _____ The kinetic energy of a gas is related to its volume.

2. _____ The molecules of a gas are moving extremely fast.

3. _____ The collisions of gas molecules with the walls of their container create pressure.

4. _____ Gas molecules are close together and move in straight-line patterns.

5. _____ We consider gas molecules to have no attractions between them.

6. When a gas is heated in a closed metal container, the
   A. pressure increases   B. pressure decreases
   C. volume increases   D. volume decreases
   E. number of molecules increases

7. The pressure of a gas will increase when
   A. the volume increases   B. the temperature decreases
   C. more molecules of gas are added   D. molecules of gas are removed
   E. none of these

8. If the temperature of a gas is increased
   A. the pressure will decrease   B. the volume will increase
   C. the volume will decrease   D. the number of molecules will increase
   E. none of these

9. The relationship that the volume of a gas is inversely related to its pressure at constant temperature is known as
   A. Boyle's law   B. Charles' law   C. Gay-Lussac's law
   D. Dalton's law   E. Avogadro's law

10. What is the pressure (atm) of a gas with a pressure of 1200 mm Hg?
    A. 0.63 atm   B. 0.79 atm   C. 1.2 atm
    D. 1.6 atm   E. 2.0 atm

11. A 6.00-L sample of oxygen has a pressure of 660. mm Hg. When the volume is reduced to 2.00 liters at constant temperature, it will have a new pressure of
    A. 1980 mm Hg   B. 1320 mm Hg   C. 330. mm Hg
    D. 220. mm Hg   E. 110. mm Hg

12. A sample of nitrogen gas at 180 K has a pressure of 1.0 atm. When the temperature is increased to 360 K at constant volume, the new pressure will be
    A. 0.50 atm   B. 1.0 atm   C. 1.5 atm
    D. 2.0 atm   E. 4.0 atm

13. If two gases have the same volume, temperature, and pressure, they also have the same
    A. density   B. number of molecules   C. molar mass
    D. speed   E. size molecules

14. A gas sample with a volume of 4.00 L has a pressure of 750 mm Hg and a temperature of 77°C. What is its new volume at 277°C and 250 mm Hg?

A. 7.6 L   **B.** 19 L   **C.** 2.1 L
D. 0.000 56 L   **E.** 3.3 L

15. If the temperature of a gas does not change, but its volume doubles, its pressure will
     A. double
     B. triple
     C. decrease to one-half the original pressure
     D. decrease to one-fourth the original pressure
     E. not change

16. A sample of oxygen with a pressure of 400 mm Hg contains 2.0 moles gas and has a volume of 4.0 L. What will the new pressure be when the volume expands to 5.0 L and when 3.0 moles helium gas are added while temperature is constant?
     A. 160 mm Hg   **B.** 250 mm Hg   **C.** 800 mm Hg
     D. 1000 mm Hg   **E.** 1560 mm Hg

17. A sample of 2.00 moles gas initially at STP is converted to a volume of 5.0 L and a temperature of 27°C. What is its new pressure in atm?
     A. 0.12 atm   **B.** 5.5 atm   **C.** 7.5 atm
     D. 8.9 atm   **E.** 9.8 atm

18. The conditions for standard temperature and pressure (STP) are
     A. 0 K, 1 atm   **B.** 0°C, 10 atm   **C.** 25°C, 1 atm
     D. 273 K, 1 atm   **E.** 273 K, 0.5 atm

19. The volume occupied by 1.50 moles CH_4 at STP is
     A. 44.8 L   **B.** 33.6 L   **C.** 22.4 L
     D. 11.2 L   **E.** 5.60 L

20. How many grams of oxygen gas (O_2) are present in 44.8 L oxygen at STP?
     A. 8.0 g   **B.** 16.0 g   **C.** 32.0 g
     D. 48.0 g   **E.** 64.0 g

21. What is the volume in liters of 0.50 moles nitrogen gas (N_2) at 25°C and 2.0 atm?
     A. 0.51 L   **B.** 1.0 L   **C.** 4.2 L
     D. 6.1 L   **E.** 24 L

22. A gas mixture contains helium with a partial pressure of 0.80 atm, oxygen with a partial pressure of 450 mm Hg, and nitrogen with a partial pressure of 230 mm Hg. What is the total pressure in atm for the gas mixture?
     A. 1.10 atm   **B.** 1.39 atm   **C.** 1.69 atm
     D. 2.00 atm   **E.** 8.00 atm

23. A mixture of oxygen and nitrogen has a total pressure of 840 mm Hg. If the oxygen has a partial pressure of 510 mm Hg, what is the partial pressure of the nitrogen?
     A. 240 mm Hg   **B.** 330 mm Hg   **C.** 775 mm Hg
     D. 1040 mm Hg   **E.** 1350 mm Hg

24. The exchange of gases between the alveoli, blood, and tissues of the body is a result of
     A. pressure gradients
     B. different molecular weights
     C. shapes of molecules
     D. altitude
     E. all of these

25. Oxygen moves into the tissues from the blood because its partial pressure
     A. in arterial blood is higher than in the tissues
     B. in venous blood is higher than in the tissues
     C. in arterial blood is lower than in the tissues
     D. in venous blood is lower than in the tissues
     E. is equal in the blood and in the tissues

Answers to the Practice Test

1. F	**2.** T	**3.** T	**4.** F	**5.** T
6. A	**7.** C	**8.** B	**9.** A	**10.** D
11. A	**12.** D	**13.** B	**14.** B	**15.** C
16. C	**17.** E	**18.** D	**19.** B	**20.** E
21. D	**22.** C	**23.** B	**24.** A	**25.** A

Answers and Solutions to Selected Text Problems

7.1 **a.** Gaseous particles have greater kinetic energies at higher temperatures. Because kinetic energy is a measure of the energy of motion, the gaseous particles must be moving faster at higher temperatures than at lower values.

b. Because particles in a gas are very far apart, gases can be easily compressed without the particles bumping into neighboring gas particles. Neighboring particles are much closer together in solids and liquids, and they will "bump" into each other and repel each other if the sample is compressed.

7.3 **a.** temperature   **b.** volume   **c.** amount of gas   **d.** pressure

7.5 Some units used to describe the pressure of a gas are pounds per square inch (lb/in.^{2}, which is also abbreviated as psi), atmospheres (abbreviated atm), torr, mm Hg, and kilopascals.

7.7 **a.** $2.00 \text{ atm} \times \dfrac{760 \text{ torr}}{1 \text{ atm}} = 1520 \text{ torr}$

b. $2.00 \text{ atm} \times \dfrac{760 \text{ mm Hg}}{1 \text{ atm}} = 1520 \text{ mm Hg}$

7.9 The gases in the diver's lungs (and dissolved in the blood) will expand because pressure decreases as the diver ascends. Unless the diver exhales, the expanding gases could rupture the membranes in the lung tissues. In addition, the formation of gas bubbles in the bloodstream could cause "the bends."

7.11 **a.** According to Boyle's law, for the pressure to increase while temperature and quantity of gas remain constant, the gas volume must decrease. Thus, cylinder A would represent the final volume.

b.

	Initial	**Final**
P	650 mm Hg	1.2 atm
V	220 mL	160 mL

Because $P_1V_2 = P_2V_2$, then $V_2 = P_1V_1/P_2$

$V_2 = 220 \text{ mL} \times \dfrac{650 \text{ mm Hg}}{1.2 \text{ atm}} \times \dfrac{1 \text{ atm}}{760 \text{ mm Hg}} = 160 \text{ mL}$

7.13 **a.** The pressure doubles when the volume is halved.

b. The pressure falls to one-third the initial pressure when the volume expands to three times its initial volume.

c. The pressure increases to 10 times the original pressure when the volume decreases to 1/10 of its initial volume.

7.15 From Boyle's law we know that pressure is inversely related to volume. (For example, the pressure increases when the volume decreases.)

a. volume increases; pressure must decrease

$655 \text{ mm Hg} \times \dfrac{10.0 \text{ L}}{20.0 \text{ L}} = 328 \text{ mm Hg}$

b. volume decreases; pressure must increase

$$655 \text{ mm Hg} \times \frac{10.0 \cancel{L}}{2.50 \cancel{L}} = 2620 \text{ mm Hg}$$

c. The mL units must be converted to L for unit cancellation in the calculation, and because the volume decreases; pressure must increase.

$$655 \text{ mm Hg} \times \frac{10.0 \cancel{L}}{1500 \cancel{mL}} \times \frac{1000 \cancel{mL}}{1 \cancel{L}} = 4400 \text{ mm Hg}$$

7.17 From Boyle's law we know that pressure is inversely related to volume.
a. Pressure increases; volume must decrease.

$$50.0 \text{ L} \times \frac{760 \cancel{\text{mm Hg}}}{1500 \cancel{\text{mm Hg}}} = 25 \text{ L}$$

b. The mm Hg units must be converted to atm for unit cancellation in the calculation, and because the pressure increases, volume must decrease.

$$760 \cancel{\text{mm Hg}} \times \frac{1 \text{ atm}}{760 \cancel{\text{mm Hg}}} = 1.00 \text{ atm}$$

$$50.0 \text{ L} \times \frac{1.00 \cancel{\text{atm}}}{2.0 \cancel{\text{atm}}} = 25 \text{ L}$$

c. The mm Hg units must be converted to atm for unit cancellation in the calculation, and because the pressure decreases, volume must increase.

$$760 \cancel{\text{mm Hg}} \times \frac{1 \text{ atm}}{760 \cancel{\text{mm Hg}}} = 1.00 \text{ atm}$$

$$50.0 \text{ L} \times \frac{1.00 \cancel{\text{atm}}}{0.500 \cancel{\text{atm}}} = 100. \text{ L}$$

7.19 $50.0 \text{ L} \times \dfrac{5.0 \cancel{\text{atm}}}{1.0 \cancel{\text{atm}}} = 25 \text{ L}$

7.21 **a.** Inspiration begins when the diaphragm flattens, causing the lungs to expand. The increased volume reduces the pressure in the lungs such that air flows into the lungs.
b. Expiration occurs as the diaphragm relaxes, causing a decrease in the volume of the lungs. The pressure of the air in the lungs increases, and air flows out of the lungs.
c. Inspiration occurs when the pressure in the lungs is less than the pressure of the air in the atmosphere.

7.23 According to Charles' law, there is a direct relationship between temperature and volume. For example, volume increases when temperature increases while the pressure and amount of gas remains constant.
a. Diagram C describes an increased volume corresponding to an increased temperature.
b. Diagram A describes a decreased volume corresponding to a decrease in temperature.
c. Diagram B shows no change in volume, which corresponds to no change in temperature.

7.25 Heating a gas in a hot air balloon increases the volume of gas, which reduces its density and allows the balloon to rise above the ground.

7.27 According to Charles' law, gas volume is directly proportional Kelvin temperature when P and n are constant. In all gas law computations, temperatures must be in Kelvin units. (Temperatures in °C are converted to K by the addition of 273.)

a. When temperature decreases, volume must also decrease.

$75°C + 273 = 348 \text{ K} \quad 55°C + 273 = 328 \text{ K}$

$$2500 \text{ mL} \times \frac{328 \, K}{348 \, K} = 2400 \text{ mL}$$

b. When temperature increases, volume must also increase.

$$2500 \text{ mL} \times \frac{680 \, K}{348 \, K} = 4900 \text{ mL}$$

c. $-25°C + 273 = 248 \text{ K}$

$$2500 \text{ mL} \times \frac{248 \, K}{348 \, K} = 1800 \text{ mL}$$

d. $2500 \text{ mL} \times \dfrac{240 \, K}{348 \, K} = 1700 \text{ mL}$

7.29 Because gas pressure increases with an increase in temperature, the gas pressure in an aerosol can may exceed the tolerance of the can when it is heated and cause it to explode.

7.31 When the temperature of the oxygen in the tanks increases, the pressure also increases, which may cause the tanks to explode.

7.33 According to Gay-Lussac's law, temperature is directly related to pressure. For example, temperature increases when the pressure increases. In all gas law computations, temperatures must be in Kelvin units. (Temperatures in °C are converted to K by the addition of 273.)

a. $155°C + 273 = 428 \text{ K} \quad 0°C + 273 = 273 \text{ K}$

$$1200 \text{ torr} \times \frac{273 \, K}{428 \, K} = 770 \text{ torr}$$

b. $12°C + 273 = 285 \text{ K} \quad 35°C + 273 = 308 \text{ K}$

$$1.40 \text{ atm} \times \frac{308 \, K}{285 \, K} = 1.51 \text{ atm}$$

7.35   **a.** boiling point   **b.** vapor pressure
       c. atmospheric pressure   **d.** boiling point

7.37   **a.** On the top of a mountain, the atmospheric or external pressure is less than 760 mm Hg. Therefore, the external pressure is equaled by a vapor pressure that is less than 760 mm Hg, which means that boiling occurs at a temperature below 100°C.
       b. The pressure inside a pressure cooker is greater than one atmosphere; therefore water boils above 100°C. Foods cook faster at higher temperatures.

7.39 $T_1 = 25°C + 273 = 298 \text{ K}; \quad V_1 = 6.50 \text{ L}; \quad P_1 = 845 \text{ mm Hg (1.11 atm)}$

a. $T_2 = 325 \text{ K}; \quad V_2 = 1.85 \text{ L}$

$$1.11 \text{ atm} \times \frac{6.50 \, L}{1.85 \, L} \times \frac{325 \, K}{298 \, K} = 4.25 \text{ atm}$$

b. $T_2 = 12°C + 273 = 285 \text{ K}; \quad V_2 = 2.25 \text{ L}$

$$1.11 \text{ atm} \times \frac{6.50 \, L}{2.25 \, L} \times \frac{285 \, K}{298 \, K} = 3.07 \text{ atm}$$

c. $T_2 = 47.°C + 273 = 320 \text{ K}; \quad V_2 = 12.8 \text{ L}$

$$1.11 \text{ atm} \times \frac{6.50 \, L}{12.8 \, L} \times \frac{320 \, K}{298 \, K} = 0.605 \text{ atm}$$

7.41 $T_1 = 225°C + 273 = 498$ K; $V_1 = 100.0$ mL; $P_1 = 1.80$ atm

$T_2 = -25°C + 273 = 248.$ K; $V_2 = ?$ $P_2 = 0.80$

$$P_2 = 100.0 \text{ mL} \times \frac{1.80 \text{ atm}}{0.80 \text{ atm}} \times \frac{248. \text{ K}}{498 \text{ K}} = 110 \text{ mL}$$

7.43 Addition of more air molecules to a tire or basketball will increase its volume.

7.45 According to Avogadro's law, a change in a gas's volume is directly proportional to the change in the number of moles of gas.

a. $8.00 \text{ L} \times \dfrac{2.00 \text{ moles}}{4.00 \text{ moles}} = 4.00 \text{ L}$

b. $25.0 \text{ g neon} \times \dfrac{1 \text{ mole neon}}{20.2 \text{ g neon}} = 1.24 \text{ moles Ne added}$

$1.50 \text{ moles} + 1.24 \text{ moles} = 2.74 \text{ moles}$

$8.00 \text{ L} \times \dfrac{2.74 \text{ moles}}{1.50 \text{ moles}} = 14.6 \text{ L}$

c. $1.50 \text{ moles} + 3.50 \text{ moles} = 5.00 \text{ moles of gases}$

$8.0 \text{ L} \times \dfrac{5.00 \text{ moles}}{1.50 \text{ moles}} = 26.7 \text{ L}$

7.47 At STP, the molar volume of any gas is 22.4 L per mole.

a. $44.8 \text{ L} \times \dfrac{1 \text{ mole O}_2}{22.4 \text{ L}} = 2.00 \text{ moles O}_2$

b. $4.00 \text{ L} \times \dfrac{1 \text{ mole CO}_2}{22.4 \text{ L}} = 0.179 \text{ mole CO}_2$

c. $6.40 \text{ g O}_2 \times \dfrac{1 \text{ mole O}_2}{32.0 \text{ g O}_2} \times \dfrac{22.4 \text{ L}}{1 \text{ mole O}_2} = 4.48 \text{ L}$

d. $50.0 \text{ g Ne} \times \dfrac{1 \text{ mole Ne}}{20.2 \text{ g Ne}} \times \dfrac{22.4 \text{ L}}{1 \text{ mole Ne}} \times \dfrac{1000 \text{ mL}}{1 \text{ L}} = 55\,400 \text{ mL}$

7.49 $8.25 \text{ g Mg} \times \dfrac{1 \text{ mole Mg}}{24.3 \text{ g Mg}} \times \dfrac{1 \text{ mole H}_2}{1 \text{ mole Mg}} \times \dfrac{22.4 \text{ L}}{1 \text{ mole H}_2} = 7.60 \text{ L H}_2$

7.51 $P = \dfrac{nRT}{V} = \dfrac{(2.00 \text{ moles})(0.0821 \text{ L} \cdot \text{atm})(300 \text{ K})}{(10.0 \text{ L})(\text{mole} \cdot \text{K})} = 4.93 \text{ atm}$

7.53 $n = \dfrac{PV}{RT} = \dfrac{(845 \text{ mm Hg})(20.0 \text{ L})}{\left(\dfrac{62.4 \text{ L} \cdot \text{mm Hg}}{\text{mole} \cdot \text{K}}\right)(295 \text{ K})} \times \dfrac{32.0 \text{ g O}_2}{1 \text{ mole O}_2} = 29.4 \text{ g O}_2$

7.55 $n = 25.0 \text{ g N}_2 \times \dfrac{1 \text{ mole N}_2}{28.0 \text{ g}} = 0.893 \text{ mole}$

$T = \dfrac{PV}{nR} \quad \dfrac{(630 \text{ mm Hg})(50.0 \text{ L})}{(0.893 \text{ mole})\left(\dfrac{62.4 \text{ L} \cdot \text{mm Hg}}{\text{mole} \cdot \text{K}}\right)} = 565 \text{ K } (= 292°C)$

7.57 Each gas particle in a gas mixture exerts a pressure as it strikes the walls of the container. The total gas pressure for any gaseous sample is thus a sum of all of the individual pressures. When the portion of the pressure due to a particular type of gaseous particle is discussed, it is only part of the total. Accordingly, these "portions" are referred to as "partial" pressures.

7.59 To obtain the total pressure in a gaseous mixture, add up all of the partial pressures using the same pressure unit.

$$P_{total} = P_{Nitrogen} + P_{Oxygen} + P_{Helium}$$
$$= 425 \text{ torr} + 115 \text{ torr} + 225 \text{ torr} = 765 \text{ torr}$$

7.61 Because the total pressure in a gaseous mixture is the sum of the partial pressures using the same pressure unit, addition and subtraction is used to obtain the "missing" partial pressure.

$$P_{Nitrogen} = P_{total} - (P_{Oxygen} + P_{Helium})$$
$$= 925 \text{ torr} - (425 \text{ torr} + 75 \text{ torr}) = 425 \text{ torr}$$

7.63 **a.** If oxygen cannot readily cross from the lungs into the bloodstream, then the partial pressure of oxygen will be lower in the blood of an emphysema patient.
b. An increase in the partial pressure of oxygen in the air supplied to the lungs will result in an increase in the partial pressure of oxygen in the bloodstream (addition of reactant causes the formation of more product). Because an emphysema patient has a lower partial pressure of oxygen in the blood, the use of a portable oxygen tank helps to bring the oxygenation of the patient's blood to a more desirable level.

7.65 **a.** 2 Fewest number of gas particles exerts the lowest pressure.
b. 1 Greatest number of gas particles exerts the highest pressure.

7.67 **a.** A Volume decreases when temperature decreases.
b. C Volume increases when pressure decreases.
c. A Volume decreases when the moles of gas decrease.
d. B Doubling temperature doubles the volume, but losing half the gas particles decreases the volume by half. The two effects cancel, and no change in volume occurs.
e. C Increasing the moles increases the volume to keep T and P constant.

7.69 **a.** The volume of the chest and lungs will decrease when compressed during the Heimlich maneuver.
b. A decrease in volume causes the pressure to increase. A piece of food would be dislodged with a sufficiently high pressure.

7.71 Recall that all temperatures *must* be in kelvins in computations involving gas laws!

$$10. \text{ atm} \times \frac{348 \text{ } K}{298 \text{ } K} \times = 12 \text{ atm}$$

7.73 Remember to use Kelvin temperature units in the calculation and convert to Celsius degrees after completing the calculation!

$$400. \text{ K} \times \frac{0.25 \text{ atm}}{2.00 \text{ atm}} = 50. \text{ K} \quad 50. \text{ K} - 273 = -223°\text{C}$$

7.75 $$n = \frac{PV}{RT} = \frac{(2500 \text{ mm Hg})(2.00 \text{ } L)}{(62.4 \text{ } L \cdot \text{mm Hg})(291 \text{ } K)} = 0.28 \text{ mole CH}_4$$
$$\frac{}{\text{mole } K}$$

$$0.28 \text{ mole CH}_4 \times \frac{16.0 \text{ g CH}_4}{1 \text{ mole CH}_4} = 4.5 \text{ g CH}_4$$

7.77 $n = \dfrac{PV}{RT} = \dfrac{(12 \text{ atm})(35.0 \text{ L})}{\dfrac{(0.0821 \text{ L} \cdot \text{atm} \; (278 \text{ K})}{\text{mole K}}} = 1.8 \text{ mole CO}_2$

$1.8 \text{ moles CO}_2 \times \dfrac{6.02 \times 10^{23} \text{ molecules}}{1 \text{ mole CO}_2} = 1.1 \times 10^{24} \text{ molecules CO}_2$

7.79 The mole–mole conversion factor is obtained from the reaction and used to convert to moles of gas, and the STP molar volume conversion factor is used to convert moles of gas into liters of gas, as shown below:

$2.00 \text{ moles CaCO}_3 \times \dfrac{1 \text{ mole CO}_2}{1 \text{ mole CaCO}_3} \times \dfrac{22.4 \text{ L}}{1 \text{ mole CO}_2} = 44.8 \text{ L CO}_2$

7.81 $425 \text{ mL} \times \dfrac{745 \text{ mm Hg}}{0.115 \text{ atm}} \times \dfrac{1 \text{ atm}}{760 \text{ mm Hg}} \times \dfrac{178 \text{ K}}{297 \text{ K}} = 2170 \text{ mL}$

7.83 $5.4 \text{ g Al} \times \dfrac{1 \text{ mole Al}}{27.0 \text{ g Al}} \times \dfrac{3 \text{ moles O}_2}{4 \text{ moles Al}} \times \dfrac{22.4 \text{ L O}_2 \text{ (STP)}}{1 \text{ mole O}_2} = 3.4 \text{ L O}_2 \text{ (g)}$

7.85 The partial pressure of each gas is proportional to the number of particles of each type of gas that is present. Thus, a ratio of partial pressure to total pressure is equal to the ratio of moles of that gas to the total number of moles of gases that are present:

$P_{\text{Helium}}/P_{\text{total}} = n_{\text{Helium}}/n_{\text{total}}$

Solving the equation for the partial pressure of helium yields:

$P_{\text{Helium}} = 2400 \text{ torr} \times \dfrac{2.0 \text{ moles}}{8.0 \text{ moles}} = 600 \text{ torr} \; (6.0 \times 10^2 \text{ torr})$

And for oxygen:

$P_{\text{Oxygen}} = 2400 \text{ torr} \times \dfrac{6.0 \text{ moles}}{8.0 \text{ moles}} = 1800 \text{ torr}$

7.87 Because the partial pressure of nitrogen is to be reported in torr, the atm and mm Hg units (for oxygen and argon, respectively) must be converted to torr, as follows:

$0.60 \text{ atm} \times \dfrac{760 \text{ torr}}{1 \text{ atm}} = 460 \text{ torr}$

$425 \text{ mm Hg} \times \dfrac{1 \text{ torr}}{1 \text{ mm Hg}} = 425 \text{ torr}$

and $P_{\text{Nitrogen}} = P_{\text{total}} - (P_{\text{Oxygen}} + P_{\text{Argon}})$
$= 1250 \text{ torr} - (460 \text{ torr} + 425 \text{ torr}) = 370 \text{ torr}$

7.89 $T_1 = 15°\text{C} + 273 = 288 \text{ K}; \quad P_1 = 745 \text{ mm Hg}; \quad V_1 = 4250 \text{ mL}$

$P_2 = 1.20 \text{ atm} \times \dfrac{760 \text{ mm Hg}}{1 \text{ atm}} = 912 \text{ mm Hg}; \quad V_2 = 2.50 \text{ L} \times \dfrac{1000 \text{ mL}}{1 \text{ L}} = 2.50 \times 10^3 \text{ mL}$

$288 \text{ K} \times \dfrac{2500 \text{ mL}}{4250 \text{ mL}} \times \dfrac{912 \text{ mm Hg}}{745 \text{ mm Hg}} = 207 \text{ K} - 273 = -66°\text{C}$

7.91 $132 \text{ g NaN}_3 \times \dfrac{1 \text{ mole NaN}_3}{65.0 \text{ g NaN}_3} \times \dfrac{3 \text{ moles N}_2}{2 \text{ moles NaN}_3} \times \dfrac{22.4 \text{ L}}{1 \text{ mole N}_2} = 68.2 \text{ L at STP}$

7.93 $T = 297\ \text{K}$ $V = 4.60\ \text{L}$

$$1.00\ \text{g CO}_2 \times \frac{1\ \text{mole CO}_2}{44.0\ \text{g CO}_2} = 0.0227\ \text{mole CO}_2$$

$$P = \frac{nRT}{V} = \frac{(0.0227\ \text{mole})(0.0821\ \text{L} \cdot \text{atm})(297\ \text{K})}{(4.60\ \text{L})(\text{mole K})} = 0.120\ \text{atm} \times \frac{760\ \text{mm Hg}}{1\ \text{atm}} = 91.5\ \text{mm Hg}$$

7.95 $$12.0\ \text{g Mg} \times \frac{1\ \text{mole Mg}}{24.3\ \text{g Mg}} \times \frac{1\ \text{mole H}_2}{1\ \text{mole Mg}} = 0.494\ \text{mole H}_2$$

$$V = \frac{nRT}{P} = \frac{(0.494\ \text{mole})(62.4\ \text{L mm Hg})(297\ \text{K})}{(835\ \text{mm Hg})(\text{mole K})} = 11.0\ \text{L}$$

Study Goals

- Identify the solute and solvent in a solution.
- Describe hydrogen bonding in water.
- Describe electrolytes in a solution.
- Define solubility.
- Identify a salt as soluble or insoluble.
- Write an equation (molecular or ionic) to show the formation of an insoluble salt.
- Calculate the percent concentrations and molarity of a solution.
- Use the molarity of a solution in a chemical reaction to calculate the volume or quantity of a reactant or product.
- Distinguish between a solution, a colloid, and a suspension.
- Describe osmosis and dialysis.

Think About It

1. Why is salt used to preserve foods?

2. Why do raisins or dried prunes swell when placed in water?

3. Why are pickles made in a brine solution with a high salt concentration?

4. Why can't you drink seawater?

5. How do your kidneys remove toxic substances from the blood but retain the usable substances?

Key Terms

Match the following terms with the correct statement shown below:

    a. solution   **b.** concentration   **c.** molarity
    d. osmosis   **e.** electrolyte

1. _____ a substance that dissociates into ions when it dissolves in water

2. _____ the flow of solvent through a semipermeable membrane into a solution with a higher solute concentration

3. _____ the amount of solute that is dissolved in a specified amount of solution

4. _____ the number of moles of solute in one liter of solution

5. _____ a mixture of at least two components called a solute and a solvent

Answers   **1.** e   **2.** d   **3.** b   **4.** c   **5.** a

8.1 Solutions

- A polar solute is soluble in a polar solvent; a nonpolar solute is soluble in a nonpolar solvent; "like dissolves like."
- A solution forms when a solute dissolves in a solvent.
- The partial positive charge of hydrogen and the partial negative charge of oxygen permits water molecules to hydrogen bond to other water molecules.
- An ionic solute dissolves in water, a polar solvent, because the polar water molecules attract and pull the positive and negative ions into solution. In solution, water molecules surround the ions due to a process called hydration.

◆ Learning Exercise 8.1A

Indicate the solute and solvent in each of the following:

		Solute	**Solvent**
a.	10 g KCl dissolved in 100 g water	_____	_____
b.	soda water, $CO_2(g)$, dissolved in water	_____	_____
c.	an alloy composed of 80% Zn and 20% Cu	_____	_____
d.	a mixture of O_2 (200 mm Hg) and He (500 mm Hg)	_____	_____
e.	a solution of 40 mL CCl_4 and 2 mL Br_2	_____	_____

Answers　　**a.** KCl; water　　**b.** CO_2; water　　**c.** Cu; Zn
　　　　　　　d. oxygen; helium　　**e.** Br_2; CCl_4

◆ Learning Exercise 8.1B

ESSAY: How does the polarity of the water molecule allow it to hydrogen bond?

Answer　　The O—H bonds in water molecules are polar because the hydrogen atoms are partially positive and the oxygen atoms are partially negative. Hydrogen bonding occurs because the partially positive hydrogen atoms in one water molecule are attracted to partially negative oxygen atoms of other water molecules.

◆ Learning Exercise 8.1C

Water is polar and hexane is nonpolar. In which solvent is each of the following soluble?

- **a.** bromine, Br_2, nonpolar _____
- **b.** HCl, polar _____
- **c.** cholesterol, nonpolar _____
- **d.** vitamin D, nonpolar _____
- **e.** vitamin C, polar _____

Answers　　**a.** hexane　　**b.** water　　**c.** hexane　　**d.** hexane　　**e.** water

8.2 Electrolytes and Nonelectrolytes

- Electrolytes conduct an electrical current because they produce ions in aqueous solutions.
- Strong electrolytes are nearly completely ionized, whereas weak electrolytes are slightly ionized. Nonelectrolytes do not form ions in solution but dissolve as molecules.
- An equivalent is the amount of an electrolyte that carries 1 mole of electrical charge.
- There are 1, 2, or 3 equivalents per mole of a positive or negative ion depending on the charge.

◆ Learning Exercise 8.2A

Write an equation for the formation of an aqueous solution of each of the following strong electrolytes:

a. $LiCl$ _____

b. $Mg(NO_3)_2$ _____

c. Na_3PO_4 _____

d. K_2SO_4 _____

e. $MgCl_2$ _____

Answers

a. $LiCl(s) \xrightarrow{H_2O} Li^+(aq) + Cl^-(aq)$

b. $Mg(NO_3)_2(s) \xrightarrow{H_2O} Mg^{2+}(aq) + 2NO_3^-(aq)$

c. $Na_3PO_4(s) \xrightarrow{H_2O} 3Na^+(aq) + PO_4^{3-}(aq)$

d. $K_3SO_4(s) \xrightarrow{H_2O} 2K^+(aq) + SO_4^{2-}(aq)$

e. $MgCl_2(s) \xrightarrow{H_2O} Mg^{2+}(aq) + 2Cl^-(aq)$

◆ Learning Exercise 8.2B

Indicate whether an aqueous solution of each of the following contains mostly ions, molecules only, or mostly molecules with some ions. Write an equation for the formation of the solution:

a. glucose, $C_6H_{12}O_6$, a nonelectrolyte _____

b. NaOH, a strong electrolyte _____

c. K_2SO_4, a strong electrolyte _____

d. HF, a weak electrolyte _____

Answers

a. $C_6H_{12}O_6(s) \rightarrow C_6H_{12}O_6(aq)$ molecules only

b. $NaOH(s) \rightarrow Na^+(aq) + OH^-(aq)$ mostly ions

c. $K_2SO_4(s) \rightarrow 2K^+(aq) + SO_4^{2-}(aq)$ mostly ions

d. $HF + H_2O \rightleftarrows H_3O^+ + F^-$ mostly molecules and a few ions

◆ Learning Exercise 8.2C

Calculate the following:

a. number of equivalents in 1 mole Mg^{2+}

b. number of equivalents of Cl^- in 2.5 moles Cl^-

c. number of equivalents of Ca^{2+} in 2.0 moles Ca^{2+}

Answers **a.** 2 Eq **b.** 2.5 Eq **c.** 4.0 Eq

8.3 Solubility

- The amount of solute that dissolves depends on the nature of the solute and solvent.
- Solubility describes the maximum amount of a solute that dissolves in 100 g of solvent at a given temperature.
- A saturated solution contains the maximum amount of dissolved solute at a certain temperature.
- An increase in temperature increases the solubility of most solids but decreases the solubility of gases in water.
- The solubility rules describe the kinds of ionic combinations that are soluble and insoluble in water. If a salt contains Li^+, Na^+, K^+, NO_3^-, or NH_4^+ ion, it is soluble in water. Most halides and sulfates are soluble.

◆ Learning Exercise 8.3A

Identify each of the following as a saturated solution (S) or an unsaturated solution (U):

1. A sugar cube dissolves when added to a cup of coffee. _____

2. A KCl crystal added to a KCl solution does not change in size. _____

3. A layer of sugar forms in the bottom of a glass of iced tea. _____

4. The rate of crystal formation equals the rate of solution. _____

5. Upon heating, all the sugar dissolves. _____

Answers **1.** U **2.** S **3.** S **4.** S **5.** U

◆ Learning Exercise 8.3B

Use the KNO_3 solubility chart for the following problems:

Solubility of KNO₃

Temperature (°C)	g KNO₃/100 g H₂O
0	15
20	30
40	65
60	110
80	170
100	250

a. How many grams of KNO_3 will dissolve in 100 g water at 40°C?

b. How many grams of KNO_3 will dissolve in 300 g water at 60°C?

c. A solution is prepared using 200 g water and 350 g KNO_3 at 80°C. Will any solute remain undissolved? If so, how much?

d. Will 200 g KNO_3 dissolve when added to 100 g water at 100°C?

Answers   **a.** 65 g   **b.** 330 g
            c. Yes, 10 g KNO_3 will not dissolve.   **d.** Yes, all 200 g KNO_3 will dissolve.

◆ Learning Exercise 8.3C

Predict whether the following salts are soluble (S) or insoluble (I) in water:

1. _____ NaCl   **2.** _____ AgNO₃   **3.** _____ PbCl₂

4. _____ Ag₂S   **5.** _____ BaSO₄   **6.** _____ Na₂CO₃

7. _____ K₂S   **8.** _____ MgCl₂   **9.** _____ BaS

Answers   **1.** S   **2.** S   **3.** I   **4.** I   **5.** I
            6. S   **7.** S   **8.** S   **9.** I

◆ **Learning Exercise 8.3D**

Predict whether an insoluble salt forms in the following mixtures of soluble salts. If so, write the formula of the solid.

1. $NaCl(aq)$ and $Pb(NO_3)_2(aq)$ _____

2. $BaCl_2(aq)$ and $Na_2SO_4(aq)$ _____

3. $K_3PO_4(aq)$ and $Na(NO_3)_2(aq)$ _____

4. $Na_2S(aq)$ and $AgNO_3(aq)$ _____

Answers   **1.** yes; $PbCl_2$ **2.** yes; $BaSO_4$ **3.** none   **4.** yes; Ag_2S

8.4 Percent Concentration

• The concentration of a solution is the relationship between the amount of solute (g or mL) and the amount (g or mL) of solution.

• A mass percent (mass/mass) expresses the ratio of the mass of solute to the mass of solution multiplied by 100:

$$\text{Percent (m/m)} = \frac{\text{grams of solute}}{\text{grams of solution}} \times 100$$

• Percent concentrations can also be expressed as a mass/volume ratio:

$$\text{Percent (m/v)} = \frac{\text{grams of solute}}{\text{volume (mL) of solution}} \times 100$$

Study Note

Calculate mass percent concentration (% m/m) as

$$\frac{\text{grams of solute}}{\text{grams of solution}} \times 100$$

Example: What is the percent (mass/mass) when 2.4 g $NaHCO_3$ dissolves in 120 g solution?

Solution: $\dfrac{2.4 \text{ g } NaHCO_3}{120 \text{ g solution}} \times 100 = 2.0\% \text{ (m/m)}$

◆ **Learning Exercise 8.4A**

Determine the percent concentration of the following solutions:

a. The mass/mass % of 18.0 g NaCl in 90.0 g solution.

b. The mass/volume % of 5.0 g KCl in 2.0 liters solution.

c. The mass/mass % of 4.0 g KOH in 50.0 g solution.

d. The mass/volume % of 0.25 kg glucose in 5.0 L solution.

Answers **a.** 20.0% **b.** 0.25% **c.** 8.0% **d.** 5.0%

Study Note

In solution problems, the percent concentration is useful as a conversion factor. The factor is obtained by rewriting the % as g solute/100 g (or mL) solution.

Example 1: How many g of KI are needed to prepare 250 mL of a 4% (m/v) KI solution?

Solution: $250 \text{ mL solution} \times \dfrac{4 \text{ g KI}}{100 \text{ mL solution}} = 10 \text{ g KI}$

% (m/v)factor

Example 2: How many grams of a 25% (m/m) NaOH solution can be prepared from 75 g NaOH?

Solution: $75 \text{ g NaOH} \times \dfrac{100 \text{ g NaOH solution}}{25 \text{ g NaOH}} = 300 \text{ g NaOH solution}$

% (m/m) factor (inverted)

◆ Learning Exercise 8.4B

Calculate the number of grams of solute needed to prepare each of the following solutions:

a. How many grams of glucose are needed to prepare 400. mL of a 10.0% (m/v) solution?

b. How many grams of lidocaine hydrochloride are needed to prepare 50.0 g of a 2.0% (m/m) solution?

c. How many grams of KCl are needed to prepare 0.80 liter of a 0.15% (m/v) KCl solution?

d. How many grams of NaCl are needed to prepare 250 mL of a 1.0% (m/v) solution?

Answers **a.** 40.0 g **b.** 1.0 g **c.** 1.2 g **d.** 2.5 g

◆ Learning Exercise 8.4C

Use percent–concentration factors to calculate the volume (mL) of each solution that contains the amount of solute stated in each problem.

    a. 2.00 g NaCl from a 1.00% (m/v) NaCl solution.

    b. 25 g glucose from a 5% (m/v) glucose solution.

    c. 1.5 g KCl from a 0.50% (m/v) KCl solution.

    d. 75.0 g NaOH from a 25.0% (m/v) NaOH solution.

Answers   **a.** 200. mL   **b.** 500 mL   **c.** 300 mL   **d.** 300. mL

8.5 Molarity and Dilution

- Molarity is a concentration term that describes the number of moles of solute dissolved in 1 L (1000 mL) of solution.

$$M = \frac{\text{moles of solute}}{\text{L solution}}$$

- *Dilution* is the process of mixing a solution with solvent to obtain a lower concentration.
- For dilutions, use the expression $C_1V_1 = C_2V_2$ or $M_1V_1 = M_2V_2$ and solve for the unknown value.
- The molarity and volume of a solution can be used to calculate the amount of a reactant or a product in a reaction.

◆ Learning Exercise 8.5A

Calculate the molarity of the following solutions:

    a. 2.0 mole HCl in 1.0 L

    b. 10.0 mole glucose ($C_6H_{12}O_6$) in 2.0 L

    c. 80.0 g NaOH in 4.0 L (hint: find moles NaOH)

Answers **a.** 2.0 M HCl **b.** 5.0 M glucose **c.** 0.50 M NaOH

Study Note

Molarity can be used as a conversion factor to convert between the amount of solute and the volume of solution.

Example 1: How many grams of NaOH are in 0.20 L of a 4.0-M NaOH solution?

Solution: The concentration 4.0 M can be expressed as the conversion factors

$$\frac{4.0 \text{ mole NaOH}}{1 \text{ L NaOH}} \quad \text{and} \quad \frac{1 \text{ L NaOH}}{4.0 \text{ mole NaOH}}$$

$$0.20 \text{ L NaOH} \times \frac{4.0 \text{ mole NaOH}}{1 \text{ L NaOH}} \times \frac{40.0 \text{ g NaOH}}{1 \text{ mole NaOH}} = 32 \text{ g NaOH}$$

Example 2: How many mL of a 6 M HCl solution will provide 0.36 mole HCl?

Solution: $0.36 \text{ mole HCl solution} \times \underbrace{\frac{1 \text{ L}}{6 \text{ mole HCl}}}_{\text{Molarity factor (inverted)}} \times \frac{1000 \text{ mL}}{1 \text{ L}} = 60 \text{ mL HCl solution}$

◆ **Learning Exercise 8.5B**

Calculate the quantity of solute in the following solutions:

a. How many moles of HCl are in 1.50 L of a 2.50-M HCl solution?

b. How many moles of KOH are in 125 mL of a 2.40-M KOH solution?

c. How many grams of NaOH are needed to prepare 225 mL of a 3.00-M NaOH solution? (Hint: Find moles of NaOH.)

d. How many grams of NaCl are in 415 mL of a 1.30-M NaCl solution?

Answers **a.** 43.75 moles HCl **b.** 0.300 moles KOH **c.** 27.0 g NaOH **d.** 31.6 g NaCl

◆ Learning Exercise 8.5C

Calculate the milliliters needed of each solution to obtain each of the following:

    a. 0.200 mole of $Mg(OH)_2$ from a 2.50-M $Mg(OH)_2$ solution

    b. 0.125 mole of glucose from a 5.00-M glucose solution

    c. 0.250 mole of KI from a 4.00-M KI solution

    d. 16.0 g NaOH from a 3.20-M NaOH solution

Answers   **a.** 80.0 mL   **b.** 25.0 mL   **c.** 62.5 mL   **d.** 125 mL

◆ Learning Exercise 8.5D

Solve each of the following dilution problems (assume the volumes add):

    a. What is the final concentration after 100 mL of a 5.0-M KCl solution is diluted with water to give a final volume of 200 mL?

    b. What is the final concentration of the diluted solution if 5.0 mL of a 15% (m/v) KCl solution is diluted to 25 mL?

c. What is the final concentration after 250 mL of 8% (m/v) NaOH is diluted with 750 mL water?

d. 160 mL of water is added to 40 mL of 1.0-M NaCl solution. What is the final concentration?

e. What volume of water must be added to 2.0 L of 12% (m/v) KCl to obtain a 4.0% (m/v) KCl solution? What is the total volume of the solution?

f. What volume of 6.0 M HCl is needed to prepare 300. mL of 1.0 M HCl? How much water must be added?

Answers   **a.** 2.5 M   **b.** 3.0% (m/v)   **c.** 2% (m/m)
                d. 0.20 M   **e.** add 4.0 L; V_2 = 6.0 L   **f.** V_1 = 50 mL; add 250 mL water

◆ Learning Exercise 8.5E

For the following reaction, $2AgNO_3(aq) + H_2SO_4(s) \rightarrow Ag_2SO_4(s) + 2H_2O(l)$:

a. How many milliliters of 1.5 M $AgNO_3$ will react with 40.0 mL of 1.0 M H_2SO_4?

b. How many grams of Ag_2SO_4 will be produced?

Answers   **a.** $40.0 \text{ mL H}_2\text{SO}_4 \times \dfrac{1 \text{ L H}_2\text{SO}_4}{1000 \text{ mL H}_2\text{SO}_4} \times \dfrac{1.0 \text{ moles H}_2\text{SO}_4}{1 \text{ L H}_2\text{SO}_4} \times \dfrac{2 \text{ moles AgNO}_3}{1 \text{ mole H}_2\text{SO}_4}$

$\times \dfrac{1000 \text{ mL AgNO}_3}{1.5 \text{ moles AgNO}_3} = 53 \text{ mL}$

b. $40.0 \text{ mL H}_2\text{SO}_4 \times \dfrac{1 \text{ L H}_2\text{SO}_4}{1000 \text{ mL H}_2\text{SO}_4} \times \dfrac{1.0 \text{ mole H}_2\text{SO}_4}{1 \text{ L H}_2\text{SO}_4} \times \dfrac{1 \text{ mole Ag}_2 \text{ SO}_4}{1 \text{ mole H}_2\text{SO}_4}$

$\times \dfrac{311.9 \text{ g AgSO}_4}{1 \text{ mole Ag}_2\text{SO}_4} = 12 \text{ g Ag}_2\text{SO}_4$

◆ Learning Exercise 8.5F

For the following reaction, calculate the milliliters of 1.8-M KOH that react with 18.5 mL of 2.2 M HCl:

$HNO_3(aq) + KOH(aq) \rightarrow KNO_3(aq) + H_2O(l)$

Answer   **b.** $18.5 \text{ mL HCl} \times \dfrac{1 \text{ L HCl}}{1000 \text{ mL HCl}} \times \dfrac{2.2 \text{ moles HCl}}{1 \text{ L HCl}} \times \dfrac{1 \text{ mole KOH}}{1 \text{ mole HCl}}$

$\times \dfrac{1000 \text{ mL KOH}}{1.8 \text{ moles KOH}} = 22.6 \text{ mL KOH}$

8.6 Properties of Solutions

- Colloids contain particles that do not settle out and pass through filters but not through semipermeable membranes.
- Suspensions are composed of large particles that settle out of solution.
- In the process of osmosis, water (solvent) moves through a semipermeable membrane from the solution that has a lower solute concentration to a solution where the solute concentration is higher.
- Osmotic pressure is the pressure that prevents the flow of water into a more concentrated solution.
- Isotonic solutions have osmotic pressures equal to those of body fluids. A hypotonic solution has a lower osmotic pressure than body fluids; a hypertonic solution has a higher osmotic pressure.
- A red blood cell maintains its volume in an isotonic solution, but it swells (hemolysis) in a hypotonic solution and shrinks (crenation) in a hypertonic solution.
- In dialysis, water and small solute particles can pass through a dialyzing membrane, whereas larger particles are retained.

◆ Learning Exercise 8.6A

Identify each of the following as a solution, colloid, or suspension:

1. _____ contains single atoms, ions, or small molecules
2. _____ settles out with gravity
3. _____ retained by filters
4. _____ cannot diffuse through a cellular membrane
5. _____ aggregates of atoms, molecules, or ions larger in size than solution particles
6. _____ large particles that are visible

Answers   **1.** solution   **2.** suspension   **3.** suspension
4. colloid   **5.** colloid   **6.** suspension

◆ Learning Exercise 8.6B

Fill in the blanks:

In osmosis, the direction of solvent flow is from the (1) _____ solvent concentration to the (2) _____ solvent concentration. A semipermeable membrane separates 5% and 10% sucrose solutions. The (3) _____% solution has the greater osmotic pressure. Water will move from the (4) _____% solution into the (5) _____% solution. The compartment that contains the (6) _____% solution increases in volume.

Answers   (1) higher   (2) lower   (3) 10
(4) 5   (5) 10   (6) 10

◆ **Learning Exercise 8.6C**

What occurs when 2% (A) and a 10% (B) starch solutions are separated by a semipermeable membrane?

Semipermeable
membrane

2% starch starch **A**	10% starch **B**

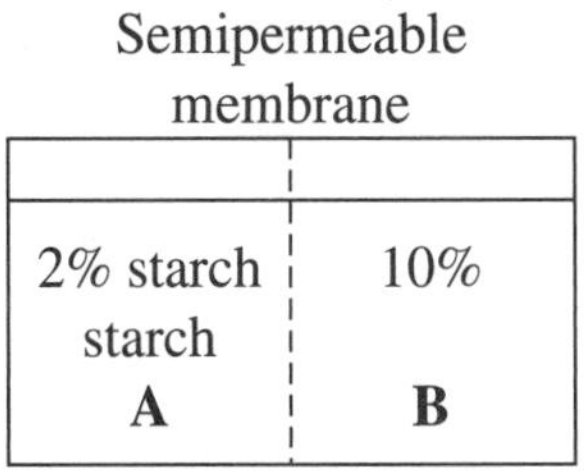

a. Water will flow from side _____ to side _____ .

b. The volume in compartment _____ will increase and decrease in compartment _____ .

c. The final concentration of the solutions in both compartments will be _____ .

Answers   **a.** A, B   **b.** B, A   **c.** 6%

◆ **Learning Exercise 8.6D**

Fill in the blanks:

A (1) _____ % NaCl solution and a (2) _____ % glucose solution are isotonic to the body fluids. A red blood cell placed in these solutions does not change in volume because these solutions are (3) _____ tonic. When a red blood cell is placed in water, it undergoes (4) _____ because water is (5) _____ tonic. A 20% glucose solution will cause a red blood cell to undergo (6) _____ because the 20% glucose solution is (7) _____ tonic.

Answers   (1) 0.9   (2) 5   (3) iso   (4) hemolysis
             (5) hypo   (6) crenation   (7) hyper

◆ **Learning Exercise 8.6E**

Indicate whether the following solutions are

1. hypotonic   2. hypertonic   3. isotonic

a. ____ 5% (m/v) glucose   b. ____ 3% (m/v) NaCl   c. ____ 2% (m/v) glucose

d. ____ water   e. ____ 0.9% (m/v) NaCl   f. ____ 10% (m/v) glucose

Answers   **a.** 3   **b.** 2   **c.** 1   **d.** 1   **e.** 3   **f.** 2

◆ **Learning Exercise 8.6F**

Indicate whether the following solutions will cause a red blood cell to undergo

1. crenation   2. hemolysis   3. no change (stays the same)

a. ____ 10% (m/v) NaCl   b. ____ 1% (m/v) glucose   c. ____ 5% (m/v) glucose

d. ____ 0.5% (m/v) NaCl   e. ____ 10% (m/v) glucose   f. water

Answers   **a.** 1   **b.** 2   **c.** 3   **d.** 2   **e.** 1   **f.** 2

◆ **Learning Exercise 8.6G**

A dialysis bag contains starch, glucose, NaCl, protein, and urea.

    a. When the dialysis bag is placed in water, which of the components would you expect to dialyze through the bag? Why?

    b. Which components will stay inside the dialysis bag? Why?

Answers   **a.** Glucose, NaCl, urea; they are solution particles.
                    b. Starch, protein; colloids are retained by semipermeable membranes.

Checklist for Chapter 8

You are ready to take the practice test for Chapter 8. Be sure that you have accomplished the following learning goals for this chapter. If you are not sure, review the section listed at the end of the goal. Then apply your new skills and understanding to the practice test.

After studying Chapter 8, I can successfully:

_____   Describe hydrogen bonding in water (8.1).

_____   Identify the solute and solvent in a solution (8.1).

_____   Describe the process of dissolving an ionic solute in water (8.1).

_____   Identify the components in solutions of electrolytes and nonelectrolytes (8.2).

_____   Calculate the number of equivalents for an electrolyte (8.2).

_____   Identify a saturated and an unsaturated solution (8.3).

_____   Identify a salt as soluble or insoluble (8.3).

_____   Write an equation (molecular or ionic) to show the formation of an insoluble salt (8.3).

_____   Describe the effects of temperature and nature of the solute on its solubility in a solvent (8.3).

_____   Calculate the percent concentration of a solute in a solution and use percent concentration to calculate the amount of solute or solution (8.4).

_____   Calculate the diluted volume of a solution (8.4).

_____   Calculate the molarity of a solution (8.5).

_____   Use molarity as a conversion factor to calculate between the mole (or grams) of a solute and the volume of the solution (8.5).

_____   Use the molarity of a solution in a chemical reaction to calculate the volume or quantity of a reactant or product (8.5).

_____   Identify a mixture as a solution, a colloid, or a suspension (8.6).

_____   Explain the processes of osmosis and dialysis (8.6).

Practice Test for Chapter 8

Indicate if the following are more soluble in (A) water (polar solvent) or (B) benzene (nonpolar solvent).

1. _____ I_2 (g), nonpolar   2. _____ NaBr(s), polar

3. _____ KI(s), polar   4. _____ C_6H_{12}, nonpolar

5. When dissolved in water, $Ca(NO_3)_2$ dissociates into
   A. $Ca^{2+} + (NO_3)_2^{2-}$ B. $Ca^+ + NO_3^-$ C. $Ca^{2+} + 2NO_3^-$
   D. $Ca^{2+} + 2N^{5+} + 2O_3^{6-}$ E. $CaNO_3^+ + NO_3^-$

6. What is the number of equivalents in 2 moles of Mg^{2+}?
   A. 0.50 equiv   B. 1 equiv   C. 1.5 equiv
   D. 2 equiv   E. 4 equiv

7. CH_3CH_2OH, ethyl alcohol, is a nonelectrolyte. When placed in water, it
   A. dissociates completely   B. dissociates partially   C. does not dissociate
   D. makes the solution acidic   E. makes the solution basic

8. The solubility of NH_4Cl is 46 g in 100 g of water at 40°C. How much NH_4Cl can dissolve in 500 g of water at 40°C?
   A. 9.2 g   B. 46 g   C. 100 g   D. 184 g   E. 230 g

Indicate if the following are soluble (S) or not soluble (N) in water:

9. _____ NaCl   10. _____ AgCl

11. _____ $BaSO_4$ 12. _____ FeO

13. A solution containing 1.20 g sucrose in 50.0 mL of solution has a percent concentration of
    A. 0.600%   B. 1.20%   C. 2.40%   D. 30.0%   E. 41.6%

14. The amount of lactose in 250 mL of a 3.0% lactose solution of infant formula is
    A. 0.15 g   B. 1.2 g   C. 6.0 g   D. 7.5 g   E. 30 g

15. The volume needed to obtain 0.40 g of glucose from a 5.0% glucose solution is
    A. 1.0 mL   B. 2.0 mL   C. 4.0 mL   D. 5.0 mL   E. 8.0 mL

16. The amount of NaCl needed to prepare 50.0 mL of a 4.00% NaCl solution is
    A. 20.0 g   B. 15.0 g   C. 10.0 g   D. 4.00 g   E. 2.00 g

17. A solution containing 6.0 g NaCl in 1500 mL of solution has a mass-volume percent concentration of
    A. 0.40 (m/v)%   B. 0.25 (m/v)%   C. 4.0 (m/v)%   D. 0.90 (m/v)%   E. 2.5 (m/v)%

For questions 18–22, indicate whether each statement describes a
    A. solution   B. colloid   C. suspension

18. _____ Contains single atoms, ions, or small molecules of solute.

19. _____ Settles out upon standing.

20. _____ Can be separated by filtering.

21. _____ Can be separated by semipermeable membranes.

22. _____ Passes through semipermeable membranes.

23. The separation of colloids from solution particles by use of a membrane is called
    A. osmosis   B. dispersion   C. dialysis   D. hemolysis   E. collodian

24. Any two solutions that have identical osmotic pressures are
    A. hypotonic   B. hypertonic   C. isotonic   D. isotopic   E. blue

25. In osmosis, water flows
    A. between solutions of equal concentrations
    B. from higher solute concentrations to lower solute concentrations
    C. from lower solute concentrations to higher solute concentrations
    D. from colloids to solutions of equal concentrations
    E. from lower solvent concentrations to higher solvent concentrations

26. A normal red blood cell will shrink when placed in a solution that is
    A. isotonic   B. hypotonic   C. hypertonic   D. colloidal   E. semitonic

27. A red blood cell undergoes hemolysis when placed in a solution that is
    A. isotonic   B. hypotonic   C. hypertonic   D. colloidal   E. semitonic

28. A solution that has the same osmotic pressure as body fluids is
    A. 0.1% NaCl   B. 0.9% NaCl   C. 5% NaCl   D. 10% glucose   E. 15% glucose

29. Which of the following is hypertonic to red blood cells?
    A. 0.5% NaCl   B. 0.9% NaCl   C. 1% glucose   D. 5% glucose   E. 10% glucose

30. Which of the following is hypotonic to red blood cells?
    A. 2.0% NaCl   B. 0.9% NaCl   C. 1% glucose   D. 5% glucose   E. 10% glucose

For questions 31–35, select the correct term from the following:
    A. isotonic   B. hypertonic   C. hypotonic   D. osmosis   E. dialysis

31. _____ a solution with a higher osmotic pressure than the blood

32. _____ a solution of 10% NaCl surrounding a red blood cell

33. _____ a 1% glucose solution

34. _____ the cleansing process of the artificial kidney

35. _____ the flow of water up the stem of a plant

36. In dialysis,
    A. dissolved salts and small molecules are separated from colloids
    B. nothing but water passes through the membrane
    C. only ions pass through a membrane
    D. two kinds of colloids are separated
    E. colloids are separated from suspensions

37. A dialyzing membrane
    A. is a semipermeable membrane
    B. allows only water and true solution particles to pass through
    C. does not allow colloidal particles to pass through
    D. all of the above
    E. none of the above

38. Which substance will remain inside a dialysis bag?
    A. water   B. NaCl   C. starch   D. glucose   E. Mg^{2+}

39. Waste removal in hemodialysis is based on
    A. concentration gradients between the bloodstream and the dialysate
    B. a pH difference between the bloodstream and the dialysate
    C. use of an osmotic membrane
    D. greater osmotic pressure in the bloodstream
    E. renal compensation

40. The moles of KOH needed to prepare 2400 mL of a 2.0 M KOH solution is
    A. 1.2 moles   B. 2.4 moles   C. 4.8 moles   D. 12 moles   E. 48 moles

41. The amount in grams of NaOH needed to prepare 7.5 mL of a 5.0 M NaOH is
    A. 1.5 g   B. 3.8 g   C. 6.7 g   D. 15 g   E. 38 g

For questions 42–44, consider a 20.0-mL sample of a solution that contains 2.0 g NaOH.

42. The % concentration of the solution is
    A. 1.0%   **B.** 4.0%   **C.** 5%   **D.** 10%   **E.** 20%

43. The number of moles of NaOH in the sample is
    A. 0.050 mole   **B.** 0.40 mole   **C.** 1.0 mole   **D.** 2.5 moles   **E.** 4.0 moles

44. The molarity of the sample is
    A. 0.10 M   **B.** 0.5 M   **C.** 1.0 M   **D.** 1.5 M   **E.** 2.5 M

45. What mass of Ag_2SO_4 is formed when 25.0 mL of 0.111-M $AgNO_3$ solution reacts?

$$2AgNO_3(aq) + H_2SO_4 \rightarrow Ag_2SO_4(s) + 2H_2O(l)$$

    A. 0.866 g   **B.** 1.74 g   **C.** 866 g   **D.** 0.433 g   **E.** 2.78 g

Answers to the Practice Test

1. B	**2.** A	**3.** A	**4.** B	**5.** C
6. E	**7.** C	**8.** E	**9.** S	**10.** N
11. N	**12.** N	**13.** C	**14.** D	**15.** E
16. E	**17.** A	**18.** A	**19.** C	**20.** C
21. B	**22.** A	**23.** C	**24.** C	**25.** C
26. C	**27.** B	**28.** B	**29.** E	**30.** C
31. B	**32.** B	**33.** C	**34.** E	**35.** D
36. A	**37.** D	**38.** C	**39.** A	**40.** C
41. A	**42.** D	**43.** A	**44.** E	**45.** D

Answers and Solutions to Selected Problems

8.1 The component present in the smaller amount is the solute; the larger amount is the solvent.
    a. sodium chloride, solute; water, solvent
    b. water, solute; ethanol, solvent
    c. oxygen, solute; nitrogen, solvent

8.3 The K^+ and I^- ions at the surface of the solid are pulled into solution by the polar water molecules, where the hydration process surrounds separate ions with water molecules.

8.5 **a.** Potassium chloride, an ionic solute, would be soluble in water (a polar solvent).
    b. Iodine, a nonpolar solute would be soluble in carbon tetrachloride (a nonpolar solvent).
    c. Sugar, a polar solute would be soluble in water, which is a polar solvent.
    d. Gasoline, a nonpolar solute, would be soluble in carbon tetrachloride, CCl_4, which is a nonpolar solvent.

8.7 The salt KF dissociates into ions when it dissolves in water. The weak acid HF exists as mostly molecules along with some ions when it dissolves in water.

8.9 Strong electrolytes dissociate into ions.

    a. $KCl(s) \xrightarrow{H_2O} K^+(aq) + Cl^-(aq)$

    b. $CaCl_2(s) \xrightarrow{H_2O} Ca^{2+}(aq) + 2Cl^-(aq)$

    c. $K_3PO_4(s) \xrightarrow{H_2O} 3K^+(aq) + PO_4^-(aq)$

    d. $Fe(NO_3)_3(s) \xrightarrow{H_2O} Fe^{3+}(aq) + 3NO_3^-(aq)$

8.11 **a.** In solution, a weak electrolyte exists mostly as molecules with a few ions.
b. Sodium bromide is a strong electrolyte and forms ions in solution.
c. A nonelectrolyte does not dissociate and forms only molecules in solution.

8.13 **a.** strong electrolyte because only ions are present in the K_2SO_4 solution
b. weak electrolyte because both ions and molecules are present in the NH_4OH solution
c. nonelectrolyte because only molecules are present in the $C_6H_{12}O_6$ solution

8.15 **a.** $1 \text{ mole K}^+ \times \dfrac{1 \text{ Eq K}^+}{1 \text{ mole K}^+} = 1 \text{ Eq K}^+$

b. $2 \text{ moles OH}^- \times \dfrac{1 \text{ Eq OH}^-}{1 \text{ mole OH}^-} = 2 \text{ Eq OH}^-$

c. $1 \text{ mole Ca}^{2+} \times \dfrac{2 \text{ Eq Ca}^+}{1 \text{ mole Ca}^{2+}} = 2 \text{ Eq Ca}^{2+}$

d. $3 \text{ moles CO}_3{}^{2-} \times \dfrac{2 \text{ Eq CO}_3{}^{2-}}{1 \text{ mole CO}_3{}^{2-}} = 6 \text{ Eq CO}_3{}^{2-}$

8.17 $1.00 \text{ L} \times \dfrac{154 \text{ mEq}}{1 \text{ L}} \times \dfrac{1 \text{ Eq}}{1000 \text{ mEq}} \times \dfrac{1 \text{ mole Na}^+}{1 \text{ Eq}} = 0.154 \text{ mole Na}^+$

$1.00 \text{ L} \times \dfrac{154 \text{ mEq}}{1 \text{ L}} \times \dfrac{1 \text{ Eq}}{1000 \text{ mEq}} \times \dfrac{1 \text{ mole Cl}^-}{1 \text{ Eq}} = 0.154 \text{ mole Cl}^-$

8.19 The total equivalents of anions must be equal to the equivalents of cations in any solution.
mEq of anions = 40. mEq Cl^-/L + 15 mEq $HPO_4{}^{2-}$/L = 55 mEq/L
mEq Na^+ = mEq anions = 55 mEq Na^+/L

8.21 **a.** The solution must be saturated because no additional solute dissolves.
b. The solution was unsaturated because the sugar cube dissolves.

8.23 **a.** It is unsaturated because 34.0 g KCl is the maximum that dissolves in 100 g H_2O at 20°C.
b. Adding 11.0 g $NaNO_3$ in 100 g H_2O. At 20°C, 88.0 g Na_2CO_3 can dissolve, so the solution is unsaturated.
c. Adding 400.0 g sugar to 125 g H_2O is 320 g in 100 g H_2O. At 20°C, only 203.9 g sugar can dissolve, which is less than 320 g. The sugar solution is saturated, and excess undissolved sugar is present.

8.25 **a.** $\dfrac{34.0 \text{ g KCl}}{100 \text{ g H}_2O} \times 200 \text{ g H}_2O = 68.0 \text{ g KCl}$ (This will dissolve at 20°C.)

At 20°C 68.0 g, KCl can dissolve in 200 g H_2O.
b. Since 80.0 g of KCl dissolves at 50°C and 68.0 g is in solution at 20°C, the mass of solid is 80.0 g − 68.0 g = 12.0 g KCl.

8.27 **a.** In general, the solubility of solid ionic solutes increases as temperature is increased.
b. The solubility of a gaseous solute (CO_2) decreases as the temperature is increased.
c. The solubility of a gaseous solute is lowered as temperature increases. When the can of warm soda is opened, more CO_2 is released, producing more spray.

8.29 **a.** Li^+ salts are soluble.
b. The Cl^- salt containing Ag^+ is insoluble.
c. Salts containing $CO_3{}^{2-}$ are usually insoluble.
d. Salts containing K^+ ions are soluble.
e. Salts containing $NO_3{}^-$ ions are soluble.

8.31 **a.** No solid forms; a salt containing K^+ and Na^+ is soluble.

b. Solid silver sulfide forms:

$2AgNO_3(aq) + K_2S(aq) \rightarrow Ag_2S(s) + 2KNO_3(aq)$

$2Ag^+(aq) + S^{2-}(aq) \rightarrow Ag_2S(s)$

c. Solid calcium sulfate forms:

$CaCl_2(aq) + Na_2SO_4(aq) \rightarrow CaSO_4(s) + 2NaCl(aq)$

$Ca^{2+}(aq) + SO_4^{2-}(aq) \rightarrow CaSO_4(s)$

8.33 A 5% (m/m) glucose solution contains 5 g glucose in 100 g of solution (5 g glucose + 95 g water), whereas a 5% (m/v) glucose solution contains 5 g glucose in 100 mL solution.

8.35 **a.** $\dfrac{25 \text{ g of KCl}}{150 \text{ g solution}} \times 100 = 17\% \text{ (m/m)}$

b. $\dfrac{12 \text{ g sugar}}{225 \text{ g solution}} \times 100 = 5.3\% \text{ (m/m)}$

8.37 **a.** $\dfrac{75 \text{ g Na}_2\text{SO}_4}{250 \text{ mL solution}} \times 100 = 30.\% \text{ (m/v)}$

b. $\dfrac{39 \text{ g sucrose}}{355 \text{ mL solution}} \times 100 = 11\% \text{ (m/v)}$

8.39 **a.** $50.0 \text{ mL solution} \times \dfrac{5.0 \text{ g KCl}}{100 \text{ mL solution}} = 2.5 \text{ g KCl}$

b. $1250 \text{ mL solution} \times \dfrac{4.0 \text{ g NH}_4\text{Cl}}{100 \text{ mL solution}} = 50. \text{ g NH}_4\text{Cl}$

8.41 $355 \text{ mL solution} \times \dfrac{22.5 \text{ mL alcohol}}{100 \text{ mL alcohol}} = 79.9 \text{ mL alcohol}$

8.43 **a.** $1 \text{ hr} \times \dfrac{100 \text{ mL solution}}{1 \text{ hr}} \times \dfrac{20 \text{ g mannitol}}{100 \text{ mL solution}} = 20 \text{ g mannitol}$

b. $15 \text{ hr} \times \dfrac{100 \text{ mL solution}}{1 \text{ hr}} \times \dfrac{20 \text{ g mannitol}}{100 \text{ mL solution}} = 300 \text{ g mannitol}$

8.45 $100 \text{ g glucose} \times \dfrac{100 \text{ mL solution}}{5 \text{ g glucose}} \times \dfrac{1 \text{ L}}{1000 \text{ mL}} = 2 \text{ L solution}$

8.47 molarity = moles of solute/L of solution

a. $\dfrac{2.0 \text{ mole glucose}}{4.0 \text{ L solution}} = 0.50 \text{ M glucose}$

b. $\dfrac{4.0 \text{ g KOH}}{2.0 \text{ L solution}} \times \dfrac{1 \text{ mole KOH}}{56.1 \text{ g KOH}} = 0.036 \text{ M KOH}$

8.49 **a.** $1.0 \text{ L solution} \times \dfrac{3.0 \text{ moles NaCl}}{1 \text{ L solution}} = 3.0 \text{ moles NaCl}$

b. $0.40 \text{ L solution} \times \dfrac{1.0 \text{ mole KBr}}{1 \text{ L solution}} = 0.40 \text{ mole KBr}$

8.51 **a.** $2.0 \, \cancel{L} \times \dfrac{1.5 \, \cancel{\text{moles NaOH}}}{1 \, \cancel{L}} \times \dfrac{40.0 \, \text{g NaOH}}{1 \, \cancel{\text{mole NaOH}}} = 120 \, \text{g NaOH}$

    b. $4.0 \, \cancel{L} \times \dfrac{0.20 \, \cancel{\text{mole KCl}}}{1 \, \cancel{L}} \times \dfrac{74.6 \, \text{g KCl}}{1 \, \cancel{\text{mole KCl}}} = 60. \, \text{g KCl}$

8.53 **a.** $3.0 \, \cancel{\text{moles NaOH}} \times \dfrac{1 \, \text{L}}{2 \, \cancel{\text{moles NaOH}}} = 1.5 \, \text{L NaO}$

    b. $15 \, \cancel{\text{moles NaCl}} \times \dfrac{1 \, \text{L}}{1.5 \, \cancel{\text{moles NaCl}}} = 10. \, \text{L NaCl}$

8.55 The concentration of a diluted solution can be calculated using the following relationship:

$$\% \, (m/v) \text{ of dilute solution} = \dfrac{\text{grams of solute}}{\text{volume dilute solution}} \times 100.$$

or molarity of dilute solution $= \dfrac{\text{moles of solute}}{\text{volume dilute solution in L}}$

    a. From the initial solution: moles solute is $2.0 \, \text{L} \times 6.0$ moles HCl/L $= 12$ moles HCl.

        Molarity of the dilute solution $= \dfrac{12 \, \text{moles HCl}}{6.0 \, \text{L}} = 2.0 \, \text{M HCl}.$

    b. The moles of solute is 12 moles NaOH/$\cancel{L} \times 0.50 \, \cancel{L} = 6.0$ moles NaOH.

        Final molarity is $\dfrac{6.0 \, \text{moles NaOH}}{3.0 \, \text{L}} = 2.0 \, \text{M NaOH}.$

    c. Initial grams of solute is $10.0 \, \cancel{\text{ml solution}} \times \dfrac{25 \, \text{g KOH}}{100 \, \cancel{\text{ml solution}}} = 2.5 \, \text{g KOH}.$

        Final % (m/v) is $\dfrac{2.5 \, \text{g KOH}}{100.0 \, \text{mL}} \times 100 = 25\% \, (m/v) \, \text{KOH}.$

    d. Initial grams of solute is $50.0 \, \cancel{\text{ml}} \times \dfrac{15 \, \text{g H}_2\text{SO}_4}{100 \, \cancel{\text{ml}}} = 7.5 \, \text{g H}_2\text{SO}_4.$

        Final % (m/v) is $\dfrac{7.5 \, \text{g H}_2\text{SO}_4}{50.0 \, \text{mL}} \times 100 = 3.0\% \, (m/v) \, \text{H}_2\text{SO}_4.$

8.57 The final volume of a diluted solution can be found by using the following relationship: $C_1V_1 = C_2V_2$, where C_1 is the concentration (M or $\%$) of the initial (concentrated) and final (dilute) solution and V_1 is the volume of the solution. Solving for V_2 gives the volume of the dilute solution.

    a. $V_2 = \dfrac{M_1V_1}{M_2} = \dfrac{6.0 \, \cancel{\text{moles/L}}}{0.20 \, \cancel{\text{mole/L}}} \times 0.0200 \, \text{L} = 0.60 \, \text{L}$

    b. $V_2 = \dfrac{\%_1V_1}{\%_2} = \dfrac{10.0 \, \cancel{\%}}{2.0 \, \cancel{\%}} \times 50.0 \, \cancel{\text{mL}} \times \dfrac{1 \, \text{L}}{1000 \, \cancel{\text{mL}}} = 0.25 \, \text{L}$

    c. $V_2 = \dfrac{M_1V_1}{M_2} = \dfrac{6.0 \, \cancel{\text{moles/L}}}{0.50 \, \cancel{\text{mole/L}}} \times 0.500 \, \text{L} = 6.0 \, \text{L}$

8.59 **a.** $50.0 \, \cancel{\text{mL}} \times \dfrac{1 \, \text{L}}{1000 \, \cancel{\text{mL}}} = 0.0500 \, \cancel{L} \times \dfrac{1.50 \, \text{moles KCl}}{1 \, \cancel{L}} = 0.0750 \, \text{mole KCl}$

      $0.0750 \, \cancel{\text{mole KCl}} \times \dfrac{1 \, \cancel{\text{mole PbCl}_2}}{2 \, \cancel{\text{moles KCl}}} \times \dfrac{278.1 \, \text{g}}{1 \, \cancel{\text{mole PbCl}_2}} = 10.4 \, \text{g PbCl}_2$

b. $50.0 \text{ mL} \times \dfrac{1 \text{ L}}{1000 \text{ mL}} = 0.0500 \text{ L} \times \dfrac{1.50 \text{ moles KCl}}{1 \text{ L}} = 0.0750 \text{ mole KCl}$

$0.0750 \text{ mole KCl} \times \dfrac{1 \text{ mole Pb(NO}_3)_2}{2 \text{ moles KCl}} \times \dfrac{1 \text{ L solution}}{2.00 \text{ moles Pb(NO}_3)_2} = 0.0188 \text{ L solution}$

$0.0188 \text{ L} \times \dfrac{1000 \text{ mL}}{1 \text{ L}} = 18.8 \text{ mL solution}$

$0.0613 \text{ mole NaOH} \times \dfrac{1 \text{ mole Ni(OH)}_2}{2 \text{ moles NaOH}} \times \dfrac{92.7 \text{ g}}{1 \text{ mole Ni(OH)}_2} = 2.84 \text{ g Ni(OH)}_2$

8.61 **a.** $15.0 \text{ g Mg} \times \dfrac{1 \text{ mole Mg}}{24.3 \text{ g Mg}} = 0.617 \text{ mole Mg}$

$0.617 \text{ mole Mg} \times \dfrac{2 \text{ moles HCl}}{1 \text{ mole Mg}} = 1.23 \text{ moles HCl} \times \dfrac{1 \text{ L}}{6.00 \text{ moles HCl}} = 0.206 \text{ L}$

$0.206 \text{ L} \times \dfrac{1000 \text{ mL}}{1 \text{ L}} = 206 \text{ mL HCl solution}$

b. $\dfrac{2.00 \text{ moles HCl}}{1 \text{ L solution}} \times 0.500 \text{ L} = 1.00 \text{ mole HCl} \times \dfrac{1 \text{ mole H}_2}{2 \text{ moles HCl}} = 0.500 \text{ mole H}_2 \text{ gas}$

8.63 **a.** A solution cannot be separated by a semipermeable membrane.
b. A suspension settles as time passes.

8.65 **a.** The 10% (m/v) starch solution has a higher osmotic pressure than pure water.
b. The water will initially flow into the starch solution to dilute solute concentration.
c. The volume of the starch solution will increase due to inflow of water.

8.67 Water flows out of the solution with the higher solvent concentration (which corresponds to a lower solute concentration) to the solution with the lower solvent concentration (which corresponds to a higher solute concentration).
a. Water flows into compartment B, which contains the 10% (m/v) glucose solution.
b. Water flows into compartment B, which contains the 8% (m/v) albumin solution.
c. Water flows into compartment B, which contains the 10% (m/v) NaCl solution.

8.69 A red blood cell has osmotic pressure of a 5% (m/v) glucose solution or a 0.9% (m/v) NaCl solution. In a hypotonic solution (lower osmotic pressure), solvent flows from the hypotonic into the red blood cell. When a red blood cell is placed in a hypertonic solution (higher osmotic pressure), solvent (water) flows from the red blood cell to the hypertonic solution. Isotonic solutions have the same osmotic pressure, and a red blood cell in an isotonic solution will not change volume because the flow of solvent into and out of the cell is equal.
a. Distilled water is a hypotonic solution when compared with a red blood cell's contents.
b. A 1% (m/v) glucose solution is a hypotonic solution.
c. A 0.9% (m/v) NaCl solution is isotonic with a red blood cell's contents.
d. A 5% (m/v) glucose solution is an isotonic solution.

8.71 Colloids cannot pass through the semipermeable dialysis membrane; water and solutions freely pass through semipermeable membranes.
a. Sodium and chloride ions will both pass through the membrane into the distilled water.
b. The amino acid alanine can pass through a dialysis membrane; the colloid starch will not.
c. Sodium and chloride ions will both be present in the water surrounding the dialysis bag; the colloid starch will not.
d. Urea will diffuse through the dialysis bag into the water.

8.73 **a.** 3 (no dissociation)
  b. 1 (some dissociation, a few ions)
  c. 2 (all ionized)

8.75 A "brine" salt water solution has a high concentration of Na^+Cl^-, which is hypertonic to the pickle. Therefore, water flows from the cucumber into the hypertonic salt solution that surrounds it. The loss of water causes the cucumber to become a wrinkled pickle.

8.77 **a.** 2 To halve the % concentration, the volume would double.
  b. 3 To go to one-fourth the % concentration, the volume would be four times the initial volume.

8.79 **a.** 2 Water will flow into the B (8%) side.
  b. 1 Water will continue to flow equally in both directions; no change in volumes.
  c. 3 Water will flow into the A (5%) side.
  d. 2 Water will flow into the B (1%) side.

8.81 Iodine is a nonpolar molecule and needs a nonpolar solvent, such as hexane. Iodine does not dissolve in water because water is a polar solvent.

8.83 $80.0 \text{ g NaCl} \times \dfrac{100 \text{ g water}}{36.0 \text{ g NaCl}} = 222 \text{ g water}$

8.85 **a.** unsaturated solution – 200 g H_2O can dissolve up to 68 g KNO_3
  b. saturated solution – this is equal to 34 g KNO_3 in 100 g H_2O
  c. saturated solution – this is equal to 58 g KNO_3 in 100 g H_2O, exceeding the 34 g KNO_3 maximum that can dissolve in 100 g H_2O at 20°C.

8.87 $\dfrac{15.5 \text{ g Na}_2\text{SO}_4}{15.5 \text{ g Na}_2\text{SO}_4 + 75.5 \text{ g water}} \times 100 = 17.0\% \text{ (m/m)}$

8.89 **a.** $24 \text{ hr} \times \dfrac{750 \text{ mL solution}}{12 \text{ hr}} \times \dfrac{4 \text{ g amino acids}}{100 \text{ mL solution}} = 60 \text{ g amino acids}$

  $24 \text{ hr} \times \dfrac{750 \text{ mL solution}}{12 \text{ hr}} \times \dfrac{25 \text{ g glucose}}{100 \text{ mL solution}} = 380 \text{ g glucose}$

  $24 \text{ hr} \times \dfrac{500 \text{ mL solution}}{12 \text{ hr}} \times \dfrac{10 \text{ g lipid}}{100 \text{ mL solution}} = 100 \text{ g lipid}$

  b. $60 \text{ g} \times \dfrac{4 \text{ kcal}}{1 \text{ g}} = 240 \text{ kcal}$

  $380 \text{ g} \times \dfrac{4 \text{ kcal}}{1 \text{ g}} = 1520 \text{ kcal}$

  $100 \text{ g lipid (fat)} \times \dfrac{9 \text{ kcal}}{1 \text{ g fat}} = 900 \text{ kcal}$

  For a total of 240 kcal + 1520 kcal + 900 kcal = (2660) = 2700 kcal per day

8.91 $4.5 \text{ mL propyl alcohol} \times \dfrac{100 \text{ mL solution}}{12 \text{ mL propyl alcohol}} = 38 \text{ mL of solution}$

8.93 $250 \text{ mL} \times \dfrac{1 \text{ L}}{1000 \text{ mL}} \times \dfrac{2.00 \text{ moles KCl}}{1 \text{ L}} \times \dfrac{74.6 \text{ g KCl}}{1 \text{ mole KCl}} = 37.3 \text{ g KCl}$

To make a 2.00-M KCl solution, weigh out 37.3 g KCl (0.500 mole) and place in a volumetric flask. Add water to dissolve the KCl and give a final volume of 0.250 L.

8.95 Mass of solution: 70.0 g solute + 130.0 g solvent = 200.0 g.

  a. $\dfrac{70.0 \text{ g HNO}_3}{(70.0 \text{ g } + 130.0 \text{ g})} = \dfrac{70.0 \text{ g}}{200.0 \text{ g}} = 35.0\%$

  b. $200.0 \text{ g solution} \times \dfrac{1 \text{ mL solution}}{1.21 \text{ g solution}} = 165 \text{ mL solution}$

  c. $\dfrac{70.0 \text{ g HNO}_3}{165 \text{ mL solution}} \times 100 = 42.4\% \text{ (m/v) HNO}_3$

  d. $\dfrac{70.0 \text{ g HNO}_3}{0.165 \text{ L solution}} \times \dfrac{1 \text{ mole HNO}_3}{63.0 \text{ g HNO}_3} = 6.73 \text{ M HNO}_3$

8.97 **a.** $2.5 \text{ L} \times \dfrac{3.0 \text{ moles Al(NO}_3)_3}{1 \text{ L}} \times \dfrac{213 \text{ g Al(NO}_3)_3}{1 \text{ mole Al(NO}_3)_3} = 1600 \text{ g Al(NO}_3)_3$

  b. $75 \text{ mL} \times \dfrac{1 \text{ L}}{1000 \text{ mL}} \times \dfrac{0.50 \text{ mole C}_6\text{H}_{12}\text{O}_6}{1 \text{ L}} \times \dfrac{180 \text{ g C}_6\text{H}_{12}\text{O}_6}{1 \text{ mole C}_6\text{H}_{12}\text{O}_6} = 6.8 \text{ g of C}_6\text{H}_{12}\text{O}_6$

8.99 **a.** $2.52 \text{ L} \times \dfrac{3.00 \text{ moles KNO}_3}{1 \text{ L}} \times \dfrac{101.1 \text{ g KNO}_3}{1 \text{ mole KNO}_3} = 764 \text{ g KNO}_3$

  b. $0.075 \text{ L} \times \dfrac{0.506 \text{ mole Na}_2\text{SO}_4}{1 \text{ L}} \times \dfrac{142.0 \text{ g Na}_2\text{SO}_4}{1 \text{ mole Na}_2\text{SO}_4} = 5.39 \text{ g Na}_2\text{SO}_4$

  c. $0.452 \text{ L} \times \dfrac{1.80 \text{ moles HCl}}{1 \text{ L}} \times \dfrac{36.5 \text{ g HCl}}{1 \text{ mole HCl}} = 2.97 \text{ g HCl}$

8.101 When solutions of $NaNO_3$ and KCl are mixed, no insoluble product forms because all of the possible combinations of salts are soluble. When KCl and $Pb(NO_3)_2$ solutions are mixed, the insoluble salt $PbCl_2$ forms.

8.103 **a.** $Ag^+(aq) + Cl^-(aq) \rightarrow AgCl(s)$
  b. none
  c. $Ba^{2+}(aq) + SO_4^{2-}(aq) \rightarrow BaSO_4(s)$

8.105 $M_1V_1 = M_2V_2$

  a. $M_2 = \dfrac{M_1V_1}{V_2} = \dfrac{(0.200 \text{ M})(25.0 \text{ mL})}{50.0 \text{ mL}} = 0.100 \text{ M NaBr}$

  b. $M_2 = \dfrac{M_1V_1}{V_2} = \dfrac{(1.20 \text{ M})(15.0 \text{ mL})}{40.0 \text{ mL}} = 0.450 \text{ M K}_2\text{SO}_4$

  c. $M_2 = \dfrac{M_1V_1}{V_2} = \dfrac{(6.00 \text{ M})(75.0 \text{ mL})}{255 \text{ mL}} = 1.76 \text{ M NaOH}$

8.107 **a.** $M_1V_1 = M_2V_2 \quad V_2 = \dfrac{M_1V_1}{M_2} = \dfrac{(5.00 \text{ M})(25.0 \text{ mL})}{2.50 \text{ M}} = 50.0 \text{ mL HCl}$

  b. $M_1V_1 = M_2V_2 \quad V_2 = \dfrac{M_1V_1}{M_2} = \dfrac{(5.00 \text{ M})(25.0 \text{ mL})}{1.00 \text{ M}} = 125 \text{ mL HCl}$

  c. $M_1V_1 = M_2V_2 \quad V_2 = \dfrac{M_1V_1}{M_2} = \dfrac{(5.00 \text{ M})(25.0 \text{ mL})}{0.500 \text{ M}} = 250. \text{ mL HCl}$

8.109 $60.0 \text{ mL Al(OH)}_3 \times \dfrac{1 \text{ L}}{1000 \text{ mL Al(OH)}_3} \times \dfrac{1.00 \text{ mole Al(OH)}_3}{1 \text{ L}} \times \dfrac{3 \text{ moles HCl}}{1 \text{ mole Al(OH)}_3}$

$\times \dfrac{1000 \text{ mL HCl}}{6.00 \text{ moles HCl}} = 30.0 \text{ mL HCl solution}$

8.111 A solution with a high salt (solute) concentration will dry flowers because water (solvent) flows out of the flowers' cells and into the salt solution to dilute the salt concentration.

8.113 Drinking seawater, which is hypertonic, will cause water to flow out of the body cells and dehydrate the body's cells.

8.115 **a.** Na^+ salts are soluble.
   b. The halide salts containing Pb^{2+} are insoluble.
   c. K^+ salts are soluble.
   d. Salts containing NH_4^+ ions are soluble.
   e. Salts containing CO_3^{2-} are usually insoluble.
   f. Salts containing PO_4^{3-} and Fe^{3+} are insoluble

8.117 **a.** Mass of NaCl is $25.50 \text{ g} - 24.10 \text{ g} = 1.40 \text{ g}$.
   Mass of solution is $36.15 \text{ g} - 24.10 \text{ g} = 12.05 \text{ g}$.

$\dfrac{1.40 \text{ g NaCl}}{12.05 \text{ g solution}} \times 100 = 11.6\% \text{ (m/m)}$

   b. $1.40 \text{ g NaCl} \times \dfrac{1 \text{ mole NaCl}}{58.5 \text{ g NaCl}} = 0.0239 \text{ mole NaCl}$

$\dfrac{0.0239 \text{ mole NaCl}}{0.0100 \text{ L}} = 2.39 \text{ M}$

   c. $M_1V_1 = M_2V_2 \quad M_2 = \dfrac{M_1V_1}{V_2} = \dfrac{(2.39 \text{ M})(10.0 \text{ mL})}{60.0 \text{ mL}} = 0.383 \text{ M}$

8.119 Mass of solution: $22.0 \text{ g solute} + 118.0 \text{ g solvent} = 140.0 \text{ g}$

   a. $\dfrac{22.0 \text{ g NaOH}}{140.0 \text{ g solution}} \times 100 = 15.7\% \text{ (m/m) NaOH}$

   b. $140.0 \text{ g solution} \times \dfrac{1 \text{ mL}}{1.15 \text{ g solution}} = 122 \text{ mL}$

   c. $22.0 \text{ g NaOH} \times \dfrac{1 \text{ mole NaOH}}{40.0 \text{ g NaOH}} \times \dfrac{1}{0.122 \text{ L}} = \dfrac{4.51 \text{ mole}}{1 \text{ L}} = 4.51 \text{ M}$

8.121 $75.0 \text{ mL} \times \dfrac{1 \text{ L}}{1000 \text{ mL}} \times \dfrac{1.50 \text{ moles}}{1 \text{ L}} \times \dfrac{102.9 \text{ g}}{1 \text{ mole}} = 11.6 \text{ g NaBr}$

8.123 $80.0 \text{ mL} \times \dfrac{1 \text{ L}}{1000 \text{ mL}} \times \dfrac{4.00 \text{ moles}}{1 \text{ L}} = 0.320 \text{ mole HNO}_3$

$0.320 \text{ mole HNO}_3 \times \dfrac{2 \text{ moles NO}}{8 \text{ moles HNO}_3} \times \dfrac{30.0 \text{ g NO}}{1 \text{ mole NO}} = 2.40 \text{ g NO}$

Chemical Equilibrium

Study Goals

- Describe how temperature, concentration, and catalysts affect the rate of a reaction.
- Use the concept of reversible reactions to explain chemical equilibrium.
- Calculate the equilibrium constant for a reversible reaction using the concentrations of reactants and products at equilibrium.
- Use an equilibrium constant to predict the extent of reaction and to calculate equilibrium concentrations.
- Use LeChâtelier's principle to describe the shifts in equilibrium concentrations when reaction conditions change.

Think About It

1. Why does a high temperature cook food faster than a low temperature?

2. Why do automobile engines now use a catalytic converter?

3. What does the size of an equilibrium constant tell you about the reactants and products?

Key Terms

Match the following terms with the statements below:

  a. activation energy   **b.** equilibrium   **c.** catalyst
  d. equilibrium constant **e.** collision theory **f.** heterogeneous equilibrium

1. _____ A substance that lowers the activation energy and increases the rate of reaction

2. _____ Equilibrium components are present in at least two different states.

3. _____ The ratio of the concentrations of products to that of the reactants raised to an exponent equal to their coefficients

4. _____ The energy required to convert reactants to products in a chemical reaction

5. _____ A reaction requires that reactants collide to form products.

6. _____ The rate of the forward reaction is equal to the rate of the reverse reaction.

Answers **1.** c   **2.** f   **3.** d
      4. a   **5.** e   **6.** b

9.1 Rates of Reaction

- The rate of a reaction is the speed at which products form.
- At higher temperatures, reaction rates increase because reactants move faster, collide more often, and produce more collisions with the required energy of activation.

- Increasing the concentration of reactants or lowering the energy of activation by adding a catalyst increases the rate of a reaction.
- The reaction rate slows when the temperature or the concentration of reactants is decreased.

◆ Learning Exercise 9.1A

Indicate the effect of each of the following on the rate of a chemical reaction:

      increase (I)   decrease (D)   no effect (N)

1. _____ adding a catalyst
2. _____ running the reaction at a lower temperature
3. _____ doubling the concentrations of the reactants
4. _____ removing a catalyst
5. _____ running the experiment in a different laboratory
6. _____ increasing the temperature
7. _____ using a container with a different shape
8. _____ using lower concentrations of reactants

Answers	**1.** I	**2.** D	**3.** I	**4.** D
	5. N	**6.** I	**7.** N	**8.** D

◆ Learning Exercise 9.1B

For the following reaction, $NO_2(g) + CO(g) \rightarrow NO(g) + CO_2(g)$, indicate the effect of each as

      increase (I)   decrease (D)   no effect (N)

1. _____ adding CO
2. _____ running the experiment on Wednesday
3. _____ removing NO_2
4. _____ adding a catalyst
5. _____ adding NO_2

Answers	**1.** I	**2.** N	**3.** D	**4.** I	**5.** I

9.2 Chemical Equilibrium

- Chemical equilibrium is achieved when the rate of the forward reaction becomes equal to the rate of the reverse reaction.
- In a system at equilibrium, there is no change in the concentrations of reactants and products.
- At equilibrium, the concentrations of reactants and products are typically greater or less than the concentrations of products; they are not usually equal.

◆ Learning Exercise 9.2

Indicate if each of the following indicates a system at equilibrium (E) or not (NE).

    a. _____ The rate of the forward reaction is faster than the rate of the reverse reaction.

    b. _____ There is no change in the concentrations of reactants and products.

c. ____ The rate of the forward reaction is equal to the rate of the reverse reaction.

d. ____ The concentrations of reactants are decreasing.

e. ____ The concentrations of products are increasing.

Answers   **a.** NE   **b.** E   **c.** E   **d.** NE   **e.** NE

9.3 Equilibrium Constants

- The equilibrium constant expression for a system at equilibrium is the ratio of the concentrations of the products to the concentrations of the reactants with the concentration of each substance raised to a power equal to its coefficient in the equation.
- For the general equation aA + bB $\rightleftarrows$ cC + dD, the equilibrium constant is written as follows:

$$K_c = \frac{[C]^c[D]^d}{[A]^a[B]^b}$$

◆ Learning Exercise 9.3A

Write the expression for the equilibrium constant (K_c) for each of the following reactions:

a. $2SO_3(g) \rightleftarrows 2SO_2(g) + O_2(g)$

b. $2NO(g) + Br_2(g) \rightleftarrows 2NOBr(g)$

c. $N_2(g) + 3H_2(g) \rightleftarrows 2NH_3(g)$

d. $2NO_2(g) \rightleftarrows N_2O_4(g)$

Answers   **a.** $K_c = \dfrac{[SO_2]^2[O_2]}{[SO_3]^2}$ **b.** $K_c = \dfrac{[NOBr]^2}{[NO]^2[Br_2]}$

c. $K_c = \dfrac{[NH_3]^2}{[N_2][H_2]^3}$ **d.** $K_c = \dfrac{[N_2O_4]}{[NO_2]^2}$

◆ Learning Exercise 9.3B

Write the expression for the equilibrium constant (K_c) for the following heterogeneous equilibria:

a. $H_2(g) + S(s) \rightleftarrows H_2S(g)$

b. $SiO_2(g) + 3C(s) \rightleftarrows SiC(s) + 2CO(g)$

c. $2PbS(s) + 3O_2(g) \rightleftarrows 2PbO(s) + 2SO_2(g)$

d. $SiH_4(g) + 2O_2(g) \rightleftarrows SiO_2(s) + 2H_2O(g)$

Answers   **a.** $K_c = \dfrac{[H_2S]}{[H_2]}$ **b.** $K_c = \dfrac{[CO]^2}{[SiO_2]}$

c. $K_c = \dfrac{[SO_2]^2}{[O_2]^3}$ **d.** $K_c = \dfrac{[H_2O]^2}{[SiH_4][O_2]^2}$

◆ Learning Exercise 9.3C

Calculate the K_c value for each of the following equilibrium concentrations:

a. $H_2(g) + I_2(g) \rightleftharpoons 2HI(g)$

$[H_2] = 0.28\ M$ $[I_2] = 0.28\ M$ $[HI] = 2.0\ M$

b. $2NO_2(g) \rightleftharpoons\ + N_2(g) + 2O_2(g)$

$[NO_2] = 0.60\ M$ $[N_2] = 0.010\ M$ $[O_2] = 0.020\ M$

c. $N_2(g) + 3H_2(g) \rightleftharpoons 2NH_3(g)$

$[N_2] = 0.50\ M$ $[H_2] = 0.20\ M$ $[NH_3] = 0.80\ M$

Answers   **a.** $K_c = \dfrac{[HI]^2}{[H_2][I_2]} = \dfrac{[2.0]^2}{[0.28][0.28]} = 51$

b. $K_c = \dfrac{[N_2][O_2]^2}{[NO_2]^2} = \dfrac{[0.010][0.020]^2}{[0.60]^2} = 1.1 \times 10^{-5}$

c. $K_c = \dfrac{[NH_3]^2}{[N_2][H_2]^3} = \dfrac{[0.80]^2}{[0.50][0.20]^3} = 1.6 \times 10^2$

9.4 Using Equilibrium Constants

- A large K_c results when a reaction favors products; a small K_c results when a reaction favors reactants.
- The concentration of a component in an equilibrium mixture is calculated from the K_c and the concentrations of all of the other components.

◆ Learning Exercise 9.4A

Consider the reaction $2NOBr(g) \rightleftarrows 2NO(g) + Br_2(g)$.

a. Write the expression for the equilibrium constant for the reaction.

b. If the equilibrium constant is 2×10^3, does the equilibrium mixture contain mostly reactants, mostly products, or both reactants and products and favor the products or the reactants? Explain.

Answers   **a.** $K_c = \dfrac{[NO]^2[Br_2]}{[NOBr]^2}$

        b. A large K_{eq} (>1) means that the mixture contains mostly products.

◆ Learning Exercise 9.4B

Consider the reaction $2HI(g) \rightleftarrows H_2(g) + I_2(g)$.

a. Write the expression for the equilibrium constant for the reaction.

b. If the equilibrium constant is 1.6×10^{-2}, does the equilibrium mixture contain mostly reactants, mostly products, or both reactants and products and favor the products or the reactants? Explain.

Answers   **a.** $K_c = \dfrac{[H_2][I_2]}{[HI]^2}$

        b. A small K_c (<1) means that the mixture contains mostly reactants.

◆ Learning Exercise 9.4C

Calculate the concentration of the indicated component for each of the following equilibrium systems:

a. $PCl_5(g) \rightleftarrows PCl_3(g) + Cl_2(g)$ $K_c = 1.2 \times 10^{-2}$

$[PCl_5] = 2.50\ M$ $[PCl_3] = 0.50\ M$ $[Cl_2] = ?$

b. $CO(g) + H_2O(g) \rightleftharpoons CO_2(g) + H_2(g)$ $K_c = 1.6$

$[CO] = 1.0$ M $[H_2O] = 0.80$ M $[CO_2] = ?$ $[H_2] = 1.2$ M

Answers

a. $K_c = \dfrac{[PCl_3][Cl_2]}{[PCl_5]}$ $[Cl_2] = \dfrac{K_c[PCl_5]}{[PCl_3]} = \dfrac{1.2 \times 10^{-2}\,[2.5]}{[0.50]} = 0.060$ M $= 6.0 \times 10^{-2}$ M

b. $K_c = \dfrac{[CO_2][H_2]}{[CO][H_2O]}$ $[CO_2] = \dfrac{K_c[CO][H_2O]}{[H_2]} = \dfrac{1.6[1.0][0.80]}{[1.2]} = 1.1$ M

9.5 Changing Equilibrium Conditions: LeChâtelier's Principle

- A change in the concentration of a reactant or product, temperature, or volume shifts the equilibrium in the direction to relieve the stress.

◆ Learning Exercise 9.5A

Identify the effect of each of the following on the equilibrium of the following reaction:

$$N_2(g) + O_2(g) + 180 \text{ kJ} \rightleftharpoons 2NO(g)$$

A. shift towards products	**B.** shift towards reactants	**C.** no change

1. _____ adding $O_2(g)$ **2.** _____ removing $N_2(g)$

3. _____ removing $NO(g)$ **4.** _____ adding heat

5. _____ reducing the volume of the container   **6.** _____ increasing the volume

Answers   **1.** A   **2.** B   **3.** A   **4.** A   **5.** A   **6.** B

◆ Learning Exercise 9.5B

Identify the effect of the each of the following on the equilibrium of the following reaction:

$$2NOBr(g) \rightleftharpoons 2NO(g) + Br_2(g) + 81 \text{ kcal}$$

A. shift towards products	**B.** shift towards reactants	**C.** no change

1. _____ adding $NO(g)$ **2.** _____ removing $Br_2(g)$

3. _____ removing $NOBr(g)$ **4.** _____ adding heat

5. _____ lowering the temperature   **6.** _____ increasing the volume

Answers   **1.** B   **2.** A   **3.** B   **4.** B   **5.** A   **6.** A

Checklist for Chapter 9

You are ready to take the self-test for chapter 9. Be sure that you have accomplished the following learning goals for this chapter. If you are not sure, review the section listed at the end of the goal. Then apply your new skills and understanding to the self-test.

After studying chapter 9, I can successfully:

_____ Describe the factors that increase or decrease the rate of a reaction (9.1).

_____ Write the forward and reverse reactions of a reversible reaction (9.2).

_____ Explain how equilibrium occurs when the rate of a forward reaction is equal to the rate of a reverse reaction (9.2).

_____ Write the equilibrium constant expression for a reaction system at equilibrium (9.3).

_____ Calculate the equilibrium constant from the equilibrium concentrations (9.3).

_____ Use the equilibrium constant to determine whether a reaction favors the reactants or products (9.4).

_____ Use the equilibrium constant to determine the equilibrium concentration of a component in the reaction (9.4).

_____ Use Le Châtelier's Principle to describe the shift in a system at equilibrium when stress is applied to the system (9.5).

Practice Test for Chapter 9

1. The number of molecular collisions increases when
   A. more reactants are added
   B. products are removed
   C. the energy of collision is below the energy of activation
   D. the reaction temperature is lowered
   E. the reacting molecules have an incorrect orientation upon impact

2. The energy of activation is lowered when
   A. more reactants are added
   B. products are removed
   C. a catalyst is used
   D. the reaction temperature is lowered
   E. the reaction temperature is raised

3. Food deteriorates more slowly in a refrigerator because
   A. more reactants are added
   B. products are removed
   C. the energy of activation is higher
   D. fewer collisions have the energy of activation
   E. collisions they have the wrong orientation upon impact

4. A reaction reaches equilibrium when
   A. the rate of the forward reaction is faster than the rate of the reverse reaction
   B. the rate of the reverse reaction is faster than the rate of the forward reaction
   C. the concentrations of reactants and products are changing
   D. fewer collisions have the energy of activation
   E. the rate of the forward reaction is equal to the rate of the reverse reaction

5. The equilibrium constant expression for the following reaction is

$$2NOCl(g) \rightleftarrows 2NO(g) + Cl_2(g)$$

A. $\dfrac{[NO][Cl_2]}{[NOCl]}$ **B.** $\dfrac{[NOCl_2]^2}{[NO]^2[Cl_2]}$ **C.** $\dfrac{[NOCl_2]}{[NO][Cl_2]}$

D. $\dfrac{[NO]^2Cl_2]}{[NOCl]}$ **E.** $\dfrac{[NO]^2[Cl_2]}{[NOCl]^2}$

6. The equilibrium constant expression for the following reaction is

$$MgO(s) \rightleftarrows CO_2(g) + MgCO_3(s)$$

A. $[CO_2]$ **B.** $\dfrac{[CO_2][MgCO_3]}{[MgO]}$ **C.** $\dfrac{[MgO]}{[CO_2][MgCO_3]}$

D. $\dfrac{1}{[CO_2]}$ **E.** $\dfrac{[CO_2]}{[MgO]}$

7. The equilibrium constant expression for the following reaction is

$$2PbS(s) + 3O_2(g) \rightleftarrows 2PbO(s) + 2SO_2(g)$$

A. $\dfrac{[PbO][SO_2]}{[PbS][O_2]}$ **B.** $\dfrac{[PbO]^2[SO_2]^2}{[PbS]^2[O_2]^3}$ **C.** $\dfrac{[SO_2]^2}{[O_2]^3}$

D. $\dfrac{[SO_2]}{[O_2]}$ **E.** $\dfrac{[O_2]^3}{[SO_2]^2}$

8. The equilibrium equation that has the following equilibrium constant expression is

$$\dfrac{[H_2S]^2}{[H_2]^2[S_2]}$$

A. $H_2S(g) \rightleftarrows H_2(g) + S_2(g)$
B. $2H_2S(g) \rightleftarrows H_2(g) + S_2(g)$
C. $2H_2(g) + S_2(g) \rightleftarrows 2H_2S(g)$
D. $2H_2S(g) \rightleftarrows 2H_2(g)$
E. $2H_2(g) \rightleftarrows 2H_2S(g)$

9. The value of the equilibrium constant for the following equilibrium is

$$COBr_2(g) \rightleftarrows CO(g) + Br_2(g)$$

$[COBr_2] = 0.93$ M $[CO] = [Br_2] = 0.42$ M
A. 0.19   **B.** 0.39   **C.** 0.42
D. 2.2   **E.** 5.3

10. The value of the equilibrium constant for the following equilibrium is

$$2NO(g) + O_2(g) \rightleftarrows 2NO_2(g)$$

$[NO] = 2.7$ M $[O_2] = 1.0$ $[NO_2] = 3.0$ M
A. 0.81   **B.** 1.1   **C.** 1.2
D. 8.1   **E.** 9.0

11. Calculate the $[PCl_5]$ for the decomposition of PCl_5 that has a $K_c = 0.050$.

$$PCl_5(g) \rightleftarrows PCl_3(g) + Cl_2(g)$$

$[PCl_3] = [Cl_2] = 0.20$ M
A. 0.01 M   **B.** 0.050 M   **C.** 0.20 M
D. 0.40 M   **E.** 0.80 M

12. The reaction that has a much greater concentration of products at equilibrium has a K_c value of
   A. 1.6×10^{-15} **B.** 2×10^{-11} **C.** 1.2×10^{-5}
   D. 3×10^{-3} **E.** 1.4×10^{5}

13. The reaction that has a much greater concentration of reactants at equilibrium has a K_c value of
   A. 1.1×10^{-11} **B.** 2×10^{-2} **C.** 1.2×10^{2}
   D. 2×10^{4} **E.** 1.3×10^{12}

14. The reaction that has about the same concentration of reactant and products at equilibrium has a K_c value of
   A. 1.4×10^{-12} **B.** 2×10^{8} **C.** 1.2
   D. 3×10^{2} **E.** 1.3×10^{7}

For questions 15–19, indicate how each of the following affects the equilibrium of the following reaction:

   $PCl_5(g) + \text{Heat} \rightleftarrows PCl_3(g) + Cl_2(g)$

   A. shifts toward products   **B.** shifts toward reactants   **C.** no change

15. _____ add more Cl_2 **16.** _____ cool the reaction   **17.** _____ remove some PCl_3

18. _____ add more PCl_5 **19.** _____ remove some PCl_5

For questions 20–24, indicate whether the equilibrium will

   A. shift toward products   **B.** shift toward reactants   **C.** not change

   $2NO(g) + O_2(g) \rightleftarrows 2NO_2(g) + \text{Heat}$

20. _____ add more NO   **21.** _____ increase temperature

22. _____ add a catalyst   **23.** _____ add some O_2

24. _____ remove NO_2

Answers to the Practice Test

1. A	**2.** C	**3.** D	**4.** E	**5.** E
6. A	**7.** C	**8.** C	**9.** A	**10.** C
11. E	**12.** E	**13.** A	**14.** C	**15.** B
16. B	**17.** A	**18.** A	**19.** B	**20.** A
21. B	**22.** C	**23.** A	**24.** A	

Answers and Solutions to Selected Text Problems

9.1   **a.** The rate of a reaction relates the speed at which reactants are transformed into products.
   b. Because fewer reactants will have the energy necessary to proceed to products (the activation energy) at refrigerator temperature than at room temperature, the rate of formation of mold will be slower at a cooler temperature in a refrigerator.

9.3   Adding Br_2 increases the concentration of reactants, which allows increases in the number of collisions that take place between the reactants.

9.5   **a.** Adding more reactant increases the reaction rate.
   b. Increasing the temperature increases the number of collisions with the energy of activation, which increases the rate of reaction.
   c. Adding a catalyst increases the reaction rate.
   d. Removing a reactant decreases the reaction rate.

9.7 If a reaction takes place in both a forward and reverse direction, it is called a reversible reaction.

9.9 **a.** Broken glass cannot be put back together; it is not reversible.
    b. In this physical process, heat melts the solid form of water, whereas removing heat can change liquid water back to solid. It is reversible.
    c. A pan is warmed when heated and cooled when heat is removed; it is reversible.

9.11 In the expression for K_c, the products are divided by the reactants with each concentration raised to a power that equals the coefficient in the equation

    a. $K_c = \dfrac{[CS_2][H_2]^4}{[CH_4][H_2S]^2}$ **b.** $K_c = \dfrac{[N_2][O_2]}{[NO]^2}$ **c.** $K_c = \dfrac{[CS_2][O_2]^4}{[SO_3]^2[CO_2]}$

9.13 **a.** only one state (gases) is present; homogeneous
    b. solid and gaseous states; heterogeneous
    c. only one state (gases) is present; homogeneous
    d. gas and liquid states; heterogeneous

9.15 **a.** $K_c = \dfrac{[O_2]^3}{[O_3]^2}$ **b.** $K_c = [CO_2][H_2O]$

    c. $K_c = \dfrac{[CO][H_2]^3}{[H_2O][CH_4]}$ **d.** $K_c = \dfrac{[Cl_2]^2}{[HCl]^4[O_2]}$

9.17 $K_c = \dfrac{[NO_2]^2}{[N_2O_4]} = \dfrac{[0.21]^2}{[0.030]} = 1.5$

9.19 $K_c = \dfrac{[H_2O][CH_4]}{[H_2]^3[CO]} = \dfrac{[2.0][1.8]}{[0.30]^3[0.51]} = 260$

9.21 **a.** A large K_c indicates that the equilibrium mixture contains mostly products.
    b. A K_c of about 1 indicates that the equilibrium mixture contains both reactants and products.
    c. A small K_c indicates that the equilibrium mixture contains mostly reactants.

9.23 $K_c = \dfrac{[HI]^2}{[H_2][I_2]}$

Rearrange K_c to solve for $[H_2]$ and substitute concentrations to calculate $[H_2]$.

$[H_2] = \dfrac{[HI]^2}{K_c\,[I_2]} = \dfrac{[0.030]^2}{[54][0.015]} = 1.1 \times 10^{-3}\,M$

9.25 $K_c = \dfrac{[Br_2][NO]^2}{[NOBr]^2}$

Rearrange K_c to solve for $[NOBr]$.

$[NOBr]^2 = \dfrac{[Br_2][NO]^2}{K_c} = \dfrac{[1.0][2.0]^2}{[2.0]} = 2.0$

$[NOBr] = \sqrt{2.0} = 1.4\,M$

9.27 **a.** When more reactant is added to an equilibrium mixture, the product/reactant ratio is initially less than K_c.
   b. According to Le Châtelier's Principle, equilibrium is reestablished when the forward reaction shifts to products to make the product/reactant ratio equal the K_c again.

9.29 **a.** Adding more reactant shifts equilibrium to products.
   b. Adding more product shifts equilibrium to reactants.
   c. Adding heat, a reactant, shifts equilibrium to products.
   d. Decreasing volume favors products with fewer moles.
   e. A catalyst does not shift equilibrium.

9.31 **a.** Adding more reactant shifts equilibrium to products.
   b. Adding heat, a reactant, shifts equilibrium to products.
   c. Removing product shifts equilibrium to products.
   d. A catalyst does not shift equilibrium.
   e. Removing reactant shifts equilibrium to reactants.

9.33 There are mostly reactants and a few products, which gives a small equilibrium constant.

9.35 **a.** There are more products, which means that heat must be reduced; T_2 is lower than T_1.
   b. Because the equilibrium mixture at T_2 has more products, the K_c for T_2 is larger than the K_c for the equilibrium mixture at T_1.

9.37 **a.** Adding heat, a product, shifts equilibrium towards reactants.
   b. Decreasing volume favors products with fewer moles.
   c. Adding a catalyst does not shift equilibrium.
   d. Adding a reactant shifts equilibrium towards products.

9.39 **a.** $K_c = \dfrac{[CO_2][H_2O]^2}{[CH_4][O_2]^2}$

   b. $K_c = \dfrac{[N_2]^2\,[H_2O]^6}{[NH_3]^4[O_2]^3}$

   c. $K_c = \dfrac{[CH_4]}{[H_2]^2}$

9.41 **a.** An equilibrium mixture with a large K_c consists of mostly products.
   b. An equilibrium mixture with a K_c of about 1 consists of both products and reactants.
   c. An equilibrium mixture with a small K_c consists of mostly reactants.

9.43 The numerator in the K_c expression gives the products in the equation, and the denominator gives the reactants.
   a. $SO_2Cl_2(g) \rightleftarrows SO_2(g) + Cl_2(g)$
   b. $Br_2(g) + Cl_2(g) \rightleftarrows 2BrCl(g)$
   c. $CO(g) + 3H_2(g) \rightleftarrows CH_4(g) + H_2O(g)$
   d. $2O_2(g) + 2NH_3(g) \rightleftarrows N_2O(g) + 3H_2O(g)$

9.45 **a.** $K_c = \dfrac{[N_2][H_2]^3}{[NH_3]^2}$

   b. $K_c = \dfrac{[3.0][0.50]^3}{[0.20]^2} = 9.4$

9.47 $K_c = \dfrac{[N_2O_4]}{[NO_2]^2}$ Rearranging K_c: $[N_2O_4] = K_c[NO_2]^2$

$[N_2O_4] = 5.0[0.50]^2 = 1.3 \text{ M}$

9.49 a. Adding a reactant shifts equilibrium to products.
b. Adding a product shifts equilibrium to reactants.
c. Adding a reactant shifts equilibrium to products.
d. Adding a product shifts equilibrium to reactants.

9.51 Decreasing the volume of an equilibrium mixture shifts the equilibrium to the side of the reaction that has the fewer number of moles. No shift occurs when there are an equal number of moles on both sides of the equation.
a. Three moles gas on the reactant side and two moles gas on the product side shifts equilibrium to products.
b. Two moles gas on the reactant side and three moles gas on the product side shifts equilibrium to reactants.
c. Six moles gas on reactant side and zero moles gas on the product side shifts equilibrium to products.
d. Four moles gas on the reactant side and five moles gas on the product side shifts equilibrium to reactants.

9.53 a. A small K_c indicates that the equilibrium mixture contains mostly reactants.
b. A large K_c indicates that the equilibrium mixture contains mostly products.

9.55 a. $\dfrac{[PCl_3][Cl_2]}{[PCl_5]} = \dfrac{[0.050 \text{ M}][0.050 \text{ M}]}{[0.10 \text{ M}]} = 0.025$, which is not equal to K_c (0.0042). This mixture is not at equilibrium.
b. Since 0.025 is greater than K_c, the new equilibrium mixture must have more PCl_5 and less Cl_2 and PCl_3; the reaction will proceed in the reverse direction.

9.57 a. $K_c = \dfrac{[PCl_3][Cl_2]}{[PCl_5]}$

b. Since PCl_3 and Cl_2 are formed in a 1:1 ratio, 0.16 mole Cl_2 is formed and 0.16 mole PCl_5 is reacted, leaving $1.00 - 0.16 = 0.84$ mole PCl_5.
At equilibrium, the concentrations are $[PCl_3] = [Cl_2] = 0.16 \text{ M}$, $[PCl_5] = 0.84 \text{ M}$.

c. $K_c = \dfrac{[PCl_3][Cl_2]}{[PCl_5]} = \dfrac{[0.16][0.16]}{[0.84]} = 0.030$

d. When Cl_2 is added to the equilibrium mixture, the shift will be toward the reactant and $[PCl_5]$ will increase.

9.59 a. $K_c = \dfrac{[CO]^2}{[CO_2]} = \dfrac{[0.030]^2}{[0.060]} = 0.015$

b. If more CO_2 is added, the reaction will shift toward the products.
c. If the container volume is decreased, the equilibrium will shift to the side with the least number of moles, which is the reactant side.

10

Acids and Bases

Study Goals

- Describe the characteristics of acids and bases.
- Identify conjugate acid–base pairs in Brønsted-Lowry acids and bases.
- Use the ion product of water to calculate $[H_3O^+]$, $[OH^-]$, and pH.
- Write balanced equations for reactions of an acid with metals, carbonates, and bases.
- Predict if a salt solution will be acidic, basic, or neutral.
- Calculate the concentration of an acid solution from titration data.
- Describe the function of a buffer.

Think About It

1. Why do lemon, grapefruit, and vinegar taste sour?

2. What do antacids do? What are some bases listed on the labels of antacids?

3. Why are some aspirin products buffered?

Key Terms

    A. acid   **B.** base   **C.** pH   **D.** neutralization   **E.** buffer

1. _____ a substance that forms hydroxide ions (OH^-) in water and/or accepts protons (H^+)

2. _____ a reaction between an acid and a base to form a salt and water

3. _____ a substance that forms hydrogen ions (H^+) in water

4. _____ a mixture of a weak acid (or base) and its salt that maintains the pH of a solution

5. _____ a measure of the acidity (H_3O^+) of a solution

Answers   **1.** B   **2.** D   **3.** A   **4.** E   **5.** C

10.1 Acids and Bases

- In water, an Arrhenius acid produces H_3O^+ and an Arrhenius base produces OH^-.
- According to the Brønsted-Lowry theory, acids are proton (H^+) donors and bases are proton acceptors.
- Protons form hydronium ions, H_3O^+, in water when they bond to polar water molecules.

◆ **Learning Exercise 10.1A**

Indicate if the following characteristics describe an (A) acid or (B) base.

1. ____ turns blue litmus red　　　　　　　2. ____ tastes sour

3. ____ contains more OH^- ions than H_3O^+ ions　　4. ____ neutralizes bases

5. ____ tastes bitter　　　　　　　　　　6. ____ turns red litmus blue

7. ____ contains more H_3O^+ ions than OH^- ions　　8. ____ neutralizes acids

Answers　　1. A　　2. A　　3. B　　4. A
　　　　　　5. B　　6. B　　7. A　　8. B

◆ **Learning Exercise 10.1B**

Fill in the blanks with the formula or name of an acid or base:

1. HCl _____

2. ____ sodium hydroxide

3. ____ sulfurous acid

4. ____ nitric acid

5. $Ca(OH)_2$ _____

6. H_2CO_3 _____

7. $Al(OH)_3$ _____

8. ____ potassium hydroxide

Answers　　1. hydrochloric acid　2. NaOH　　　3. H_2SO_3
　　　　　　4. HNO_3　　　　5. calcium hydroxide　6. carbonic acid
　　　　　　7. aluminum hydroxide　8. KOH

10.2 Brønsted-Lowry Acids and Bases

- According to the Brønsted-Lowry theory, acids donate protons (H^+) to bases.
- Conjugate acid–base pairs are molecules or ions linked by the loss and gain of a proton.

Study Note

Identify the conjugate acid–base pairs in the following equation:

$$HCl + H_2O \rightarrow H_3O^+ + Cl^-$$

Solution: HCl (proton donor) and Cl^- (proton acceptor)
　　　　　 H_2O (proton acceptor) and H_3O^+ (proton donor)

◆ Learning Exercise 10.2A

Complete the following conjugate acid–base pairs:

Conjugate Acid	Conjugate Base
1. H_2O	____
2. HSO_4^-	____
3. ____	F^-
4. ____	CO_3^{2-}
5. HNO_3	____
6. NH_4^+	____
7. ____	HS^-
8. ____	$H_2PO_4^-$

Answers   1. OH^- 2. SO_4^{2-} 3. HF 4. HCO_3^-
5. NO_3^- 6. NH_3 7. H_2S 8. H_3PO_4

◆ Learning Exercise 10.2B

Identify the conjugate acid–base pairs in each of the following:

1. $HF + H_2O \rightleftarrows H_3O^+ + F^-$
2. $NH_4^+ + SO_4^{2-} \rightleftarrows NH_3^+ + HSO_4^-$
3. $NH_3 + H_2O \rightleftarrows NH_4^+ + OH^-$
4. $HNO_3 + OH^- \rightleftarrows H_2O^+ + NO_3^-$

Answers   1. HF/F^- and H_2O/H_3O^+ 2. NH_4/NH_3 and SO_4^{2-}/HSO_4^-
3. NH_3/NH_4^+ and H_2O/OH^- 4. HNO_3/NO_3^- and OH^-/H_2O

10.3 Strengths of Acids and Bases

- In aqueous solution, a strong acid donates nearly all of its protons to water whereas a weak acid donates only a small percentage of protons to water.
- Most hydroxides of Groups 1A (1) and 2A (2) are strong bases, which dissociate nearly completely in water. In an aqueous ammonia solution, NH_3, which is a weak base, accepts only a small percentage of protons to form NH_4^+.

Study Note

Only six common acids are strong acids; other acids are considered as weak acids.

HCl	HNO_3
HBr	H_2SO_4 (first H)
HI	$HClO_4$

Example: Is H_2S a strong or weak acid?
Solution: H_2S is a weak acid because it is not one of the six strong acids.

◆ Learning Exercise 10.3A

Identify each of the following as a strong or weak acid or base:

1. HNO_3 _____   2. H_2CO_3 _____   3. $H_2PO_4^-$ _____

4. NH_3 _____   5. $LiOH$ _____   6. H_3BO_3 _____

7. $Ca(OH)_2$ _____   8. H_2SO_4 _____

Answers   1. strong acid   2. weak acid   3. weak acid   4. weak base
                 5. strong base   6. weak acid   7. strong base   8. strong acid

◆ Learning Exercise 10.3B

Using Table 10.3, identify the stronger acid in each of the following pairs of acids:

1. HCl or H_2CO_3 _____   2. HNO_2 or HCN _____

3. H_2S or HBr _____   4. H_2SO_4 or HSO_4^- _____

5. HF or H_3PO_4 _____

Answers   1. HCl 2. HNO_2 3. HBr 4. H_2SO_4 5. H_3PO_4

◆ Learning Exercise 10.3C

Write the equation for the dissociation and the acid dissociation constant for the ionization of the following weak acids:

1. HCN 2. HNO_2

Answers   1. $HCN + H_2O \rightleftarrows H_3O^+ + CN^-$

$$K_a = \frac{[H_3O^+][CN^-]}{[HCN]}$$

2. $HNO_2 + H_2O \rightleftarrows H_3O^+ + NO_2^-$

$$K_a = \frac{[H_3O^+][NO_2^-]}{[HNO_2]}$$

10.4 Ionization of Water

- In pure water, a few water molecules transfer a proton to other water molecules, producing small but equal amounts of $[H_3O^+]$ and $[OH^-] = 1 \times 10^{-7}$ moles/L.
- K_w, the ion product $[H_3O^+][OH^-] = [1 \times 10^{-7}][1 \times 10^{-7}] = 1 \times 10^{-14}$, applies to all aqueous solutions.
- In acidic solutions, the $[H_3O^+]$ is greater than the $[OH^-]$. In basic solutions, the $[OH^-]$ is greater than the $[H_3O^+]$.

Study Note

Example: What is the $[H_3O^+]$ in a solution that has $[OH^-] = 2.0 \times 10^{-9}$ M?

Solution: $[H_3O^+] = \dfrac{1.0 \times 10^{-14}}{2.0 \times 10^{-9}} = 5.0 \times 10^{-6}$ M

◆ Learning Exercise 10.4

Write the $[H_3O^+]$ when the $[OH^-]$ has the following values:

    a. $[OH^-] = 1.0 \times 10^{-10}$ M $[H_3O^+] =$

    b. $[OH^-] = 2.0 \times 10^{-5}$ M $[H_3O^+] =$

    c. $[OH^-] = 4.5 \times 10^{-7}$ M $[H_3O^+] =$

    d. $[OH^-] = 8.0 \times 10^{-4}$ M $[H_3O^+] =$

    e. $[OH^-] = 5.5 \times 10^{-8}$ M $[H_3O^+] =$

Answers   **a.** 1.0×10^{-4} M   **b.** 5.0×10^{-10} M   **c.** 2.2×10^{-8} M
                     d. 1.3×10^{-11} M   **e.** 1.8×10^{-7} M

10.5 The pH Scale

- The pH scale is a range of numbers from 0 to 14 related to the $[H_3O^+]$ of the solution.
- A neutral solution has a pH of 7. In acidic solutions, the pH is below 7, and in basic solutions, the pH is above 7.
- Mathematically, pH is the negative logarithm of the hydronium ion concentration:

$$pH = -\log [H_3O^+]$$

◆ Learning Exercise 10.5A

State whether the following pH values are acidic, basic, or neutral:

    1. _____ plasma, pH = 7.4   **2.** _____ soft drink, pH = 2.8

    3. _____ maple syrup, pH = 6.8   **4.** _____ beans, pH = 5.0

    5. _____ tomatoes, pH = 4.2   **6.** _____ lemon juice, pH = 2.2

    7. _____ saliva, pH = 7.0   **8.** _____ eggs, pH = 7.8

    9. _____ lime, pH = 12.4   **10.** _____ strawberries, pH = 3.0

Answers   **1.** basic   **2.** acidic   **3.** acidic   **4.** acidic   **5.** acidic
                     6. acidic   **7.** neutral   **8.** basic   **9.** basic   **10.** acidic

◆ **Learning Exercise 10.5B**

Calculate the pH of each of the following solutions:

a. $[H_3O^+] = 1 \times 10^{-8}$ M ____   **b.** $[OH^-] = 1 \times 10^{-12}$ M ____

c. $[H_3O^+] = 1 \times 10^{-3}$ M ____   **d.** $[OH^-] = 1 \times 10^{-10}$ M ____

Answers   **a.** 8.0   **b.** 2.0   **c.** 3.0   **d.** 4.0

◆ **Learning Exercise 10.5C**

Calculate the pH of each of the following solutions:

a. $[H_3O^+] = 1.0 \times 10^{-3}$ M   **b.** $[OH^-] = 1.9 \times 10^{-6}$ M

c. $[H_3O^+] = 1 \times 10^{-8}$ M   **d.** $[OH^-] = 1 \times 10^{-10}$ M

Answers   **a.** 3.0   **b.** 8.0   **c.** 8.0   **d.** 4.0

◆ **Learning Exercise 10.5D**

Complete the following table:

	$[H_3O^+]$	$[OH^-]$	pH
a.	_____	1×10^{-12} M	_____
b.	_____	_____	8.0
c.	1×10^{-10} M	_____	_____
d.	_____	_____	7.0
e.	_____	_____	1.0

Answers	$[H_3O^+]$	$[OH^-]$	pH
a.	1×10^{-2} M	1×10^{-12} M	2.0
b.	1×10^{-8} M	1×10^{-6} M	8.0
c.	1×10^{-10} M	1×10^{-4} M	10.0
d.	1×10^{-7} M	1×10^{-7} M	7.0
e.	1×10^{-1} M	1×10^{-13} M	1.0

10.6 Reactions of Acids and Bases

- Acids react with many metals to yield hydrogen gas (H_2) and the salt of the metal.
- Acids react with carbonates and bicarbonates to yield CO_2, H_2O, and the salt of the metal.
- Acids neutralize bases in a reaction that produces water and a salt.
- The net ionic equation for any neutralization is $H^+ + OH^- \rightarrow H_2O$.

- In a balanced neutralization equation, an equal number of moles of H^+ and OH^- must react.
- The concentration of an acid can be determined by titration.

◆ Learning Exercise 10.6A

Complete and balance each of the following reactions of acids:

1. _____ $Zn(s)$ + _____ $HCl \rightarrow$ _____ $ZnCl_2$ + _____

2. _____ HCl + _____ $Li_2CO_3 \rightarrow$ _____ + _____

3. _____ HCl + _____ $NaHCO_3 \rightarrow$ _____ CO_2 + _____ H_2O + _____ $NaCl$

4. _____ Al + _____ $H_2SO_4 \rightarrow$ _____ $Al_2(SO_4)_3$ + _____

Answers
1. $1 Zn(s) + 2 HCl \rightarrow 1 ZnCl_2 + H_2$
2. $2 HCl + 1 Li_2CO_3 \rightarrow 1 CO_2 + 1 H_2O + 2 LiCl$
3. $1 HCl + 1 NaHCO_3 \rightarrow 1 CO_2 + 1 H_2O + 1 NaCl$
4. $2 Al + 3 H_2SO_4 \rightarrow 1 Al_2(SO_4)_3 + 3 H_2$

◆ Learning Exercise 10.6B

Balance each of the following neutralization reactions:

1. _____ $NaOH$ + _____ $H_2SO_4 \rightarrow$ _____ Na_2SO_4 + _____ H_2O

2. _____ $Mg(OH)_2$ + _____ $HCl \rightarrow$ _____ $MgCl_2$ + _____ H_2O

3. _____ $Al(OH)_3$ + _____ $HNO_3 \rightarrow$ _____ $Al(NO_3)_3$ + _____ H_2O

4. _____ $Ca(OH)_2$ + _____ $H_3PO_4 \rightarrow$ _____ $Ca_3(PO_4)_2$ + _____ H_2O

Answers
1. $2 NaOH + 1 H_2SO_4 \rightarrow 1 Na_2SO_4 + 2 H_2O$
2. $1 Mg(OH)_2 + 2 HCl \rightarrow 1 MgCl_2 + 2 H_2O$
3. $1 Al(OH)_3 + 3 HNO_3 \rightarrow 1 Al(NO_3)_3 + 3 H_2O$
4. $3 Ca(OH)_2 + 2 H_3PO_4 \rightarrow 1 Ca_3(PO_4)_2 + 6 H_2O$

◆ Learning Exercise 10.6C

Complete each of the following neutralization reactions and then balance:

a. _____ KOH + _____ $H_3PO_4 \rightarrow$ _____ + _____ H_2O

b. _____ $NaOH$ + _____ $\rightarrow$ _____ Na_2SO_4 + _____

c. _____ + _____ $\rightarrow$ _____ $AlCl_3$ + _____

d. _____ + _____ $\rightarrow$ _____ $Fe_2(SO_4)_3$ + _____

Answers
a. $3 KOH + 1 H_3PO_4 \rightarrow K_3PO_4 + 3 H_2O$
b. $2 NaOH + 1 H_2SO_4 \rightarrow 1 Na_2SO_4 + 2 H_2O$
c. $Al(OH)_3 + 3 HCl \rightarrow 1 AlCl_3 + 3 H_2O$
d. $2 Fe(OH)_3 + 3 H_2SO_4 \rightarrow 1 Fe_2(SO_4)_3 + 6 H_2O$

◆ **Learning Exercise 10.6D**

1. A 24.6-ml sample of HCl reacts with 33.0 ml of 0.222-M NaOH solution. What is the molarity of the HCl solution?

2. A 15.7-ml sample of H_2SO_4 reacts with 27.7 ml of 0.187-M KOH solution. What is the molarity of the H_2SO_4 solution?

Answers   1. 0.298 M HCl   2. 0.165 M H_2SO_4

10.7 Acid–Base Properties of Salt Solutions

- Salts of strong acids and strong bases produce neutral, aqueous solutions.
- Salts of weak acids and strong bases form basic, aqueous solutions.
- Salts of strong acids and weak bases form acidic, aqueous solutions.

Study Note

Use the cation and anion of a salt to determine the acidity of its aqueous solution.

Example: Will the salt Na_2CO_3 form an acidic, basic, or neutral aqueous solution?

Solution: A salt of a strong base (NaOH) and a weak acid (HCO_3^-) remove protons from water to produce a basic solution:

$$CO_3^{2-}(aq) + H_2O(l) \rightarrow HCO_3^-(aq) + OH^-(aq)$$

◆ **Learning Exercise 10.7A**

Identify solutions of each of the following salts as acidic, basic, or neutral:

1. NaBr _____   2. KNO_2 _____

3. NH_4Cl _____   4. Li_2SO_4 _____

5. KF _____

Answers   1. neutral   2. basic   3. acidic   4. basic   5. basic

◆ **Learning Exercise 10.7B**

Determine if each of the following salts dissolved in water forms a solution that is acidic, basic, or neutral. If acidic or basic, write an equation for the reaction.

		Acidic, basic, or neutral	**Equation**
1.	NaCN	_____	_____
2.	LiBr	_____	_____
3.	NH_4NO_3	_____	_____
4.	Na_2S	_____	_____
5.	$BaCl_2$	_____	_____

Answers   1. NaCN   basic $CN^-(aq) + H_2O(l) \rightarrow HCN(aq) + OH^-(aq)$
           2. LiBr   neutral
           3. NH_4NO_3 acidic $NH_4^+(aq) + H_2O(l) \rightarrow H_3O^+(aq) + NH_3(aq)$
           4. Na_2S basic $S^{2-}(aq) + H_2O(l) \rightarrow HS^-(aq) + OH^-(aq)$
           5. $BaCl_2$ neutral

10.8 Buffers

- A buffer solution resists a change in pH when small amounts of acid or base are added.
- A buffer contains either (1) a weak acid and its salt or (2) a weak base and its salt. The weak acid picks up excess OH^-, and the anion of the salt picks up excess H_3O^+.
- The pH of a buffer can be calculated by rearranging the K_a for $[H_3O^+]$.

◆ Learning Exercise 10.8

State whether each of the following represents a buffer system or not.

   a. HCl + NaCl   **b.** K_2SO_4 **c.** H_2CO_3 **d.** H_2CO_3 + $NaHCO_3$

Answers   **a.** No. A strong acid is not a buffer.
             b. No. A salt alone cannot act as a buffer.
             c. No. A weak acid alone cannot act as a buffer.
             d. Yes. A weak acid and its salt act as a buffer system.

Checklist for Chapter 10

You are ready to take the practice test for Chapter 10. Be sure that you have accomplished the following learning goals for this chapter. If you are not sure, review the section listed at the end of the goal. Then apply your new skills and understanding to the practice test.

After studying Chapter 10, I can successfully:

_____   Describe the properties of Arrhenius acids and bases and write their names (10.1).

_____   Describe the Brønsted-Lowry concept of acids and bases; write conjugate acid–base pairs for an acid–base reaction (10.2).

_____   Write equations for the ionization of strong and weak acids and bases (10.3).

_____   Use the ion product of water to calculate $[H_3O^+]$ and $[OH^-]$ (10.4).

_____   Calculate pH from the $[H_3O^+]$ of a solution (10.5).

_____   Write a balanced equation for the reactions of acids with metals, carbonates, and/or bases (10.6).

_____   Determine if a salt dissolved in water forms a solution that is acidic, basic, or neutral (10.7).

_____   Describe the role of buffers in maintaining the pH of a solution and calculate the pH of a buffer solution (10.8).

Practice Test for Chapter 10

1. An acid is a compound that, when placed in water, yields this characteristic ion:
   A. H_3O^+ **B.** OH^- **C.** Na^+ **D.** Cl^- **E.** CO_3^{2-}

2. $MgCl_2$ would be classified as a(n)
   A. acid   **B.** base   **C.** salt   **D.** buffer   **E.** nonelectrolyte

3. $Mg(OH)_2$ would be classified as a
   A. weak acid   **B.** strong base   **C.** salt   **D.** buffer   **E.** nonelectrolyte

4. In the K_w expression for pure H_2O, the $[H_3O^+]$ has the value
    A. 1×10^{-7} M   **B.** 1×10^{-1} M   **C.** 1×10^{-14} M   **D.** 1×10^{-6} M   **E.** 1×10^{-12} M

5. Of the following pH values, which is the most acidic?
    A. 8.0   **B.** 5.5   **C.** 1.5   **D.** 3.2   **E.** 9.0

6. Of the following pH values, which is the most basic pH?
    A. 10.0   **B.** 4.0   **C.** 2.2   **D.** 11.5   **E.** 9.0

For questions 7–9, consider a solution with $[H_3O^+] = 1 \times 10^{-11}$ M.

7. The pH of the solution is
    A. 1.0   **B.** 2.0   **C.** 3.0   **D.** 11.0   **E.** 14.0

8. The hydroxide ion concentration is
    A. 1×10^{-1} M   **B.** 1×10^{-3} M   **C.** 1×10^{-4} M   **D.** 1×10^{-7} M   **E.** 1×10^{-11} M

9. The solution is
    A. acidic   **B.** basic   **C.** neutral   **D.** a buffer   **E.** neutralized

For questions 10–12, consider a solution with a $[OH^-] = 1 \times 10^{-5}$ M.

10. The hydrogen ion concentration of the solution is
    A. 1×10^{-5} M   **B.** 1×10^{-7} M   **C.** 1×10^{-9} M   **D.** 1×10^{-10} M   **E.** 1×10^{-14} M

11. The pH of the solution is
    A. 2.0   **B.** 5.0   **C.** 9.0   **D.** 11   **E.** 14

12. The solution is
    A. acidic   **B.** basic   **C.** neutral   **D.** a buffer   **E.** neutralized

13. Acetic acid is a weak acid because
    A. it forms a dilute acid solution   **B.** it is isotonic
    C. it is less than 50% ionized in water   **D.** it is a nonpolar molecule
    E. it can form a buffer

14. A weak base when added to water
    A. makes the solution slightly basic   **B.** does not affect the pH
    C. dissociates completely   **D.** does not dissociate
    E. makes the solution slightly acidic

15. Which is an equation for neutralization?
    A. $CaCO_3 \rightarrow CaO + CO_2$
    B. $Na_2SO_4(s) \rightarrow 2Na^+ + SO_4{}^{2-}$
    C. $H_2SO_4 + 2NaOH \rightarrow Na_2SO_4 + 2H_2O$
    D. $Na_2O + SO_3 \rightarrow Na_2SO_4$
    E. $H_2CO_3 \rightarrow CO_2 + H_2O$

16. What is the name given to components in the body that keep blood pH within its normal 7.35 to 7.45 range?
    A. nutrients   **B.** buffers   **C.** metabolites   **D.** regufluids   **E.** neutralizers

17. What is true of a typical buffer system?
    A. It maintains a pH of 7.0.
    B. It contains a weak base.
    C. It contains a salt.
    D. It contains a strong acid and its salt.
    E. It maintains the pH of a solution.

18. Which of the following would act as a buffer system?
    A. HCl   **B.** Na_2CO_3 **C.** $NaOH + NaNO_3$
    D. NH_4OH **E.** $NaHCO_3 + H_2CO_3$

19. Which of the following pairs is a conjugate acid–base pair?
  A. HCl/HNO_3 **B.** HNO_3/NO_3^- **C.** NaOH/KOH   **D.** HSO_4^-/HCO_3^- **E.** Cl^-/F^-

20. The conjugate base of HSO_4^- is
  A. SO_4^{2-} **B.** H_2SO_4 **C.** HS^- **D.** H_2S **E.** SO_3^{2-}

21. In which reaction does H_2O act as an acid?
  A. $H_3PO_4 + H_2O \rightarrow H_3O^+ + H_2PO_4^-$
  B. $H_2SO_4 + H_2O \rightarrow H_3O^+ + HSO_4^-$
  C. $H_2O + HS^- \rightarrow H_3O^+ + S^{2-}$
  D. $NaOH + HCl \rightarrow NaCl + H_2O$
  E. $NH_3 + H_2O \rightarrow NH_4^+ + OH^-$

22. 23.7 ml of HCl reacts with 19.6 ml of 0.179 M NaOH. The molarity of the HCl solution is
  A. 6.76 M   **B.** 0.216 M   **C.** 0.148 M   **D.** 0.163 M   **E.** 0.333 M

For questions 23–25, will each salt dissolved in water make a solution which will be acidic (A), basic (B), or neutral (N)?

23. NaCl

24. KF

25. NH_4Cl

Answers to the Practice Test

1. A	**2.** C	**3.** B	**4.** A	**5.** C
6. D	**7.** D	**8.** B	**9.** B	**10.** C
11. C	**12.** B	**13.** C	**14.** A	**15.** C
16. B	**17.** E	**18.** E	**19.** B	**20.** A
21. E	**22.** C	**21.** N	**22.** B	**21.** A

Answers and Solutions to Selected Text Problems

10.1 **a.** Acids taste sour.   **b.** Acids neutralize bases.
        c. Acids produce H^+ ions in water.   **d.** Potassium hydroxide is the name of a base.

10.3 The names of non-oxy acids begin with *hydro-*, followed by the name of the anion. The names of oxyacids use the element root with $-ic\ acid$. Acids with one oxygen less than the common $-ic$ *acid* name are named as $-ous\ acids$.
        a. hydrochloric acid   **b.** calcium hydroxide
        c. carbonic acid   **d.** nitric acid
        e. sulfurous acid

10.5 **a.** $Mg(OH)_2$ **b.** HF   **c.** H_3PO_4 **d.** LiOH   **e.** $Cu(OH)_2$

10.7 The acid donates a proton (H^+), whereas the base accepts a proton.
        a. acid (proton donor) HI   proton acceptor (base) H_2O
        b. acid (proton donor) H_2O proton acceptor (base) F^-

10.9 To form the conjugate base, remove a proton (H^+) from the acid.
        a. F^-, fluoride ion   **b.** OH^-, hydroxide ion
        c. HCO_3^-, bicarbonate ion   **d.** SO_4^{2-}, sulfate ion

10.11 To form the conjugate acid, add a proton (H^+) to the base.
        a. HCO_3^- bicarbonate ion   **b.** H_3O^+ hydronium ion
        c. H_3PO_4 phosphoric acid   **d.** HBr hydrobromic acid

10.13 The conjugate acid is a proton donor, and the conjugate base is a proton acceptor.
    a. acid H_2CO_3; conjugate base HCO_3^-; base H_2O; conjugate acid H_3O^+
    b. acid NH_4^+; conjugate base NH_3; base H_2O; conjugate acid H_3O^+
    c. acid HCN; conjugate base CN^-; base NO_2^-; conjugate acid HNO_2

10.15 A strong acid is a good proton donor, whereas its conjugate base is a poor proton acceptor.

10.17 Use Table 10.3 to answer.
    a. HBr   **b.** HSO_4^- **c.** H_2CO_3

10.19 Use Table 10.3 to answer.
    a. HSO_4^- **b.** HF   **c.** HCO_3^-

10.21 **a.** From Table 10.3, we see that H_2O is a weaker base than HCO_3^- and that H_2CO_3 is a weaker acid than H_3O^+. Thus, the reactants are favored.
    b. From Table 10.3, we see that NH_4^+ is a weaker acid than H_3O^+ and H_2O is a weaker base than NH_3. Thus, the reactants are favored.
    c. From Table 10.3, we see that NH_4^+ is a weaker acid than HCl and that Cl^- is a weaker base than NH_3. Thus, the products are favored.

10.23 The reactants are favored because NH_4^+ is a weaker acid than HSO_4^-.

$$NH_4^-(aq) + SO_4^{2-}(aq) \rightleftarrows NH_3(aq) + HSO_4^-(aq)$$

10.25 The smaller the K_a, the weaker the acid. The weaker acid has the stronger conjugate base.
    a. H_2SO_3, which has a larger K_a than HS^-, is a stronger acid.
    b. The conjugate base forms by removing a proton from the acid, HSO_3^-.
    c. The stronger acid, H_2SO_3, has a weaker conjugate base, HSO_3^-.
    d. The weaker acid, HS^-, has a stronger conjugate base.
    e. H_2SO_3, the stronger acid, produces more ions.

10.27 $H_3PO_4(aq) + H_2O(l) \rightleftarrows H_3O^+(aq) + H_2PO_4^-(aq)$
The K_a is the ratio of the [products] divided by the [reactants] with [H_2O] considered constant and part of the K_a.

$$K_a = \frac{[H_3O^+][H_2PO_4^-]}{[H_3PO_4]}$$

10.29 In pure water, a small fraction of the water molecules break apart to form H^+ and OH^-. The H^+ combines with H_2O to form H_3O^+. Every time a H^+ is formed, a OH^- is also formed. Therefore, the concentration of the two must be equal in pure water.

10.31 In an acidic solution, [H_3O^+] is greater than [OH^-], which means that [H_3O^+] is greater than 1×10^{-7} M and [OH^-] is less than 1×10^{-7} M.

10.33 A neutral solution has [OH^-] = [H_3O^+] = 1.0×10^{-7} M. If [OH^-] is greater than 1×10^{-7}, the solution is basic; if [H_3O^+] is greater than 1×10^{-7} M, the solution is acidic.
    a. acidic; [H_3O^+] is greater than 1×10^{-7} M
    b. basic; [H_3O^+] is less than 1×10^{-7} M
    c. basic; [OH^-] is greater than 1×10^{-7} M
    d. acidic; [OH^-] is less than 1×10^{-7} M

10.35 The [H_3O^+] multiplied by the [OH^-] is equal to K_w, which is 1.0×10^{-14}. When [H_3O^+] is known, the [OH^-] can be calculated. Rearranging the K_w gives [OH^-] = $K_w/[H_3O^+]$
    a. 1.0×10^{-9} M   **b.** 1.0×10^{-6} M
    c. 2.0×10^{-5} M   **d.** 4.0×10^{-13} M

10.37 The value of the $[H_3O^+]$ multiplied by the value of the $[OH^-]$ is always equal to K_w, which is 1×10^{-14}. When $[H_3O^+]$ is known, the $[OH^-]$ can be calculated. Rearranging the K_w gives $[OH^-] = K_w/[H_3O^+]$.

a. 1.0×10^{-11} M
b. 2.0×10^{-9} M
c. 5.6×10^{-3} M
d. 2.5×10^{-2} M

10.39 In neutral solutions, $[H_3O^+] = 1.0 \times 10^{-7}$ M. pH $= -\log[1.0 \times 10^{-7}] = 7.00$. The pH value contains two *decimal places*, which represent the two significant figures in the coefficient 1.0.

10.41 An acidic solution has a pH less than 7. A neutral solution has a pH equal to 7. A basic solution has a pH greater than 7.
a. basic
b. acidic
c. basic
d. acidic

10.43 pH $= -\log[H_3O^+]$

The value of $[H_3O^+][OH^-] = K_w$, which is 1.0×10^{-14}. If $[H_3O^+]$ needs to be calculated from $[OH^-]$, then rearranging the K_w for $[H_3O^+]$ gives

$$[H_3O^+] = \frac{1.0 \times 10^{-14}}{[OH^-]}$$

a. pH $= -\log[1.0 \times 10^{-4}] = 4.00$

b. pH $= -\log[3.0 \times 10^{-9}] = 8.52$

c. $[H_3O^+] = \dfrac{1.0 \times 10^{-14}}{[1.0 \times 10^{-5}]} = 1.0 \times 10^{-9}$ pH $= -\log[1.0 \times 10^{-9}] = 9.00$

d. $[H_3O^+] = \dfrac{1.0 \times 10^{-14}}{[2.5 \times 10^{-11}]} = 4.0 \times 10^{-4}$ pH $= -\log[4.0 \times 10^{-4}] = 3.40$

10.45 On a calculator, pH is calculated by entering $-\log$, followed by the coefficient EE (EXP) key and the power of 10 follow by the change sign ($+/-$) key. On some calculators, the concentration is entered first (coefficient EXP $-$ power) followed by log and $+/-$ key.

$$[H_3O^+] = \frac{1.0 \times 10^{-14}}{[OH^-]} \qquad\qquad [OH^-] = \frac{1.0 \times 10^{-14}}{[H_3O^+]}$$

pH $= -\log[H_3O^+]$

$[H_3O^+]$	$[OH^-]$	pH	Acidic, Basic, or Neutral?
1.0×10^{-8} M	1.0×10^{-6} M	8.00	Basic
1.0×10^{-3} M	1.0×10^{-11} M	3.00	Acidic
2.8×10^{-5} M	3.6×10^{-10} M	4.55	Acidic
1.0×10^{-12} M	1.0×10^{-2} M	12.00	Basic

10.47 Acids react with active metals to form H_2 and a salt of the metal. The reaction of acids with carbonates yields CO_2, H_2O, and a salt of the metal. In a neutralization reaction, an acid and a base react to form a salt and H_2O.
a. $ZnCO_3(s) + 2HBr(aq) \rightarrow ZnBr_2(aq) + CO_2(g) + H_2O(l)$
b. $Zn(s) + 2HCl(aq) \rightarrow ZnCl_2(aq) + H_2(g)$
c. $HCl(aq) + NaHCO_3(s) \rightarrow NaCl(aq) + H_2O(l) + CO_2(g)$
d. $H_2SO_4(aq) + Mg(OH)_2(s) \rightarrow MgSO_4(aq) + 2\,H_2O(l)$

10.49 In balancing a neutralization equation, the number of H^+ and OH^- must be equalized by placing coefficients in front of the formulas for the acid and base.
    a. $2HCl(aq) + Mg(OH)_2(s) \rightarrow MgCl_2(aq) + 2H_2O(l)$
    b. $H_3PO_4(aq) + 3LiOH(aq) \rightarrow Li_3PO_4(aq) + 3H_2O(l)$

10.51 In balancing a neutralization equation, the number of H^+ and OH^- must be equalized by placing coefficients in front of the formulas for the acid and base.
    a. $H_2SO_4(aq) + 2NaOH(aq) \rightarrow Na_2SO_4(aq) + 2H_2O(l)$
    b. $3HCl(aq) + Fe(OH)_3(aq) \rightarrow FeCl_3(aq) + 3H_2O(l)$
    c. $H_2CO_3(aq) + Mg(OH)_2(s) \rightarrow MgCO_3(aq) + 2H_2O(l)$

10.53 In the equation, one mole HCl reacts with one mole NaOH.

$$\text{NaOH: } 28.6 \ \cancel{mL} \times \frac{1 \text{ L}}{1000 \ \cancel{mL}} = 0.0286 \ \cancel{L} \times \frac{0.145 \text{ mole NaOH}}{1 \ \cancel{L}} = 0.00415 \text{ mole NaOH}$$

$$0.004\ 15 \ \cancel{\text{mole NaOH}} \times \frac{1 \text{ mole HCl}}{1 \ \cancel{\text{mole NaOH}}} = 0.004\ 15 \text{ mole HCl}$$

$$\text{M HCl: } 5.00 \ \cancel{mL} \times \frac{1 \text{ L}}{1000 \ \cancel{mL}} = 0.005\ 00 \text{ L} \qquad \frac{0.004\ 15 \text{ mole HCl}}{0.005\ 00 \text{ L}} = 0.829 \text{ M}$$

10.55 In the equation, one mole H_2SO_4 reacts with two moles KOH.

$$\text{KOH: } 38.2 \ \cancel{mL} \times \frac{1 \text{ L}}{1000 \ \cancel{mL}} = 0.0382 \ \cancel{L} \times \frac{0.163 \text{ mole KOH}}{1 \ \cancel{L}} = 0.006\ 23 \text{ mole KOH}$$

$$\text{Moles of } H_2SO_4: 0.006\ 23 \ \cancel{\text{mole KOH}} \times \frac{1 \text{ mole } H_2SO_4}{2 \ \cancel{\text{moles KOH}}} = 0.003\ 12 \text{ mole } H_2SO_4$$

$$\text{Volume of } H_2SO_4: 25.0 \ \cancel{mL} \times \frac{1 \text{ L}}{1000 \ \cancel{mL}} = 0.0250 \text{ L}$$

$$\text{Molarity of } H_2SO_4: \frac{0.003\ 12 \text{ mole } H_2SO_4}{0.0250 \text{ L}} = 0.125 \text{ M}$$

10.57 In the equation, one mole H_3PO_4 reacts with three moles NaOH.

$$\text{Moles of NaOH: } 6.4 \ \cancel{mL} \times \frac{1 \text{ L}}{1000 \ \cancel{mL}} = 0.0164 \ \cancel{L} \times \frac{0.204 \text{ mole NaOH}}{1 \ \cancel{L}} = 0.003\ 35 \text{ mole NaOH}$$

$$\text{Moles of } H_3PO_4: 0.003\ 35 \ \cancel{\text{mole NaOH}} \times \frac{1 \text{ mole } H_3PO_4}{3 \ \cancel{\text{moles NaOH}}} = 0.001\ 12 \text{ mole } H_3PO_4$$

$$\text{Volume of } H_3PO_4: 50.0 \ \cancel{mL} \times \frac{1 \text{ L}}{1000 \ \cancel{mL}} = 0.0500 \text{ L}$$

$$\text{Molarity of } H_3PO_4: \frac{0.001\ 12 \text{ mole } H_3PO_4}{0.0500 \text{ L}} = 0.0223 \text{ M}$$

10.59 The anion of a weak acid removes a proton from H_2O to make a basic solution.

10.61 A solution of a salt with an anion from a strong acid and a cation from a weak base will form an acidic solution. A salt with an anion from a weak acid and a cation from a strong base will form a basic solution. Solutions of salts with ions of strong acids and strong bases are neutral.
    a. neutral: Mg^{2+} is the cation of a strong base; Cl^- is the anion of a strong acid.
    b. acidic: $NH_4^+(aq) + H_2O(l) \rightleftarrows NH_3(aq) + H_3O^+(aq)$
    c. basic: $CO_3^{2-}(aq) + H_2O(l) \rightleftarrows HCO_3^-(aq) + OH^-(aq)$
    d. basic: $S^{2-}(aq) + H_2O(l) \rightleftarrows HS^-(aq) + OH^-(aq)$

10.63 A buffer system contains a weak acid and its salt, or a weak base and its salt.
    a. This is not a buffer system because it only contains a strong base.
    b. This is a buffer system; it contains the weak acid H_2CO_3 and its salt $NaHCO_3$.
    c. This is a buffer system; it contains HF, a weak acid, and its salt KF.
    d. This is not a buffer system because it contains the salts KCl and NaCl.

10.65   **a.** A buffer system keeps the pH of a solution constant.
    b. The salt of the acid in a buffer is needed to neutralize any acid added.
    c. When H^+ is added to the buffer, the F^- from NaF, the salt of the weak acid, reacts with the acid to neutralize it.

$$F^- + H_3O^+ \rightarrow HF + H_2O$$

    d. When OH^- is added to the buffer solution, HF (weak acid) reacts to neutralize the OH^-.

$$HF(aq) + OH^-(aq) \rightarrow F^-(aq) + H_2O$$

10.67 Rearrange the K_a for $[H_3O^+]$ and use it to calculate the pH.

$$[H_3O^+] = 4.5 \times 10^{-4} \times \frac{[0.10 \text{ M}]}{[0.10 \text{ M}]} = 4.5 \times 10^{-4} \quad pH = -\log[4.5 \times 10^{-4}] = 3.35$$

10.69 Rearrange the K_a for $[H_3O^+]$ and use it to calculate the pH.

$$[H_3O^+] = 7.2 \times 10^{-4} \times \frac{[0.10 \text{ M}]}{[0.10 \text{ M}]} = 7.2 \times 10^{-4} \quad pH = -\log[7.2 \times 10^{-4}] = 3.14$$

$$[H_3O^+] = 7.2 \times 10^{-4} \times \frac{[0.060 \text{ M}]}{[0.120 \text{ M}]} = 3.6 \times 10^{-4} \quad pH = -\log[3.6 \times 10^{-4}] = 3.44$$

The solution with 0.10 M HF is more acidic.

10.71   **a.** This diagram represents a weak acid; only a few HX molecules separate into H_3O^+ and X^- ions.
    b. This diagram represents a strong acid; all of the HX molecules separate H_3O^+ and X^- ions.
    c. This diagram represents a weak acid; only a few HX molecules separate H_3O^+ and X^- ions.

10.73   **a.** During hyperventilation, a person will lose CO_2 and the blood pH will rise.
    b. Breathing into a paper bag will increase the CO_2 concentration and lower the blood pH.

10.75 The name of an acid from a simple nonmetallic anion is formed by adding the prefix *hydro-* to the name of the anion and changing the anion ending to *-ic acid.* If the acid has polyatomic anion, the name of the acid uses the name of the polyatomic anion and ends in $-ic\ acid$ or $-ous\ acid$. There is no prefix *hydro.* Bases are named as ionic compounds containing hydroxide anions.
    a. sulfuric acid   **b.** potassium hydroxide   **c.** calcium hydroxide
    d. hydrochloric acid   **e.** nitrous acid

10.77 Both strong and weak acids dissolve in water to give H_3O^+. They both neutralize bases and turn litmus red and phenolphthalein clear. Both taste sour and are electrolytes in solution. However, weak acids are only slightly dissociated in solution and are weak electrolytes. Strong acids, which are nearly completely dissociated in solution, are strong electrolytes.

10.79   **a.** $Mg(OH)_2$ is a strong base because all the base that dissolves is dissociated in aqueous solution.
    b. $Mg(OH)_2(s) + 2HCl(aq) \rightarrow 2H_2O(l) + MgCl_2(aq)$

10.81   **a.** HF   **b.** H_3O^+ **c.** HNO_2 **d.** HCO_3^-

10.83 The pH $= -\log[H_3O^+]$,
    a. pH 7.70   **b.** pH 1.30   **c.** pH 10.54   **d.** pH 11.73

10.85 If the pH is given, the $[H_3O^+]$ can be found by using the relationship $[H_3O^+] = 1.0 \times 10^{-pH}$. The $[OH^-]$ can be found from $[H_3O^+][OH^-] = 1 \times 10^{-14}$.

    a. pH = 3.00 $[H_3O^+] = 1.0 \times 10^{-3}$ M $[OH^-] = 1.0 \times 10^{-11}$ M

    b. $[H_3O^+] = 3.3 \times 10^{-7}$ M $[OH^-] = 3.0 \times 10^{-8}$ M

       $[H_3O^+] = 6.48 \pm$ 2nd *function* 10^x (or *inv log*) $= 3.3 \times 10^{-7}$ M

$$[OH^-] = \frac{1.0 \times 10^{-14}}{3.3 \times 10^{-7}} = 3.0 \times 10^{-8} \text{ M}$$

    c. $[H_3O^+] = 1.4 \times 10^{-9}$ M $[OH^-] = 7.1 \times 10^{-6}$ M

    d. $[H_3O^+] = 1.0 \times 10^{-11}$ M $[OH^-] = 1.0 \times 10^{-3}$ M

10.87 The concentration of OH^- can be calculated from the moles of NaOH and volume of the solution.

$$0.225 \text{ g NaOH} \times \frac{1 \text{ mole NaOH}}{40.0 \text{ g NaOH}} = 0.005\ 63 \text{ mole NaOH}$$

$$\frac{0.005\ 63 \text{ mole NaOH}}{0.0250 \text{ L}} = 0.225 \text{ M NaOH}$$

10.89 $2.5 \text{ g HCl} \times \dfrac{1 \text{ mole HCl}}{36.5 \text{ g HCl}} = 0.069 \text{ mole HCl}$

$$\frac{0.069 \text{ mole HCl}}{0.425 \text{ L}} = 0.16 \text{ M HCl}$$

Since HCl is a strong acid, the $[H_3O^+]$ is also 0.16 M.

pH $= -\log[1.6 \times 10^{-1} \text{ M}] = 0.80$

10.91   **a.** One mole HCl reacts with one mole NaOH.

$$\text{HCl: } 25.0 \text{ mL} \times \frac{1 \text{ L}}{1000 \text{ mL}} = 0.0250 \text{ L} \times \frac{0.288 \text{ mole HCl}}{1 \text{ L}} = 0.007\ 20 \text{ mole HCl}$$

$$0.00720 \text{ mole HCl} \times \frac{1 \text{ mole NaOH}}{1 \text{ mole HCl}} = 0.007\ 20 \text{ mole NaOH}$$

$$\text{Volume of NaOH: } 0.007\ 20 \text{ mole} \times \frac{1 \text{ L}}{0.150 \text{ mole}} \times \frac{1000 \text{ mL}}{1 \text{ L}} = 48.0 \text{ mL}$$

    b. One mole H_2SO_4 reacts with two moles NaOH.

$$H_2SO_4\text{: } 10.0 \text{ mL} \times \frac{1 \text{ L}}{1000 \text{ mL}} = 0.0100 \text{ L} \times \frac{0.560 \text{ mole}}{1 \text{ L}} = 0.005\ 60 \text{ mole } H_2SO_4$$

$$0.00560 \text{ mole } H_2SO_4 \times \frac{2 \text{ moles NaOH}}{1 \text{ mole } H_2SO_4} = 0.0112 \text{ mole NaOH}$$

$$\text{Volume of NaOH: } 0.0112 \text{ mole} \times \frac{1 \text{ L}}{0.150 \text{ mole}} \times \frac{1000 \text{ mL}}{1 \text{ L}} = 74.7 \text{ mL}$$

10.93 One mole H_2SO_4 reacts with two moles NaOH.

$$\text{NaOH: } 45.6 \text{ mL} \times \frac{1 \text{ L}}{1000 \text{ mL}} = 0.0456 \text{ L} \times \frac{0.205 \text{ mole}}{1 \text{ L}} = 0.009\ 35 \text{ mole NaOH}$$

$$\text{Moles of } H_2SO_4\text{: } 0.009\ 35 \text{ mole NaOH} \times \frac{1 \text{ mole } H_2SO_4}{2 \text{ moles KOH}} = 0.004\ 68 \text{ mole } H_2SO_4$$

$$\text{M } H_2SO_4\text{: } 20.0 \text{ mL} \times \frac{1 \text{ L}}{1000 \text{ mL}} = 0.0200 \text{ L} \quad \frac{0.004\ 68 \text{ mole } H_2SO_4}{0.0200 \text{ L}} = 0.234 \text{ M}$$

10.95 a. The solution will be basic. K^+ is the cation of a strong acid; no effect on pH. The anion, F^-, reacts with water to form the weak acid, HF and OH^-.

$F^-(aq) + H_2O \rightarrow HF(aq) + OH(aq)$

b. The solution will be basic. Na^+ is the cation of a strong acid; no effect on pH. CN^-, the anion, reacts with water to form the weak acid, HCN and OH^-.

$CN^-(aq) + H_2O(l) \rightarrow HCN(aq) + OH(aq)$

c. The solution will be acidic. NH_4^+ is the cation of a weak base, NH_4OH. The anion, NO_3^-, is from a strong acid and does not change the pH.

d. The solution will be neutral. The cation is from a strong base and the anion is from a strong acid. None of the ions of the salt will change the pH.

10.97 In a buffer, the anion accepts H^+ and the cation provides H^+.
a. $H_2PO_4^-(aq) + H_3O^+(aq) \rightarrow H_3PO_4(aq) + H_2O(l)$
b. $H_3PO_4(aq) + OH^-(aq) \rightarrow H_2PO_4^-(aq) + H_2O(l)$

c. $[H_3O^+] = 7.5 \times 10^{-3} \times \dfrac{[0.10 \text{ M}]}{[0.10 \text{ M}]} = 7.5 \times 10^{-3}$ pH $= -\log(7.5 \times 10^{-3}) = 2.12$

10.99 a. 1) HS^- 2) $H_2PO_4^-$ 3) CO_3^{2-}

b. 1) $\dfrac{[H_3O^+][HS^-]}{[H_2S]}$ 2) $\dfrac{[H_3O^+][H_2PO_4^-]}{[H_3PO_4]}$

    3) $\dfrac{[CO_3^{2-}][H_3O^+]}{[HCO_3^-]}$

c. H_2S (see Table 10.3)
d. H_3PO_4 (see Table 10.3)

10.101 a. $ZnCO_3(s) + H_2SO_4(aq) \rightarrow ZnSO_4(aq) + CO_2(g) + H_2O(l)$
b. $2Al(s) + 6HCl(aq) \rightarrow 2AlCl_3(aq) + 3H_2(g)$
c. $2H_3PO_4(aq) + 3Ca(OH)_2(s) \rightarrow Ca_3(PO_4)_2(aq) + 6H_2O(l)$
d. $KHCO_3(s) + HNO_3(aq) \rightarrow KNO_3(aq) + CO_2(g) + H_2O(l)$

10.103 $KOH \rightarrow K^+ + OH^-$
$[OH^-] = 0.050$ M $= 5.0 \times 10^{-2}$ M

a. $[H_3O^+] = \dfrac{1.0 \times 10^{-14}}{[5.0 \times 10^{-2}]} = 2.0 \times 10^{-13}$ M

b. pH $= -\log[2.0 \times 10^{13}] = 12.70$
c. $3KOH(aq) + H_3PO_4(aq) \rightarrow K_3PO_4(aq) + 3H_2O(l)$

d. H_2SO_4 40.0 mL $\times \dfrac{1 \text{ L}}{1000 \text{ mL}} = 0.0400$ L $\times \dfrac{0.035 \text{ mole}}{1 \text{ L}} = 0.0014$ mole H_2SO_4

0.0014 mole $H_2SO_4 \times \dfrac{2 \text{ moles KOH}}{1 \text{ mole } H_2SO_4} \times \dfrac{1000 \text{ mL KOH}}{0.0500 \text{ mole KOH}} = 56$ mL KOH

Introduction to Organic Chemistry: Alkanes

Study Goals

- Identify the number of bonds for carbon and other atoms in organic compounds.
- Describe the tetrahedral shape of carbon with single bonds in organic compounds.
- Draw expanded and condensed structural formulas for alkanes.
- Write the IUPAC names for alkanes and cycloalkanes.
- Describe the physical properties of alkanes.
- Write equations for the combustion and halogenation of alkanes.
- Describe the properties that are characteristic of organic compounds.
- Identify the functional groups in organic compounds.

Think About It

1. What is the meaning of the term "organic"?

2. What two elements are found in all organic compounds?

3. In a salad dressing, why is there a layer of vegetable oil floating on the vinegar and water layer?

Key Terms

1. Match the statements shown below with the following key terms.

a. alkene	**b.** isomers	**c.** hydrocarbon
d. alcohol	**e.** functional group	**f.** alkane
g. condensed structural formula	**h.** main chain	**i.** combustion
j. cycloalkane		

1. _____ an atom or group of atoms that influences the chemical reactions of an organic compound

2. _____ a class of organic compounds with one or more hydroxyl (—OH) groups

3. _____ a type of hydrocarbon with one or more carbon–carbon double bonds

4. _____ organic compound consisting of only carbon and hydrogen atoms

5. _____ compounds having the same molecular formula but a different arrangements of atoms

6. _____ a hydrocarbon that contains only carbon–carbon single bonds

7. _____ an alkane that exists as a cyclic structure

8. _____ the chemical reaction of an alkane and oxygen that yields CO_2, H_2O, and heat

9. _____ the type of formula that shows the arrangement of the carbon atoms grouped with their attached H atoms

10. _____ the longest continuous chain of carbon atoms in a structural formula

Answers	**1.** e	**2.** d	**3.** a	**4.** c	**5.** b
	6. f	**7.** j	**8.** i	**9.** g	**10.** h

11.1 Organic Compounds

- Organic compounds are compounds of carbon and hydrogen that have covalent bonds, have low melting and boiling points, burn vigorously, are nonelectrolytes, and are usually more soluble in nonpolar solvents than in water.
- Each carbon in an alkane has four bonds arranged so that the bonded atoms are in the corners of a tetrahedron.

◆ Learning Exercise 11.1A

Identify the following as typical of organic (O) or inorganic (I) compounds:

1. _____ have covalent bonds
2. _____ have low boiling points
3. _____ burn in air
4. _____ are soluble in water
5. _____ have high melting points
6. _____ are soluble in nonpolar solvents
7. _____ have ionic bonds
8. _____ form long chains
9. _____ contain carbon
10. _____ are not very combustible
11. _____ have a formula of Na_2SO_4
12. _____ have a formula of $CH_3-CH_2-CH_3$

Answers   **1.** O   **2.** O   **3.** O   **4.** I   **5.** I   **6.** O
                7. I   **8.** O   **9.** O   **10.** I   **11.** I   **12.** O

◆ Learning Exercise 11.1B

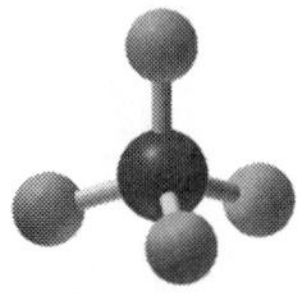

1. What is the name of the three-dimensional structure of methane shown above?

2. Draw the expanded structural formula (two-dimensional) for methane.

Answers   **1.** tetrahedron

2. 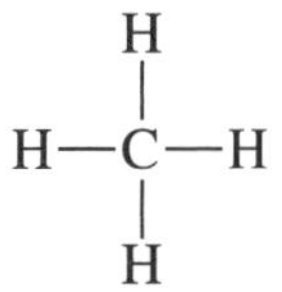
$$\begin{array}{c} \text{H} \\ | \\ \text{H}-\text{C}-\text{H} \\ | \\ \text{H} \end{array}$$

11.2 Alkanes

- In an IUPAC name, the stem indicates the number of carbon atoms, and the suffix describes the family of the compound. For example, in the name *propane,* the stem *prop* indicates a chain of three carbon atoms and the ending *ane* indicates single bonds (alkane). The names of the first six alkanes follow:

Name	Carbon Atoms	Condensed Structural Formula
Methane	1	CH_4
Ethane	2	CH_3-CH_3
Propane	3	$CH_3-CH_2-CH_3$
Butane	4	$CH_3-CH_2-CH_2-CH_3$
Pentane	5	$CH_3-CH_2-CH_2-CH_2-CH_3$
Hexane	6	$CH_3-CH_2-CH_2-CH_2-CH_2-CH_3$

- An expanded structural formula shows a separate line to each bonded atom; a condensed structural formula depicts each carbon atom and its attached hydrogen atoms as a group. A molecular formula gives the total numbers of atoms.

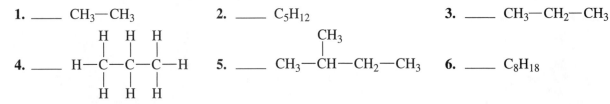

Expanded Structural Formula   **Condensed Structural Formula**   **Molecular Formula**

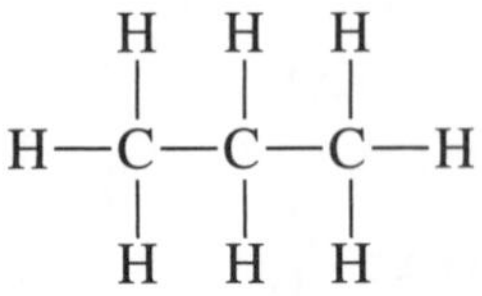

$CH_3-CH_2-CH_3$

or C_3H_8

$CH_3CH_2CH_3$

◆ Learning Exercise 11.2A

Indicate if each of the following is a molecular formula (M), an expanded structural formula (E), or a condensed structural formula (C):

1. _____ CH_3-CH_3 **2.** _____ C_5H_{12} **3.** _____ $CH_3-CH_2-CH_3$

4. _____ (expanded structure)   **5.** _____ $CH_3-CH-CH_2-CH_3$ (with CH_3 branch)   **6.** _____ C_8H_{18}

Answers   **1.** C   **2.** M   **3.** C   **4.** E   **5.** C   **6.** M

◆ Learning Exercise 11.2B

Write the condensed formulas for the following structural formulas:

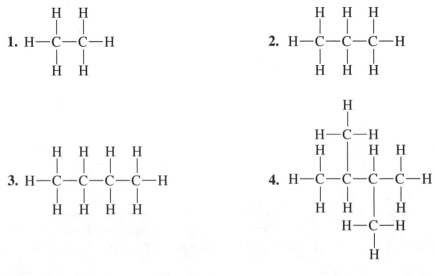

Answers   **1.** CH_3-CH_3 **2.** $CH_3-CH_2-CH_3$

3. $CH_3-CH_2-CH_2-CH_3$

4.
$$CH_3-\underset{\underset{CH_3}{|}}{\overset{\overset{CH_3}{|}}{CH}}-CH-CH_3$$

◆ Learning Exercise 11.2C

Write the condensed structure and name for the straight-chain alkane of each of the following formulas:

1. C_2H_6 _____

2. C_3H_8 _____

3. C_4H_{10} _____

4. C_5H_{12} _____

5. C_6H_{14} _____

Answers
1. CH_3-CH_3, ethane
2. $CH_3-CH_2-CH_3$, propane
3. $CH_3-CH_2-CH_2-CH_3$, butane
4. $CH_3-CH_2-CH_2-CH_2-CH_3$, pentane
5. $CH_3-CH_2-CH_2-CH_2-CH_2-CH_3$, hexane

◆ Learning Exercise 11.2D

Write the IUPAC name for each of the following cycloalkanes:

Answers   **1.** cyclohexane   **2.** cyclobutane   **3.** cyclopentane   **4.** cyclopropane

11.3 Alkanes with Substituents

- The IUPAC system is a set of rules used to name organic compounds in a systematic manner.
- Each substituent is numbered and listed alphabetically in front of the name of the longest chain.
- Carbon groups that are substituents are named as alkyl groups or alkyl substituents. An alkyl group is named by replacing the *ane* of the alkane name with *yl*. For example, CH_3- is named as methyl (from CH_4 methane), and CH_3-CH_2- is named as an ethyl group (from CH_3-CH_3 ethane).
- Structural isomers have the same molecular formula but differ in the sequence of atoms in each of their structural formulas.
- In a haloalkane, a halogen atom, F, Cl, Br, or I, replaces a hydrogen atom in an alkane.
- A halogen atom is named as a substituent (fluoro, chloro, bromo, iodo) attached to the alkane chain.

Study Note

Example: Write the IUPAC name for the following compound:

$$CH_3-CH_2-\underset{\underset{CH_3}{|}}{\overset{\overset{CH_3}{|}}{CH}}-CH_3$$

Solution: The four-carbon chain butane is numbered from the end nearest the side group, which places the *methyl* substituent on carbon 2: *2-methylbutane*.

◆ **Learning Exercise 11.3A**

Provide a correct IUPAC name for each of the following compounds:

$$
\begin{array}{c}
\quad\quad CH_3 \\
\quad\quad | \\
\mathbf{1.}\ CH_3-CH-CH_3
\end{array}
$$ _____

$$
\begin{array}{c}
\quad\quad CH_3 \quad\quad\quad CH_3 \\
\quad\quad | \quad\quad\quad\quad\ | \\
\mathbf{2.}\ CH_3-CH-CH_2-CH-CH_2-CH_3
\end{array}
$$ _____

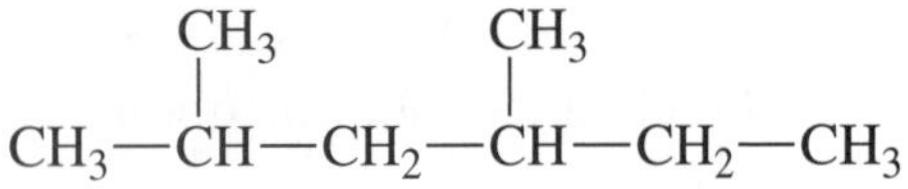

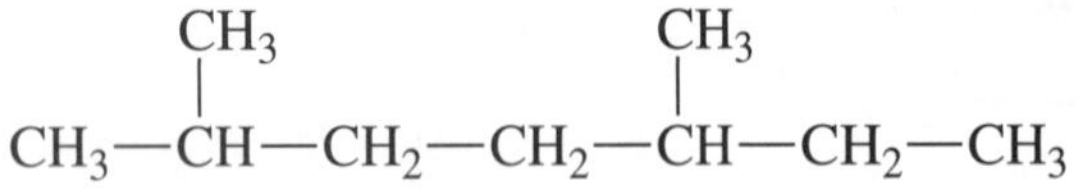

$$
\begin{array}{c}
\quad\quad CH_3 \quad\quad\quad\quad\quad CH_3 \\
\quad\quad | \quad\quad\quad\quad\quad\quad\quad | \\
\mathbf{3.}\ CH_3-CH-CH_2-CH_2-CH-CH_2-CH_3
\end{array}
$$ _____

$$
\begin{array}{c}
\quad\quad CH_3 \\
\quad\quad | \\
\mathbf{4.}\ CH_3-C-CH_2-CH_3 \\
\quad\quad | \\
\quad\quad CH_3
\end{array}
$$ _____

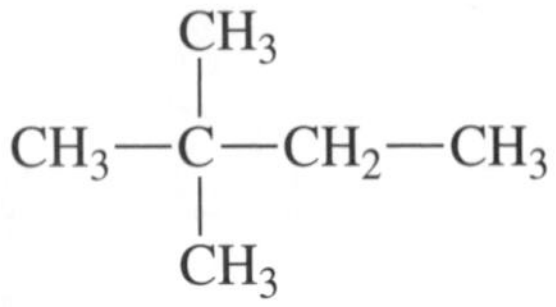

Answers   **1.** 2-methylpropane   **2.** 2,4-dimethylhexane   **3.** 2,5-dimethylheptane
4. 2,2-dimethylbutane

◆ **Learning Exercise 11.3B**

Write the condensed formula for each of the following compounds:

1. hexane   **2.** methane

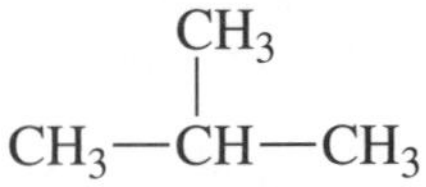

3. 2,4-dimethylpentane   **4.** propane

Answers   **1.** $CH_3-CH_2-CH_2-CH_2-CH_2-CH_3$ **2.** CH_4

$$
\begin{array}{c}
\quad\quad\quad CH_3 \quad\quad\quad CH_3 \\
\quad\quad\quad | \quad\quad\quad\quad\ | \\
\mathbf{3.}\ CH_3-CH-CH_2-CH-CH_3
\end{array}
$$ **4.** $CH_3-CH_2-CH_3$

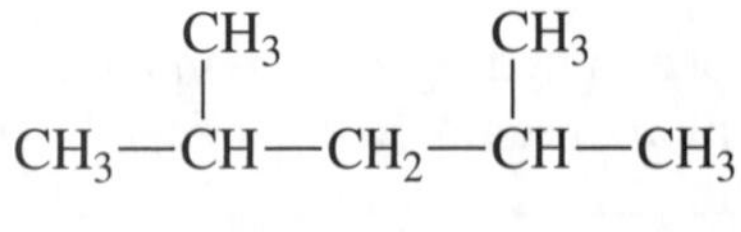

◆ **Learning Exercise 11.3C**

Write the condensed structural formula for each of the following alkanes or cycloalkanes:

1. pentane   **2.** 2-methylpentane

3. 4-ethyl-2-methylhexane   **4.** 2,2,4-trimethylhexane

5. 1,2-dichlorocyclobutane   **6.** methylcyclohexane

Answers

1. $CH_3—CH_2—CH_2—CH_3—CH_3$

2. 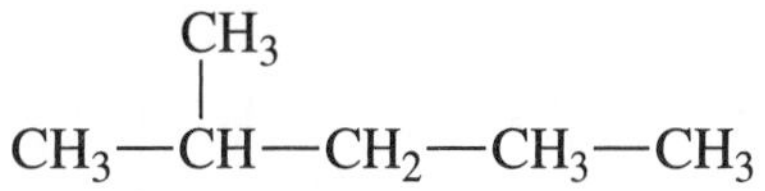
$$CH_3$$
$$|$$
$$CH_3—CH—CH_2—CH_3—CH_3$$

3.
$$CH_3 \qquad CH_2—CH_3$$
$$| \qquad\qquad |$$
$$CH_3—CH—CH_2—CH—CH_2—CH_3$$

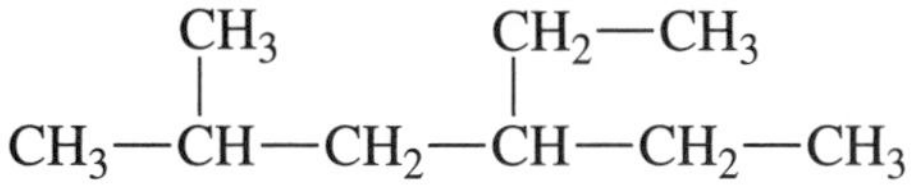

4. 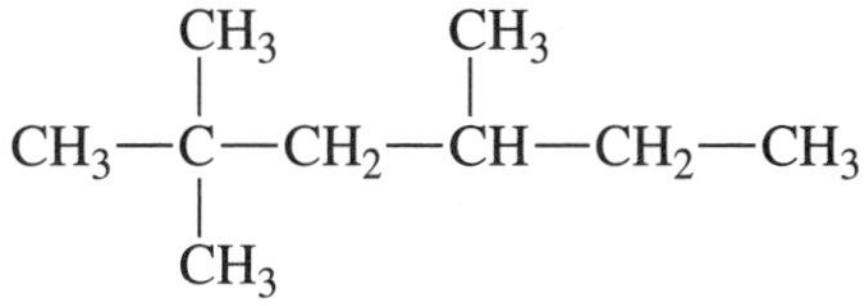
$$CH_3 \qquad CH_3$$
$$| \qquad\qquad |$$
$$CH_3—C—CH_2—CH—CH_2—CH_3$$
$$|$$
$$CH_3$$

5. 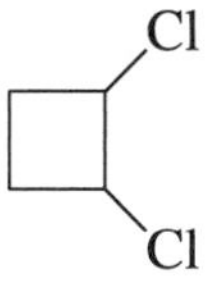
Cl — on cyclobutane ring
Cl

6. 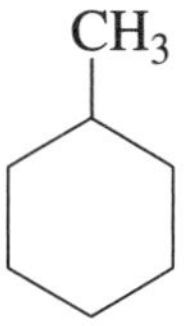
CH₃ — on cyclohexane ring

◆ Learning Exercise 11.3D

Write a correct IUPAC (or common name) for the following:

1. $CH_3—CH_2—Br$

2. 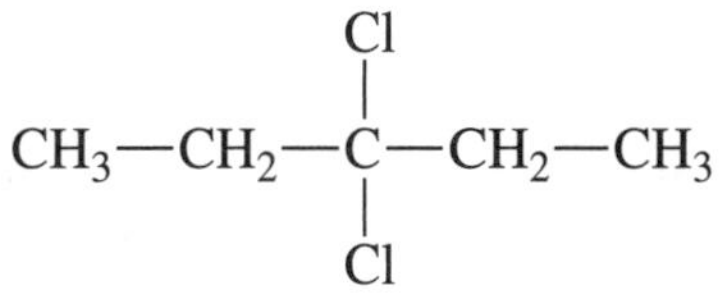
$$Cl$$
$$|$$
$$CH_3—CH_2—C—CH_2—CH_3$$
$$|$$
$$Cl$$

3.
$$Cl \qquad\qquad Br$$
$$| \qquad\qquad\quad |$$
$$CH_3—CH_2—CH—CH_2—CH—CH_3$$

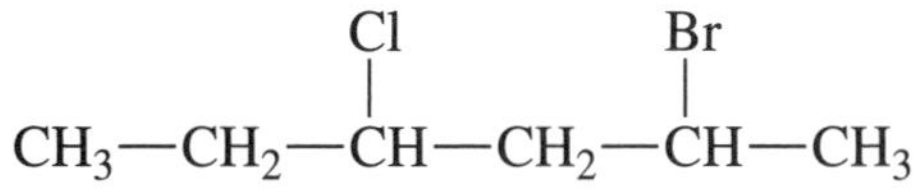

4. 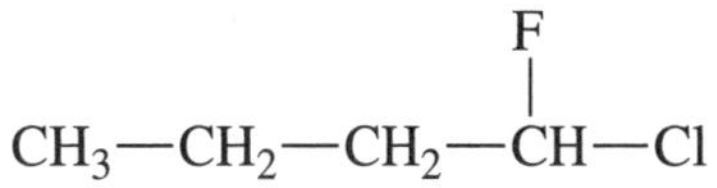
$$F$$
$$|$$
$$CH_3—CH_2—CH_2—CH—Cl$$

5.  Br

Answers   **1.** bromoethane (ethyl bromide)   **2.** 3,3-dichloropentane
                3. 2-bromo-4-chlorohexane   **4.** 1-chloro-1-fluorobutane
                5. bromocyclopropane

◆ Learning Exercise 11.3E

Write the condensed formula for each of the following haloalkanes:

1. ethyl chloride   **2.** bromomethane

3. 3-bromo-1-chloropentane   **4.** 1,1-dichlorohexane

5. 2,2,3-trichlorobutane   **6.** 2,4-dibromo-2,4-dichloropentane

Answers   **1.** CH_3-CH_2-Cl **2.** CH_3-Br

3. 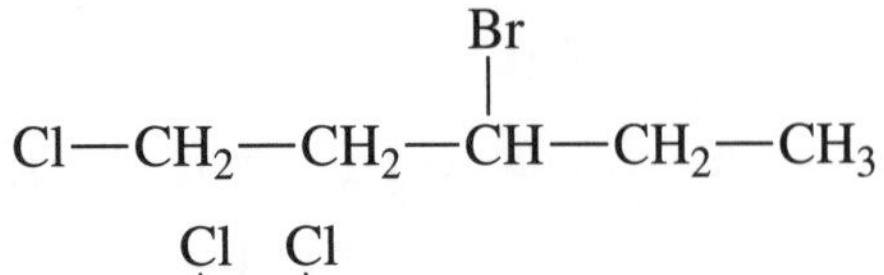
$$Cl-CH_2-CH_2-\overset{\overset{\displaystyle Br}{|}}{CH}-CH_2-CH_3$$

4. 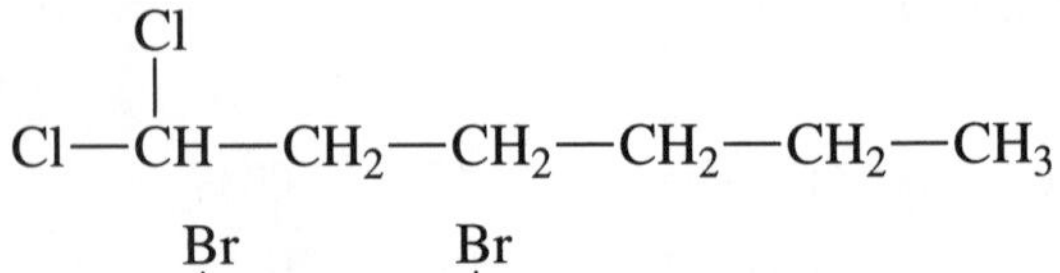
$$Cl-\overset{\overset{\displaystyle Cl}{|}}{CH}-CH_2-CH_2-CH_2-CH_2-CH_3$$

5. 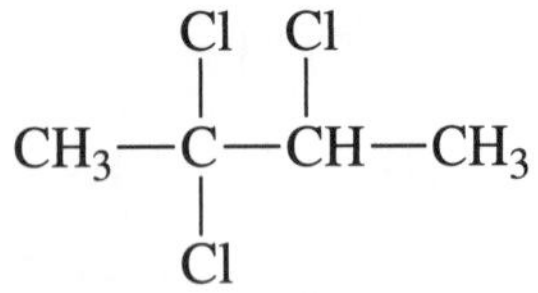
$$CH_3-\overset{\overset{\displaystyle Cl}{|}}{\underset{\underset{\displaystyle Cl}{|}}{C}}-\overset{\overset{\displaystyle Cl}{|}}{CH}-CH_3$$

6. 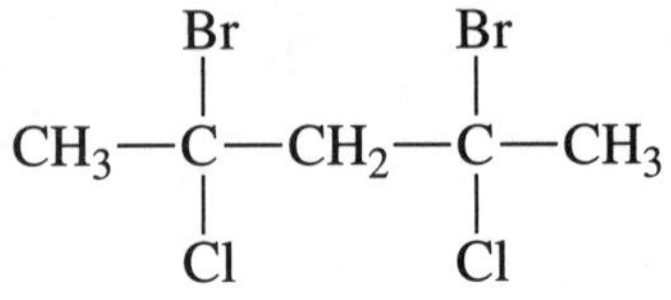
$$CH_3-\overset{\overset{\displaystyle Br}{|}}{\underset{\underset{\displaystyle Cl}{|}}{C}}-CH_2-\overset{\overset{\displaystyle Br}{|}}{\underset{\underset{\displaystyle Cl}{|}}{C}}-CH_3$$

11.4 Properties of Alkanes

• The alkanes are nonpolar, less dense than water, and mostly unreactive, except that they burn vigorously.
• Alkanes are found in natural gas, gasoline, and diesel fuels.
• In combustion, an alkane at a high temperature reacts rapidly with oxygen to produce carbon dioxide, water, and a great amount of heat.
• In halogenation, an atom of a halogen will replace one or more hydrogen atoms.

Study Note

Example: Write the equation for the combustion of methane.

Solution: Write the molecular formulas for the following reactants: methane (CH_4) and oxygen (O_2). Write the products CO_2 and H_2O and balance the equation.

$$CH_4(g) + O_2(g) \rightarrow CO_2(g) + H_2O(g) + \text{Heat}$$

$$CH_4(g) + 2O_2(g) \rightarrow CO_2(g) + 2H_2O(g) + \text{Heat (balanced)}$$

◆ **Learning Exercise 11.4A**

Write a balanced equation for the complete combustion of the following:

1. propane_____

2. hexane_____

3. pentane_____

4. cyclobutane_____

Answers
1. $C_3H_8 + 5O_2 \rightarrow 3CO_2 + 4H_2O$ + Heat
2. $2C_6H_{14} + 19O_2 \rightarrow 12CO_2 + 14H_2O$ + Heat
3. $C_5H_{12} + 8O_2 \rightarrow 5CO_2 + 6H_2O$ + Heat
4. $C_4H_8 + 6O_2 \rightarrow 4CO_2 + 4H_2O$ + Heat

◆ **Learning Exercise 11.4B**

Write the product of the monochlorination of:

1. ethane

2. methane

Answers
1. $CH_3—CH_2—Cl$

2. CH_3Cl

11.5 Functional Groups

- Organic compounds are classified by *functional groups*, which are atoms or groups of atoms where specific chemical reactions occur.
- Alkenes are hydrocarbons that contain one or more double bonds (C=C); alkynes contain a triple bond (C≡C).
- Alcohols contain a hydroxyl (—OH) group; ethers have an oxygen atom (—O—) between two alkyl groups.
- Aldehydes contain a carbonyl group (C=O) bonded to at least one H atom; ketones contain the carbonyl group bonded to two alkyl groups.
- Carboxylic acids have a carboxyl group attached to hydrogen (—COOH); esters contain the carboxyl groups attached to an alkyl group.
- Amines are derived from ammonia (NH_3) in which alkyl groups replace one or more of the H atoms.

◆ **Learning Exercise 11.5A**

Classify the organic compounds shown below according to their functional groups:

a. alkane   **b.** alkene   **c.** alcohol   **d.** ether   **e.** aldehyde

1. _____ $CH_3—CH_2—CH=CH_2$ 2. _____ $CH_3—CH_2—CH_3$

$$\overset{\displaystyle O}{\overset{\displaystyle \|}{}}$$

3. _____ $CH_3—CH_2—\overset{O}{\overset{\|}{C}}—H$ 4. _____ $CH_3—CH_2—CH_2—OH$

5. _____ $CH_3—CH_2—O—CH_2—CH_3$ 6. _____ $CH_3—CH_2—CH_2—CH_3$

Answers   1. b   2. a   3. e   4. c   5. d   6. a

◆ **Learning Exercise 11.5B**

Classify the following compounds according to their functional groups:

a. alcohol   **b.** aldehyde   **c.** ketone   **d.** ether   **e.** amine

1. ___ $CH_3—CH_2—CH_2—\overset{O}{\overset{\|}{C}}—H$ 2. ___ $CH_3—CH_2—CH_2—NH_2$

3. ___ $CH_3—CH_2—\overset{O}{\overset{\|}{C}}—CH_2—CH_3$ 4. ___ $CH_3—CH_2—O—CH_3$

195

5. _____ $CH_3-\overset{\overset{\displaystyle O}{\|}}{C}-CH_2-CH_3$

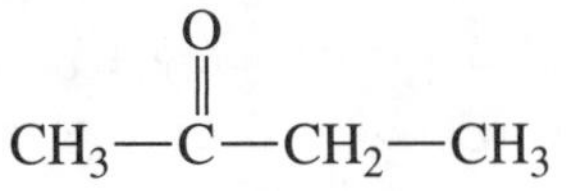

6. _____ $CH_3-\overset{\overset{\displaystyle O}{\|}}{C}-H$

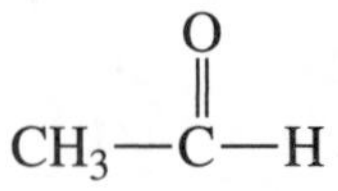

7. _____ $CH_3-CH_2-\overset{\overset{\displaystyle NH_2}{|}}{CH}-CH_3$

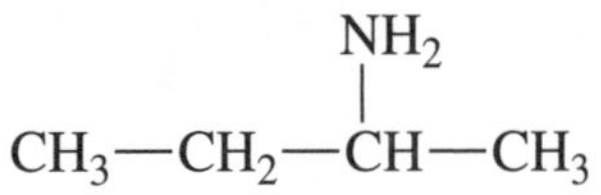

8. _____ $CH_3-CH_2-\overset{\overset{\displaystyle OH}{|}}{CH}-CH_3$

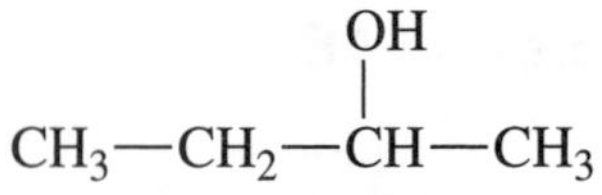

Answers	**1.** b	**2.** e	**3.** c	**4.** d
	5. c	**6.** b	**7.** e	**8.** a

Checklist for Chapter 11

You are ready to take the practice test for Chapter 11. Be sure that you have accomplished the following learning goals for this chapter. If you are not sure, review the section listed at the end of the goal. Then apply your new skills and understanding to the practice test.

After studying Chapter 11, I can successfully:

_____ Identify properties as characteristic of organic or inorganic compounds (11.1).

_____ Identify the number of bonds for carbon (11.1).

_____ Describe the tetrahedral shape of carbon in carbon compounds (11.1).

_____ Draw the expanded complete structural formula and the condensed structural formula for an alkane (11.2).

_____ Use the IUPAC system to write the names for alkanes and cycloalkanes (11.2).

_____ Use the IUPAC system to write the names for alkanes and cycloalkanes with substituents (11.3).

_____ Draw the structural formulas of alkanes from the name (11.3).

_____ Describe physical properties of alkanes (11.4).

_____ Balance equations for the combustion of alkanes (11.4).

_____ Draw the structure for the product of halogenation of an alkane (11.4).

_____ Identify the functional groups in organic compounds (11.5).

Practice Test for Chapter 11

For problems 1–8, indicate whether the following characteristics are typical of (O) organic compounds or (I) inorganic compounds.

1. _____ higher melting points

2. _____ fewer compounds

3. _____ covalent bonds

4. _____ soluble in water

5. _____ ionic bonds

6. _____ combustible

7. _____ low boiling points

8. _____ soluble in nonpolar solvents

Match the name of the hydrocarbon with each of the following structures:

A. methane   **B.** ethane   **C.** propane   **D.** pentane   **E.** heptane

9. _____ $CH_3-CH_2-CH_3$

10. _____ $CH_3-CH_2-CH_2-CH_2-CH_2-CH_2-CH_3$

11. _____ CH_4

12. _____ $CH_3-CH_2-CH_2-CH_2-CH_3$

13. _____ CH_3-CH_3

Match the name of the hydrocarbons with each of the following structures:
A. butane   **B.** methylcyclohexane   **C.** cyclopropane
D. 3,5-dimethylhexane   **E.** 2,4-dimethylhexane

14. _____ $CH_3-CH_2-CH_2-CH_3$

15. _____
$$CH_3-\overset{\overset{\displaystyle CH_3}{|}}{CH}-CH_2-\overset{\overset{\displaystyle CH_3}{|}}{CH}-CH_2-CH_3$$

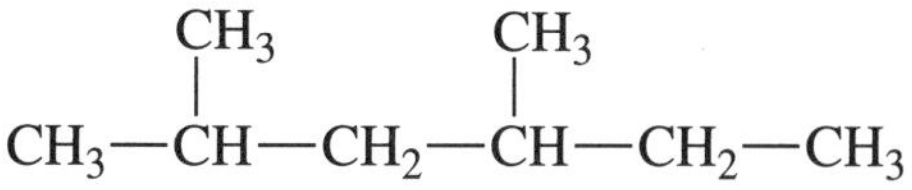

16. _____ △

17. _____

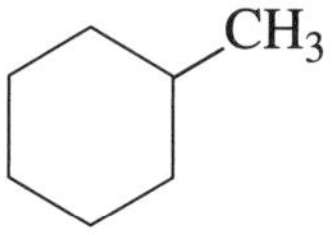

Match the name of the hydrocarbon with each of the following structures:
A. methylcyclopentane   **B.** cyclobutane
C. cyclohexane   **D.** ethylcyclopentane

18. _____   **19.** 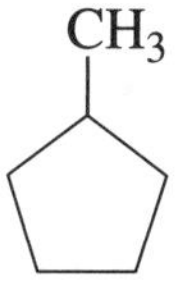 _____   **20.** _____

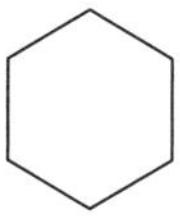

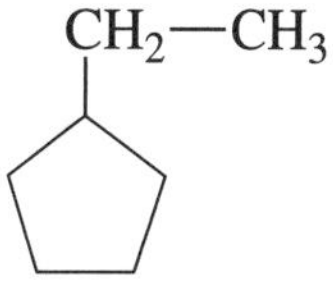

Match each of the following compounds with the correct name:
A. 2,4-dichloropentane   **B.** chlorocyclopentane
C. 1,2-dichloropentane   **D.** 4,5-dichloropentane

21. _____ 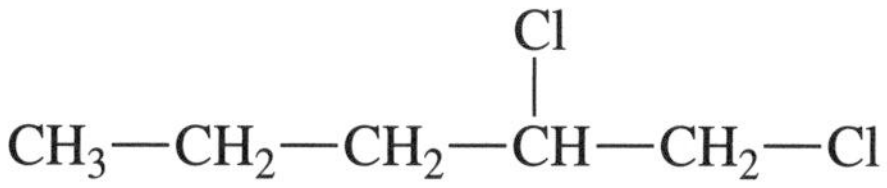
$$CH_3-CH_2-CH_2-\overset{\overset{\displaystyle Cl}{|}}{CH}-CH_2-Cl$$
        22. _____

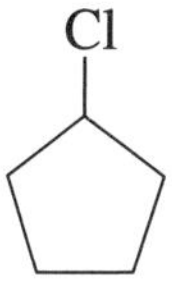

23. _____
$$CH_3-\overset{\overset{\displaystyle Cl}{|}}{CH}-CH_2-\overset{\overset{\displaystyle Cl}{|}}{CH}-CH_3$$

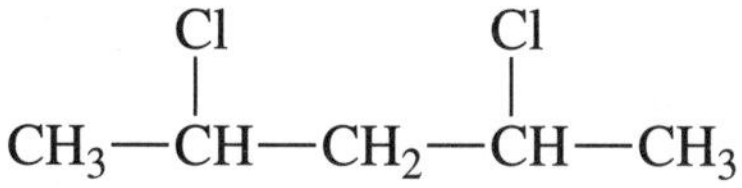

24. The correctly balanced equation for the complete combustion of ethane is
     A. $C_2H_6 + O_2 \rightarrow 2CO + 3H_2O$ **B.** $C_2H_6 + O_2 \rightarrow CO_2 + H_2O$
     C. $C_2H_6 + 2O_2 \rightarrow 2CO_2 + 3H_2O$ **D.** $2C_2H_6 + 7O_2 \rightarrow 4CO_2 + 6H_2O$
     E. $2C_2H_6 + 4O_2 \rightarrow 4CO_2 + 6H_2O$

Classify the compounds in problems 25–33 by the functional groups.
A. alkane   **B.** alkene   **C.** alcohol   **D.** aldehyde
E. ketone   **F.** ether   **G.** amine   **H.** amide

25. _____
$$CH_3-CH_2-\overset{\overset{\displaystyle O}{||}}{C}-NH_2$$

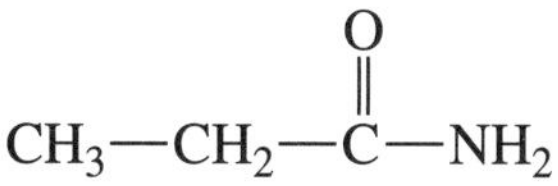

26. _____ 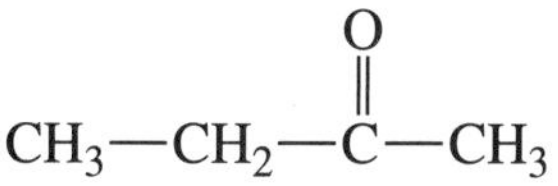
$$CH_3-CH_2-\overset{\overset{\displaystyle O}{||}}{C}-CH_3$$
        27. _____ $CH_3-CH_2-CH_2-OH$

28. _____ 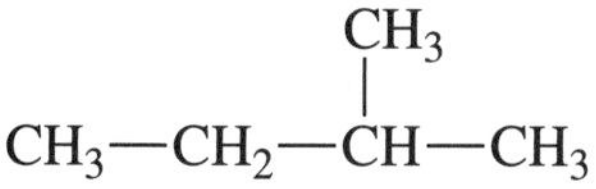
$$CH_3-CH_2-\overset{\overset{\displaystyle CH_3}{|}}{CH}-CH_3$$
        29. _____ $CH_3-CH_2-O-CH_3$

30. _____ 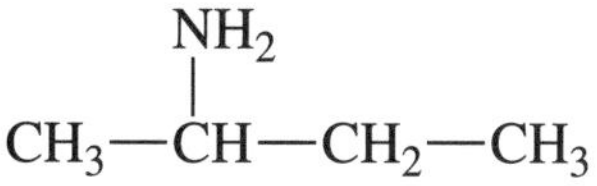
$$CH_3-\overset{\overset{\displaystyle NH_2}{|}}{CH}-CH_2-CH_3$$
        31. _____
$$CH_3-\overset{\overset{\displaystyle O}{||}}{C}-H$$

197

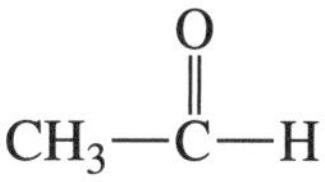

$$\overset{\displaystyle CH_3}{\underset{\displaystyle |}{\text{}}}$$

32. ____ $CH_3-CH_2-\overset{CH_3}{\underset{|}{CH}}-CH_3$ 33. ____ $CH_3-CH_2-\overset{OH}{\underset{|}{CH}}-CH_3$

Indicate whether the pairs of compounds in problems 34–38 are isomers (I), the same compound (S), or different compounds (D).

34. ____ $CH_3-CH_2-CH_2-CH_3$ and $CH_3-\overset{CH_3}{\underset{|}{CH}}-CH_3$

35. ____ CH_3-CH_2-OH and $CH_3-\overset{O}{\overset{||}{C}}-H$

36. ____ $CH_3-CH_2-NH_2$ and $CH_3-\overset{H}{\underset{|}{N}}-CH_2-CH_3$

37. ____ $CH_3-CH_2-\overset{O}{\overset{||}{C}}-OH$ and $CH_3-\overset{O}{\overset{||}{C}}-O-CH_3$

38. ____ $CH_3-CH_2-CH_2-CH_3$ and $CH_3-C\equiv C-CH_3$

Answers to Practice Test

1. I	**2.** I	**3.** O	**4.** I	**5.** I
6. O	**7.** O	**8.** O	**9.** C	**10.** E
11. A	**12.** D	**13.** B	**14.** A	**15.** E
16. C	**17.** B	**18.** D	**19.** A	**20.** E
21. C	**22.** B	**23.** A	**24.** D	**25.** H
26. E	**27.** C	**28.** A	**29.** F	**30.** G
31. D	**32.** A	**33.** C	**34.** I	**35.** D
36. D	**37.** I	**38.** D		

Answers to Selected Problems

11.1 Organic compounds contain C and H and sometimes O, N, or a halogen atom. Inorganic compounds usually contain elements other than C and H.
  a. inorganic   **b.** organic   **c.** organic
  d. inorganic   **e.** inorganic   **f.** organic

11.3 **a.** Inorganic compounds are usually soluble in water.
  b. Organic compounds have lower boiling points than most inorganic compounds.
  c. Organic compounds often burn in air.
  d. Inorganic compounds are more likely to be solids at room temperature.

11.5 **a.** ethane   **b.** ethane   **c.** NaBr   **d.** NaBr

11.7 VSEPR theory predicts that the four bonds in CH_4 will be as far apart as possible, which means that the hydrogen atoms are at the corners of a tetrahedron.

11.9 **a.** In expanded formulas, each C—H and each C—C bond is drawn separately.

$$H-\overset{H}{\underset{H}{C}}-\overset{H}{\underset{H}{C}}-\overset{H}{\underset{H}{C}}-H$$

b. A condensed formula groups hydrogen atoms with each carbon atom.

$$CH_3—CH_2—CH_2—CH_2—CH_2—CH_3$$

c. A line-bond formula shows only the bonds connecting the carbon atoms.

11.11 **a.** Pentane is a carbon chain of five (5) carbon atoms.
b. Heptane is a carbon chain of seven (7) carbon atoms.
c. Hexane is a carbon chain of six (6) carbon atoms.
d. Cyclobutane is the geometric figure with four (4) carbons.

11.13 **a.** CH_4 **b.** $CH_3—CH_3$ **c.** $CH_3—CH_2—CH_2—CH_2—CH_3$ **d.**

11.15 **a.** same molecule   **b.** isomers of C_5H_{12} **c.** isomers of C_6H_{14}

11.17 **a.** 2-methylbutane   **b.** 2,2-dimethylpropane
c. 2,3-dimethylpentane   **d.** 4-ethyl-2,2-dimethylhexane

11.19 **a.** A ring of five carbon atoms with one chlorine atom is chlorocyclopentane; no numbering is needed for a single substituent.
b. A ring of six carbon atoms with one methyl group is methylcyclohexane; no numbering is needed for a single substituent.
c. 1-bromo-3-methylcyclobutane
d. 1-bromo-2-chlorocyclopentane

11.21. Draw the main chain with the number of carbon atoms in the ending. For example, butane has a main chain of four carbon atoms, and hexane has a main chain of six carbon atoms. Attach substituents on the carbon atoms indicated. For example, in 3-methylpentane, a $CH_3—$ group is bonded to carbon 3 of a five-carbon chain.

11.23 Draw the cyclic structure first, and then attach the substituents. When there are two or more substituents, start with the first on a carbon assigned number 1 and continue around the ring.

199

11.25 In the IUPAC system, the halogen substituent is named with the prefix *halo-* on the main chain of carbon atom.
   a. bromoethane   **b.** 1-fluoropropane
   c. 2-chloropropane   **d.** trichloromethane

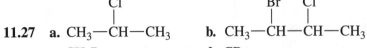

11.27   a. $CH_3—\overset{\overset{\displaystyle Cl}{|}}{CH}—CH_3$ **b.** $CH_3—\overset{\overset{\displaystyle Br}{|}}{CH}—\overset{\overset{\displaystyle Cl}{|}}{CH}—CH_3$
   c. CH_3Br **d.** CBr_4

11.29   a. $CH_3—CH_2—CH_2—CH_2—CH_2—CH_2—CH_3$
   b. liquid   **c.** insoluble in water
   d. float

11.31 Longer carbon chains have higher boiling points. The boiling points of branched alkanes are usually lower than the same number of carbon atoms in a continuous chain. Cycloalkanes have higher boiling points than continuous-chain alkanes.
   a. Heptane has a longer carbon chain.
   b. cyclopropane
   c. The continuous chain hexane has a higher boiling point than its branched-chain isomer.

11.33 In combustion, a hydrocarbon reacts with oxygen to yield CO_2 and H_2O.
   a. $2C_2H_6 + 7O_2 \rightarrow 4CO_2 + 6H_2O$ **b.** $2C_3H_6 + 9O_2 \rightarrow 6CO_2 + 6H_2O$
   c. $2C_8H_{18} + 25O_2 \rightarrow 16CO_2 + 18H_2O$ **d.** $C_6H_{12} + 9O_2 \rightarrow 6CO_2 + 6H_2O$

11.35   a. $CH_3—CH_2—Cl$ **b.**   Cl

   c. $CH_3—\overset{\overset{\displaystyle CH_3}{|}}{CH}—CH_2—Cl$ $CH_3—\overset{\overset{\displaystyle CH_3}{|}}{\underset{\underset{\displaystyle Cl}{|}}{C}}—CH_3$

11.37   a. Alcohols contain a hydroxyl group (—OH).
   b. Alkenes have carbon-carbon double bonds.
   c. Aldehydes contain a $C{=}O$ bonded to at least one H atom.
   d. Esters contain a carboxyl group attached to an alkyl group.

11.39   a. Ethers have an —O— group.
   b. Alcohols have a —OH group.
   c. Ketones have a $C{=}O$ group between alkyl groups.
   d. Carboxylic acids have a —COOH group.
   e. Amines contain a N atom.

11.41   a. aromatic, ether, alcohol, ketone
   b. aromatic, ether, alkene, ester

11.43 aromatic, ether, amide

11.45   a. Organic compounds have covalent bonds; inorganic compounds have ionic as well as polar covalent bonds, and a few have nonpolar covalent bonds.
   b. Most organic compounds are insoluble in water; inorganic compounds are soluble in water.
   c. Most organic compounds have low melting points; inorganic compounds have high melting points.
   d. Most organic compounds are flammable; inorganic compounds are not flammable.

11.47 **a.** Butane; organic compounds have low melting points.
b. Butane; organic compounds burn vigorously in air.
c. Potassium chloride; inorganic compounds have high melting points.
d. Potassium chloride; inorganic compounds (ionic) produce ions in water.
e. Butane; organic compounds are more likely to be gases at room temperature.

11.49 **a.**
$$
\begin{array}{c}
\quad\; H \;\; H \\
\quad\; | \;\;\; | \\
H-C-C-H \\
\quad\; | \;\;\; | \\
\quad\; H \;\; H
\end{array}
$$

b.
$$
\begin{array}{c}
\quad\; H \;\; H \\
\quad\; | \;\;\; | \\
H-C-C-O-H \\
\quad\; | \;\;\; | \\
\quad\; H \;\; H
\end{array}
$$

c.
$$
\begin{array}{c}
\quad\; H \;\; H \;\; O \\
\quad\; | \;\;\; | \;\;\; || \\
H-C-C-C-H \\
\quad\; | \;\;\; | \\
\quad\; H \;\; H
\end{array}
$$

d.
$$
\begin{array}{c}
\quad\; H \quad\quad H \;\; H \\
\quad\; | \quad\quad\; | \;\;\; | \\
H-C-O-C-C-H \\
\quad\; | \quad\quad\; | \;\;\; | \\
\quad\; H \quad\quad H \;\; H
\end{array}
$$

11.51 **a.** methyl **b.** propyl **c.** isopropyl **d.** ethyl

11.53 **a.** $CH_3-CH_2-\overset{\overset{\displaystyle CH_3}{|}}{CH}-CH_2-CH_2-CH_3$

b.

c. $Cl-CH_2-CH_2-\overset{\overset{\displaystyle CH_3}{|}}{\underset{\underset{\displaystyle Cl}{|}}{C}}-CH_2-CH_2-CH_2-CH_3$

d.

11.55 A line-bond formula shows only the bonds connecting the carbon atoms. The number of bonds to hydrogen atoms is understood.

a.   **b.**   **c.**

11.57 Condensed structural formula: $CH_3-\overset{\overset{\displaystyle CH_3}{|}}{\underset{\underset{\displaystyle CH_3}{|}}{C}}-CH_2-\overset{\overset{\displaystyle CH_3}{|}}{CH}-CH_3$

molecular formula: C_8H_{18}

The combustion reaction: $2C_8H_{18} + 25O_2 \rightarrow 16CO_2 + 18H_2O$

11.59 **a.** heptane **b.** cyclopentane **c.** hexane

11.61 **a.** $C_3H_8 + 5O_2 \rightarrow 3CO_2 + 4H_2O$
b. $C_5H_{12} + 8O_2 \rightarrow 5CO_2 + 6H_2O$
c. $C_4H_8 + 6O_2 \rightarrow 4CO_2 + 4H_2O$
d. $2C_8H_{18} + 25O_2 \rightarrow 16CO_2 + 18H_2O$

11.63 **a.** CH_3-CH_2-Cl

b. $CH_3-CH_2-CH_2-Cl$ and $CH_3-\overset{\overset{\displaystyle Cl}{|}}{CH}-CH_3$

c. (chlorocyclopentane)

11.65 **a.** alcohol   **b.** alkene   **c.** aldehyde   **d.** alkane
e. carboxylic acid   **f.** amine   **g.** tetrahedral

11.67 **a.** $C_5H_{12} + 8O_2 \rightarrow 5CO_2 + 6H_2O$
b. 72.0 g/mole

c. $1 \text{ gal} \times \dfrac{3.78 \text{ L}}{1 \text{ gal}} \times \dfrac{1000 \text{ mL}}{1 \text{ L}} \times \dfrac{0.63 \text{ g}}{1 \text{ mL}} \times \dfrac{1 \text{ mole } C_5H_{12}}{72.0 \text{ g}} \times \dfrac{845 \text{ kcal}}{1 \text{ mole}} = 2.8 \times 10^4 \text{ kcal}$

d. $1 \text{ gal} \times \dfrac{3.78 \text{ L}}{1 \text{ gal}} \times \dfrac{1000 \text{ mL}}{1 \text{ L}} \times \dfrac{0.63 \text{ g}}{1 \text{ mL}} \times \dfrac{1 \text{ mole } C_5H_{12}}{72.0 \text{ g}} \times \dfrac{5 \text{ moles } CO_2}{1 \text{ mole } C_5H_{12}} \times \dfrac{22.4 \text{ L}}{1 \text{ mole}} = 3700 \text{ L}$

11.69 $CH_3-\overset{\overset{\displaystyle CH_3}{|}}{CH}-\overset{\overset{\displaystyle CH_3}{|}}{CH}-CH_3 \qquad CH_3-\overset{\overset{\displaystyle CH_3}{|}}{\underset{\underset{\displaystyle CH_3}{|}}{C}}-CH_2-CH_3$

11.71 **a.** $CH_3-CH_2-CH_3$
b. $C_3H_8 + 5O_2 \rightarrow 3CO_2 + 4H_2O$

c. $12.0 \text{ L } C_3H_8 \times \dfrac{1 \text{ mole } C_3H_8}{22.4 \text{ L } C_3H_8} \times \dfrac{5 \text{ moles } O_2}{1 \text{ mole } C_3H_8} \times \dfrac{32.0 \text{ g } O_2}{1 \text{ mole } O_2} = 85.7 \text{ g } O_2$

d. $12.0 \text{ L } C_3H_8 \times \dfrac{1 \text{ mole } C_3H_8}{22.4 \text{ L } C_3H_8} \times \dfrac{3 \text{ moles } CO_2}{1 \text{ mole } C_3H_8} \times \dfrac{44.0 \text{ g } CO_2}{1 \text{ mole } CO_2} = 70.7 \text{ g } CO_2$

12
Unsaturated Hydrocarbons

Study Goals

- Classify unsaturated compounds as alkenes, cycloalkenes, and alkynes.
- Write IUPAC and common names for alkenes and alkynes.
- Write structural formulas and names for cis-trans isomers of alkenes.
- Write equations for halogenation, hydration, and hydrogenation of alkenes and alkynes.
- Describe the formation of a polymer from alkene monomers.
- Describe the bonding in benzene.
- Write structural formulas and give the names of aromatic compounds.
- Describe the physical and chemical properties of aromatic compounds.

Think About It

1. The label on a bottle of vegetable oil says the oil is unsaturated. What does this mean?

2. What are polymers?

3. A margarine is partially hydrogenated. What does that mean?

Key Terms

Match the statements shown below with the following key terms.

    a. alkene   **b.** hydrogenation   **c.** alkyne
    d. hydration   **e.** polymer

1. _____ A long-chain molecule formed by linking many small molecules.

2. _____ The addition of H_2 to a carbon–carbon double bond.

3. _____ An unsaturated hydrocarbon containing a carbon–carbon double bond.

4. _____ The addition of H_2O to a carbon–carbon double bond.

5. _____ A compound that contains a triple bond.

Answers   **1.** e   **2.** b   **3.** a   **4.** d   **5.** c

12.1 Alkenes and Alkynes

- Alkenes are unsaturated hydrocarbons that contain one or more carbon–carbon double bond.
- In alkenes, the three groups bonded to the carbons in the double bond are planar and arranged at angles of 120°.
- Alkynes are unsaturated hydrocarbons that contain a carbon–carbon triple bond.
- The atoms bonded to a carbon–carbon triple bond are linear.
- The IUPAC names of alkenes are derived by changing the *ane* ending of the parent alkane to *ene*. For example, the IUPAC name of $H_2C{=}CH_2$ is ethene. It has a common name of ethylene. In alkenes,

the longest carbon chain containing the double bond is numbered from the end nearest the double bond. In cycloalkenes with substituents, the double bond carbons are given positions of 1 and 2, and the ring is numbered to give the next lower numbers to the substituents.

$$CH_3—CH=CH_2 \qquad CH_2=CH—CH_2—CH_3 \qquad CH_3—CH=\overset{\overset{\displaystyle CH_3}{|}}{C}—CH_3$$

Propene (propylene)   1-Butene   2-Methylbutene

- The alkynes are a family of unsaturated hydrocarbons that contain a triple bond. They use naming rules similar to the alkenes, but the parent chain ends with *yne*.

$$HC\equiv CH \qquad\qquad CH_3—C\equiv CH$$
ethyne   propyne

◆ Learning Exercise 12.1A

Classify the following structural formulas as alkane, alkene, cycloalkene, or alkyne:

1. _____ $CH_3—CH_2—CH_3$

2. _____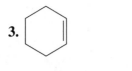

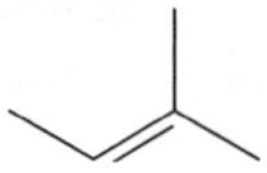

3. _____ $CH_3—C\equiv C—CH_3$

4. _____ $CH_3—CH_2—CH=\overset{\overset{\displaystyle CH_3}{|}}{C}—CH_2—CH_3$

Answers   **1.** alkane   **2.** alkene   **3.** alkyne   **4.** alkene

◆ Learning Exercise 12.1B

Write the IUPAC (and common name, if one) for each of the following alkenes:

1. $CH_3CH=CH_2$

2. $CH_3—CH=CH—CH_3$

_____   _____

3. (hexagon with double bond)

4. $CH_2=CH—\overset{\overset{\displaystyle Cl}{|}}{CH}—CH_2—\overset{\overset{\displaystyle CH_3}{|}}{CH}—CH_3$

_____   _____

5. $CH_3—CH=\overset{\overset{\displaystyle CH_3}{|}}{C}—CH_2—CH_3$

6. $CH_3—CH_2—\overset{\overset{\displaystyle CH_2}{||}}{CH}$

_____   _____

Answers   **1.** propene (propylene)   **2.** 2-butene   **3.** cyclohexene
              4. 3-chloro-5-methyl-1-hexene   **5.** 3-methyl-2-pentene   **6.** 1-butene

◆ **Learning Exercise 12.1C**

Write the IUPAC and common name (if any) of each of the following alkynes:

1. HC≡CH   **2.** CH_3—C≡CH

3. CH_3—CH_2—C≡CH

4.
$$CH_3\text{—}\underset{\underset{\displaystyle CH_3}{|}}{CH}\text{—}C≡C\text{—}CH_3$$

Answers   **1.** ethyne (acetylene)   **2.** propyne (methylacetylene)
              3. 1-butyne (ethylacetylene)   **4.** 4-methyl-2-pentyne

◆ **Learning Exercise 12.1D**

Draw the condensed structural formula for each of the following:

1. 2-pentyne   **2.** 2-chloro-2-butene

3. 3-bromo-2-methyl-2-pentene   **4.** 3-methylcyclohexene

Answers   **1.** CH_3—C≡C—CH_2—CH_3

2.
$$CH_3\text{—}CH=\underset{\underset{\displaystyle CH_3}{|}}{\overset{\overset{\displaystyle Cl}{|}}{C}}$$

3.
$$CH_3\text{—}\underset{\underset{\displaystyle CH_3}{|}}{C}=\overset{\overset{\displaystyle Br}{|}}{C}\text{—}CH_2\text{—}CH_3$$

4.

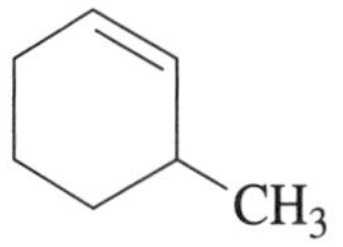

12.2 Cis-Trans Isomers

•   Cis-trans isomers are possible for alkenes because there is not rotation around the rigid double bond.
•   In the cis isomer, groups are attached on the same side of the double bond, whereas in the trans isomer, they are attached on the opposite sides of the double bond.

◆ **Learning Exercise 12.2A**

Write the cis-trans isomers of 2,3-dibromo-2-butene and name each.

Answers

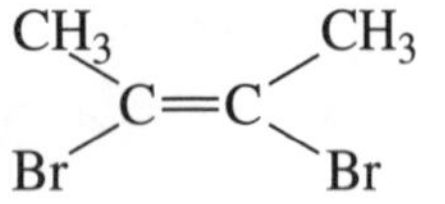

$$CH_3\diagdown_{Br}C=C\diagup^{CH_3}_{Br}\qquad CH_3\diagdown_{Br}C=C\diagup^{Br}_{CH_3}$$

cis-2,3-dibromo-2-butene 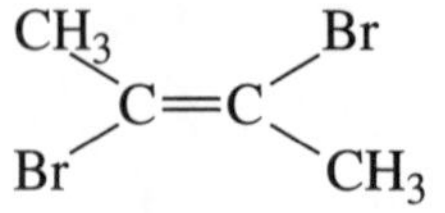   trans-2,3-dibromo-2-butene

In the cis-isomer, the bromine atoms are attached on the same side of the double bond; in the trans-isomer, they are on opposite sides.

◆ **Learning Exercise 12.2B**

Name the following alkenes using the cis-trans where isomers are possible:

1. 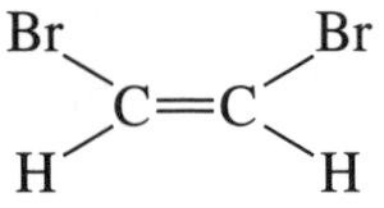
$$Br\diagdown_{H}C=C\diagup^{Br}_{H}$$

2. 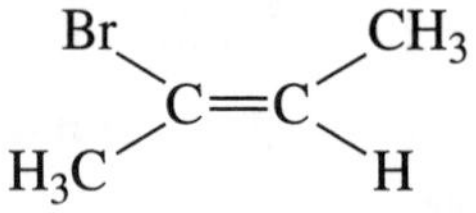
$$Br\diagdown_{H_3C}C=C\diagup^{CH_3}_{H}$$

3.
$$Cl\diagdown_{H_3C}C=C\diagup^{H}_{H}$$

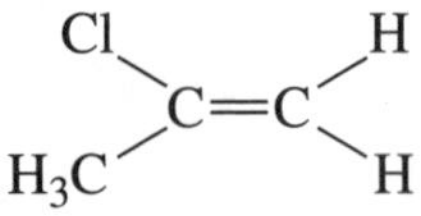

4. 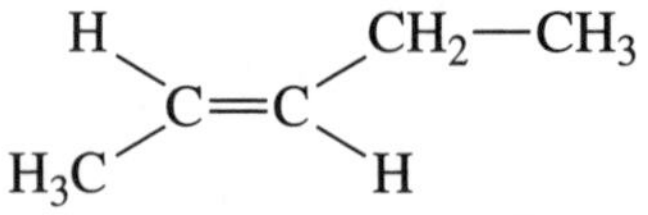
$$H\diagdown_{H_3C}C=C\diagup^{CH_2-CH_3}_{H}$$

Answers
1. *cis*-1,2-dibromoethene
3. 2-chloropropene (not a cis-trans isomer)

2. *trans*-2-butene
4. *trans*-2-pentene

12.3 Addition Reactions

- The addition of small molecules to the double bond is a characteristic reaction of alkenes.
- Hydrogenation adds hydrogen atoms to the double bond of an alkene or the triple bond of an alkyne to yield an alkane.

$$CH_2{=}CH_2 + H_2 \xrightarrow{\text{Pt}} CH_3{-}CH_3$$
$$HC{\equiv}CH + 2H_2 \longrightarrow CH_3{-}CH_3$$

- Halogenation adds bromine or chlorine atoms to produce dihaloalkanes.

$$CH_2{=}CH_2 + Br_2 \longrightarrow Br{-}CH_2{-}CH_2{-}Br$$

- Hydrohalogenation adds hydrogen halides, and hydration adds water to a double bond.

$$CH_2{=}CH_2 + HCl \longrightarrow CH_3{-}CH_2{-}Cl$$

$$CH_2{=}CH_2 + HOH \xrightarrow{H^+} CH_3{-}CH_2{-}OH$$

- According to Markovnikov's rule, the H from the reactant (HX or HOH) bonds to the carbon in the double bond that has the greater number of hydrogen atoms.

◆ **Learning Exercise 12.3A**

Write the products of the following addition reactions:

1. $CH_3{-}CH_2{-}CH{=}CH_2 + H_2 \xrightarrow{Pt}$

2.  ⬠ + $H_2 \xrightarrow{Pt}$

3. $CH_3{-}CH{=}CH{-}CH_2{-}CH_3 + Cl_2 \longrightarrow$

4. $CH_3{-}CH{=}CH_2 + H_2 \xrightarrow{Pt}$

5. $CH_3{-}CH{=}CH{-}CH_3 + Br_2 \longrightarrow$

Answers   **1.** $CH_3{-}CH_2{-}CH_2{-}CH_3$ **2.** 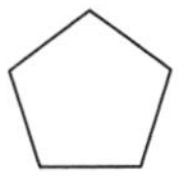 ⬠

3. $CH_3{-}\overset{\overset{\displaystyle Cl}{|}}{C}H{-}\overset{\overset{\displaystyle Cl}{|}}{C}H{-}CH_2{-}CH_3$ **4.** $CH_3{-}CH_2{-}CH_3$

5. $CH_3{-}\overset{\overset{\displaystyle Br}{|}}{C}H{-}\overset{\overset{\displaystyle Br}{|}}{C}H{-}CH_3$

◆ **Learning Exercise 12.3B**

1. $CH_3{-}CH{=}CH{-}CH_3 + HCl \longrightarrow$

2. $CH_3{-}\overset{\overset{\displaystyle CH_3}{|}}{C}{=}CH_2 + HBr \longrightarrow$

3. $CH_3{-}CH{=}CH_2 + HOH \xrightarrow{H^+}$

4. $CH_3{-}CH_2{-}CH{=}\overset{\overset{\displaystyle CH_3}{|}}{C}{-}CH_3 + HBr \longrightarrow$

5.  ⬠ + $H_2O \xrightarrow{H^+}$

Answers

1. $CH_3{-}CH_2{-}\overset{\overset{\displaystyle Cl}{|}}{C}H{-}CH_3$ **2.** $CH_3{-}\overset{\overset{\displaystyle CH_3}{|}}{\underset{\underset{\displaystyle Br}{|}}{C}}{-}CH_3$ **3.** $CH_3{-}\overset{\overset{\displaystyle OH}{|}}{C}H{-}CH_3$

$$\text{4.} \quad CH_3-CH_2-CH_2-\underset{\underset{Br}{|}}{\overset{\overset{CH_3}{|}}{C}}-CH_3 \qquad \text{5.} \quad \text{(cyclopentanol with OH)}$$

12.4 Polymerization of Alkenes

- *Polymers* are large molecules prepared from the bonding of many small units called *monomers*.
- Many synthetic polymers are made from small alkene monomers.

◆ Learning Check 12.4A

Write the formula of the alkene monomer that would be used for each of the following polymers:

1.
```
    H   H   H   H   H   H
    |   |   |   |   |   |
 —C — C — C — C — C — C—
    |   |   |   |   |   |
    H   H   H   H   H   H
```

2.
```
    H  CH3 H  CH3 H  CH3
    |   |   |   |   |   |
 —C — C — C — C — C — C—
    |   |   |   |   |   |
    H   H   H   H   H   H
```

3.
```
    F   F   F   F   F   F
    |   |   |   |   |   |
 —C — C — C — C — C — C—
    |   |   |   |   |   |
    F   F   F   F   F   F
```

Answers   1. $H_2C{=}CH_2$ 2. $H_2C{=}\overset{\overset{CH_3}{|}}{CH}$ 3. $F_2C{=}CF_2$

◆ Learning Check 12.4B

Write three sections of the polymer that would result when 1,1-difluoroethene is the monomer unit.

Answer
```
    F   H   F   H   F   H
    |   |   |   |   |   |
 —C — C — C — C — C — C—
    |   |   |   |   |   |
    F   H   F   H   F   H
```

12.5 Aromatic Compounds

- Most aromatic compounds contain benzene, a cyclic structure containing six CH units. The structure of benzene is represented as a hexagon with a circle in the center.
- The names of many aromatic compounds use the parent name benzene, although many common names were retained as IUPAC names, such as toluene, phenol, and aniline. For two branches, the positions are often shown by the prefixes *ortho* (1,2-), *meta* (1,3-), and *para* (1,4-).

◆ Learning Exercise 12.5

Write the IUPAC (or common name) for each of the following:

1.

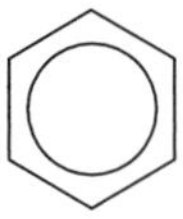

2.

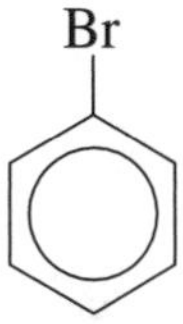

3.

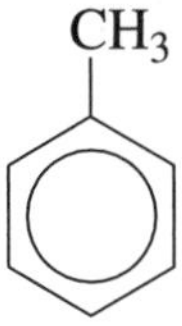

4.

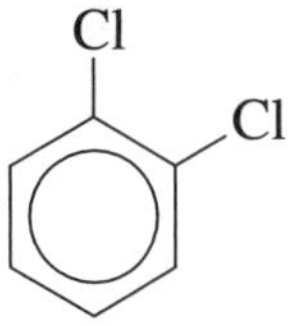

5.

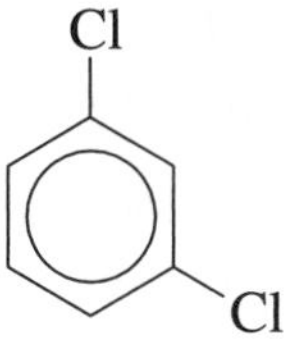

6.

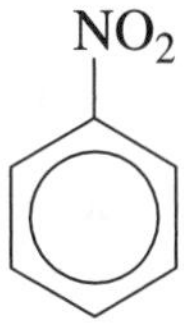

7.

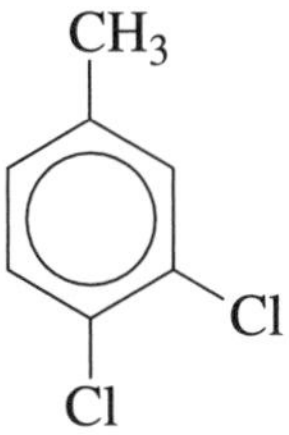

8.

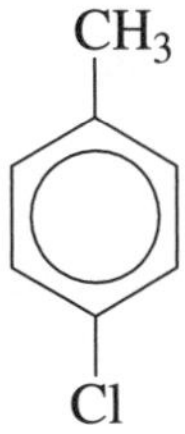

Answers   **1.** benzene   **2.** bromobenzene   **3.** methylbenzene; toluene
4. 1,2-dichlorobenzene; *o*-dichlorobenzene   **5.** 1,3-dichlorobenzene; *m*-dichlorobenzene
6. nitrobenzene   **7.** 3,4-dichlorotoluene   **8.** 4-chlorotoluene; *p*-chlorotoluene

12.6 Properties of Aromatic Compounds

- Aromatic compounds have higher melting and boiling points than cycloalkanes.
- Aromatic compounds undergo substitution reactions of halogenation, nitration, and sulfonation.

◆ Learning Exercise 12.6

Write the missing reactant, catalyst, or product for each of the following reactions:

a. Benzene and Br_2 $\xrightarrow{FeBr_2}$

b. Benzene and SO_3 $\xrightarrow{H_2SO_4}$

c. Benzene and HNO_3 $\xrightarrow{H_2SO_4}$

d.   (benzene) + ——— $\xrightarrow{???}$ (chlorobenzene, Cl) + HCl

Answers   a. (bromobenzene, Br)   b. (benzenesulfonic acid, SO_3H)   c. (nitrobenzene, NO_2)

d. (benzene) + Cl_2 $\xrightarrow{FeCl_2}$ (chlorobenzene, Cl) + HCl

Checklist for Chapter 12

You are ready to take the practice test for chapter 12. Be sure that you have accomplished the following learning goals for this chapter. If you are not sure, review the section listed at the end of the goal. Then apply your new skills and understanding to the practice test. Good luck.

After studying chapter 12, I can successfully:

_____ Identify the structural features of alkenes and alkynes (12.1).

_____ Name alkenes and alkynes using IUPAC rules and write their structural formulas (12.1).

_____ Identify alkenes that exist as cis-trans isomers; write their structural formulas and names (12.2).

_____ Write the structural formulas and names for the products of the addition of hydrogen, halogens, hydrogen halides, and water to alkenes, applying Markovnikov's rule when necessary (12.3).

_____ Describe the process of forming polymers from alkene monomers (12.4).

_____ Write the names and structures for compounds that contain a benzene ring (12.5).

_____ Write the products of substitution reactions of benzene (12.6).

Practice Test for Chapter 12

Questions 1–4 refer to $H_2C{=}CH{-}CH_3$ and $H_2C{-}CH_2$ with CH_2 forming a ring

(A)   (B)

1. These compounds are
   A. aromatic   B. alkanes   C. isomers   D. alkenes   E. cycloalkanes

2. Compound (A) is a(n)
   A. alkane   B. alkene   C. cycloalkane   D. alkyne   E. aromatic

3. Compound (B) is named
   A. propane   B. propylene   C. cyclobutane   D. cyclopropane   E. cyclopropene

4. Compound (A) is named
   A. propane   B. propene   C. 2-propene   D. propyne   E. 1-butene

In questions 5–8, match the name of the alkene with the structural formula.
A. cyclopentene   B. methylpropene
C. cyclohexene   D. ethene   E. 3-methylcyclopentene

5. $CH_2=CH_2$

6.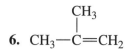

7.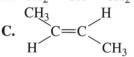

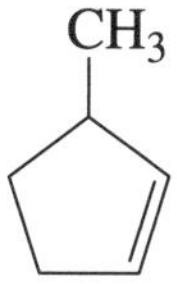

8.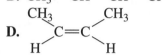

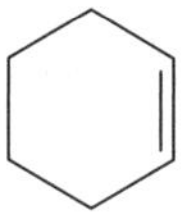

9. The cis isomer of 2-butene is
  A. $CH_2=CH-CH_2-CH_3$
  B. $CH_3-CH=CH-CH_3$
  C.
  D.
  E. 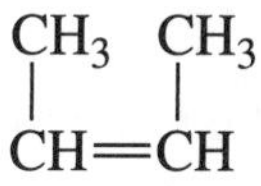 $CH_3 \quad CH_3$ $CH=CH$

10. The name of this compound is

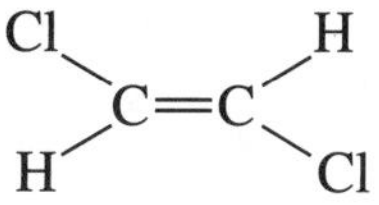

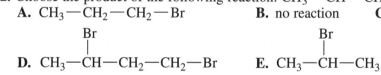

  A. dichloroethene
  B. *cis*-1,2-dichloroethene
  C. *trans*-1,2-dichloroethene
  D. *cis*-chloroethene
  E. *trans*-chloroethene

11. Hydrogenation of $CH_3-CH=CH_2$ gives
  A. $3CO_2 + 6H_2$
  B. $CH_3-CH_2-CH_3$
  C. $CH_2=CH-CH_3$
  D. no reaction
  E. $CH_3-CH_2-CH_2-CH_3$

12. Choose the product of the following reaction: $CH_3-CH=CH_2 + HBr \rightarrow$
  A. $CH_3-CH_2-CH_2-Br$
  B. no reaction
  C. $CH_3-CH_2-CH_3$
  D. $CH_3-\overset{\underset{\displaystyle Br}{|}}{CH}-CH_2-CH_2-Br$
  E. $CH_3-\overset{\underset{\displaystyle Br}{|}}{CH}-CH_3$

13. Addition of bromine (Br_2) to ethene gives
  A. CH_3-CH_2-Br
  B. $Br-CH_2-CH_2-Br$
  C. $CH_3-CH-Br_2$
  D. CH_3-CH_3
  E. no reaction

14. Hydration of 2-butene gives
  A. $CH_3-CH_2-CH_2-CH_3$
  B. $CH_3-CH_2-CH_2-CH_2-OH$
  C. 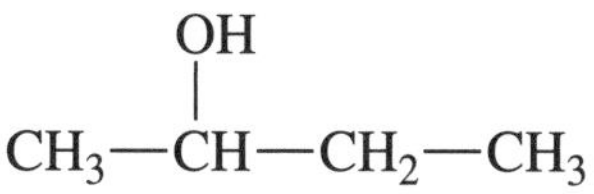 $CH_3-\overset{\underset{\displaystyle OH}{|}}{CH}-CH_2-CH_3$
  D.
  E.

15. What is the common name for the compound 1,3-dichlorobenzene?
  A. *m*-dichlorobenzene
  B. *o*-dichlorobenzene
  C. *p*-dichlorobenzene
  D. *x*-dichlorobenzene
  E. *z*-dichlorobenzene

16. What is the common name of methylbenzene?
  A. aniline
  B. phenol
  C. toluene
  D. xylene
  E. toluidine

17. What is the IUPAC name of $CH_3-CH_2-C\equiv CH$?
  A. methylacetylene
  B. propyne
  C. propylene
  D. 4-butyne
  E. 1-butyne

18. What is the product when cyclopentene reacts with Cl_2?
    A. chlorocyclopentene   **B.** 1,1-dichlorocyclopentane
    C. 1,2-dichlorocyclopentane   **D.** 1,3-dichlorocyclopentane
    E. no reaction

19. The reaction $CH_2{=}CH_2 + Cl_2 \rightarrow Cl{-}CH_2{-}CH_2{-}Cl$ is called
    A. hydrogenation   **B.** halogenation   **C.** hydrohalogenation
    D. hydration   **E.** combustion

20. The reaction in problem 19 is
    A. a hydration reaction   **B.** an oxidation reaction   **C.** a substitution reaction
    D. an addition reaction   **E.** a reduction reaction

21. The reaction $CH_3{-}CH{=}CH_2 + H_2O \longrightarrow CH_3{-}\overset{\overset{\displaystyle OH}{\displaystyle |}}{CH}{-}CH_3$ is called a
    A. hydrogenation   **B.** halogenation   **C.** hydrohalogenation of an alkene
    D. hydration of an alkene   **E.** combustion

For questions 22–25, identify the family for each compound as
A. alkane   **B.** alkene   **C.** alkyne   **D.** cycloalkene

22. $CH_3{-}CH{=}CH_2$

23.

24. $CH_3{-}CH_2{-}\overset{\overset{\displaystyle CH_3}{\displaystyle |}}{CH}{-}CH_2{-}CH_3$

25. $CH_3{-}CH_2{-}C{\equiv}CH$

Match the name of each of the following aromatic compounds with the correct structure.

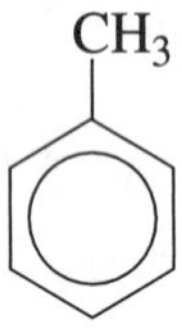

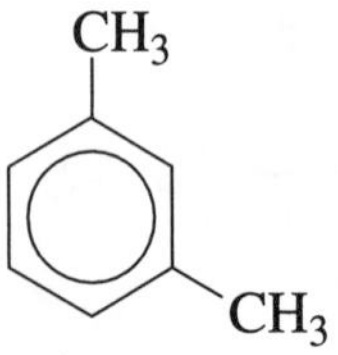

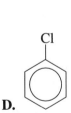

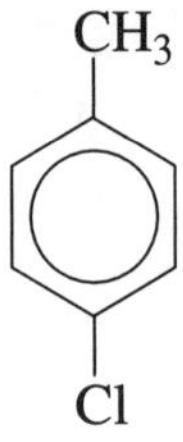

26. _____ chlorobenzene   ·   **27.** _____ benzene

28. _____ toluene   **29.** _____ *p*-chlorotoluene

30. _____ 1,3-dimethylbenzene

Answers to the Practice Test

1. C	**2.** B	**3.** D	**4.** B	**5.** D
6. B	**7.** E	**8.** C	**9.** D	**10.** C
11. B	**12.** E	**13.** B	**14.** C	**15.** A

16. C	**17.** E	**18.** C	**19.** B	**20.** D
21. D	**22.** B	**23.** D	**24.** A	**25.** C
26. D	**27.** A	**28.** B	**29.** E	**30.** C

Answers and Solutions to Selected Text Problems

12.1.   **a.** An alkene has a double bond.   **b.** An alkyne has a triple bond.
       c. An alkene has a double bond.   **d.** A cycloalkene has a double bond in a ring.

12.3   **a.** The two-carbon compound with a double bond is ethene.
       b. methylpropene
       c. 4-bromo-2-pentyne
       d. This is a four-carbon cyclic structure with a double bond. The name is cyclobutene.
       e. This is a five-carbon cyclic structure with a double bond and an ethyl group. You must count the two carbons of the double bond as 1 and 2. The name is 4-ethylcyclopentene.
       f. Count the chain from the end nearest the double bond: 4-ethyl-2-hexene.

12.5   **a.** Propene is the three-carbon alkene: $H_2C{=}CH{-}CH_3$.
       b. 1-pentene is the five-carbon compound with a double bond between carbon 1 and carbon 2.

$$H_2C{=}CH{-}CH_2{-}CH_2{-}CH_3$$

       c. 2-methyl-1-butene has a four-carbon chain with a double bond between carbon 1 and carbon 2 and a methyl attached to carbon 2.

$$\begin{array}{c} CH_3 \\ | \\ H_2C{=}C{-}CH_2{-}CH_3 \end{array}$$

       d. 3-methylcyclohexene is a six-carbon cyclic compound with a double bond between carbon 1 and carbon 2 and a methyl group attached to carbon 3.

       e. 2-chloro-3-hexyne is a six-carbon compound with a triple bond between carbon 3 and 4 and a chlorine atom bonded to carbon 2.

$$\begin{array}{c} Cl \\ | \\ CH_3{-}CH{-}C{\equiv}C{-}CH_2{-}CH_3 \end{array}$$

12.7   **a.** This compound cannot have cis-trans isomers since there are two identical hydrogen atoms attached to the first carbon.
       b. This compound can have cis-trans isomers since there are different groups attached to each carbon atom in the double bond.
       c. This compound cannot have cis-trans isomers since there are two of the same groups attached to each carbon.

12.9   **a.** *cis*-2-butane. This is a four-carbon compound with a double bond between carbon 2 and carbon 3. Both methyl groups are on the same side of the double bond; it is cis.
       b. *trans*-3-octene. This compound has eight carbons with a double bond between carbon 3 and carbon 4. The alkyl groups are on opposite sides of the double bond; it is trans.
       c. *cis*-3-heptene. This is a seven-carbon compound with a double bond between carbon 3 and carbon 4. Both alkyl groups are on the same side of the double bond; it is cis.

213

12.11 **a.** *trans*-2-butene has a four-carbon chain with a double bond between carbon 2 and carbon 3. The trans isomer has two methyl groups on opposite sides of the double bond.

$$CH_3\diagdown_{} \qquad_{} \diagup H$$
$$C=C$$
$$H \diagup \qquad \diagdown CH_3$$

b. *cis*-2-pentene has a five-carbon chain with a double bond between carbon 2 and carbon 3. The cis isomer has alkyl groups on the same side of the double bond.

$$CH_3\diagdown_{} \qquad_{} \diagup CH_2—CH_3$$
$$C=C$$
$$H \diagup \qquad \diagdown H$$

c. *trans*-3-heptene has a seven carbon chain with a double bond between carbon 3 and carbon 4. The trans isomer has the alkyl groups on opposite sides of the double bond.

$$CH_3—CH_2\diagdown_{} \qquad_{} \diagup H$$
$$C=C$$
$$H \diagup \qquad \diagdown CH_2—CH_2—CH_3$$

12.13 **a.** $CH_3—CH_2—CH_2—CH_2—CH_3$ pentane

b.
$$\overset{\text{Cl}}{\underset{\underset{\text{CH}_3}{|}}{\overset{|}{Cl—CH_2—C—CH_2—CH_3}}}$$ 1,2-dichloro-2-methylbutane

c. The product is a four-carbon cycloalkane with bromine atoms attached to carbon 1 and carbon 2. The name is 1,2-dibromocyclobutane.

d. When H_2 is added to a cycloalkene, the product is a cycloalkane. Cyclopentene would form cyclopentane.

cyclopentene   cyclopentane

e. When Cl_2 is added to an alkene, the product is a dichloroalkane. The product is a four-carbon chain with chlorine atoms attached to carbon 2 and carbon 3 and a methyl group attached to carbon 2. The name of the product is 2,3-dichloro-2-methylbutane.

$$\overset{\text{CH}_3}{\overset{|}{CH_3—C=CH—CH_2}} + Cl_2 \longrightarrow \overset{\text{CH}_3}{\underset{\underset{\text{Cl} \quad \text{Cl}}{| \quad |}}{\overset{|}{CH_3—C—CH—CH_3}}}$$

2-methyl-2-butene   2,3-dichloro-2-methylbutane

f. $CH_3—CH_2—CH_2—CH_2—CH_3$ pentane

12.15 **a.** When HBr is added to an alkene, the product is a bromoalkane. In this case, we do not need to use Markovnikov's rule.

$$CH_3—CH_2—\overset{\overset{\displaystyle Br}{\displaystyle |}}{C}H—CH_3$$

b. When H_2O is added to an alkene, the product is an alcohol. In this case, we do not need to use Markovnikov's rule.

c. When HCl is added to an alkene, the product is a chloroalkane. We need to use Markovnikov's rule, which says that hydrogen adds to the carbon with the greater number of hydrogens; in this case that is carbon 1.

$$CH_3—\overset{\overset{\displaystyle Cl}{\displaystyle |}}{C}H—CH_2—CH_3$$

d. When HI is added to an alkene, the product is a iodoalkane. In this case, we do not need to use Markovnikov's rule.

$$CH_3—\overset{\overset{\displaystyle CH_3}{\displaystyle |}}{C}H—\overset{\overset{\displaystyle I}{\displaystyle |}}{C}H—CH_3$$

e. When HBr is added to an alkene, the product is a bromoalkane. We need to use Markovnikov's rule, which says that hydrogen adds to the carbon with the greatest number of hydrogens; in this case that is carbon 2.

$$CH_3—CH_2—\overset{\overset{\displaystyle Br}{\displaystyle |}}{\underset{\underset{\displaystyle CH_3}{\displaystyle |}}{C}}—CH_2—CH_3$$

f. Using Markovnikov's rule, the H from HOH goes to the carbon 2 in the cyclohexane ring, which has more hydrogen atoms. The —OH then goes to carbon 1.

12.17 **a.** Hydrogenation of an alkene gives the saturated compound, the alkane.

$$CH_2{=}\overset{\overset{\displaystyle CH_3}{\displaystyle |}}{C}—CH_3 + H_2 \xrightarrow{\text{Pt}} CH_3—\overset{\overset{\displaystyle CH_3}{\displaystyle |}}{C}H—CH_3$$

b. The addition of HCl to a cycloalkene gives a chlorocycloalkane.

215

c. The addition of bromine (Br_2) to an alkene gives a dibromoalkane.

$$CH_3-CH=CH-CH_2-CH_3 + Br_2 \longrightarrow CH_3-\overset{\overset{\displaystyle Br}{|}}{C}H-\overset{\overset{\displaystyle Br}{|}}{C}H-CH_2-CH_3$$

d. Hydration (the addition of H_2O) to an alkene gives an alcohol. In this case, we use Markovnikov's rule and attach hydrogen to carbon 1.

$$CH_2=CH-CH_3 + H_2O \xrightarrow{H^+} CH_3-\overset{\overset{\displaystyle OH}{|}}{C}H-CH_3$$

e. $CH_3-C\equiv C-CH_3 + 2Cl_2 \longrightarrow CH_3-\overset{\overset{\displaystyle Cl}{|}}{\underset{\underset{\displaystyle Cl}{|}}{C}}-\overset{\overset{\displaystyle Cl}{|}}{\underset{\underset{\displaystyle Cl}{|}}{C}}-CH_3$

f.

12.19   A polymer is a long-chain molecule consisting of many repeating smaller units. These smaller units are called monomers.

12.21   Teflon is a polymer of the monomer tetrafluoroethene.

12.23   1,1-difluoroethene is the two-carbon alkene with two fluorine atoms attached to carbon 1.

12.25   Cyclohexane, C_6H_{12}, is a cycloalkane in which six carbon atoms are linked by single bonds in a ring. In benzene, C_6H_6, an aromatic system, links the six carbon atoms in a ring.

12.27   The six carbon ring with alternating single and double bonds is benzene. If the groups are in the 1,2 position, this is ortho (*o*); 1,3 is meta (*m*), and 1,4 is para (*p*).
   a. 1-chloro-2-methylbenzene; *o*-chlorotoluene
   b. ethylbenzene
   c. 1,3,5-trichlorobenzene
   d. *m*-xylene; *m*-methyltoluene; 1,3-dimethylbenzene
   e. 1-bromo-3-chloro-5-methylbenzene; 3-bromo-5-chlorotoluene
   f. isopropyl benzene

12.29   a.   **b.**   The prefix *m* means that the two chloro groups are in the 1 and 3 position.

c. 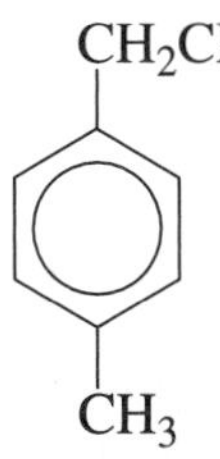 **d.** 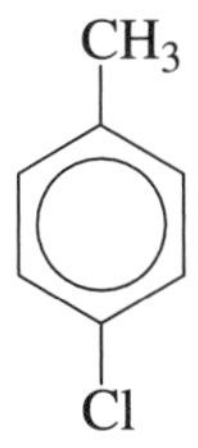

The prefix *p* means that the two groups are in the 1 and 4 position.

12.31 Benzene undergoes substitution reactions because a substitution reaction allows benzene to retain the stability of the aromatic system.

12.33 **a.** 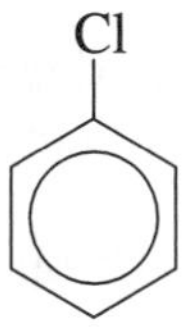 **b.** 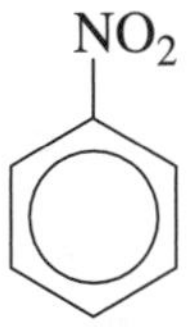

12.35 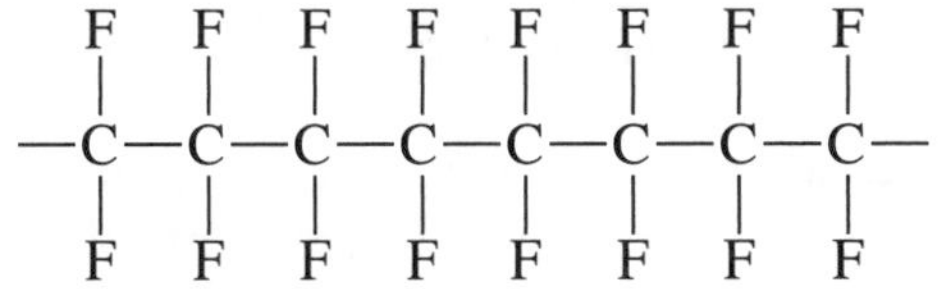

12.37 **a.** 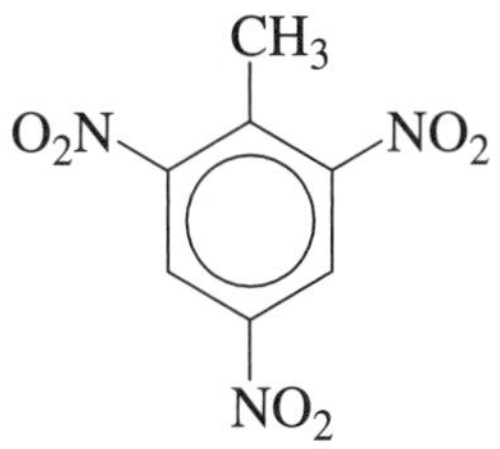

b. 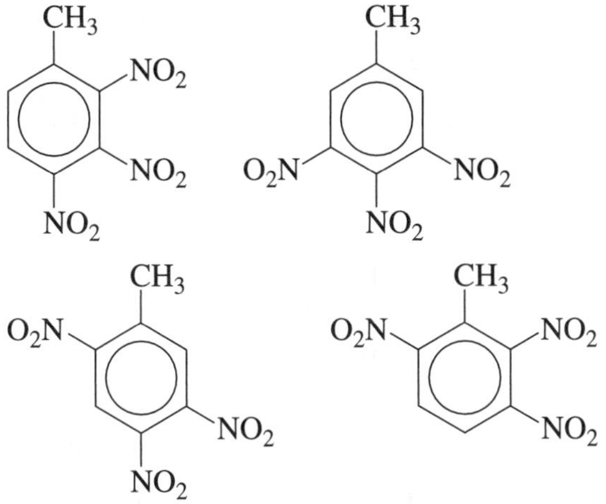

12.39 Propane is the three-carbon alkane with the formula C_3H_8. All the carbon–carbon bonds in propane are single bonds. Cyclopropane is the three-carbon cycloalkane with the formula C_3H_6. All of the carbon–carbon bonds in cyclopropane are single bonds. Propene is the three-carbon compound that has a carbon–carbon double bond. The formula of propene is C_3H_6. Propyne is the three-carbon compound with a carbon–carbon triple bond. The formula of propyne is C_3H_4.

12.41 **a.** This compound has a chlorine atom attached to a cyclopentane; the IUPAC name is chlorocyclopentane.
b. This compound has a five-carbon chain with a chlorine atom attached to carbon 2 and a methyl group attached to carbon 4. The IUPAC name is 2-chloro-4-methylpentane.

    c. This compound contains a five-carbon chain with a double bond between carbon 1 and carbon 2 and a methyl group attached to carbon 2. The IUPAC name is 2-methyl-1-pentene.

    d. This compound contains a five-carbon chain with a triple bond between carbon 2 and carbon 3. The IUPAC name is 2-pentyne.

    e. This compound contains a five-carbon cycloalkene with a chlorine atom attached to carbon 1. The IUPAC name is 1-chlorocyclopentene.

    f. This compound contains a five-carbon chain with a double bond between carbon 2 and carbon 3. The alkyl groups are on opposite sides of the double bond. The IUPAC name is *trans*-2-pentene.

    g. This compound contains a six-carbon ring with a double bond and chlorine atoms attached to carbon 1 and carbon 3. The IUPAC name is 1,3-dichlorocyclohexene.

12.43   **a.** These structures represent a pair of constitutional isomers. In one isomer, the chlorine is attached to one of the carbons in the double bond; in the other isomer, the carbon bonded to the chlorine is not part of the double bond.

    b. These structures are cis-trans isomers. In the cis isomer, the two methyl groups are on the same side of the double bond. In the trans isomer, the methyl groups are on opposite sides of the double bond.

    c. These structures are identical and not isomers. Both have five carbon chains with a double bond between carbon 1 and carbon 2.

    d. These structures represent a pair of constitutional isomers. Both have the molecular formula C_7H_{16}. One isomer is a six-carbon chain with a methyl group attached, whereas the other is a five-carbon chain with two methyl groups attached.

12.45   The structure of methylcyclopentane is

It can be formed by the hydrogenation of four cycloalkenes.

12.47 **a.**

cis-2-pentene; both alkyl groups are on the same side of the double bond.

trans-2-pentene; both alkyl groups are on opposite sides of the double bond.

    b.

cis-3-hexene; both alkyl groups are on the same side of the double bond.

trans-3-hexene; both alkyl groups are on opposite sides of the double bond.

    c.

cis-2-butene; both alkyl groups are on the same side of the double bond.

trans-2-butene; both alkyl groups are on opposite sides of the double bond.

d.
$$CH_3 \quad\quad CH_2CH_2CH_3$$
$$\diagdown\; C{=}C\; \diagup$$
$$H \quad\quad\quad H$$

cis-2-hexene; both alkyl groups are on the same side of the double bond.

$$CH_3 \quad\quad H$$
$$\diagdown\; C{=}C\; \diagup$$
$$H \quad\quad\quad CH_2CH_2CH_3$$

trans-2-hexene; both alkyl groups are on opposite sides of the double bond.

12.49 **a.** The reaction of H_2 in the presence of a Ni catalyst changes alkenes into alkanes. The reactant must be cyclohexene.

b. Br_2 adds to alkenes to give a dibromoalkane. Since there are bromine atoms on carbon 2 and carbon 3, the double bond in the reactant must have been between carbons 2 and 3.

$$CH_3{-}CH{=}CH{-}CH_2{-}CH_3$$

c. HCl adds to alkenes to give a chloroalkane. The product has three carbons, and the double bond must be between carbons 1 and 2.

$$CH_2{=}CH{-}CH_3$$

d. An alcohol is formed when H_2O adds to an alkene in the presence of acid (H^+). The alkene that adds water to form the alcohol is cyclopentene.

12.51 Styrene is $H_2C{=}CH$ ⬡ and acrylonitrile is $H_2C{=}CH$ with CN. A section copolymer of styrene and acrylonitrile would be the following:

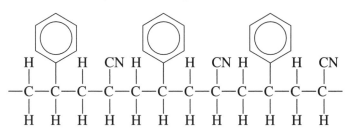

12.53 **a.** chlorobenzene
c. benzenesulfonic acid
b. *o*-bromotoluene, *m*-bromotoluene, *p*-bromotoluene
d. no products

12.55 **a.** methylbenzene; toluene
b. 1-chloro-2-methylbenzene; *o*-chlorotoluene (1,2 position is *ortho, o*)
c. 1-ethyl-4-methylbenzene; *p*-ethyltoluene (1,4 position is *para,p*)
d. 1,3-diethylbenzene; *m*-diethylbenzene (1,3 position is *meta,m*)

12.57 $CH_3-CH=CH-CH_2-CH_3$ *cis*-2-pentene or *trans*-2-pentene

   $H_2C=CH-CH_2-CH_2-CH_3$ 1-pentene

$$H_2C=\overset{\overset{\displaystyle CH_3}{|}}{C}-CH_2-CH_3 \qquad \text{2-methyl-1-butene}$$

$$CH_3-\overset{\overset{\displaystyle CH_3}{|}}{C}=CH-CH_3 \qquad \text{2-methyl-2-butene}$$

$$CH_3-\overset{\overset{\displaystyle CH_3}{|}}{CH}-CH=CH_2 \qquad \text{3-methyl-1-butene}$$

12.59   Bombykol $C_{16}H_{30}O = 238.3$

$$50 \text{ ng} \times \frac{1 \text{ g}}{10^9 \text{ ng}} \times \frac{1 \text{ mole}}{238 \text{ g}} \times \frac{6.02 \times 10^{23} \text{ molecules}}{1 \text{ mole}} = 1 \times 10^{14} \text{ molecules}$$

13

Alcohols, Phenols, Thiols, and Ethers

Study Goals

- Classify alcohols as primary, secondary, or tertiary.
- Name and write the condensed structural formulas for alcohols, phenols, and thiols.
- Identify the uses of some alcohols and phenols.
- Name and write the condensed structural formulas for ethers.
- Describe the solubility in water, density, and boiling points of alcohols, phenols, and ethers.
- Write equations for combustion, dehydration, and oxidation of alcohols.

Think About It

1. What are the functional groups of alcohols, phenols, ethers, and thiols?

2. Phenol is sometime used in mouthwashes. Why does it form a solution with water?

3. What reaction of ethanol takes place when you make a fondue dish or a flambé dessert?

Key Terms

Match the following terms with the statements shown below.

a. primary alcohol   **b.** thiol   **c.** ether
d. phenol   **e.** tertiary alcohol

1. _____ An organic compound with one alkyl group bonded to the carbon with the —OH group

2. _____ An organic compound that contains an —SH group

3. _____ An organic compound that contains an oxygen atom —O— attached to two alkyl groups

4. _____ An organic compound with three alkyl groups bonded to the carbon with the —OH group

5. _____ An organic compound that contains a benzene ring bonded to a hydroxyl group

Answers   **1.** a   **2.** b   **3.** c   **4.** e   **5.** d

13.1 Alcohols, Phenols, and Thiols

- Alcohols are classified according to the number of alkyl groups attached to the carbon bonded to the —OH group. Phenols have a hydroxyl group attached to an aromatic ring. Thiols have an —SH functional group.
- In a primary alcohol, there is one alkyl group attached to the carbon atom bonded to the —OH. In a secondary alcohol, there are two alkyl groups, and in a tertiary alcohol, there are three alkyl groups attached to the carbon atom with the —OH functional group.
- In the IUPAC system, alcohols are named by replacing the *ane* of the alkane name with *ol*. The location of the —OH group is given by numbering the carbon chain. Simple alcohols are generally named

by their common names with the alkyl name preceding the term *alcohol.* For example, CH_3—OH is methyl alcohol, and CH_3—CH_2—OH is ethyl alcohol.

CH_3—OH
methanol
(methyl alcohol)

CH_3—CH_2—OH
ethanol
(ethyl alcohol)

CH_3—CH_2—CH_2—OH
1-propanol
(propyl alcohol)

- To name a thiol, give the alkane name of the chain, followed by *thiol.*

CH_3—SH
methanethiol

CH_3—CH_2—SH
ethanethiol

Study Note

Example   Identify the following as primary, secondary, or tertiary alcohols.
Solution   Determine the number of alkyl group attached to the hydroxyl carbon atom.

$$CH_3\text{—}CH_2\text{—}OH \qquad CH_3\overset{CH_3}{\underset{}{—}CH}\text{—}OH \qquad CH_3\overset{CH_3}{\underset{CH_3}{—}\overset{|}{C}}\text{—}OH$$

primary (1°)   secondary (2°) 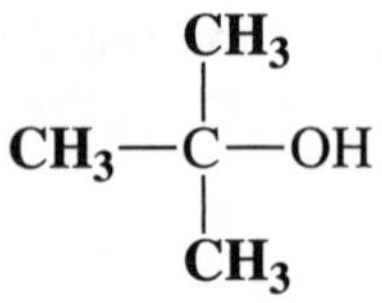   tertiary (3°)

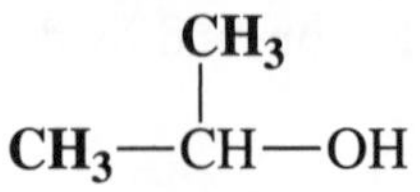

◆ Learning Exercise 13.1A

Classify each of the following alcohols as primary (1°), secondary (2°), or tertiary (3°):

1. CH_3—CH_2—OH _____

2. 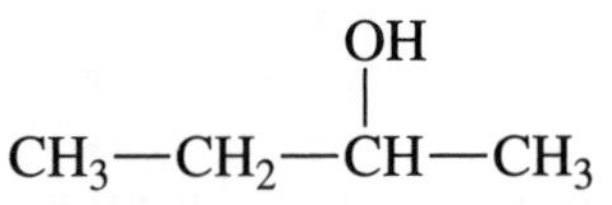 CH_3—CH_2—$\overset{OH}{\overset{|}{CH}}$—$CH_3$ _____

3. CH_3—$\overset{OH}{\underset{CH_3}{\overset{|}{\underset{|}{C}}}}$—$CH_2$—$CH_3$ _____

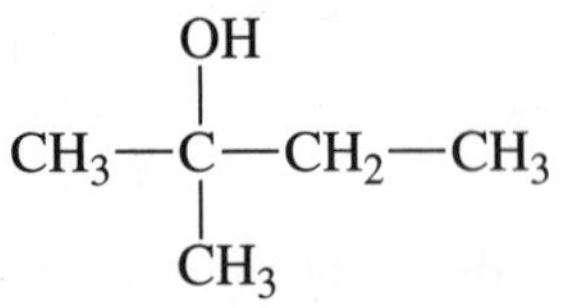

4. 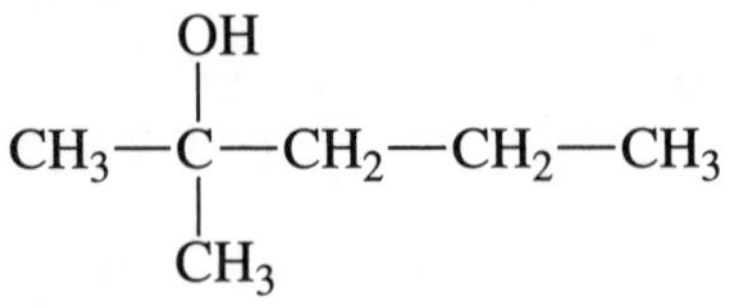 CH_3—$\overset{OH}{\underset{CH_3}{\overset{|}{\underset{|}{C}}}}$—$CH_2$—$CH_2$—$CH_3$ _____

5. 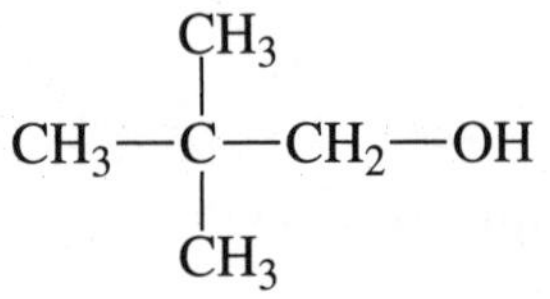 CH_3—$\overset{CH_3}{\underset{CH_3}{\overset{|}{\underset{|}{C}}}}$—$CH_2$—OH _____

6. 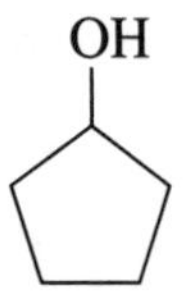 (cyclopentane with OH) _____

Answers   1. primary(1°)   2. secondary (3°)   3. tertiary (3°)
              4. tertiary (3°)   5. primary (1°)   6. secondary (2°)

◆ Learning Exercise 13.1B

Give the correct IUPAC and common name (if any) for each of the following compounds:

1. CH_3—CH_2—OH

2. CH_3—CH_2—CH_2—OH

3. 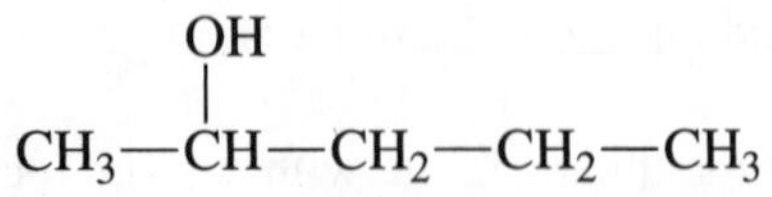 CH_3—$\overset{OH}{\overset{|}{CH}}$—$CH_2$—$CH_2$—$CH_3$

4. 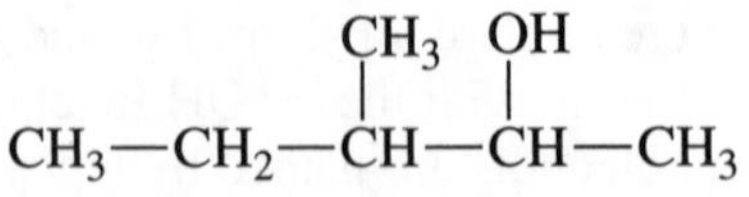 CH_3—CH_2—$\overset{CH_3}{\overset{|}{CH}}$—$\overset{OH}{\overset{|}{CH}}$—$CH_3$

5. 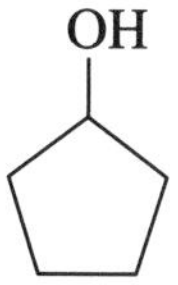
OH

6. 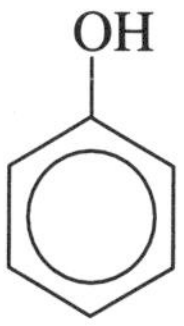
OH

Answers **1.** ethanol (ethyl alcohol) **2.** 1-propanol (propyl alcohol)
3. 2-pentanol **4.** 3-methyl-2-pentanol
5. cyclopentanol **6.** phenol

◆ Learning Exercise 13.1C

Write the correct condensed structural formula for each of the following compounds:

1. 2-butanol

2. 2-chloro-1-propanol

3. 2,4-dimethyl-1-pentanol

4. cyclohexanol

5. 3-methylcyclopentanol

6. *o*-chlorophenol

Answers **1.** CH$_3$—$\overset{\text{OH}}{\underset{|}{\text{CH}}}$—CH$_2$—CH$_3$ **2.** CH$_3$—$\overset{\text{Cl}}{\underset{|}{\text{CH}}}$—CH$_2$—OH

3. CH$_3$—$\overset{\text{CH}_3}{\underset{|}{\text{CH}}}$—CH$_2$—$\overset{\text{CH}_3}{\underset{|}{\text{CH}}}$—CH$_2$—OH **4.** 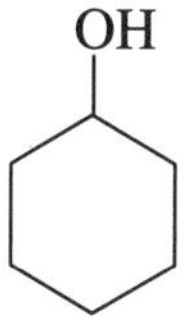
OH

5.

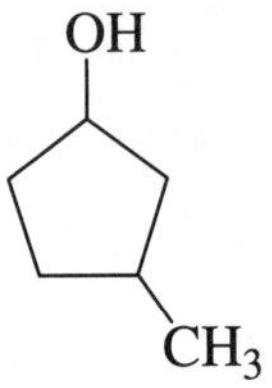

6.

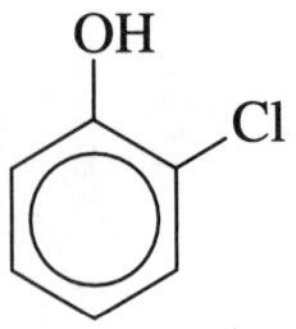

◆ Learning Exercise 13.1D

Give the correct IUPAC name for the following thiols:

1. CH_3-CH_2-SH _____

2. $CH_3-CH_2-CH_2-SH$ _____

3. $CH_3-CH_2-\overset{\displaystyle SH}{\underset{|}{C}H}-CH_3$ _____

4. _____

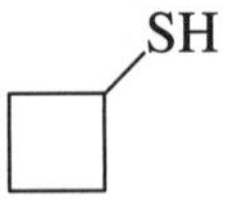

Answers   **1.** ethanethiol   **2.** 1-propanethiol
          3. 2-butanethiol   **4.** cyclobutanethiol

13.2 Ethers

- In ethers, an oxygen atom is connected by single bonds to two alkyl or aromatic groups.
- In the IUPAC name, the smaller alkyl group and the oxygen are named as an *alkoxy group* attached to the longer alkane chain, which is numbered to give the location of the alkoxy group. In the common names of ethers, the alkyl groups are listed alphabetically followed by the name *ether.*

Study Note

Example Write the common and IUPAC names for $CH_3-CH_2-O-CH_3$.
Solution The common name lists the alkyl groups alphabetically before the name *ether.* Using the IUPAC system, the smaller alkyl group and the oxygen are named as a substituent *methoxy* attached to the two-carbon chain ethane.

Ethyl group *methyl group*	*Ethane* *Methoxy group*
$CH_3-CH_2-O-CH_3$.	$CH_3-CH_2-O-CH_3$
Common: ethyl methyl ether	IUPAC: methoxy ethane

◆ Learning Exercise 13.2A

Write an IUPAC and common name, if any, for the following ethers:

1. CH_3-O-CH_3 **2.** $CH_3-CH_2-O-CH_2-CH_3$

3. $CH_3-CH_2-CH_2-CH_2-O-CH_3$ **4.** $CH_3-O-CH_2-CH_3$

5. 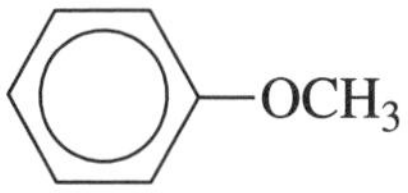 ⬡—OCH₃

Answers   1. methoxymethane; (di)methyl ether   2. ethoxyethane; (di)ethyl ether
3. 1-methoxybutane; butyl methyl ether   4. methoxyethane; ethyl methyl ether
5. methoxybenzene; methyl phenyl ether (anisole)

◆ Learning Exercise 13.2B

Write the structural formula for each of the following ethers:

1. ethyl propyl ether

2. 2-methoxypropane

3. ethyl methyl ether

4. 3-ethoxypentane

Answers   **1.** $CH_3-CH_2-O-CH_2-CH_2-CH_3$

2. $CH_3-\overset{\overset{O-CH_3}{|}}{CH}-CH_3$

3. $CH_3-O-CH_2-CH_3$

4. $CH_3-CH_2-\overset{\overset{O-CH_2-CH_3}{|}}{CH}-CH_2-CH_3$

◆ Learning Exercise 13.2C

Identify each of the following heterocyclic structures as a furan, pyran, or dioxane:

1.

2.

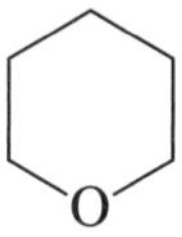

3.

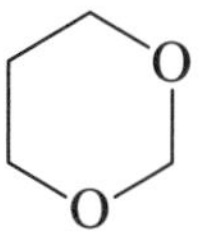

4.

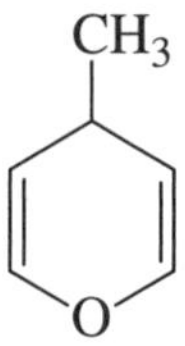

Answers   **1.** furan   **2.** pyran   **3.** dioxane   **4.** pyran

◆ Learning Exercise 13.2D

Identify each of the following pairs of compounds as structural isomers, the same compound, or different compounds.

1. CH_3-O-CH_3 and CH_3-CH_2-OH _____

$$\overset{\displaystyle OH}{\underset{\displaystyle |}{}}$$

2. $CH_3-O-CH_2-CH_3$ and $CH_3-CH-CH_3$ _____

$$\overset{\displaystyle CH_3}{\underset{\displaystyle |}{}} \qquad \overset{\displaystyle OH}{\underset{\displaystyle |}{}}$$

3. $CH_3-CH-OH$ and $CH_3-CH-CH_3$ _____

4. $CH_3-CH_2-O-CH_3$ and $CH_3-CH_2-CH_2-CH_2-OH$ _____

Answers   **1.** structural isomers   **2.** structural isomers
         3. the same compound   **4.** different compounds

13.3 Physical Properties of Alcohols, Phenols, and Ethers

- The polar $-OH$ group gives alcohols higher boiling points than alkanes and ethers of similar mass.
- Alcohols with one to four carbons are soluble in water because the $-OH$ group forms hydrogen bonds with water molecules.
- Phenol is soluble in water and acts as a weak acid.
- Because ethers are less polar than alcohols, they have boiling points similar to alkanes. Ethers are soluble in water due to hydrogen bonding. Ethers are widely used as solvents but can be dangerous to use because their vapors are highly flammable.

◆ Learning Exercise 13.3A

Circle the compound in each pair that is the more soluble in water.

1. _____ CH_3-CH_3 or CH_3-CH_2-OH

2. _____ $CH_3-CH_2-CH_2-OH$ or $CH_3-CH_2-CH_2-CH_2-CH_2-OH$

3. _____ $CH_3-CH_2-CH_2-CH_3$ or $CH_3-CH_2-CH_2-CH_2-OH$

4. _____ Benzene or phenol

Answers   **1.** CH_3-CH_2-OH **2.** $CH_3-CH_2-CH_2-OH$
         3. $CH_3-CH_2-CH_2-CH_2-OH$ **4.** phenol

◆ Learning Exercise 13.3B

Select the compound in each pair with the higher boiling point.

1. $CH_3-CH_2-CH_3$ or CH_3-CH_2-OH
2. 2-butanol or 2-hexanol
3. $CH_3-O-CH_2-CH_3$ or $CH_3-CH_2-CH_2-OH$
4. $CH_3-CH_2-CH_2-OH$ or $CH_3-CH_2-CH_2-CH_3$

Answers   **1.** CH_3-CH_2-OH **2.** 2-hexanol
         3. $CH_3-CH_2-CH_2-OH$ **4.** $CH_3-CH_2-CH_2-OH$

13.4 Reactions of Alcohols and Thiols

- At high temperatures, an alcohol dehydrates in the presence of an acid to yield an alkene and water.

$$CH_3-CH_2-OH \xrightarrow[\text{Heat}]{H^+} H_2C{=}CH_2 + H_2O$$

- Ethers are produced from primary alcohols in the presence of acid and at lower temperatures than needed for dehydration.

$$CH_3-OH + HO-CH_3 \xrightarrow[\text{Heat}]{H^+} CH_3-O-CH_3 + H_2O$$

- Using an oxidizing agent [O], primary alcohols oxidize to aldehydes, which usually oxidize further to carboxylic acids. Secondary alcohols are oxidized to ketones, but tertiary alcohols do not oxidize.

$$CH_3-CH_2-OH \xrightarrow{[O]} \underset{\text{aldehyde}}{CH_3-\overset{\overset{\textstyle O}{\|}}{C}-H} + H_2O$$

$$\underset{\text{1° alcohol}}{CH_3-CH_2-OH}$$

$$\underset{\text{2° alcohol}}{CH_3-\overset{\overset{\textstyle OH}{|}}{CH}-CH_3} \xrightarrow{[O]} \underset{\text{ketone}}{CH_3-\overset{\overset{\textstyle O}{\|}}{C}-CH_3} + H_2O$$

- Thiols undergo oxidation and lose hydrogen from the —SH group to form disulfides.

◆ Learning Exercise 13.4A

Write the condensed structural formulas of the products expected from dehydration of each of the following reactants:

1. $CH_3-CH_2-CH_2-CH_2-OH \xrightarrow{H^+,\ heat}$

2. $\xrightarrow{H^+,\ heat}$

3. $CH_3-\overset{\overset{\textstyle OH}{|}}{CH}-CH_3 \xrightarrow{H^+,\ heat}$

4. $CH_3-CH_2-\overset{\overset{\textstyle OH}{|}}{CH}-CH_2-CH_3 \xrightarrow{H^+,\ heat}$

Answers **1.** $CH_3-CH_2-CH{=}CH_2$ **2.**

3. $CH_3-CH{=}CH_2$ **4.** $CH_3-CH_2-CH{=}CH-CH_3$

◆ **Learning Exercise 13.4B**

Write the structure of the ether formed in the following reactions:

1. $CH_3-CH_2-OH + HO-CH_2-CH_3 \xrightarrow{\text{H}^+,\ \text{heat}}$

2. $CH_3-OH + HO-CH_3 \xrightarrow{\text{H}^+,\ \text{heat}}$

Answers   1. $CH_3-CH_2-O-CH_2-CH_3$ 2. CH_3-O-CH_3

◆ **Learning Exercise 13.4C**

Write the condensed structural formulas of the products expected in the oxidation reaction of each of the following reactants:

1. $CH_3-CH_2-CH_2-CH_2-OH \xrightarrow{\text{[O]}}$

2. 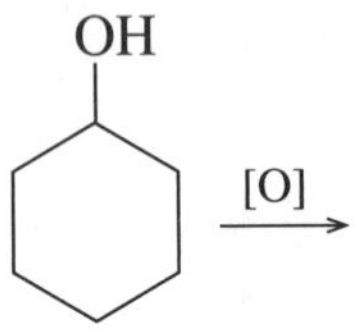 $\xrightarrow{\text{[O]}}$

3.
$$\underset{\text{}}{CH_3}-\overset{\overset{\displaystyle OH}{|}}{CH}-CH_3 \xrightarrow{\text{[O]}}$$

4.
$$CH_3-\overset{\overset{\displaystyle OH}{|}}{CH_2}-CH-CH_2-CH_3 \xrightarrow{\text{[O]}}$$

Answers   1. $CH_3-CH_2-CH_2-\overset{\overset{\displaystyle O}{||}}{C}-H$ 2.

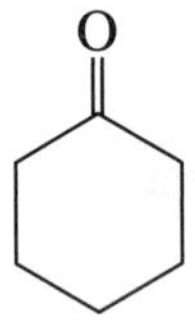

3. $CH_3-\overset{\overset{\displaystyle O}{||}}{C}-CH_3$

4. $CH_3-CH_2-\overset{\overset{\displaystyle O}{||}}{C}-CH_2-CH_3$

Checklist for Chapter 13

You are ready to take the practice test for chapter 13. Be sure that you have accomplished the following learning goals for this chapter. If you are not sure, review the section listed at the end of the goal. Then apply your new skills and understanding to the practice test. Good luck.

After studying chapter 13, I can successfully:

_____ Classify an alcohol as primary, secondary, or tertiary (13.1).

_____ Give the IUPAC or common name of an alcohol, phenol, or thiol; draw the condensed structural formula from the name (13.1).

228

_____ Write the IUPAC or common name of an ether; write the condensed structural formula from the name (13.2).

_____ Describe the solubility of alcohols, phenols, and ethers in water; compare their boiling points (13.3).

_____ Write the products of alcohols that undergo dehydration, ether formation, and oxidation (13.4).

Practice Test for Chapter 13

Match the names of the following compounds with their structures.
A. 1-propanol   **B.** cyclobutanol   **C.** 2-propanol
D. ethyl methyl ether   **E.** diethyl ether

1.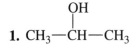

2. $CH_3-CH_2-CH_2-OH$

3. $CH_3-O-CH_2-CH_3$

4. ⌐ with OH

5. $CH_3-CH_2-O-CH_2-CH_3$

6. The compound 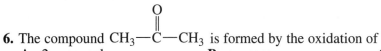 is formed by the oxidation of
    A. 2-propanol   **B.** propane   **C.** 1-propanol
    D. dimethyl ether   **E.** methyl ethyl ketone

7. Why are short-chain alcohols water soluble?
    A. They are nonpolar.   **B.** They can hydrogen bond.   **C.** They are organic.
    D. They are bases.   **E.** They are acids.

8. Phenol is
    A. the alcohol of benzene   **B.** the aldehyde of benzene
    C. the phenyl group of benzene   **D.** the ketone of benzene   **E.** cyclohexanol

9. $CH_3-CH_2-OH + HO-CH_2-CH_3 \xrightarrow{H^+}$ [   ] $+ H_2O$
    A. an alkane   **B.** an aldehye   **C.** a ketone
    D. an ether   **E.** a phenol

10. The dehydration of cyclohexanol gives
    A. cyclohexane   **B.** cyclohexene   **C.** cyclohexyne
    D. benzene   **E.** phenol

11. The formula of ethanethiol is
    A. CH_3-SH **B.** CH_3-CH_2-OH **C.** CH_3-CH_2-SH
    D. $CH_3-CH_2-S-CH_3$ **E.** CH_3-S-OH

In questions 12–16, classify each alcohol as

A. primary (1°)   **B.** secondary (2°)   **C.** tertiary (3°)

12. $CH_3-CH_2-CH_2-OH$ **13.**   **14.**

15.

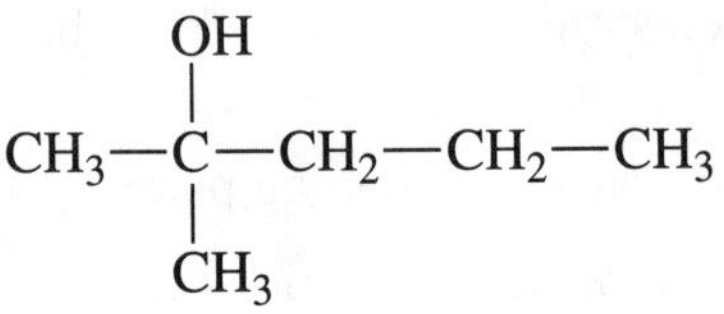

$$CH_3-\overset{\displaystyle OH}{\underset{\displaystyle CH_3}{\overset{\displaystyle |}{\underset{\displaystyle |}{C}}}}-CH_2-CH_2-CH_3$$

16.

$$CH_3-\overset{\displaystyle OH}{\overset{\displaystyle |}{CH}}-CH_2-CH_2-CH_2-CH_3$$

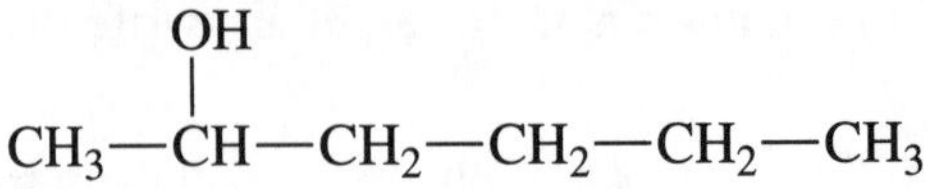

Complete questions 17–20 by indicating one of the products (A–E) formed in each of the following reactions:

A. primary alcohol   **B.** secondary alcohol   **C.** aldehyde   **D.** ketone   **E.** carboxylic acid

17. _____ oxidation of a primary alcohol

18. _____ oxidation of a secondary alcohol

19. _____ oxidation of an aldehyde

20. _____ hydration of 1-propene

Answers to Practice Test

1. C	**2.** A	**3.** D	**4.** B	**5.** E
6. A	**7.** B	**8.** A	**9.** D	**10.** B
11. C	**12.** A	**13.** B	**14.** C	**15.** C
16. B	**17.** C	**18.** D	**19.** E	**20.** B

Answers and Solutions to Selected Text Problems

13.1 The carbon bonded to the hydroxyl group (—OH) is attached to one alkyl group in a primary (1°) alcohol, except for methanol; to two alkyl groups in a secondary alcohol (2°); and to three alkyl groups in a tertiary alcohol (3°).
   a. 1°   **b.** 1°   **c.** 3°   **d.** 2°

13.3 **a.** This compound has a two-carbon chain (ethane). The final −e is dropped and −ol added to indicate an alcohol. The IUPAC name is ethanol.
   b. This compound has a four-carbon chain with a hydroxyl attached to carbon 2. The IUPAC name is 2-butanol.
   c. This compound has a five-carbon chain with a hydroxyl attached to carbon 2. The IUPAC name is 2-pentanol.
   d. This compound is a six-carbon cycloalkane with a hydroxyl attached to carbon 1 and a methyl group attached to carbon 4. Since the hydroxyl is always attached to carbon 1, the number 1 is omitted in the name. The IUPAC name is 4-methylcyclohexanol.

13.5 **a.** 1-propanol has a three-carbon chain with a hydroxyl attached to carbon 1.

$$CH_3-CH_2-CH_2-OH$$

   b. Methyl alcohol has a hydroxyl attached to a one-carbon alkane CH_3-OH.
   c. 3-pentanol has a five-carbon chain with a hydroxyl attached to carbon 3.

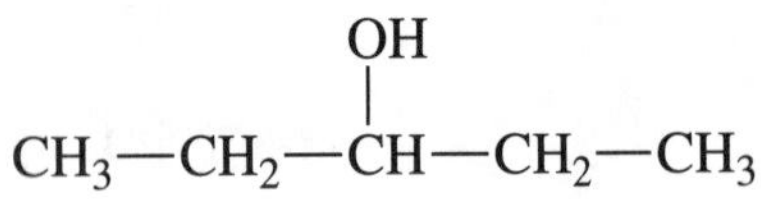

$$CH_3-CH_2-\overset{\displaystyle OH}{\overset{\displaystyle |}{CH}}-CH_2-CH_3$$

   d. 2-methyl-2-butanol has a four-carbon chain with a methyl and hydroxyl attached to carbon 2.

$$CH_3-\overset{\displaystyle OH}{\underset{\displaystyle CH_3}{\overset{\displaystyle |}{\underset{\displaystyle |}{C}}}}-CH_2-CH_3$$

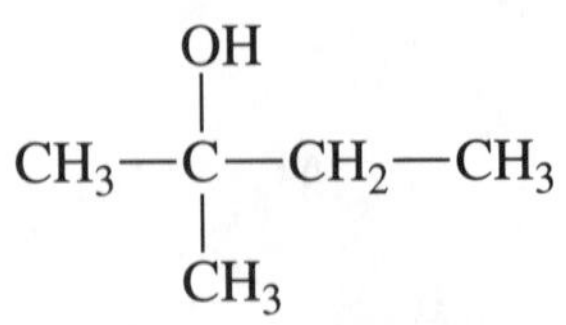

   e. Cyclohexanol has a six-carbon cycloalkane with a hydroxyl attached.

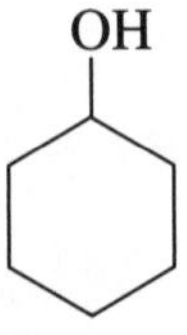

13.7   A benzene ring with a hydroxyl group is called *phenol*. Substituents are numbered from the carbon bonded to the hydroxyl group as carbon 1. Common names use the prefixes *ortho*, *meta*, and *para*.

   a. phenol

   b. 2-bromophenol, *ortho*-bromophenol (groups on the 1 and 2 positions are ortho)

   c. 3,5-dichlorophenol

   d. 3-bromophenol, *meta*-bromophenol (groups on the 1 and 3 positions are meta)

13.9   **a.** The *m* (meta) indicates that the two groups have a 1,3 arrangement.

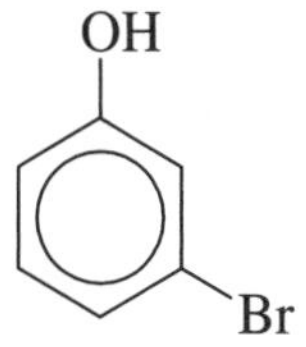

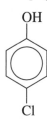

   b. The *p* (para) indicates that the two groups have a 1,4 arrangement.

   c. Two chlorine atoms are attached to the aromatic system, one on carbon 2 and the other on carbon 5, with the hydroxyl attached to carbon 1.

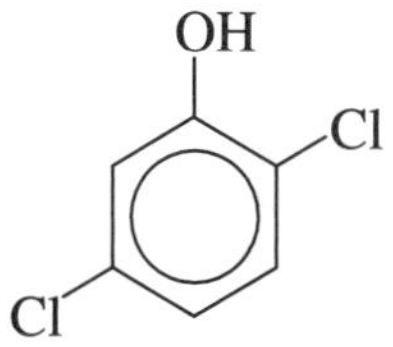

   d. The *o* (ortho) indicates that the two groups are in the 1,2 arrangement.

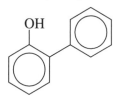

13.11 **a.** This is a one-carbon alkane with a thiol (—SH) group. The IUPAC name is methanethiol.

   b. This thiol has a three-carbon alkane with the thiol group attached to carbon 2. The IUPAC name is 2-propanethiol.

   c. This compound has a four-carbon alkane with methyl groups attached to carbon 2 and carbon 3 and the thiol attached to carbon 1. The IUPAC name is 2,3-dimethyl-1-butanethiol.

   d. This compound has a thiol attached to a cyclobutane. The IUPAC name is cyclobutanethiol.

13.13 **a.** methoxyethane, ethyl methyl ether

   b. methoxycyclohexane, cyclohexyl methyl ether

   c. ethoxycyclobutane, cyclobutyl ethyl ether

   d. 1-methoxypropane, methyl propyl ether

13.15 **a.** Ethyl propyl ether has a two-carbon group and a three-carbon group attached to oxygen by single bonds: $CH_3 — CH_2 — O — CH_2 — CH_2 — CH_3$.

   b. Ethyl cyclopropyl ether has a two-carbon group and a three-carbon cyclo alkyl group attached to oxygen by single bonds.

$$CH_3-CH_2-O-\triangleleft$$

c. Methoxycyclopentane has a one-carbon group and a five-carbon cycloalkyl group attached to oxygen by single bonds.

OCH$_3$

d. 1-ethoxy-2-methylbutane has a four-carbon chain with a methyl attached to carbon 2 and an ethoxy attached to carbon 1.

$$CH_3-CH_2-O-CH_2-\overset{\overset{\displaystyle CH_3}{|}}{CH}-CH_2-CH_3$$

e. 2,3-dimethoxypentane has a five-carbon chain with two methoxy groups attached; one to carbon 2 and the other to carbon 3.

$$CH_3-\overset{\overset{\displaystyle O-CH_3}{|}}{CH}-\overset{\underset{\displaystyle O-CH_3}{|}}{CH}-CH_2-CH_3$$

13.17 **a.** Isomers ($C_5H_{12}O$) have the same formula but different arrangements.
b. Different compounds have different molecular formulas.
c. Isomers ($C_5H_{12}O$) have the same formula but different arrangements.

13.19 The heterocyclic ethers with five atoms including one oxygen are named *furan*; six atoms including one oxygen are *pyrans*. A six-atom cyclic ether with two oxygen atoms is *dioxane*.
a. tetrahydrofuran   **b.** 3-methylfuran   **c.** 5-methyl-1,3-dioxane

13.21 **a.** Methanol; hydrogen bonding of alcohols gives higher boiling points than alkanes.
b. 1-butanol; alcohols hydrogen bond, but ethers cannot.
c. 1-butanol; hydrogen bonding of alcohols gives higher boiling points than alkanes.

13.23 **a.** Yes; alcohols with 1–4 carbon atoms hydrogen bond with water.
b. Yes; the water can hydrogen bond to the O in ether.
c. No; a carbon chain longer than 4 carbon atoms diminishes the effect of the —OH group.
d. Yes; the —OH in phenol ionizes in water, which makes it soluble.

13.25 Dehydration is the removal of an —OH and a —H from adjacent carbon atoms.

a. $CH_3-CH_2-CH=CH_2$ **b.**

c. In c, there are two possible products, A and B. B will be the major product, since the hydrogen is removed from the carbon that has the smaller number of hydrogens.

A   B

d. In d, there are two possible products, A and B. B will be the major product, since the hydrogen is removed from the carbon that has the smaller number of hydrogens.

$$CH_3-CH_2-CH_2-CH=CH_2 \qquad CH_3-CH_2-CH=CH-CH_3$$
                A   B

13.27 An ether is formed when H_2O is eliminated from two alcohols; the alkyl portion of one alcohol combines with the alkoxy portion of the other alcohol.

a. CH_3-O-CH_3 **b.** $CH_3-CH_2-CH_2-O-CH_2-CH_2-CH_3$

13.29 Alcohols can produce alkenes and ethers by the loss of water (dehydration).

a. CH_3-CH_2-OH

b. Since this ether has two different alkyl groups, it must be formed from two alcohols.

$CH_3-OH + CH_3-CH_2-OH$

c.

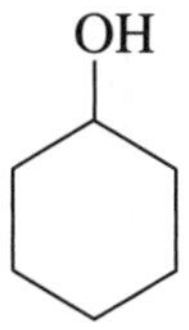

13.31 **a.** A primary alcohol oxidizes to an aldehyde and then to a carboxylic acid.

$CH_3-CH_2-CH_2-CH_2-C(=O)-H$ then $CH_3-CH_2-CH_2-CH_2-C(=O)-OH$

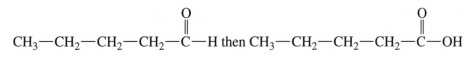

b. A secondary alcohol oxidizes to a ketone. $CH_3-CH_2-C(=O)-CH_3$

c. A secondary alcohol oxidizes to a ketone.

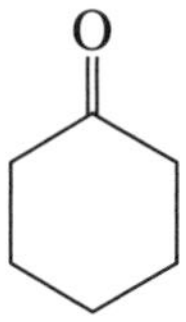

d. A secondary alcohol oxidizes to a ketone. $CH_3-C(=O)-CH_2-CH(CH_3)-CH_3$

e. A primary alcohol oxidizes to an aldehyde and then to a carboxylic acid.

$CH_3-CH(CH_3)-CH_2-C(=O)-H$ then $CH_3-CH(CH_3)-CH_2-C(=O)-OH$

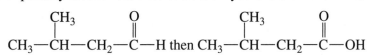

13.33 **a.** An aldehyde is the product of the oxidation of a primary alcohol: CH_3-OH.

b. A ketone is the product of the oxidation of a secondary alcohol.

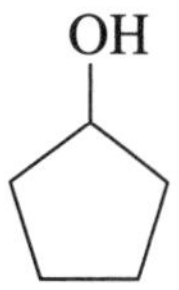

c. A ketone is the product of the oxidation of a secondary alcohol: $CH_3-CH(OH)-CH_2-CH_3$.

d. An aldehyde is the product of the oxidation of a primary alcohol.

e. A ketone is the product of the oxidation of a secondary alcohol.

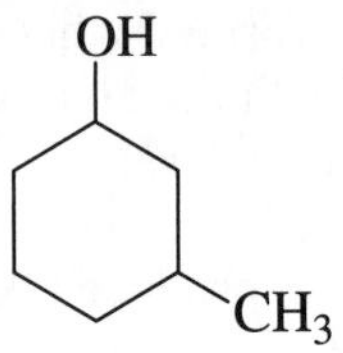

13.35

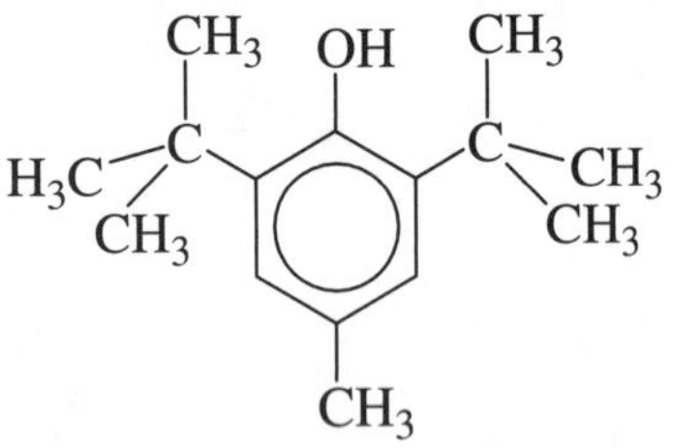

13.37 **a.** phenol   **b.** alcohol

13.39 **a.** 2°   **b.** 1°   **c.** 1°   **d.** 2°
        e. 1°   **f.** 3°

13.41 **a.** alcohol   **b.** ether   **c.** thiol   **d.** alcohol
        e. ether   **f.** cyclic ether   **g.** alcohol   **h.** phenol

13.43 **a.** 2-chloro-4-methylcyclohexanol   **b.** methyoxy benzene; methyl phenyl ether
        c. 2-propanethiol   **d.** 2,4-dimethyl-2-pentanol
        e. 1-methoxypropane; methyl propyl ether   **f.** 3-methyl furan
        g. 4-bromo-2-pentanol   **h.** *meta*-cresol

13.45 **a.**

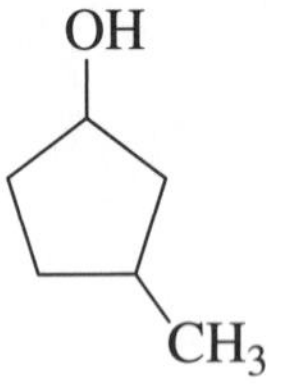

b.

c. H₃C—CH—CH—CH₂—CH₃

d.

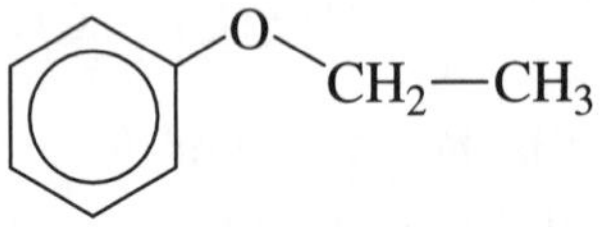

e. CH₃—CH₂—CH—CH₂—CH₃

f.

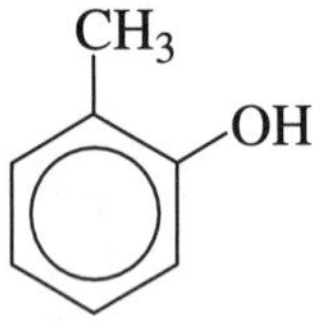

g.

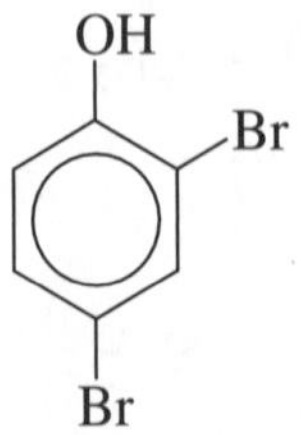

13.47 Write the carbon chain first, and place the —OH on the carbon atoms in the chain to give different structural formulas. Shorten the chain by one carbon, and attach a methyl group and —OH group to give different compounds.

$$CH_3—CH_2—CH_2—CH_2—OH \quad CH_3—\overset{\overset{\displaystyle OH}{|}}{CH}—CH_2—CH_3$$

$$\overset{\overset{\displaystyle CH_3}{|}}{CH_2}—CH—CH_2—OH \quad \overset{\overset{\displaystyle OH}{|}}{\underset{\underset{\displaystyle CH_3}{|}}{CH_2—C—CH_3}}$$

13.49 **a.** 1-propanol; hydrogen bonding   **b.** 1-propanol; hydrogen bonding
c. 1-butanol; larger molar mass

13.51 **a.** soluble; hydrogen bonding   **b.** soluble; hydrogen bonding
c. insoluble; long carbon chain diminishes effect of polar —OH on hydrogen bonding

13.53 **a.** $CH_3—CH{=}CH_2$ **b.** $CH_3—CH_2—\overset{\overset{\displaystyle O}{\|}}{C}—H$

c. $CH_3—CH{=}CH—CH_3$ **d.** $CH_3—CH_2—\overset{\overset{\displaystyle O}{\|}}{C}—CH_3$
e. $CH_3—CH_2—CH_2—O—CH_2—CH_2—CH_3$

f.   **g.**

13.55 **a.** $CH_3—CH_2—CH_2—OH \xrightarrow{H^+,\ heat} CH_2—CH{=}CH_2 + HCl \longrightarrow CH_3—\overset{\overset{\displaystyle Cl}{|}}{CH}—CH_3$

b. $CH_3—\overset{\overset{\displaystyle OH}{|}}{\underset{\underset{\displaystyle CH_3}{|}}{C}}—CH_3 \xrightarrow{H^+,\ heat} CH_3—\overset{\underset{\underset{\displaystyle CH_3}{|}}{}}{C}{=}CH_2 + H_2 \xrightarrow{Pt} CH_3—\overset{\underset{\underset{\displaystyle CH_3}{|}}{}}{CH}—CH_3$

c. $CH_3—CH_2—CH_2—OH \xrightarrow{H^+,\ heat} CH_3—CH{=}CH_2 + H_2O \xrightarrow{H^+}$

$CH_3—\overset{\overset{\displaystyle OH}{|}}{CH}—CH_3 \xrightarrow{[O]} CH_3—\overset{\overset{\displaystyle O}{\|}}{C}—CH_3$

13.57 Testosterone contains cycloalkene, alcohol, and ketone functional groups.

13.59 4-hexyl-1, 3-benzenediol tells us that there is a six-carbon group attached to carbon 4 of a benzene ring and hydroxyls attached to carbons 1 and 3.

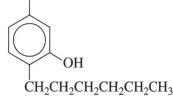

13.61 **a.** 2,5-dichlorophenol is a benzene ring with a hydroxyl on carbon 1 and chlorine atoms on carbons 2 and 5.

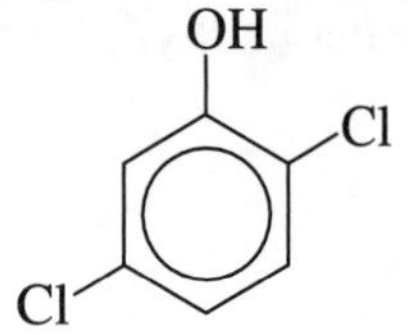
OH
Cl
Cl

a. $CH_3-CH(CH_3)-CH_2-CH_2-SH$

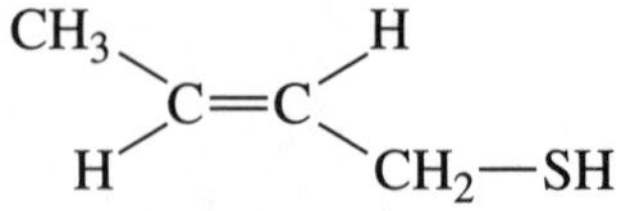
CH3
H
C=C
H
CH2—SH

c.

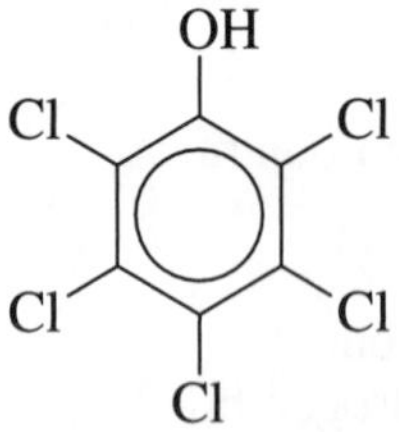
OH
Cl
Cl
Cl
Cl
Cl

13.63 $CH_3-CH(CH_3)-C(=O)-H$ 2-methylpropanal

13.65 $CH_3-CH_2-CH_2-CH_2-CH_2-OH$ 1-pentanol

$CH_3-CH(OH)-CH_2-CH_2-CH_3$ 2-pentanol

$CH_3-CH_2-CH(OH)-CH_2-CH_3$ 3-pentanol

$HO-CH_2-CH(CH_3)-CH_2-CH_3$ 2-methyl-1-butanol

$HO-CH_2-CH_2-CH(CH_3)-CH_3$ 3-methyl-1-butanol

$CH_3-C(CH_3)(OH)-CH_2-CH_3$ 2-methyl-2-butanol

$CH_3-CH(OH)-CH(CH_3)-CH_3$ 3-methyl-2-butanol

$CH_3-C(CH_3)_2-CH_2-OH$ 2,2-dimethyl-1-propanol

Aldehydes, Ketones, and Chiral Molecules

Study Goals

- Name and write the condensed structural formulas for aldehydes and ketones.
- Describe some important aldehydes and ketones.
- Identify the chiral carbon atoms in organic molecules.
- Write equations for the oxidation of aldehydes and for the reduction of aldehydes and ketones.
- Draw the structural formulas of hemiacetals and acetals produced from the addition of alcohols to aldehydes and ketones.

Think About It

1. What are the functional groups of an aldehyde and ketone?

2. How is an alcohol changed to an aldehyde or ketone?

3. When are mirror images not superimposable?

4. How are hemiacetals and acetals formed?

Key Terms

Match the following terms with the statements shown below:

    a. chiral carbon   **b.** hemiacetal   **c.** Fischer projection   **d.** aldehyde   **e.** ketone

1. _____ An organic compound with a carbonyl group attached to two alkyl groups

2. _____ A carbon that is bonded to four different groups

3. _____ The product that forms when an alcohol adds to an aldehyde or a ketone

4. _____ A system for drawing chiral molecules that uses horizontal lines for bonds coming forward and vertical lines for bonds going back with the chiral atom at the center.

5. _____ An organic compound that contains a carbonyl group and a hydrogen atom at the end of the carbon chain.

Answers   **1.** e   **2.** a   **3.** b   **4.** c   **5.** d

14.1 Aldehydes and Ketones

- In an aldehyde, the carbonyl group appears at the end of a carbon chain attached to at least one hydrogen atom.
- In a ketone, the carbonyl group occurs between carbon groups and has no hydrogens attached to it.

- In the IUPAC system, aldehydes and ketones are named by replacing the *e* in the longest chain containing the carbonyl group with *al* for aldehydes and *one* for ketones. The location of the carbonyl group in a ketone is given if there are more than four carbon atoms in the chain.

$$CH_3-\overset{\overset{\displaystyle O}{\|}}{C}-H \qquad CH_3-\overset{\overset{\displaystyle O}{\|}}{C}-CH_3$$

ethanal   propanone
(acetaldehyde)   (dimethyl ketone)

◆ Learning Exercise 14.1A

Classify each of the following compounds:

A. alcohol   **B.** aldehyde   **C.** ketone   **D.** ether   **E.** thiol

___1. $CH_3-CH_2-CH_2-\overset{\overset{\displaystyle O}{\|}}{C}-H$ ___2. $CH_3-CH_2-CH_2-OH$

___3. $CH_3-CH_2-\overset{\overset{\displaystyle O}{\|}}{C}-CH_2-CH_3$ ___4. $CH_3-CH_2-O-CH_3$

___5. $CH_3-\overset{\overset{\displaystyle O}{\|}}{C}-CH_2-CH_3$ ___6. $CH_3-\overset{\overset{\displaystyle O}{\|}}{C}-H$

___7. $CH_3-CH_2-\overset{\overset{\displaystyle SH}{|}}{CH}-CH_3$ ___8. $CH_3-CH_2-\overset{\overset{\displaystyle OH}{|}}{CH}-CH_3$

Answers   1. B   2. A   3. C   4. D
              5. C   6. B   7. E   8. A

◆ Learning Exercise 14.1B

Indicate whether the compounds in each of the following pairs are constitutional isomers (C), the same compound (S), or different compounds (D).

1. ___ $CH_3-CH_2-\overset{\overset{\displaystyle O}{\|}}{C}-H$ and $CH_3-\overset{\overset{\displaystyle O}{\|}}{C}-CH_3$

2. ___ (structures) and

3. ___ $CH_3-\overset{\overset{\displaystyle O}{\|}}{C}-CH_2-CH_3$ and $CH_3-\overset{\overset{\displaystyle O}{\|}}{C}-CH_2-CH_2-CH_3$

Answers   1. C   2. S   3. D

◆ **Learning Exercise 14.1C**

Write the correct IUPAC (or common name) for the following aldehydes:

1. 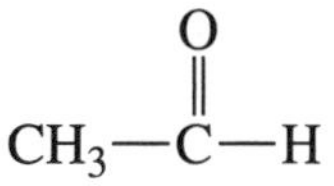 $CH_3-\overset{\displaystyle O}{\overset{\|}{C}}-H$

2. $CH_3-CH_2-CH_2-CH_2-\overset{\displaystyle O}{\overset{\|}{C}}-H$

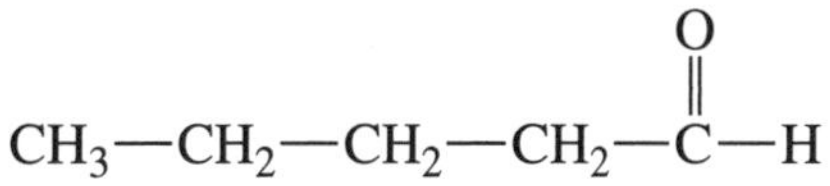

3. $CH_3-CH_2-\overset{\displaystyle CH_3}{\overset{|}{CH}}-CH_2-CH_2-\overset{\displaystyle O}{\overset{\|}{C}}-H$

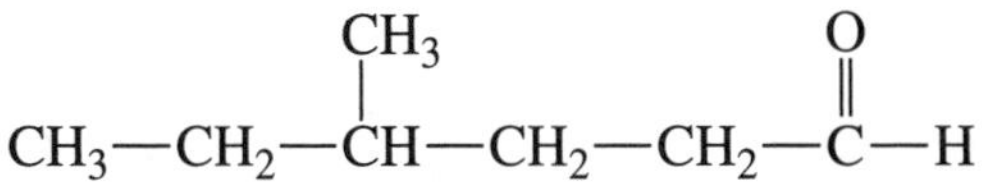

4.

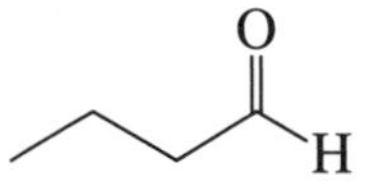

5. 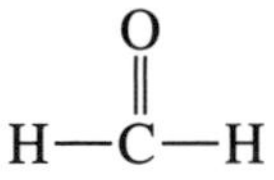 $H-\overset{\displaystyle O}{\overset{\|}{C}}-H$

Answers   **1.** ethanal; acetaldehyde   **2.** pentanal   **3.** 4-methylhexanal
             4. butanal; butyraldehyde   **5.** methanal; formaldehyde

◆ **Learning Exercise 14.1D**

Write the IUPAC (or common name) for the following ketones:

1. 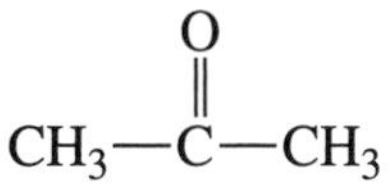 $CH_3-\overset{\displaystyle O}{\overset{\|}{C}}-CH_3$

2.

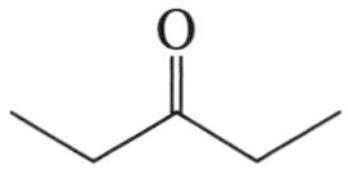

3. $CH_3-CH_2-\overset{\displaystyle O}{\overset{\|}{C}}-CH_2-CH_3$

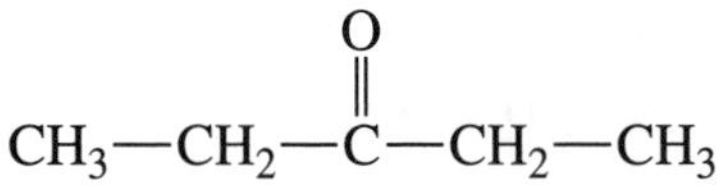

4.

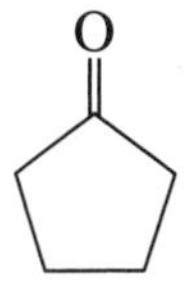

5.

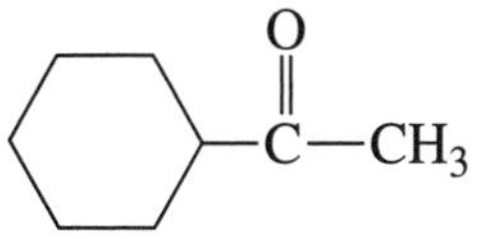

Answers   **1.** propanone; dimethyl ketone, acetone   **2.** 2-pentanone; methyl propyl ketone
             3. 3-pentanone; diethyl ketone   **4.** cyclopentanone
             5. cyclohexyl methyl ketone

◆ **Learning Exercise 14.1E**

Write the correct condensed formulas for the following:

1. ethanal

2. butyraldehyde

3. 2-chloropropanal

4. ethylmethylketone

5. 3-hexanone

6. benzaldehyde

Answers

1.
$$CH_3-\overset{\displaystyle O}{\overset{\|}{C}}-H$$

2.
$$CH_3-CH_2-CH_2-\overset{\displaystyle O}{\overset{\|}{C}}-H$$

3.
$$CH_3-\overset{Cl}{\overset{|}{CH}}-\overset{O}{\overset{\|}{C}}-H$$

4.
$$CH_3-CH_2-\overset{\displaystyle O}{\overset{\|}{C}}-CH_3$$

5.
$$CH_3-CH_2-\overset{\displaystyle O}{\overset{\|}{C}}-CH_2-CH_2-CH_3$$

6.

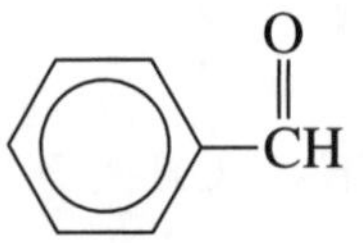

14.2 Physical Properties

• The polarity of the carbonyl group makes aldehydes and ketones of one to four carbon atoms soluble in water.

◆ **Learning Exercise 14.2A**

Indicate the compound with the highest boiling point in each of the following groups of compounds:

1. $CH_3-CH_2-\overset{\displaystyle O}{\overset{\|}{C}}-H$, $CH_3-CH_2-CH_2-OH$, or $CH_3-\overset{\displaystyle O}{\overset{\|}{C}}-CH_3$

2. acetaldehyde or propionaldehyde
3. propanone or butanone
4. methylcyclohexane or cyclohexanone

Answers   **1.** CH_3—CH_2—CH_2—OH   **2.** propionaldehyde
             3. butanone   **4.** cyclohexanone

◆ Learning Exercise 14.2B

Indicate whether each of the following compounds is soluble (S) or not soluble (NS) in water:

1. ____ 3-hexanone   **2.** ____ propanal   **3.** ____ acetaldehyde

4. ____ butanal   **5.** ____ cyclohexanone

Answers   **1.** NS   **2.** S   **3.** S   **4.** S   **5.** NS

14.3 Oxidation and Reduction

- Using an oxidizing agent, primary alcohols oxidize to aldehydes, which usually oxidize further to carboxylic acids. Secondary alcohols are oxidized to ketones, but tertiary alcohols do not oxidize.

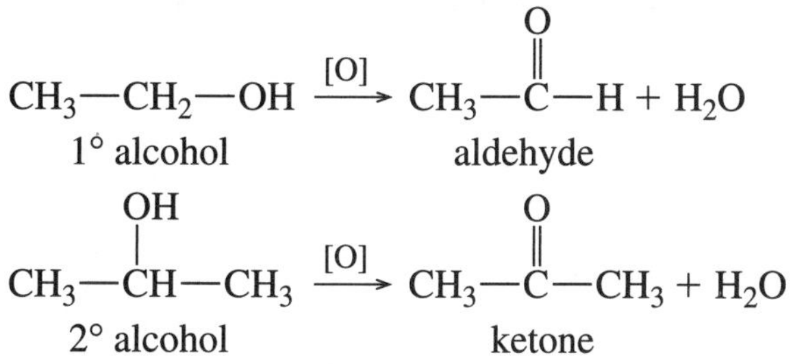

$$CH_3—CH_2—OH \xrightarrow{[O]} CH_3—\overset{\overset{\displaystyle O}{\|}}{C}—H + H_2O$$
1° alcohol   aldehyde

$$CH_3—\overset{\overset{\displaystyle OH}{|}}{CH}—CH_3 \xrightarrow{[O]} CH_3—\overset{\overset{\displaystyle O}{\|}}{C}—CH_3 + H_2O$$
2° alcohol   ketone

- Aldehydes and ketones are reduced when hydrogen is added in the presence of a metal catalyst to produce primary or secondary alcohols.

◆ Learning Exercise 14.3A

Write the structural formula of the alcohol that oxidized to give each of the following compounds:

1. 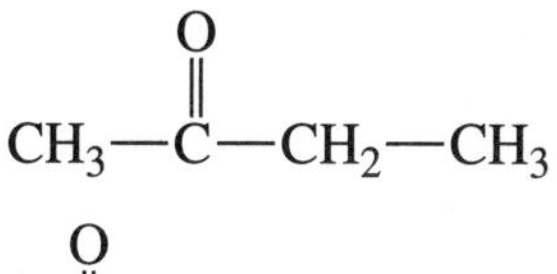 $CH_3—\overset{\overset{\displaystyle O}{\|}}{C}—CH_2—CH_3$

2.

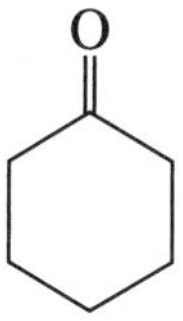

3. 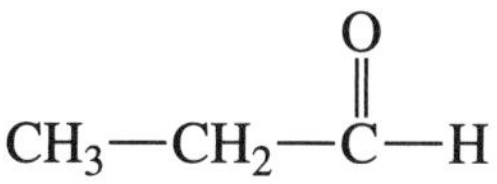 $CH_3—CH_2—\overset{\overset{\displaystyle O}{\|}}{C}—H$

Answers   **1.** 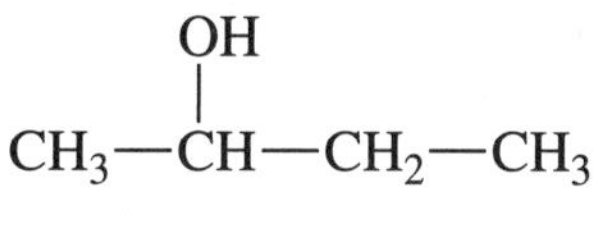 $CH_3—\overset{\overset{\displaystyle OH}{|}}{CH}—CH_2—CH_3$ **2.** 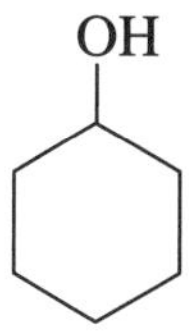   **3.** $CH_3—CH_2—CH_2—OH$

241

◆ **Learning Exercise 14.3B**

Indicate the compound in each of the following pairs that will oxidize.

1. propanal or propanone _____

2. butane or butanal _____

3. ethane or acetaldehyde _____

Answers   **1.** propanal   **2.** butanal   **3.** acetaldehyde

◆ **Learning Exercise 14.3C**

Write the reduction products for the following:

1. $CH_3-\overset{\overset{\displaystyle O}{\|}}{C}-CH_3 + H_2 \xrightarrow{Pt}$

2. $CH_3-CH_2-\overset{\overset{\displaystyle O}{\|}}{C}-H + H_2 \xrightarrow{Pt}$

3. $CH_3-\overset{\overset{\displaystyle O}{\|}}{C}-H + H_2 \xrightarrow{Pt}$

4. 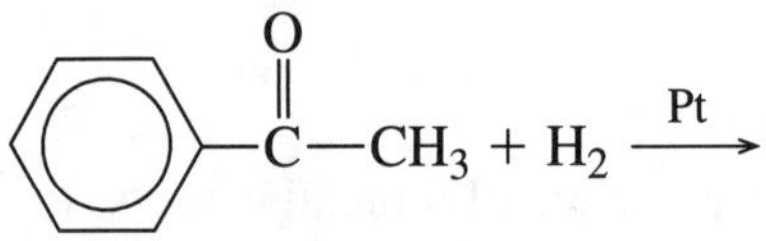 $\text{C}_6\text{H}_5-\overset{\overset{\displaystyle O}{\|}}{C}-CH_3 + H_2 \xrightarrow{Pt}$

5. (2-methylcyclopentane carbaldehyde) $+ H_2 \xrightarrow{Pt}$

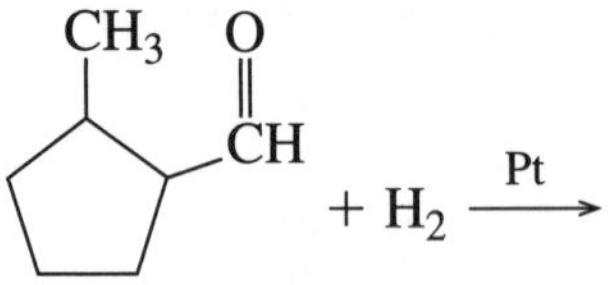

Answers   **1.** $CH_3-\overset{\overset{\displaystyle OH}{|}}{CH}-CH_3$ **2.** $CH_3-CH_2-CH_2-OH$ **3.** CH_3-CH_2-OH

4. 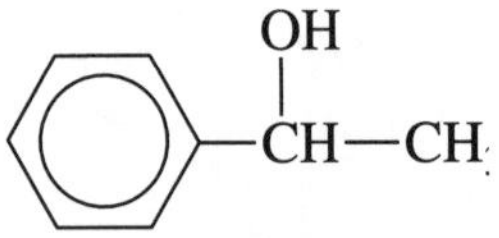 $C_6H_5-\overset{\overset{\displaystyle OH}{|}}{CH}-CH_3$ **5.** (2-methylcyclopentyl)CH_2OH

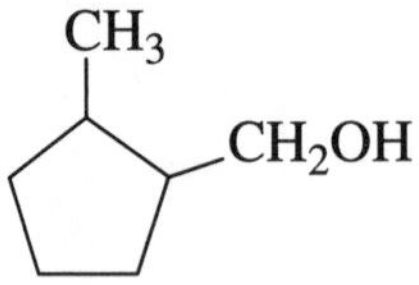

14.4 Addition Reactions

- Alcohols add to the carbonyl group of aldehyde and ketones.
- Hemiacetals form when one alcohol adds to aldehydes or ketones.
- Acetals form when a second alcohol molecule adds to hemiacetals.

◆ **Learning Exercise 14.4A**

Match the statements shown below with the following types of compounds:

A. hemiacetal   **B.** acetal

1. _____ the product from the addition of one alcohol to an aldehyde

2. _____ the product from the addition of one alcohol to a ketone

3. _____ a compound that contains two ether groups

4. _____ a compound that consists of one ether group, an alcohol group, and two alkyl groups

Answers   **1.** A   **2.** A   **3.** B   **4.** A

◆ **Learning Exercise 14.4B**

Identify each of the following structural formulas as a hemiacetal, acetal, or neither.

1. CH_3—O—CH_2—OH

2. 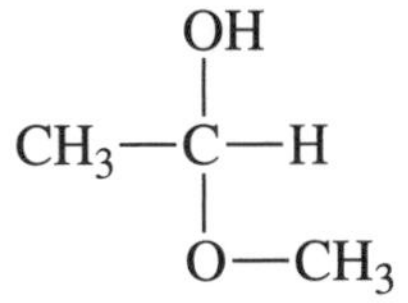
$$CH_3—\overset{\displaystyle OH}{\underset{\displaystyle O—CH_3}{C}}—H$$

3.
$$CH_3—\overset{\displaystyle O—CH_2—CH_3}{\underset{\displaystyle O—CH_2—CH_3}{C}}—CH_3$$

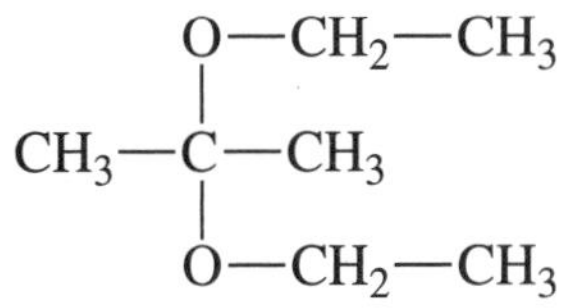

4. 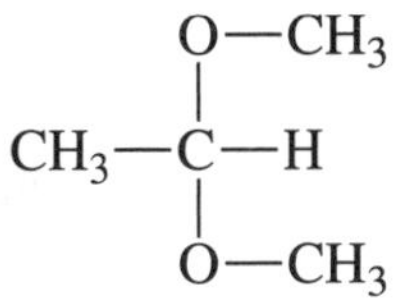
$$CH_3—\overset{\displaystyle O—CH_3}{\underset{\displaystyle O—CH_3}{C}}—H$$

Answers   **1.** hemiacetal   **2.** hemiacetal   **3.** acetal   **4.** acetal

◆ **Learning Exercise 14.4C**

Write the structural formula of the hemiacetal and acetal products when methanol adds to propanone.

Answer
$$CH_3—\overset{\displaystyle OH}{\underset{\displaystyle CH_3}{C}}—O—CH_3 \qquad CH_3—\overset{\displaystyle O—CH_3}{\underset{\displaystyle CH_3}{C}}—O—CH_3$$

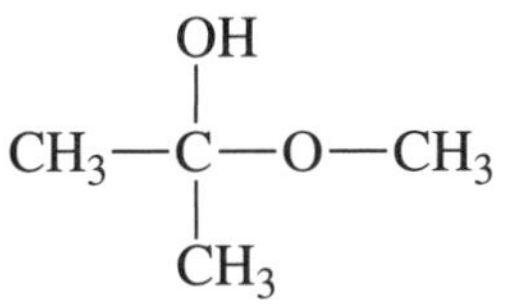

         hemiacetal 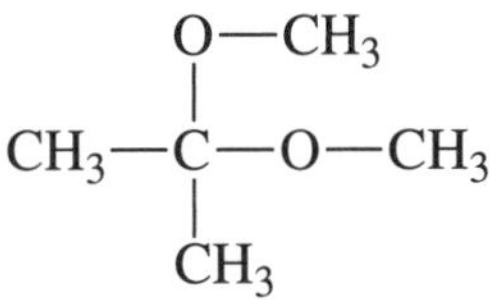   acetal

14.5 Chiral Molecules

- Chiral molecules have mirror images that cannot be superimposed.
- In a chiral molecule, there is one or more carbon atoms attached to four different atoms or groups.
- The mirror images of a chiral molecule represent two different molecules called enantiomers.

- In a Fischer projection (straight chain), the prefixes D- and L- are used to distinguish between the mirror images. In D-glyceraldehyde, the —OH is on the right of the chiral carbon; it is on the left in L-glyceraldehyde.

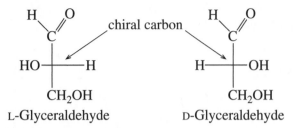

L-Glyceraldehyde   D-Glyceraldehyde

◆ Learning Exercise 14.5A

Indicate whether the following objects would be chiral or not:

1. a piece of plain computer paper _____   **2.** a glove _____

3. a baseball cap _____   **4.** a volleyball net _____

5. your left foot _____

Answers   **1.** not chiral   **2.** chiral   **3.** not chiral   **4.** not chiral   **5.** chiral

◆ Learning Exercise 14.5B

State whether each of the following molecules is chiral or not chiral:

$$\begin{array}{ccc} & Cl & \\ & | & \\ \textbf{1.} & H-C-Cl & \\ & | & \\ & CH_3 & \end{array} \qquad \begin{array}{ccc} & Cl & \\ & | & \\ \textbf{2.} & H-C-OH & \\ & | & \\ & CH_3 & \end{array} \qquad \begin{array}{ccc} & CHO & \\ & | & \\ \textbf{3.} & H-C-OH & \\ & | & \\ & CH_3 & \end{array}$$

_____   _____   _____

Answers   **1.** not chiral   **2.** chiral   **3.** chiral

◆ Learning Exercise 14.5C

Identify the following as a feature that is characteristic of a chiral compound or not:

1. the central atom is attached to two identical groups _____

2. contains a carbon attached to four different groups _____

3. has identical mirror images _____

Answers   **1.** not chiral   **2.** chiral   **3.** not chiral

◆ Learning Exercise 14.5D

Indicate whether each pair of Fischer projections represents enantiomers (E) or identical structures (I).

$$\textbf{a.} \begin{array}{c} COOH \\ HO-\!\!\!\!-\!\!\!H \\ CH_2OH \end{array} \text{and} \begin{array}{c} COOH \\ H-\!\!\!\!-\!\!\!OH \\ CH_2OH \end{array} \qquad \textbf{b.} \begin{array}{c} CH_3 \\ Cl-\!\!\!\!-\!\!\!H \\ CH_2OH \end{array} \text{and} \begin{array}{c} CH_3 \\ Cl-\!\!\!\!-\!\!\!H \\ CH_2OH \end{array}$$

$$\begin{array}{cc}
\text{CHO} & \text{CHO} \\
| & | \\
\textbf{c. } \text{Cl}\!-\!\!-\!\!\text{Br} \text{ and } \text{Br}\!-\!\!-\!\!\text{Cl} \\
| & | \\
\text{CH}_3 & \text{CH}_3
\end{array}$$

$$\begin{array}{cc}
\text{COOH} & \text{COOH} \\
| & | \\
\textbf{d. } \text{H}\!-\!\!-\!\!\text{OH} \text{ and } \text{HO}\!-\!\!-\!\!\text{H} \\
| & | \\
\text{COOH} & \text{COOH}
\end{array}$$

Answers   **1.** E   **2.** I   **3.** E   **4.** I

Checklist for Chapter 14

You are ready to take the practice test for chapter 14. Be sure that you have accomplished the following learning goals for this chapter. If you are not sure, review the section listed at the end of the goal. Then apply your new skills and understanding to the practice test. Good luck.

After studying chapter 14, I can successfully:

_____   Identify structural formulas as aldehydes and ketones (14.1).

_____   Give the IUPAC and common names of an aldehyde or ketone; draw the condensed structural formula from the name (14.1).

_____   Compare the physical properties of aldehydes and ketones with alcohols and alkanes (14.2).

_____   Write the structural formulas for reactants and products of the oxidation of alcohols or reduction of aldehydes and ketones (14.3).

_____   Write the structural formulas of the hemiacetals and acetals that form when alcohols add to aldehyde or ketones (14.4).

_____   Identify a molecule as a chiral or not; write the D and L Fischer projections (14.5).

Practice Test for Chapter 14

Match the following compounds with the names given.

A. dimethyl ether   **B.** acetaldehyde   **C.** methanal   **D.** dimethyl ketone   **E.** propanal

1. _____
$$\text{H}\!-\!\!\overset{\overset{\text{O}}{\|}}{\text{C}}\!-\!\text{H}$$

2. _____ $\text{CH}_3\!-\!\text{O}\!-\!\text{CH}_3$

3. _____
$$\text{CH}_3\!-\!\!\overset{\overset{\text{O}}{\|}}{\text{C}}\!-\!\text{CH}_3$$

4. _____
$$\text{CH}_3\!-\!\!\overset{\overset{\text{O}}{\|}}{\text{C}}\!-\!\text{H}$$

5. _____
$$\text{CH}_3\!-\!\text{CH}_2\!-\!\!\overset{\overset{\text{O}}{\|}}{\text{C}}\!-\!\text{H}$$

6. The compound with the highest boiling point is

A. $\text{CH}_3\!-\!\text{CH}_2\!-\!\text{CH}_2\!-\!\text{CH}_3$ **B.** $\text{CH}_3\!-\!\text{CH}_2\!-\!\text{CH}_2\!-\!\text{OH}$

C.
$$\text{CH}_3\!-\!\!\overset{\overset{\text{O}}{\|}}{\text{C}}\!-\!\text{CH}_3$$
     D.
$$\text{CH}_3\!-\!\text{CH}_2\!-\!\!\overset{\overset{\text{O}}{\|}}{\text{C}}\!-\!\text{H}$$

E. $\text{CH}_3\!-\!\text{CH}_2\!-\!\text{O}\!-\!\text{CH}_3$

Complete questions 7–11 by indicating one of the products (A–E) formed in each of the following reactions:

    A. primary alcohol   **B.** secondary alcohol   **C.** aldehyde
    D. ketone   **E.** carboxylic acid

  7. ____ oxidation of a primary alcohol   **8.** ____ oxidation of a secondary alcohol

  9. ____ oxidation of an aldehyde   **10.** ____ reduction of a ketone

11. ____ reduction of an aldehyde

12. Benedict's reagent will oxidize

  A. 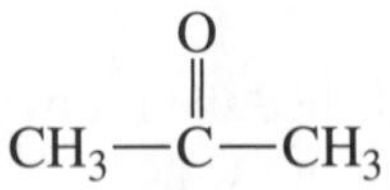 $CH_3-\overset{\overset{O}{\|}}{C}-CH_3$ **B.** $CH_3-\overset{\overset{OH}{|}}{CH}-CH_2-OH$

  C. $CH_3-\overset{\overset{O}{\|}}{C}-CH_2-OH$ **D.** 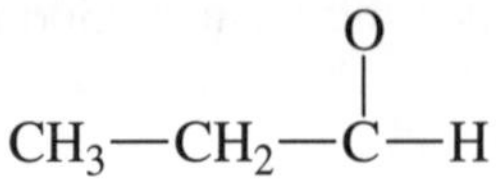 $CH_3-CH_2-\overset{\overset{O}{|}}{C}-H$

  E. 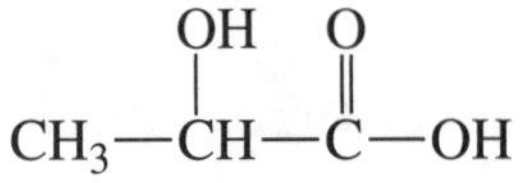 $CH_3-\overset{\overset{OH}{|}}{CH}-\overset{\overset{O}{\|}}{C}-OH$

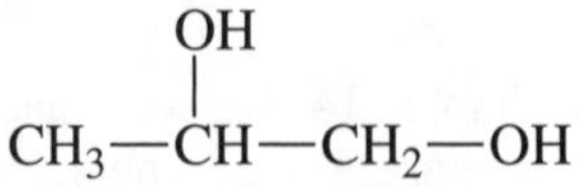

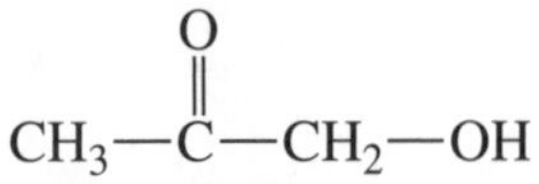

13. In the Tollen's test
    A. an aldehyde is oxidized and Ag^+ is reduced
    B. an aldehyde is reduced and Ag^+ is oxidized
    C. a ketone is oxidized and Ag^+ is reduced
    D. a ketone is reduced and Ag^+ is oxidized
    E. all of these

Identify each of the following structural formulas as

14. alcohol   **15.** ether   **16.** hemiacetal   **17.** acetal

  A. 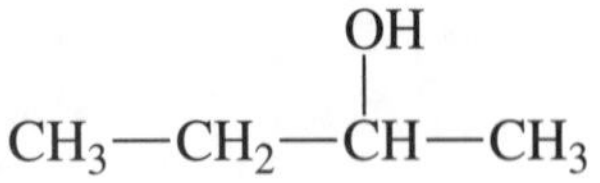 $CH_3-CH_2-\overset{\overset{OH}{|}}{CH}-CH_3$ **B.** 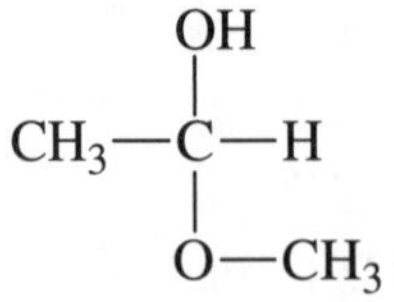 $CH_3-\overset{\overset{OH}{|}}{\underset{\underset{O-CH_3}{|}}{C}}-H$

  C. $CH_3-\overset{\overset{O-CH_2-CH_3}{|}}{\underset{\underset{O-CH_2-CH_3}{|}}{C}}-CH_3$ **D.** 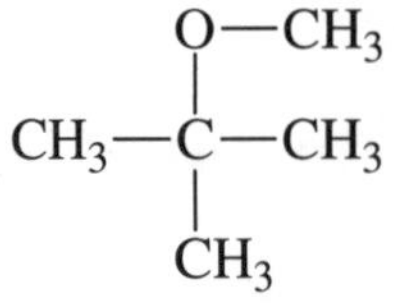 $CH_3-\overset{\overset{O-CH_3}{|}}{\underset{\underset{CH_3}{|}}{C}}-CH_3$

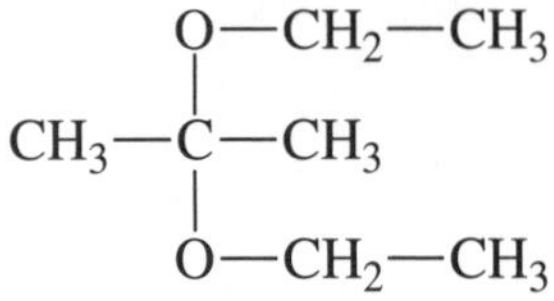

18. The structural formula for 4-bromo-3-methylcyclohexanone is

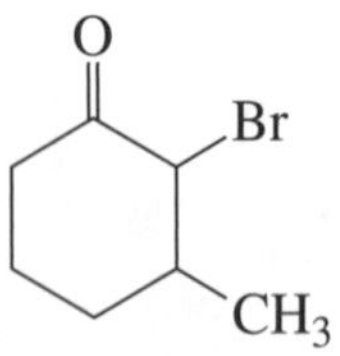

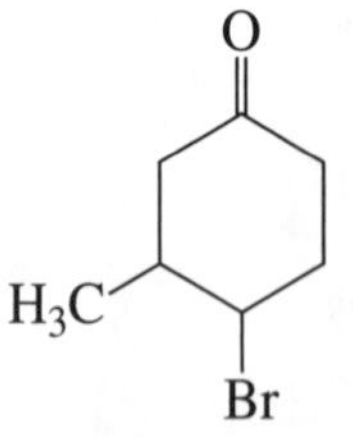

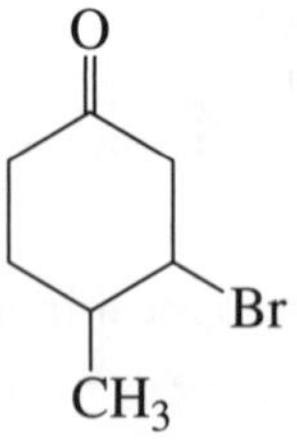

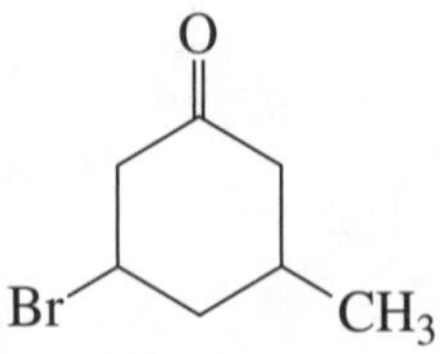

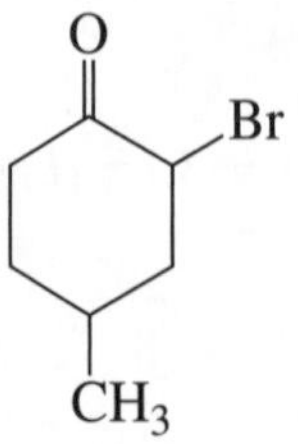

19. The name of this compound is

$$CH_3-\overset{\overset{\displaystyle CH_3}{|}}{CH}-CH_2-\overset{\overset{\displaystyle CH_3}{|}}{CH}-CH_2-\overset{\overset{\displaystyle O}{||}}{C}-H$$

   A. 3,5-dimethyl-1-hexanal   **B.** 2,4-dimethyl-6-hexanal
   C. 3,5-dimethylhexanal   **D.** 1-aldo-3,5-dimethylhexane
   E. 2,4-dimethylhexanal

20. The reaction of an alcohol with an aldehyde is called a(n)
   A. elimination   **B.** addition   **C.** substitution
   D. hydrolysis   **E.** oxidation

Identify each of the following as enantiomers (E), identical (I), or different (D) compounds:

21. 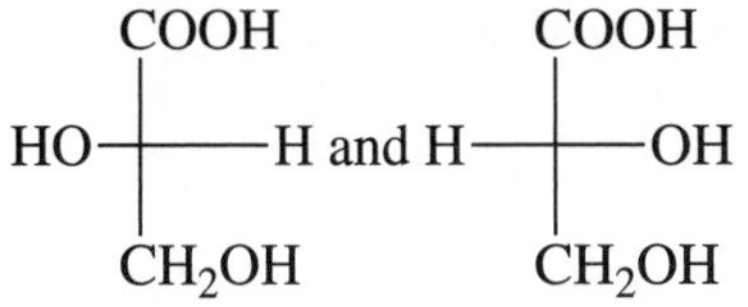 HO—|—H and H—|—OH (COOH top, CH₂OH bottom)

22. 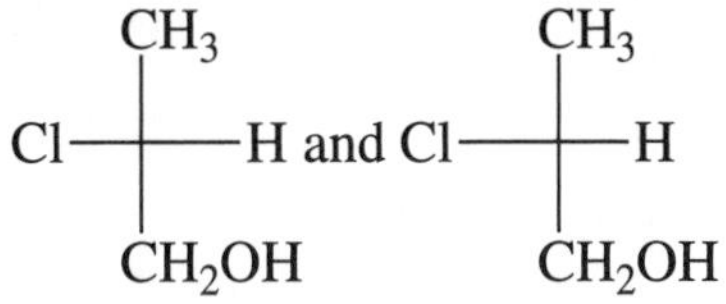 Cl—|—H and Cl—|—H (CH₃ top, CH₂OH bottom)

23. 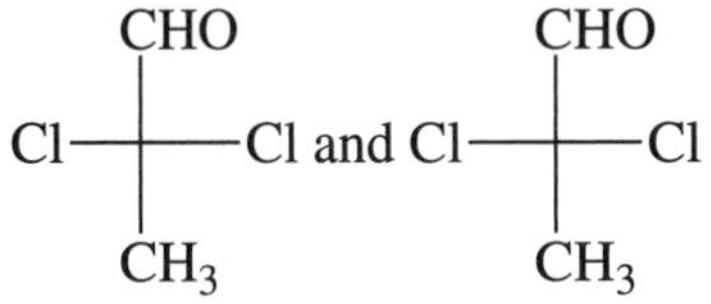 Cl—|—Cl and Cl—|—Cl (CHO top, CH₃ bottom)

24. 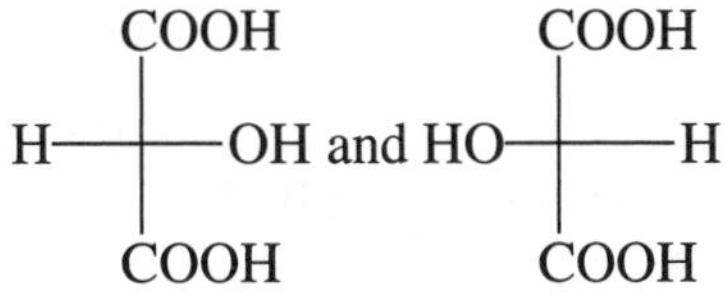 H—|—OH and HO—|—H (COOH top, COOH bottom)

25. 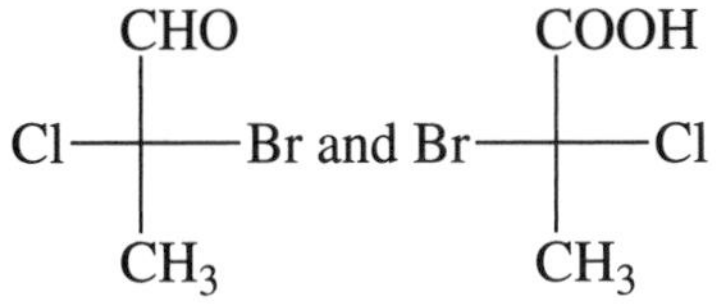 Cl—|—Br and Br—|—Cl (CHO/COOH top, CH₃ bottom)

Answers to Practice Test

1. B	**2.** A	**3.** D	**4.** B	**5.** E
6. B	**7.** C, E	**8.** D	**9.** E	**10.** B
11. A	**12.** D	**13.** A	**14.** A	**15.** D
16. B	**17.** C	**18.** B	**19.** C	**20.** B
21. E	**22.** I	**23.** I	**24.** I	**25.** D

Answers and Solutions to Selected Text Problems

14.1   **a.** ketone   **b.** aldehyde   **c.** ketone   **d.** aldehyde

14.3   **a.** 1   **b.** 1   **c.** 2

14.5   **a.** propanal   **b.** 2-methyl-3-pentanone   **c.** 3-bromobutanal
      d. 2-pentanone   **e.** 3-methylcyclohexanone   **f.** 4-chlorobenzaldehyde

14.7   **a.** acetaldehyde   **b.** methyl propyl ketone   **c.** formaldehyde

14.9 **a.** CH₃—C(=O)—H

b. CH₃—C(=O)—CH₂—CH(CH₃)—CH₃

c. CH₃—CH(Br)—CH(Br)—C(=O)—H

d. CH₃—C(=O)—CH₂—CH₂—CH₂—CH₃

e. CH₃—CH₂—CH(CH₃)—CH₂—C(=O)—H

14.11

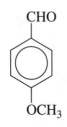

14.13 **a.** CH₃—C(=O)—H has a polar carbonyl group.

b. Pentanal has more carbons and thus a higher molar mass.

c. 1-butanol hydrogen bonds with other 1-butanol molecules.

14.15 **a.** CH₃—C(=O)—C(=O)—CH₃ : more hydrogen bonding

b. acetaldehyde; acetaldehyde can hydrogen bond

c. acetone; lower number of carbon atoms

14.17 No; the carbon chain diminishes the effect of the carbonyl group.

14.19 **a.** An aldehyde is the product of the oxidation of a primary alcohol: CH₃OH.

b. A ketone is the product of the oxidation of a secondary alcohol.

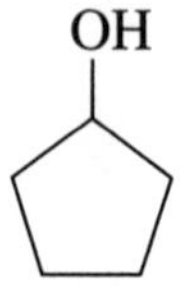

c. A ketone is the product of the oxidation of a secondary alcohol.

CH₃—CH(OH)—CH₂—CH₃

d. An aldehyde is the product of the oxidation of a primary alcohol.

e. A ketone is the product of the oxidation of a secondary alcohol.

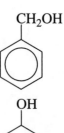

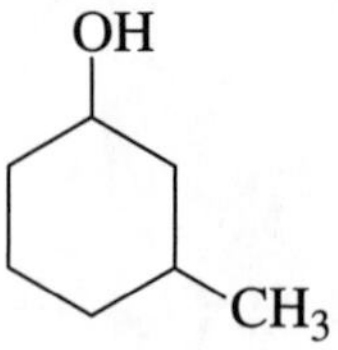

14.21 **a.** A primary alcohol will be oxidized to an aldehyde and then to a carboxylic acid.

$$CH_3-CH_2-CH_2-CH_2-\overset{\overset{\textstyle O}{\|}}{C}-H \text{ then } CH_3-CH_2-CH_2-CH_2-\overset{\overset{\textstyle O}{\|}}{C}-OH$$

b. A secondary alcohol will be oxidized to a ketone. $CH_3-CH_2-\overset{\overset{\textstyle O}{\|}}{C}-CH_3$

c. A secondary alcohol will be oxidized to a ketone.

d. A secondary alcohol will be oxidized to a ketone. $CH_3-\overset{\overset{\textstyle O}{\|}}{C}-CH_2-\overset{\overset{\textstyle CH_3}{|}}{CH}-CH_3$

e. A primary alcohol will be oxidized to an aldehyde and then to a carboxylic acid.

$$CH_3-\overset{\overset{\textstyle CH_3}{|}}{CH}-CH_2-\overset{\overset{\textstyle O}{\|}}{C}-H \text{ then } CH_3-\overset{\overset{\textstyle CH_3}{|}}{CH}-CH_2-\overset{\overset{\textstyle O}{\|}}{C}-OH$$

14.23 In reduction, an aldehyde will give a primary alcohol and a ketone will give a secondary alcohol.
a. Butyraldehyde is the four-carbon aldehyde; it will be reduced to a four carbon, primary alcohol.

$$CH_3-CH_2-CH_2-CH_2-OH$$

b. Acetone is a three-carbon ketone; it will be reduced to a three carbon secondary alcohol.

$$CH_3-\overset{\overset{\textstyle OH}{|}}{CH}-CH_3$$

c. 3-bromohexanal is a six-carbon aldehyde with bromine attached to carbon 3. It reduces to a six-carbon primary alcohol with bromine on carbon 3.

$$CH_3-CH_2-CH_2-\overset{\overset{\textstyle Br}{|}}{CH}-CH_2-CH_2-OH$$

d. 2-methyl-3-pentanone is a five-carbon ketone with a methyl group attached to carbon 2. It will be reduced to a five-carbon secondary alcohol with a methyl attached to carbon 2.

$$CH_3-\overset{\overset{\textstyle CH_3}{|}}{CH}-\overset{\overset{\textstyle OH}{|}}{CH}-CH_2-CH_3$$

14.25 **a.** $CH_3-\overset{\overset{\textstyle OH}{|}}{\underset{\underset{\textstyle OH}{|}}{C}}-H$ **b.** $H-\overset{\overset{\textstyle OH}{|}}{\underset{\underset{\textstyle OH}{|}}{C}}-H$

14.27 **a.** hemiacetal (ethanol and formaldehyde)   **b.** hemiacetal   **c.** acetal
d. hemiacetal   **e.** acetal

14.29 A hemiacetal forms when an alcohol is added to the carbonyl of an aldehyde or ketone.

a. $CH_3-\overset{\overset{\textstyle O-CH_3}{|}}{\underset{\underset{\textstyle OH}{|}}{C}}-H$ **b.** $CH_3-\overset{\overset{\textstyle O-CH_3}{|}}{\underset{\underset{\textstyle OH}{|}}{CH}}-CH$

249

c.

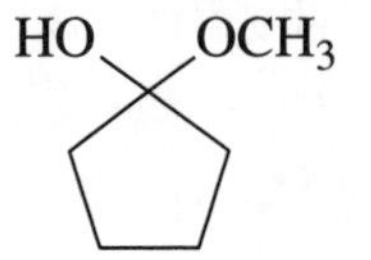

$$HO \quad OCH_3$$

(cyclopentane ring)

d. 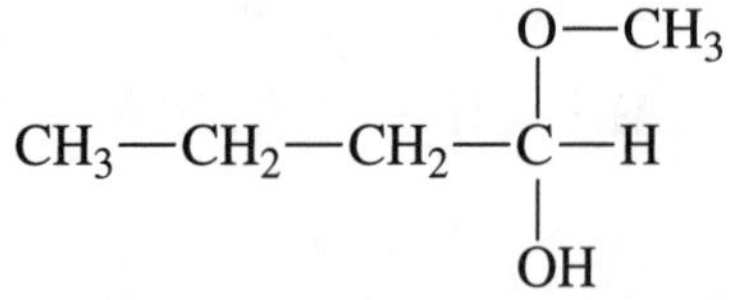 $CH_3—CH_2—CH_2—\overset{\displaystyle O—CH_3}{\underset{\displaystyle OH}{C}}—H$

14.31 An acetal forms when a second molecule of alcohol reacts with a hemiacetal.

a. 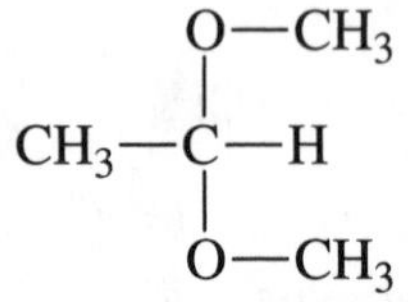 $CH_3—\overset{\displaystyle O—CH_3}{\underset{\displaystyle O—CH_3}{C}}—H$ b. $CH_3—\overset{\displaystyle O—CH_3}{\underset{\displaystyle O—CH_3}{C}}—CH_3$

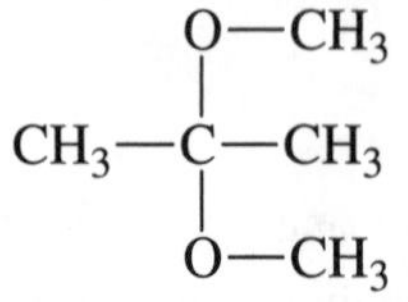

c.

$$CH_3O \quad OCH_3$$

(cyclopentane ring)

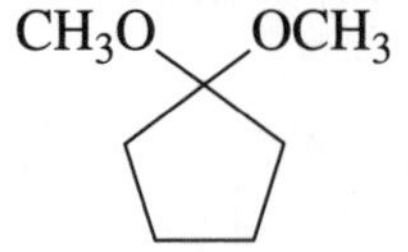

d. 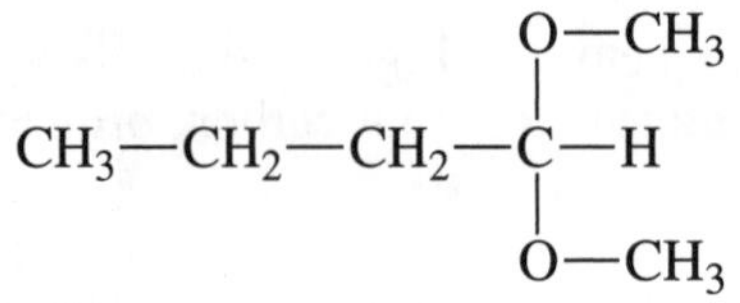 $CH_3—CH_2—CH_2—\overset{\displaystyle O—CH_3}{\underset{\displaystyle O—CH_3}{C}}—H$

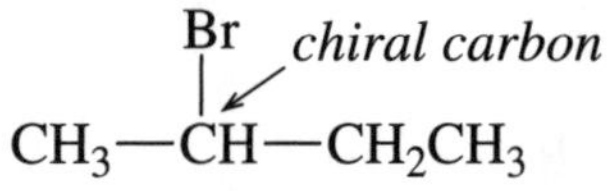

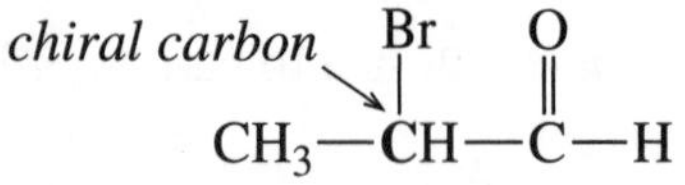

14.33 a. achiral   b. chiral $CH_3—\overset{\displaystyle \overset{Br}{|} \; chiral\ carbon}{CH}—CH_2CH_3$

c. chiral $\overset{chiral\ carbon}{\searrow}\; CH_3—\overset{\displaystyle \overset{Br}{|}}{CH}—\overset{\displaystyle \overset{O}{\|}}{C}—H$ d. achiral

14.35 a. 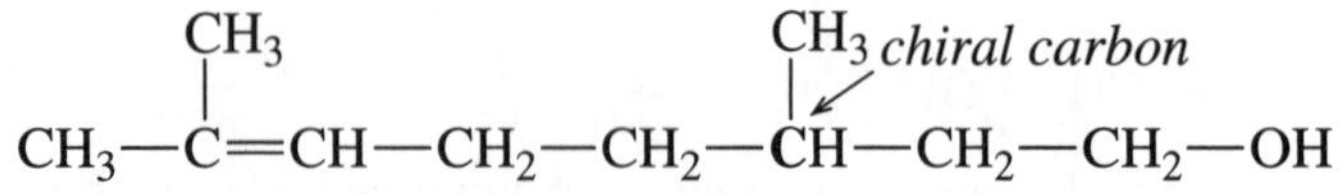 $CH_3—\overset{\displaystyle \overset{CH_3}{|}}{C}=CH—CH_2—CH_2—\overset{\displaystyle \overset{CH_3\; chiral\ carbon}{|}}{CH}—CH_2—CH_2—OH$

b. 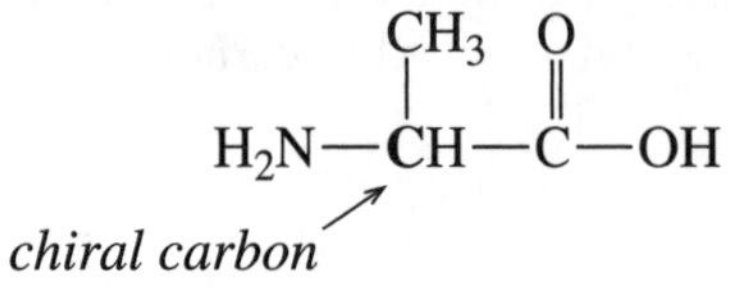 $H_2N—\overset{\displaystyle \overset{CH_3}{|}}{CH}—\overset{\displaystyle \overset{O}{\|}}{C}—OH$

   $\underset{chiral\ carbon}{\nearrow}$

14.37 a. 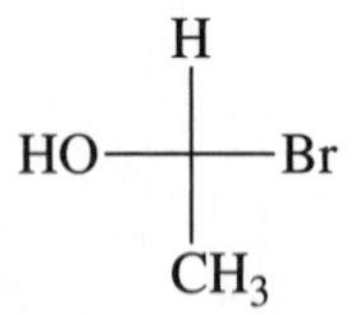 $HO—\overset{\displaystyle \overset{H}{|}}{\underset{\displaystyle \overset{|}{CH_3}}{}}—Br$ b. 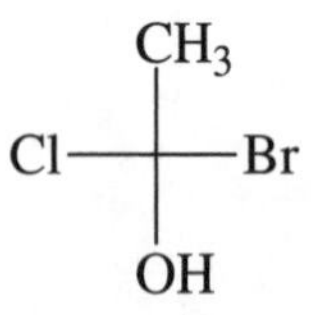 $Cl—\overset{\displaystyle \overset{CH_3}{|}}{\underset{\displaystyle \overset{|}{OH}}{}}—Br$ c. 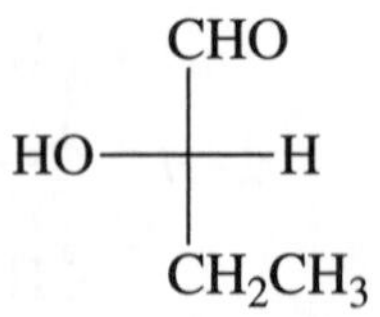 $HO—\overset{\displaystyle \overset{CHO}{|}}{\underset{\displaystyle \overset{|}{CH_2CH_3}}{}}—H$

14.39 a. identical   b. enantiomers   c. identical   d. enantiomers

14.41 **a, b,** and **f** will give positive Tollen's tests.

14.43 a. aromatic, aldehyde   b. aromatic, aldehyde, ether, phenol
        c. aromatic, aldehyde, alkene   d. cycloalkane, ketone   e. ketone

        a. 2   b. 5   c. 4   d. 3   e. 1

14.45

$$CH_3-CH_2-CH_2-\overset{\overset{\displaystyle O}{\|}}{C}-H \qquad CH_3-\overset{\overset{\displaystyle CH_3}{|}}{CH}-\overset{\overset{\displaystyle O}{\|}}{C}-H \qquad CH_3-CH_2-\overset{\overset{\displaystyle O}{\|}}{C}-CH_3$$

14.47 **a.** 2-bromo-4-chlorocyclopentanone **b.** 4-chloro-3-hydroxybenzaldehyde
c. 3-chloropropanal **d.** 5-chloro-3-hexanone
e. 2-chloro-3-pentanone

14.49 **a.** 3-methylcyclopentanone is a five-carbon cyclic structure with a methyl group located two carbons from the carbonyl group.

b. *p*-chlorobenzaldehyde is a benzene with an aldehyde group and a chlorine on carbon 4.

c. 3-chloropropionaldehyde is a three-carbon aldehyde with a chlorine located two carbons from the carbonyl group.

$$Cl-CH_2-CH_2-\overset{\overset{\displaystyle O}{\|}}{C}-H$$

d. Butanone is a four-carbon ketone.

$$CH_3-\overset{\overset{\displaystyle O}{\|}}{C}-CH_2-CH_3$$

e. This is a six-carbon aldehyde with a methyl group on carbon 3.

$$CH_3-CH_2-CH_2-\overset{\overset{\displaystyle CH_3}{|}}{CH}-CH_2-\overset{\overset{\displaystyle O}{\|}}{C}-H$$

14.51 Compounds b, c, and d are soluble in water because they have polar groups with oxygen atoms that hydrogen bond with water and fewer than five carbon atoms.

14.53 **a.** CH_3-CH_2-OH; polar $-OH$ group can hydrogen bond

b. $CH_3-CH_2-\overset{\overset{\displaystyle O}{\|}}{C}-H$; polar carbonyl group
c. $CH_3-CH_2-CH_2-OH$; polar $-OH$ group can hydrogen bond

14.55 A chiral carbon is bonded to four different groups.

a. $H-\overset{\overset{\displaystyle Cl}{|}}{\underset{\underset{\displaystyle Cl}{|}}{C}}-\overset{\overset{\displaystyle Cl}{|}}{\underset{\underset{\displaystyle H}{|}}{\textcircled{C}}}-O-H$ **b.** none **c.** none

d. 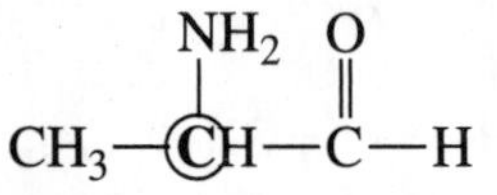 CH₃—CH—C—H (with NH₂ above CH circled, O above C)   **e.** 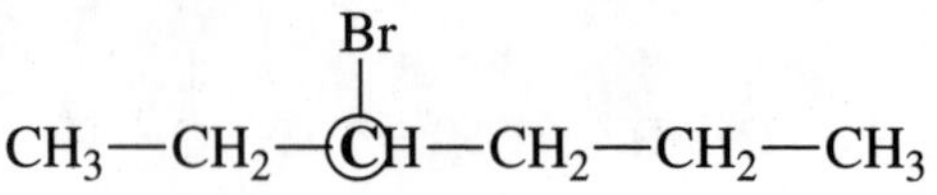 CH₃—CH₂—CH—CH₂—CH₂—CH₃ (with Br above CH circled)

f. none

14.57 Enantiomers are mirror images.

   a. identical   **b.** enantiomers

   c. enantiomers (turn 180°)   **d.** enantiomers

14.59 Primary alcohols oxidize to aldehydes and then to carboxylic acids. Secondary alcohols oxidize to ketones.

   a. 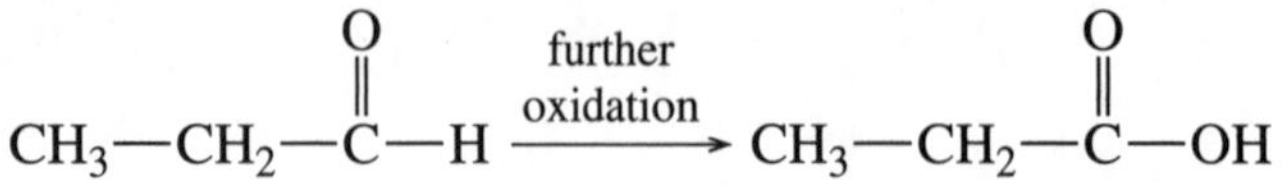 CH₃—CH₂—C—H $\xrightarrow{\text{further oxidation}}$ CH₃—CH₂—C—OH (with O above each C)

   b. 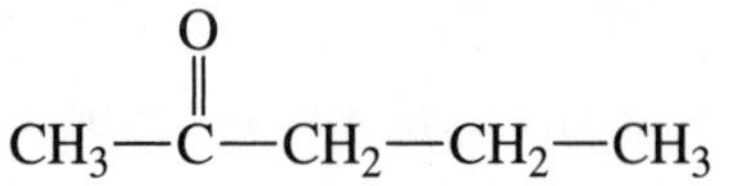 CH₃—C—CH₂—CH₂—CH₃ (with O above C)

   c. CH₃—CH₂—CH₂—C—OH (with O above C)

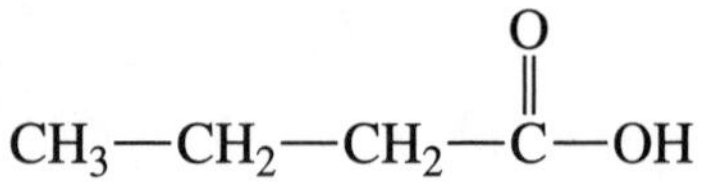

   d. 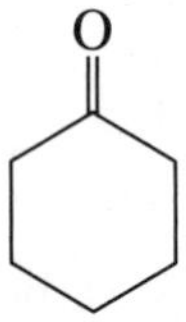 (cyclohexanone ring with O above)

14.61

   a. 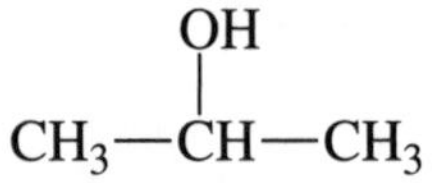 CH₃—CH—CH₃ (with OH above CH)

   b. 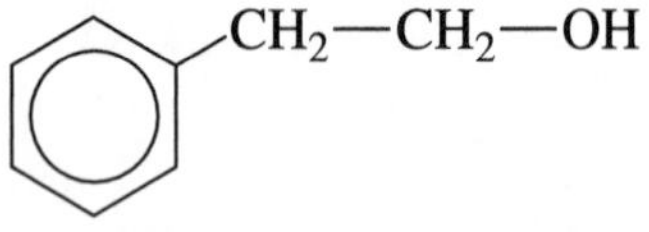 (benzene ring)—CH₂—CH₂—OH

   c. 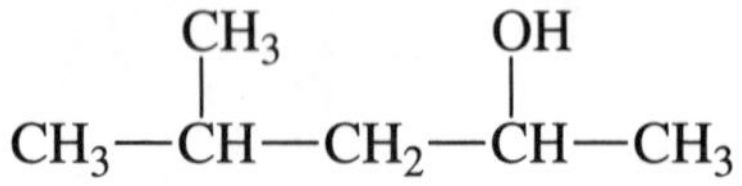 CH₃—CH—CH₂—CH—CH₃ (with CH₃ above first CH, OH above second CH)

14.63

   a. 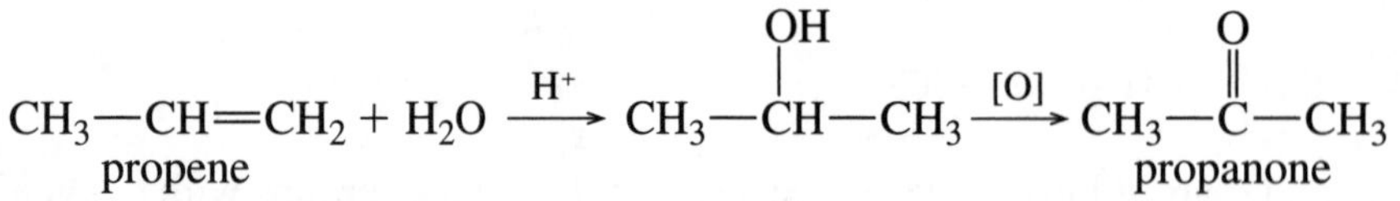 CH₃—CH=CH₂ + H₂O $\xrightarrow{\text{H}^+}$ CH₃—CH—CH₃ $\xrightarrow{\text{[O]}}$ CH₃—C—CH₃
      propene (OH above CH) (O above C) propanone

   b. 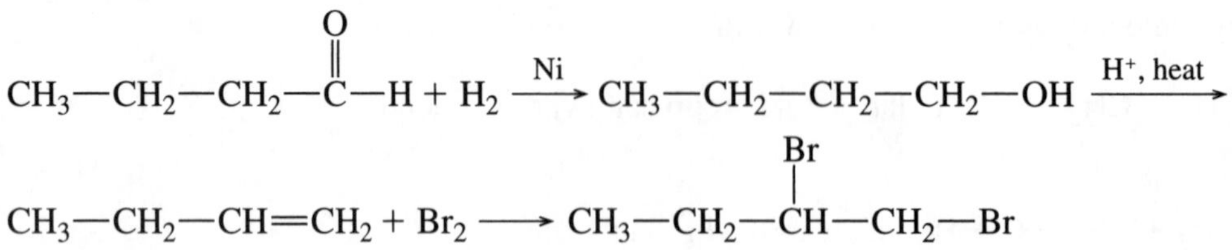 CH₃—CH₂—CH₂—C—H + H₂ $\xrightarrow{\text{Ni}}$ CH₃—CH₂—CH₂—CH₂—OH $\xrightarrow{\text{H}^+, \text{ heat}}$ (O above C)

   CH₃—CH₂—CH=CH₂ + Br₂ ⟶ CH₃—CH₂—CH—CH₂—Br (Br above CH)

   c. CH₃—CH₂—CH₂—C—H + H₂ $\xrightarrow{\text{Ni}}$ CH₃—CH₂—CH₂—CH₂—OH $\xrightarrow{\text{H}^+, \text{ heat}}$ (O above C)

   CH₃—CH₂—CH=CH₂ + H₂O ⟶ CH₃—CH₂—CH—CH₃ $\xrightarrow{\text{[O]}}$ CH₃—CH₂—C—CH₃
      (OH above CH) (O above C) butanone

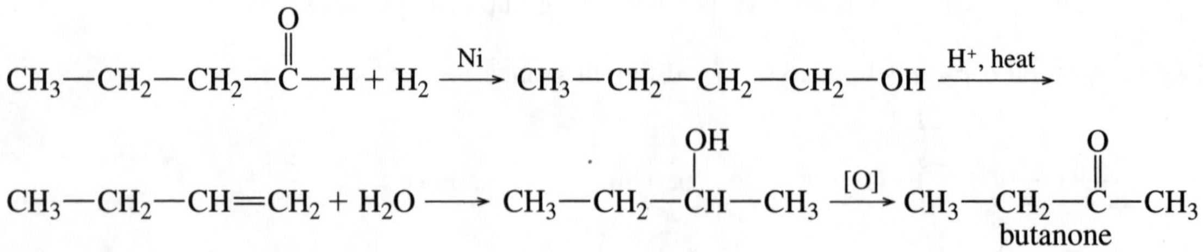

14.65 **a.** acetal; propanal and methanol
b. hemiacetal; butanone and ethanol
c. acetal; cyclohexanone and ethanol

14.67 **1.** true   **2.** false   **3.** true   **4.** true   **5.** false   **6.** true   **7.** true

14.69 $CH_3-CH_2-CH_2-OH$ A 1-propanol

$CH_3-CH=CH_2$ B propene

$$CH_3-CH_2-\overset{\overset{\textstyle O}{\|}}{C}-H$$ C propanal

$$CH_3-\overset{\overset{\textstyle OH}{|}}{CH}-CH_3$$ D 2-propanol

$$CH_3-\overset{\overset{\textstyle O}{\|}}{C}-CH_3$$ E propanone

Carbohydrates

Study Goals

- Identify the common carbohydrates in the diet.
- Distinguish between monosaccharides, disaccharides, and polysaccharides.
- Identify the chiral carbons in a carbohydrate.
- Label the Fischer projection for a monosaccharide as the D- or L-enantiomer.
- Write Haworth structures for monosaccharides.
- Describe the structural units and bonds in disaccharides and polysaccharides.

Think About It

1. What are some foods you eat that contain carbohydrates?

2. What elements are found in carbohydrates?

3. What carbohydrates are present in table sugar, milk, and wood?

4. What is meant by a "high-fiber" diet?

Key Terms

Match the following key terms with the descriptions shown below.

    A. carbohydrate   **B.** glucose   **C.** disaccharide   **D.** Haworth structure   **E.** cellulose

1. _____ A simple or complex sugar composed of a carbon chain with an aldehyde or ketone group and several hydroxyl groups

2. _____ A cyclic structure that represents the closed chain form of a monosaccharide

3. _____ An unbranched polysaccharide that cannot be digested by humans

4. _____ An aldohexose that is the most prevalent monosaccharide in the diet

5. _____ A carbohydrate that contains two monosaccharides linked by a glycosidic bond

Answers   **1.** A   **2.** D   **3.** E   **4.** B   **5.** C

15.1 Carbohydrates

- Carbohydrates are classified as monosaccharides (simple sugars), disaccharides (two monosaccharide units), and polysaccharides (many monosaccharide units).
- In a chiral molecule, there is one or more carbon atom attached to four different atoms or groups.
- Monosaccharides are polyhydroxy aldehydes (aldoses) or ketones (ketoses).
- Monosaccharides are classified by the number of carbon atoms as *trioses*, *tetroses*, *pentoses*, or *hexoses*.

◆ **Learning Exercise 15.1A**

Complete and balance the equations for the photosynthesis of

1. glucose: _____ + _____ → $C_6H_{12}O_6$ + _____

2. ribose: _____ + _____ → $C_5H_{10}O_5$ + _____

Answers   1. $6CO_2 + 6H_2O \rightarrow C_6H_{12}O_6 + 6O_2$
             2. $5CO_2 + 5H_2O \rightarrow C_5H_{10}O_5 + 5O_2$

◆ **Learning Exercise 15.1B**

Indicate the number of monosaccharide units (1, 2, or many) in each of the following carbohydrates:

1. sucrose, a disaccharide   _____   2. cellulose, a polysaccharide   _____

3. glucose, a monosaccharide   _____   4. amylose, a polysaccharide   _____

5. maltose, a disaccharide   _____

Answers   **1.** two   **2.** many   **3.** one   **4.** many   **5.** two

◆ **Learning Exercise 15.1C**

Identify the following monosaccharides as aldotrioses, ketotrioses, tetroses, pentoses, or hexoses.

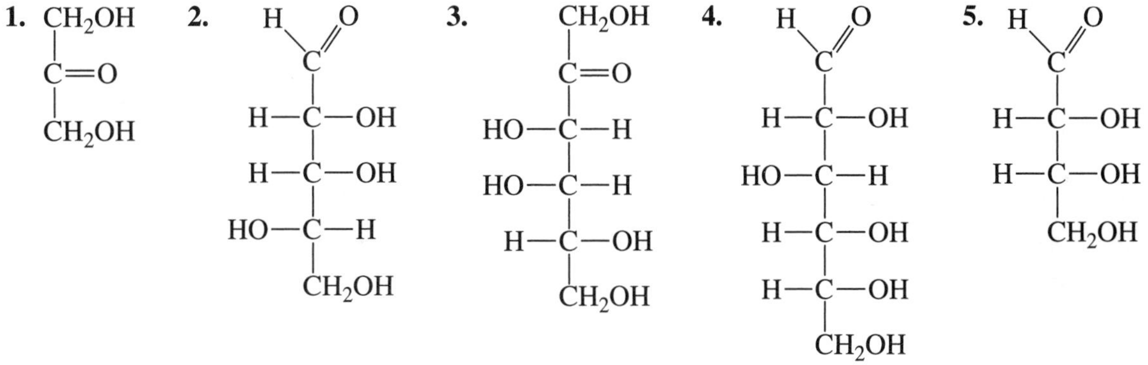

1. _____   2. _____

3. _____   4. _____

5. _____

Answers   **1.** ketotriose   **2.** aldopentose   **3.** ketohexose
             4. aldohexose   **5.** aldotetrose

15.2 Structures of Monosaccharides

- In a Fischer projection (straight chain), the prefixes D- and L- are used to distinguish between the mirror images. In D-glyceraldehyde, the —OH is on the right of the chiral carbon; it is on the left in L-glyceraldehyde.
- In the Fischer projection of a monosaccharide, the chiral —OH farthest from the carbonyl group (C=O) is on the left side in the L-isomer and on the right side in the D-isomer.
- Important monosaccharides are the aldohexoses glucose and galactose and the ketohexose fructose.

◆ Learning Exercise 15.2A

Identify each of the following sugars as the D- or L- isomer.

1. 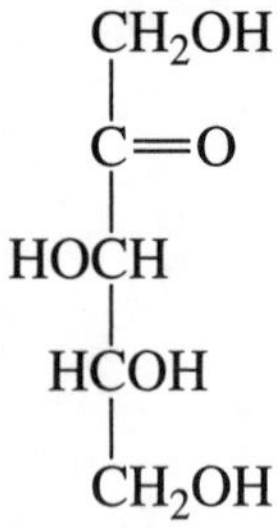
$$CH_2OH$$
$$C=O$$
$$HOCH$$
$$HCOH$$
$$CH_2OH$$

_____-xylulose

2. 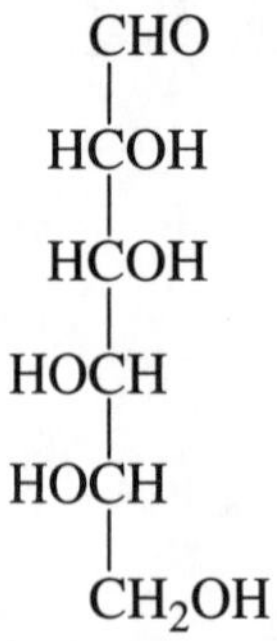
$$CHO$$
$$HCOH$$
$$HCOH$$
$$HOCH$$
$$HOCH$$
$$CH_2OH$$

_____-mannose

3. 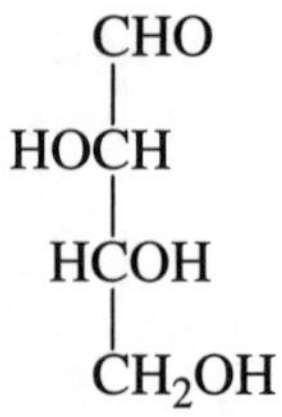
$$CHO$$
$$HOCH$$
$$HCOH$$
$$CH_2OH$$

_____-threose

4. 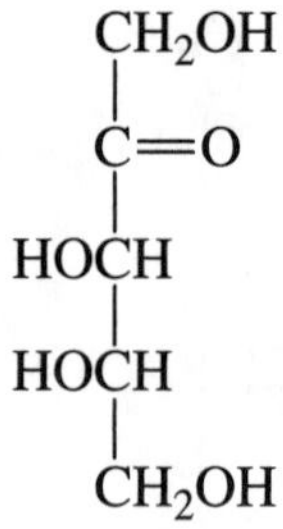
$$CH_2OH$$
$$C=O$$
$$HOCH$$
$$HOCH$$
$$CH_2OH$$

_____-ribulose

Answers   **1.** D-xylulose   **2.** L-mannose   **3.** D-threose   **4.** L-ribulose

◆ Learning Exercise 15.2B

Write the mirror image of each of the sugars in learning exercise 15.2A and give the D- or L-name.

1.   **2.**   **3.**   **4.**

Answers

1. 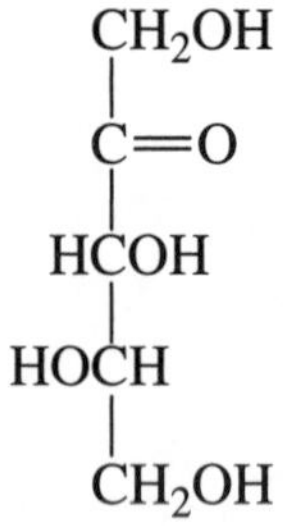
$$CH_2OH$$
$$C=O$$
$$HCOH$$
$$HOCH$$
$$CH_2OH$$
L-xylulose

2. 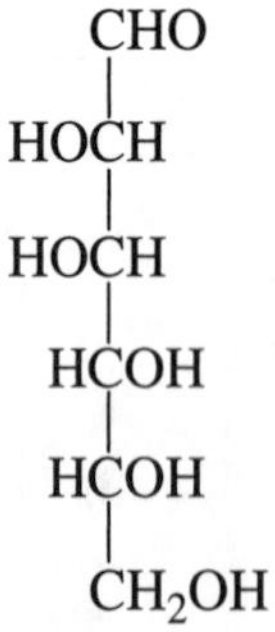
$$CHO$$
$$HOCH$$
$$HOCH$$
$$HCOH$$
$$HCOH$$
$$CH_2OH$$
D-mannose

3. 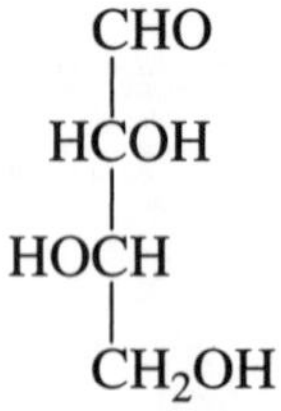
$$CHO$$
$$HCOH$$
$$HOCH$$
$$CH_2OH$$
L-threose

4. 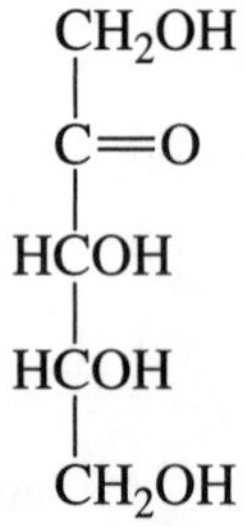
$$CH_2OH$$
$$C=O$$
$$HCOH$$
$$HCOH$$
$$CH_2OH$$
D-ribulose

◆ Learning Exercise 15.2C

Identify the monosaccharide (glucose, fructose, or galactose) that fits the following description:

1. a building block in cellulose   _____

2. also known as fruit sugar   _____

3. accumulates in the disease known as *galactosemia* _____

4. the most common monosaccharide _____

5. the sweetest monosaccharide _____

Answers   **1.** glucose   **2.** fructose   **3.** galactose   **4.** glucose   **5.** fructose

◆ Learning Exercise 15.2D

Draw the open-chain structure for the following monosaccharides:
D-glucose   L-galactose   D-fructose

Answers

D-glucose   D-galactose   D-fructose

15.3 Cyclic Structures of Monosaccharides

- The predominant form of monosaccharides is the cyclic form of five or six atoms called the Haworth structure. The cyclic structure forms by a reaction between an OH on carbon 5 in hexoses with the carbonyl group of the same molecule.
- The formation of a new hydroxyl group on carbon 1 (or 2 in fructose) gives α and β forms of the cyclic monosaccharide. Because the molecule opens and closes continuously in solution, both α and β forms are present.

◆ **Learning Exercise 15.3**

Write the Haworth structures (α-form) for the following:
1. D-glucose　　　　　2. D-galactose　　　　　3. D-fructose

Answers

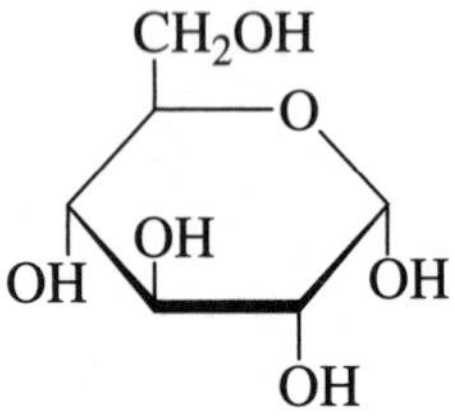

α-D-glucose　　　　α-D-galactose　　　　α-D-fructose

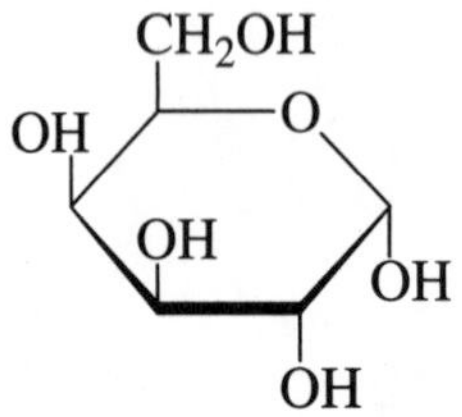

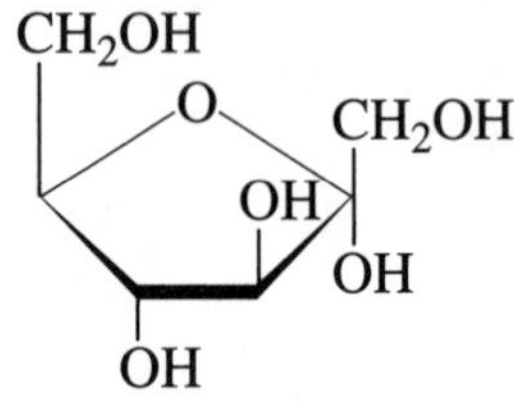

15.4 Chemical Properties of Monosaccharides

- Monosaccharides contain functional groups that undergo oxidation or reduction.
- Monosaccharides are called *reducing sugars* because the aldehyde group (also available in ketoses) is oxidized by a metal ion such as Cu^{2+} in Benedict's solution, which is reduced.
- Monosaccharides are also reduced to give sugar alcohols.

◆ **Learning Exercise 15.4**

What changes occur when a reducing sugar reacts with Benedict's reagent?

Answers　　　The carbonyl group of the reducing sugar is oxidized to a carboxylic acid group; the Cu^{2+} ion in Benedict's reagent is reduced to Cu^+, which forms a brick-red solid of Cu_2O.

15.5 Disaccharides

- Disaccharides are two monosaccharide units joined together by a glycosidic bond:

monosaccharide (1) + monosaccharide (2) → disaccharide + H_2O

- In the most common disaccharides, maltose, lactose, and sucrose, there is at least one glucose unit.
- In the disaccharide maltose, two glucose units are linked by an α-1,4 bond. The α-1,4 indicates that the —OH of the alpha form at carbon 1 was bonded to the —OH on carbon 4 of the other glucose molecule.

• When a disaccharide is hydrolyzed by water, the products are a glucose unit and one other monosaccharide.

$$\text{maltose} + H_2O \rightarrow \text{glucose} + \text{glucose}$$
$$\text{lactose} + H_2O \rightarrow \text{glucose} + \text{galactose}$$
$$\text{sucrose} + H_2O \rightarrow \text{glucose} + \text{fructose}$$

◆ Learning Exercise 15.5

a. What is a glycosidic bond?

b. For the following disaccharides, state (a) the monosaccharide units, (b) the type of glycosidic bond, and (c) the name of the disaccharide.

1.

2.

	a. Monosaccharide(s)	**b.** Type of glycosidic bond	**c.** Name of disaccharide
1.			
2.			

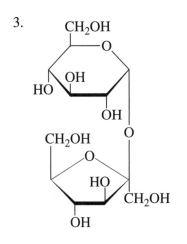

3.

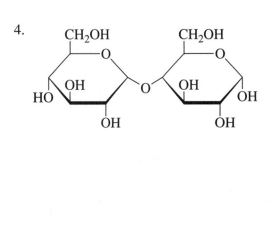

4.

	a. Monosaccharide units	**b.** Type of glycosidic bond	**c.** Name of disaccharide
3.			
4.			

Answers　**a.** A glycosidic bond forms between the OH of a sugar with the —OH of another compound, usually another sugar.

b. 1. (a) two glucose units　**(b)** α-1,4-glycosidic bond　**(c)** β-maltose
　　2. (a) galactose + glucose　**(b)** β-1,4-glycosidic bond　**(c)** α-lactose
　　3. (a) fructose + glucose　**(b)** α-1, β-2 glycosidic bond　**(c)** sucrose
　　4. (a) two glucose units　**(b)** α-1,4-glycosidic bond　**(c)** α-maltose

15.6 Polysaccharides

- Polysaccharides are polymers of monosaccharide units.
- Starches consist of amylose, an unbranched chain of glucose, and amylopectin, a branched polymer of glucose. Glycogen, the storage form of glucose in animals, is similar to amylopectin, with more branching.
- Cellulose is also a polymer of glucose, but in cellulose the glycosidic bonds are β bonds rather than α bonds as in the starches. Humans can digest starches to obtain energy but not cellulose. However, cellulose is important as a source of fiber in our diets.

◆ Learning Exercise 15.6

List the monosaccharides and describe the glycosidic bonds in each of the following carbohydrates:

	Monosaccharides	Type(s) of glycosidic bonds
1. amylose	_____	_____
2. amylopectin	_____	_____
3. glycogen	_____	_____
4. cellulose	_____	_____

Answers　**1.** glucose; α-1,4-glycosidic bonds
　　2. glucose; α-1,4- and α-1,6-glycosidic bonds
　　3. glucose; α-1,4- and α-1,6-glycosidic bonds
　　4. glucose; β-1,4-glycosidic bonds

Checklist for Chapter 15

You are ready to take the practice test for Chapter 15. Be sure that you have accomplished the following learning goals for this chapter. If you are not sure, review the section listed at the end of the goal. Then apply your new skills and understanding to the practice test.

After studying Chapter 15, I can successfully:

_____ Classify carbohydrates as monosaccharides, disaccharides, and polysaccharides (15.1).

_____ Classify a monosaccharide as aldose or ketose and indicate the number of carbon atoms (15.1).

_____ Draw and identify D- and L-Fischer projections for carbohydrate molecules (15.2).

_____ Draw the open-chain structures for D-glucose, D-galactose, and D-fructose (15.2).

_____ Draw or identify the cyclic structures of monosaccharides (15.3).

_____ Describe some chemical properties of carbohydrates (15.4).

_____ Describe the monosaccharide units and linkages in disaccharides (15.5).

_____ Describe the structural features of amylose, amylopectin, glycogen, and cellulose (15.6).

Practice Test for Chapter 15

1. The requirements for photosynthesis are
   A. sun   **B.** sun and water
   C. water and carbon dioxide   **D.** sun, water, and carbon dioxide
   E. carbon dioxide and sun

2. What are the products of photosynthesis?
   A. carbohydrates   **B.** carbohydrates and oxygen
   C. carbon dioxide and oxygen   **D.** carbohydrates and carbon dioxide
   E. water and oxygen

3. The name "carbohydrate" came from the fact that
   A. Carbohydrates are hydrates of water.
   B. Carbohydrates contain hydrogen and oxygen in a 2:1 ratio.
   C. Carbohydrates contain a great quantity of water.
   D. All plants produce carbohydrates.
   E. Carbon and hydrogen atoms are abundant in carbohydrates.

4. What functional groups are in the open chains of monosaccharides?
   A. hydroxyl groups
   B. aldehyde groups
   C. ketone groups
   D. hydroxyl and aldehyde or ketone groups
   E. hydroxyl and ether groups

5. What is the classification of the following sugar?

CH_2OH
|
$C{=}O$
|
CH_2OH

   A. aldotriose   **B.** ketotriose   **C.** aldotetrose   **D.** ketotetrose   **E.** ketopentose

Questions 6–10 refer to

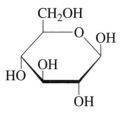

6. It is the cyclic structure of an
   A. aldotriose   **B.** ketopentose   **C.** aldopentose   **D.** aldohexose   **E.** aldoheptose

7. This is a Haworth structure of
    A. fructose   **B.** glucose   **C.** ribose   **D.** glyceraldehyde   **E.** galactose

8. It is at least one of the products of the complete hydrolysis of
    A. maltose   **B.** sucrose   **C.** lactose   **D.** glycogen   **E.** all of these

9. A Benedict's test with this sugar would
    A. be positive   **B.** be negative
    C. produce a blue precipitate   **D.** give no color change
    E. produce a silver mirror

10. It is the monosaccharide unit used to build polymers of
    A. amylose   **B.** amylopectin   **C.** cellulose   **D.** glycogen   **E.** all of these

Identify each of the carbohydrates described in 11–15 as one of the following:
    A. maltose   **B.** sucrose   **C.** cellulose   **D.** amylopectin   **E.** glycogen

11. _____ a disaccharide that is not a reducing sugar

12. _____ a disaccharide that occurs as a breakdown product of amylose

13. _____ a carbohydrate that is produced as a storage form of energy in plants

14. _____ the storage form of energy in humans

15. _____ a carbohydrate that is used for structural purposes by plants

For questions 16–20, select answers from the following:
    A. amylose   **B.** cellulose   **C.** glycogen   **D.** lactose   **E.** sucrose

16. _____ a polysaccharide composed of many glucose units linked by α-1,4-glycosidic bonds

17. _____ a sugar containing both glucose and galactose

18. _____ a sugar composed of glucose units joined by both α-1,4- and α-1,6-glycosidic bonds

19. _____ a disaccharide that is not a reducing sugar

20. _____ a carbohydrate composed of glucose units joined by β-1,4-glycosidic bonds

For questions 21–25, select answers from the following:
    A. glucose   **B.** lactose   **C.** sucrose   **D.** maltose

21. _____ a sugar composed of glucose and fructose

22. _____ also called table sugar

23. _____ found in milk and milk products

24. _____ gives sorbitol upon reduction

25. _____ gives galactose upon hydrolysis

Answers to the Practice Test

1. D	**2.** B	**3.** B	**4.** D	**5.** B
6. D	**7.** B	**8.** E	**9.** A	**10.** E
11. B	**12.** A	**13.** D	**14.** E	**15.** C
16. A	**17.** D	**18.** C	**19.** E	**20.** B
21. C	**22.** C	**23.** B	**24.** A	**25.** B

Answers and Solutions to Selected Text Problems

15.1   Photosynthesis requires CO_2, H_2O, and the energy from the sun. Respiration requires O_2 from the air and glucose from our foods.

15.3 A monosaccharide cannot be split into smaller carbohydrates. A disaccharide is composed of two monosaccharide units.

15.5 Hydroxyl groups and a carbonyl are found in all monosaccharides.

15.7 The name ketopentose tells us that the compound contains a ketone functional group and has five carbon atoms. In addition, all monosaccharides contain hydroxyl groups.

15.9 **a.** This monosaccharide is a ketose; it has a carbonyl between two carbon atoms.
   b. This monosaccharide is an aldose; it has a CHO, an aldehyde group.
   c. This monosaccharide is a ketose; it has a carbonyl between two carbon atoms.
   d. This monosaccharide is an aldose; it has a CHO, an aldehyde group.
   e. This monosaccharide is an aldose; it has a CHO, an aldehyde group.

15.11 A Fischer projection is a two-dimensional representation of the three-dimensional structure of a molecule.

15.13 **a.** This structure is a D isomer since the hydroxyl group on the chiral carbon farthest from the carbonyl is on the right.
   b. This structure is a D isomer since the hydroxyl group on the chiral carbon farthest from the carbonyl is on the right.
   c. This structure is an L isomer since the hydroxyl group on the chiral carbon farthest from the carbonyl is on the left.
   d. This structure is a D isomer since the hydroxyl group on the chiral carbon farthest from the carbonyl is on the right.

15.15 **a.**   **b.**

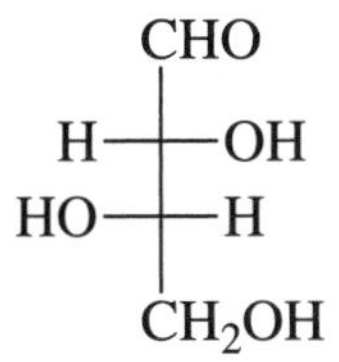

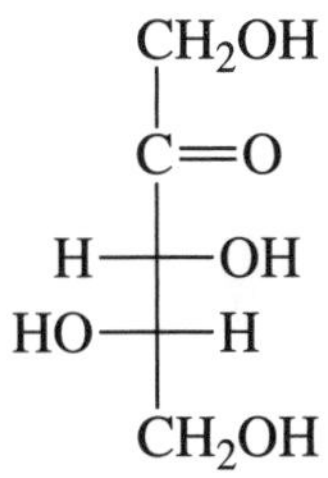

c. 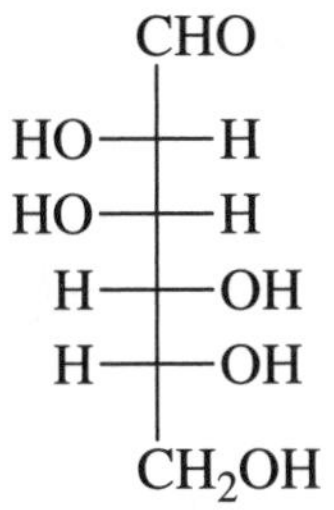   **d.**

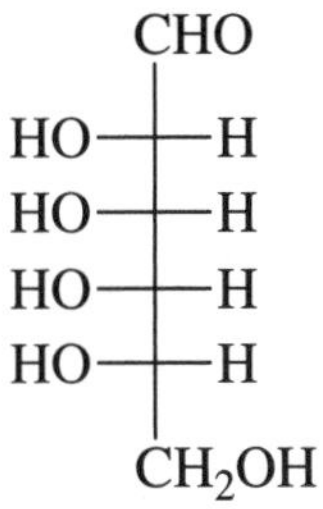

15.17 L-glucose is the mirror image of D-glucose.

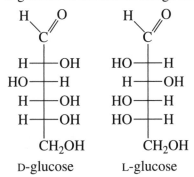

D-glucose   L-glucose

15.19 In D-galactose the hydroxyl on carbon four extends to the left; in glucose this hydroxyl group goes to the right.

15.21 **a.** Glucose is also called dextrose.
b. Galactose is not metabolized in the condition called galactosemia.
c. Another name for fructose is fruit sugar.

15.23 In the cyclic structure of glucose, there are five carbon atoms and an oxygen atom in the ring.

15.25 In the α form, the hydroxyl (—OH) on carbon 1 is down; in the β form, the hydroxyl (—OH) on carbon 1 is up.

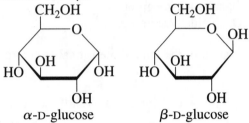

α-D-glucose　　　β-D-glucose

15.27 **a.** This is the α-form because the —OH on carbon 1 is down.
b. This is the α-form because the —OH on carbon 1 is down.

15.29

$$
\begin{array}{c}
CH_2OH \\
| \\
H-C-OH \\
| \\
HO-C-H \\
| \\
H-C-OH \\
| \\
CH_2OH
\end{array}
$$
Xylitol

15.31 Oxidation product:

$$
\begin{array}{c}
O \\
\| \\
C-OH \\
| \\
HO-C-H \\
| \\
H-C-OH \\
| \\
H-C-OH \\
| \\
CH_2OH
\end{array}
$$

Reduction product (sugar alcohol):

$$
\begin{array}{c}
CH_2OH \\
| \\
HO-C-H \\
| \\
H-C-OH \quad \text{D-arabitol} \\
| \\
H-C-OH \\
| \\
CH_2OH
\end{array}
$$

15.33 **a.** When this disaccharide is hydrolyzed, galactose and glucose are produced. The glycosidic bond is a β-1,4 bond since the ether bond is up from the 1 carbon of the galactose, which is on the left in the drawing, to the 4 carbon of the glucose on the right. β-lactose is the name of this disaccharide since the free hydroxyl is up.

b. When this disaccharide is hydrolyzed, two molecules of glucose are produced. The glycosidic bond is an α-1,4 bond since the ether bond is down from the 1 carbon of the glucose on the left to the 4 carbon of the glucose on the right. α-maltose is the name of this disaccharide since the free hydroxyl is down.

15.35 **a.** can be oxidized   **b.** can be oxidized

15.37 **a.** Another name for table sugar is sucrose.
b. Lactose is the disaccharide found in milk and milk products.
c. Maltose is also called malt sugar.
d. When lactose is hydrolyzed, the products are the monosaccharides galactose and glucose.

15.39 **a.** Amylose is an unbranched polymer of glucose units joined by α-1,4 bonds; amylopectin is a branched polymer of glucose joined by α-1,4 and α-1,6 bonds.
b. Amylopectin, produced by plants, is a branched polymer of glucose joined by α-1,4 and α-1,6 bonds. Glycogen, which is made by animals, is a highly branched polymer of glucose joined by α-1,4 and α-1,6 bonds.

15.41 **a.** Cellulose is not digestible by humans since we do not have the enzymes necessary to break the β-1,4-glycosidic bonds in cellulose.
b. Amylose and amylopectin are the storage forms of carbohydrates in plants.
c. Amylose is the polysaccharide, which contains only α-1,4 glycosidic bonds.
d. Glycogen contains many α-1,4 and α-1,6 bonds and is the most highly branched.

15.43 **a.** Isomaltose is a disaccharide.
b. Isomaltose consists of two glucose molecules.
c. The glycosidic link in isomaltose is an α-1,6 bond.
d. The structure shown is α-isomaltose.
e. I somaltose is a reducing sugar

15.45 **a.** Melezitose is a trisaccharide.
b. Melezitose contains two glucose molecules and a fructose molecule.

15.47 They differ only at carbon 4; the —OH in D-glucose is on the right side, and in D-galactose, it is on the left side.

15.49 D-galactose is the mirror image of L-galactose. In D-galactose, the —OH group on carbon 5 is on the right side, whereas in L-galactose, the —OH group on carbon 5, is on the left side.

15.51 a.

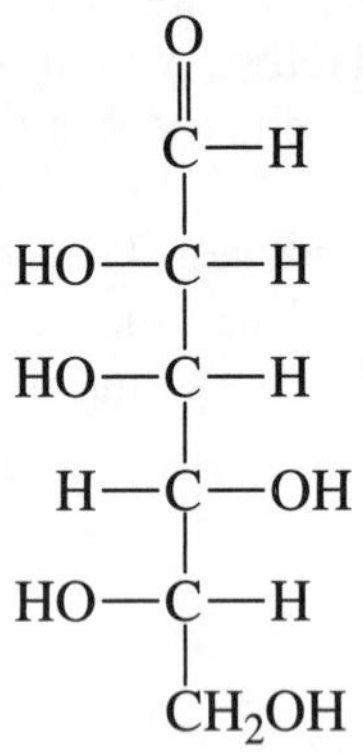

D-gulose

b.

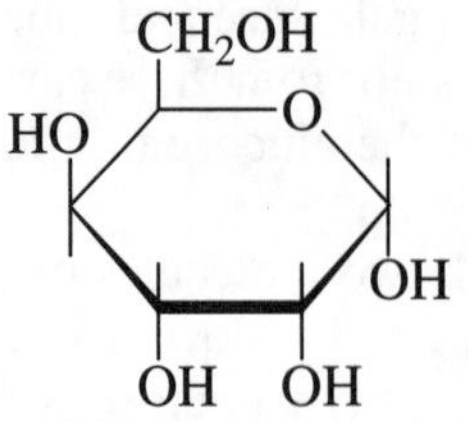

α-D-gulose β-D-gulose

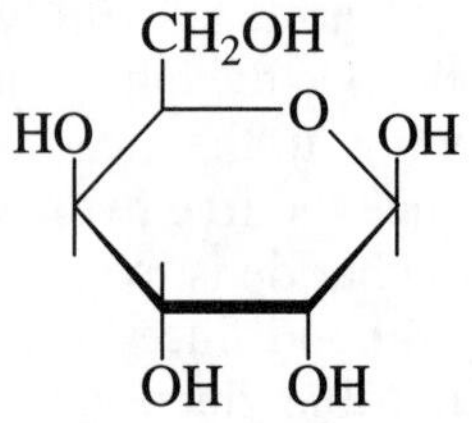

15.53 Since sorbitol can be oxidized to D-glucose, it must contain the same number of carbons with the same groups attached as glucose. The difference is that sorbitol has only hydroxyls whereas glucose has an aldehyde group. In sorbitol, the aldehyde group is changed to a hydroxyl.

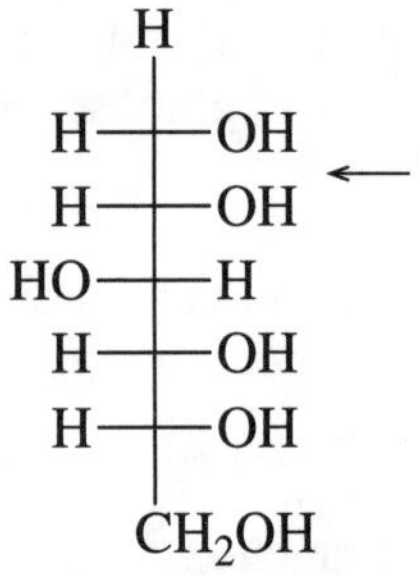

← This hydroxyl is an aldehyde in glucose.

15.55 The α-galactose forms an open chain structure, and when the chain closes, it can form both α- and β-galactose.

15.57

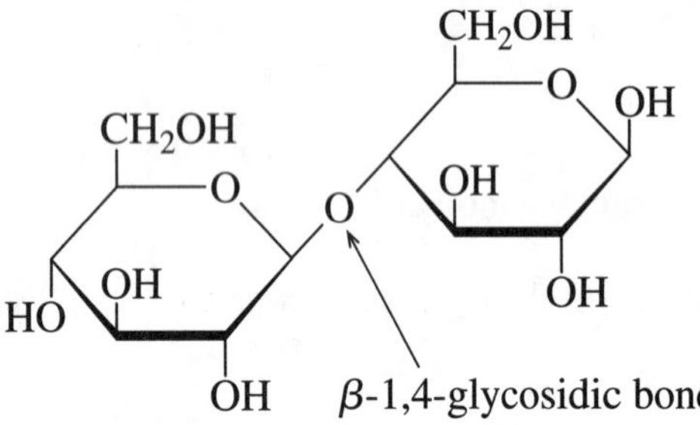

β-1,4-glycosidic bond. The bond from the glucose on the left is up (β).

15.59 a.

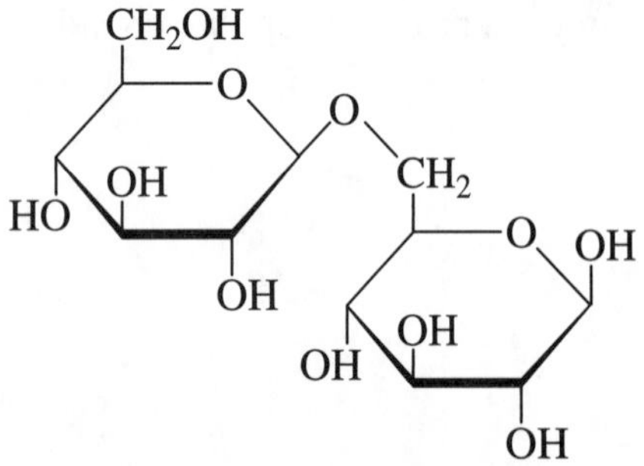

b. Yes; the ring on the right side can open up to form an aldehyde.

16
Carboxylic Acids and Esters

Study Goals

- Name and write structural formulas of carboxylic acids and esters.
- Describe the boiling points and solubility of carboxylic acids.
- Write equations for the ionization of carboxylic acids in water.
- Write equations for the esterification, hydrolysis, and saponification of esters.

Think About It

1. Why do vinegar and citrus juices taste sour?

2. What type of compound gives flowers and fruits their pleasant aromas?

Key Terms

Match the key term with the correct statement shown below.

a. carboxylic acid **b.** saponification **c.** esterification
d. hydrolysis **e.** ester

1. _____ An organic compound containing the carboxyl group (—COOH)

2. _____ A reaction of a carboxylic acid and an alcohol in the presence of an acid catalyst

3. _____ A type of organic compound that produces pleasant aromas in flowers and fruits

4. _____ The hydrolysis of an ester with a strong base producing a salt of the carboxylic acid and an alcohol

5. _____ The splitting of a molecule such as an ester by the addition of water in the presence of an acid

Answers **1.** a **2.** c **3.** e **4.** b **5.** d

16.1 Carboxylic Acids

- In the IUPAC system, a carboxylic acid is named by replacing the *ane* ending with *oic acid.* Simple acids usually are named by the common naming system using the prefixes **form** (1C), **acet** (2C), **propion** (4C), or **butyr** (4C), followed by ***ic acid.***

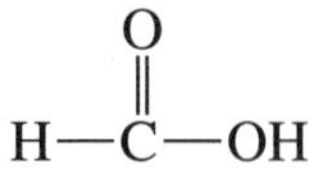
methanoic acid
(formic acid)

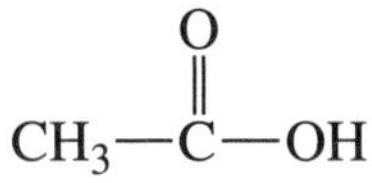
ethanoic acid
(acetic acid)

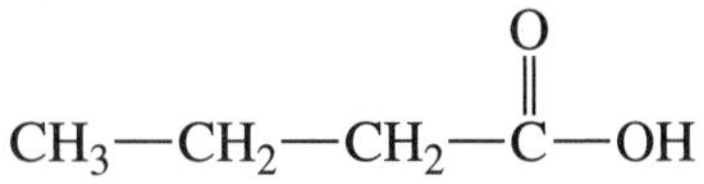
butanoic acid
(butyric acid)

- A carboxylic acid is prepared by the oxidation of a primary alcohol or an aldehyde.

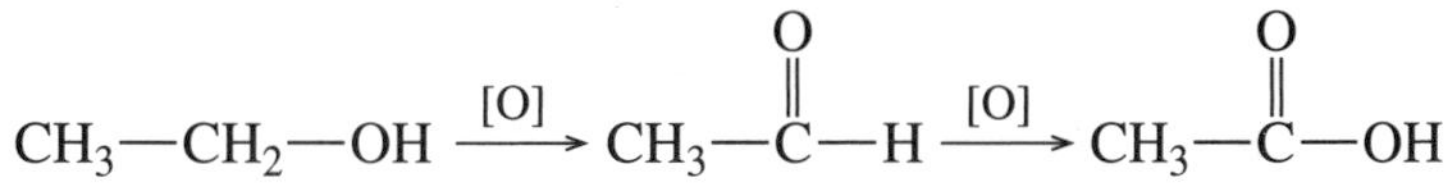

◆ Learning Exercise 16.1A

Give the IUPAC and common names for each of the following carboxylic acids:

1. $CH_3-\overset{\overset{\displaystyle O}{\|}}{C}-OH$

2. $CH_3-\overset{\overset{\displaystyle OH}{|}}{CH}-\overset{\overset{\displaystyle O}{\|}}{C}-OH$

3. $CH_3-\overset{\overset{\displaystyle CH_3}{|}}{CH}-CH_2-\overset{\overset{\displaystyle O}{\|}}{C}-OH$

4. 

Answers

1. ethanoic acid (acetic acid)
2. 2-hydroxypropanoic acid (α-hydroxypropionic acid)
3. 3-methylbutanoic acid (β-methylbutyric acid)
4. 4-chlorobenzoic acid (*p*-chlorobenzoic acid)

◆ Learning Exercise 16.1B

A. Write the formulas for the following carboxylic acids:

1. acetic acid

2. 2-ketobutanoic acid

3. benzoic acid

4. β-hydroxypropionic acid

5. formic acid

6. 3-methylpentanoic acid

Answers

1. $CH_3-\overset{\overset{\displaystyle O}{\|}}{C}-OH$

2. $CH_3-CH_2-\overset{\overset{\displaystyle O}{\|}}{C}-\overset{\overset{\displaystyle O}{\|}}{C}-OH$

3.

$$\text{C}6\text{H}_5\overset{\displaystyle O}{\overset{\|}{\text{C}}}\text{—OH}$$

4. $\text{HO—CH}_2\text{—CH}_2\overset{\displaystyle O}{\overset{\|}{\text{—C}}}\text{—OH}$

5. $\text{H}\overset{\displaystyle O}{\overset{\|}{\text{—C}}}\text{—OH}$

6. $\text{CH}_3\text{—CH}_2\overset{\displaystyle \text{CH}_3}{\overset{|}{\text{—CH}}}\text{—CH}_2\overset{\displaystyle O}{\overset{\|}{\text{—C}}}\text{—OH}$

◆ Learning Exercise 16.1C

Write the structural formula of the appropriate aldehyde to produce the following:
  1. propanoic acid   **2.** β-methylbutyric acid

Answers   **1.** $\text{CH}_3\text{—CH}_2\overset{\displaystyle O}{\overset{\|}{\text{—C}}}\text{—H}$ **2.** $\text{CH}_3\overset{\displaystyle \text{CH}_3}{\overset{|}{\text{—CH}}}\text{—CH}_2\overset{\displaystyle O}{\overset{\|}{\text{—C}}}\text{—H}$

16.2 Properties of Carboxylic Acids

- Carboxylic acids have higher boiling points than other polar compounds such as alcohols.
- Because they have two polar groups, two carboxylic acids form a dimer, which contains two sets of hydrogen bonds.
- Carboxylic acids with one to four carbon atoms are very soluble in water.
- As weak acids, carboxylic acids ionize slightly in water to form acidic solutions of H_3O^+ and a carboxylate ion.
- When bases neutralize carboxylic acids, the products are carboxylic acid salts and water.

◆ Learning Exercise 16.2A

Indicate whether each of the following carboxylic acids are soluble in water:
  1. _____ hexanoic acid   **2.** _____ acetic acid   **3.** _____ propanoic acid

  4. _____ benzoic acid   **5.** _____ formic acid   **6.** _____ octanoic acid

Answers   **1.** no   **2.** yes   **3.** yes
                4. no   **5.** yes   **6.** no

◆ Learning Exercise 16.2B

Identify the compound in each pair that has the higher boiling point.
  1. acetic acid or butyric acid   **2.**   propanoic acid or 2-propanol

  3. propanoic acid or propanone   **4.**   acetic acid or acetaldehyde

Answers   **1.** butyric acid   **2.** propanoic acid
3. propanoic acid   **4.** acetic acid

◆ Learning Exercise 16.2C

Write the products for the ionization of the following carboxylic acids in water:

1. $CH_3-CH_2-\overset{\overset{\displaystyle O}{\|}}{C}-OH + H_2O \rightleftharpoons$

2. benzoic acid + $H_2O \rightleftharpoons$

Answers   **1.** $CH_3-CH_2-\overset{\overset{\displaystyle O}{\|}}{C}-O^- + H_3O^+$ **2.** 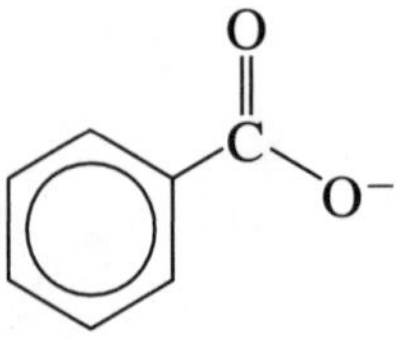 (benzoate structure) $+ H_3O^+$

◆ Learning Exercise 16.2D

Write the products and names for each of the following reactions:

1. $CH_3-CH_2-\overset{\overset{\displaystyle O}{\|}}{C}-OH + NaOH \longrightarrow$

2. formic acid + KOH $\rightarrow$

Answers   **1.** $CH_3-CH_2-\overset{\overset{\displaystyle O}{\|}}{C}-O^-Na^+ + H_2O$ **2.** $H-\overset{\overset{\displaystyle O}{\|}}{C}-O^-K^+ + H_2O$
Sodium propanoate   potassium methanoate
(sodium propionate)   (potassium formate)

16.3 Esters of Carboxylic Acids

•   In the presence of a strong acid, carboxylic acids react with alcohols to produce esters and water.

◆ Learning Exercise 16.3

Write the products of the following reactions:

1. $CH_3-\overset{\overset{\displaystyle O}{\|}}{C}-OH + CH_3-OH \xrightarrow{H^+}$

2. $H-\overset{\overset{\displaystyle O}{\|}}{C}-OH + CH_3-CH_2-OH \xrightarrow{H^+}$

3.

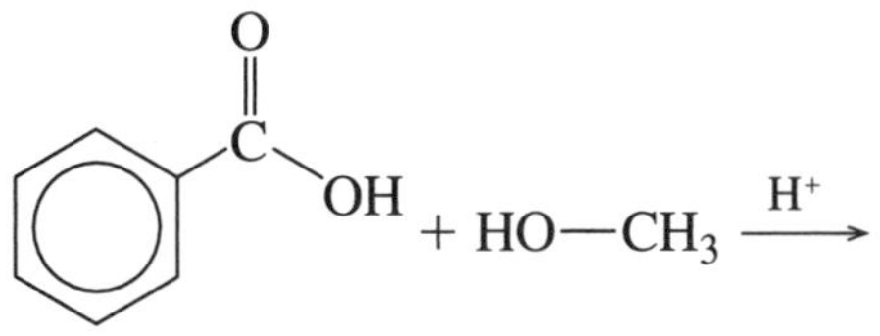

$$+ \; HO-CH_3 \; \xrightarrow{H^+}$$

4. propanoic acid and ethanol $\xrightarrow{H^+}$

Answers   **1.** $CH_3-\overset{\overset{\displaystyle O}{\|}}{C}-O-CH_3 + H_2O$ **2.** $H-\overset{\overset{\displaystyle O}{\|}}{C}-O-CH_2-CH_3 + H_2O$

3.

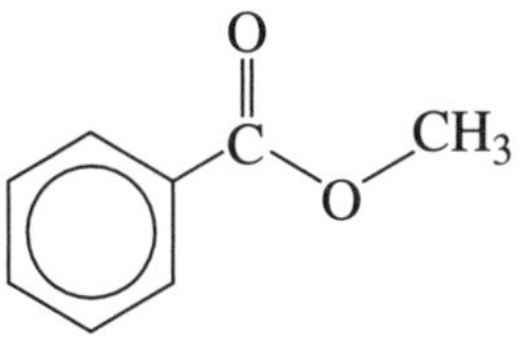

$+ \; H_2O$

4. $CH_3-CH_2-\overset{\overset{\displaystyle O}{\|}}{C}-O-CH_2-CH_3 + H_2O$

16.4 Naming Esters

- The names of esters consist of two words, one from the alcohol and the other from the carboxylic acid, with the *ic* ending replaced by *ate*.

$CH_3-\overset{\overset{\displaystyle O}{\|}}{C}-O-CH_3$ methyl ethanoate (IUPAC) or methyl acetate (common)

◆ Learning Exercise 16.4A

Name each of the following esters:

1. $CH_3-\overset{\overset{\displaystyle O}{\|}}{C}-O-CH_2-CH_3$

2. $CH_3-CH_2-CH_2-\overset{\overset{\displaystyle O}{\|}}{C}-O-CH_3$

3. $CH_3-CH_2-\overset{\overset{\displaystyle O}{\|}}{C}-O-CH_2-\overset{\overset{\displaystyle OH}{|}}{CH}-CH_3$

4.

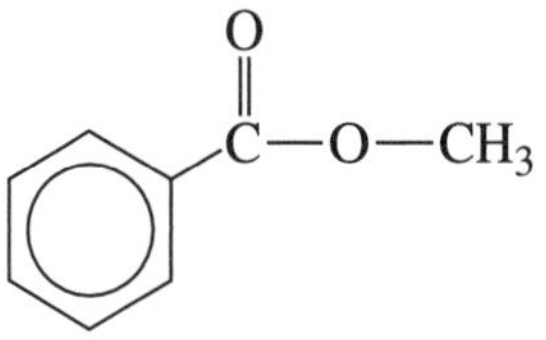

Answers   **1.** ethyl ethanoate (ethyl acetate)
   2. methylbutanoate (methylbutyrate)
   3. 2-hydroxypropylpropanoate (2-hydroxypropylpropionate)
   4. methylbenzoate

◆ **Learning Exercise 16.4B**

Write structural formulas for each of the following esters:
1. propylacetate   2. ethylbutyrate

3. ethylpropanoate   4. ethylbenzoate

Answers:

1. $CH_3-\overset{\displaystyle O}{\overset{\|}{C}}-O-CH_2-CH_2-CH_3$ 2. $CH_3-CH_2-CH_2-\overset{\displaystyle O}{\overset{\|}{C}}-O-CH_2-CH_3$

3. $CH_3-CH_2-\overset{\displaystyle O}{\overset{\|}{C}}-O-CH_2-CH_3$ 4. 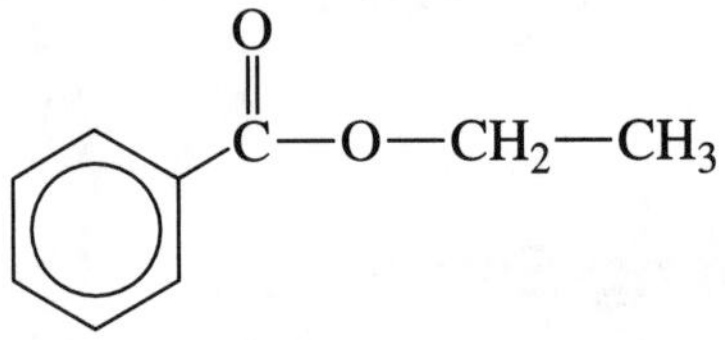 (benzene ring)$-\overset{\displaystyle O}{\overset{\|}{C}}-O-CH_2-CH_3$

16.5 Properties of Esters

- Esters shave higher boiling points than alkanes but lower than alcohols and carboxylic acids of similar mass.
- In hydrolysis, esters are split apart by a reaction with water. When the catalyst is an acid, the products are a carboxylic acid and an alcohol.

$$CH_3-\overset{\displaystyle O}{\overset{\|}{C}}-O-CH_3 + H_2O \overset{H^+}{\longrightarrow} CH_3-\overset{\displaystyle O}{\overset{\|}{C}}-OH + HO-CH_3$$

     methyl acetate   *acetic acid*   *methyl alcohol*

- Saponification is the hydrolysis of an ester in the presence of a base, which produces a carboxylate salt and an alcohol.

$$CH_3-\overset{\displaystyle O}{\overset{\|}{C}}-O-CH_3 + NaOH \longrightarrow CH_3-\overset{\displaystyle O}{\overset{\|}{C}}-O^-Na^+ + HO-CH_3$$

     methyl acetate   *sodium acetate*   *methyl alcohol*

- In saponification, long-chain fatty acids from fats react with strong bases to produce salts of the fatty acids, which are soaps.

◆ **Learning Exercise 16.5A**

Identify the compound with the higher boiling point in each of the following pairs of compounds:

1. CH_3-CH_2-OH or $H-\overset{\overset{\displaystyle O}{\|}}{C}-O-CH_3$

2. $CH_3-\overset{\overset{\displaystyle O}{\|}}{C}-O-CH_3$ or $CH_3-\overset{\overset{\displaystyle OH}{|}}{CH}-CH_2-CH_3$

3. $CH_3-\overset{\overset{\displaystyle O}{\|}}{C}-O-CH_3$ or $CH_3-CH_2-CH_2-CH_2-CH_3$

Answers   1. CH_3-CH_2-OH 2. $CH_3-\overset{\overset{\displaystyle OH}{|}}{CH}-CH_2-CH_3$

3. $CH_3-\overset{\overset{\displaystyle O}{\|}}{C}-O-CH_3$

◆ **Learning Exercise 16.5B**

Write the products of hydrolysis or saponification for the following esters:

1. $CH_3-CH_2-CH_2-\overset{\overset{\displaystyle O}{\|}}{C}-O-CH_3 + H_2O \xrightarrow{\text{H}^+}$

2. $CH_3-\overset{\overset{\displaystyle O}{\|}}{C}-O-CH_3 + NaOH \longrightarrow$

3. 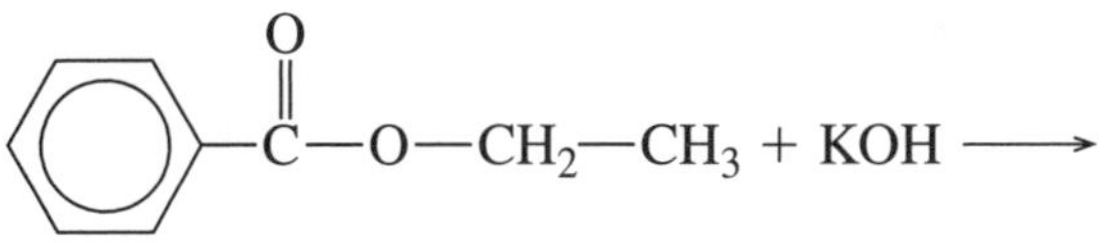 $\langle\bigcirc\rangle-\overset{\overset{\displaystyle O}{\|}}{C}-O-CH_2-CH_3 + KOH \longrightarrow$

4. 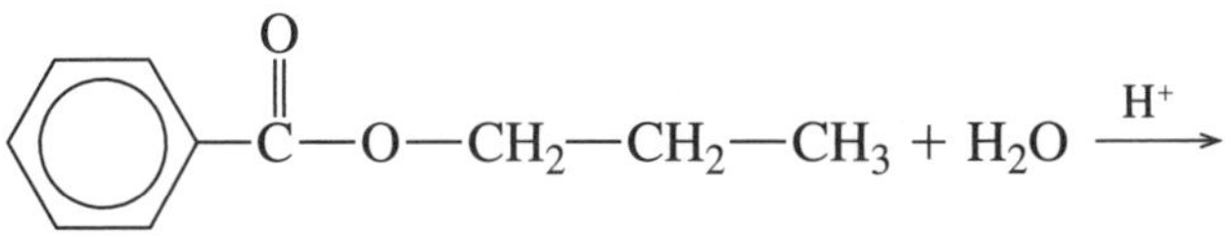 $\langle\bigcirc\rangle-\overset{\overset{\displaystyle O}{\|}}{C}-O-CH_2-CH_2-CH_3 + H_2O \xrightarrow{\text{H}^+}$

Answers   1. $CH_3-CH_2-CH_2-\overset{\overset{\displaystyle O}{\|}}{C}-OH + HO-CH_3$

2. $CH_3-\overset{\overset{\displaystyle O}{\|}}{C}-O^-Na^+ + CH_3-OH$

3. 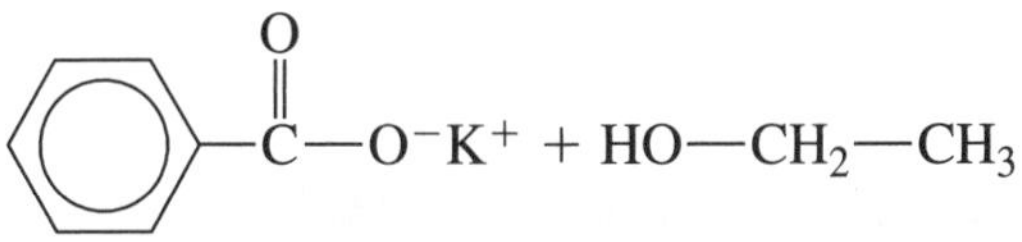 $\langle\bigcirc\rangle-\overset{\overset{\displaystyle O}{\|}}{C}-O^-K^+ + HO-CH_2-CH_3$

4. 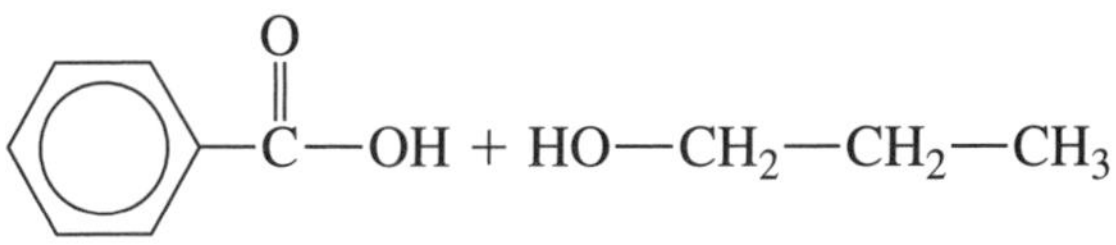 $\langle\bigcirc\rangle-\overset{\overset{\displaystyle O}{\|}}{C}-OH + HO-CH_2-CH_2-CH_3$

273

Checklist for Chapter 16

You are ready to take the practice test for chapter 16. Be sure that you have accomplished the following learning goals for this chapter. If you are not sure, review the section listed at the end of the goal. Then apply your new skills and understanding to the practice test. Good luck.

After studying chapter 16, I can successfully:

_____ Write the IUPAC and common names and draw condensed structural formula of carboxylic acids (16.1).

_____ Describe the solubility and ionization of carboxylic acids in water (16.2).

_____ Describe the behavior of carboxylic acids as weak acids and write the structural formulas for the products of neutralization (16.2).

_____ Write equations for the preparation of esters (16.3).

_____ Write the IUPAC or common names and condensed structural formulas of esters (16.4).

_____ Write equations for the hydrolysis and saponification of esters (16.5).

Practice Test for Chapter 16

Match each structure to its functional group.

A. alcohol   **B.** aldehyde   **C.** carboxylic acid   **D.** ester   **E.** ketone

1. _____ $CH_3-\overset{\overset{\displaystyle CH_3}{|}}{CH}-CH_2-OH$ **2.** _____ $CH_3-CH_2-\overset{\overset{\displaystyle O}{||}}{C}-H$

3. _____ $CH_3-\overset{\overset{\displaystyle O}{||}}{C}-CH_2-CH_3$ **4.** _____ $CH_3-CH_2-\overset{\overset{\displaystyle O}{||}}{C}-OH$

5. _____ $CH_3-\overset{\overset{\displaystyle O}{||}}{C}-O-CH_3$

Match the names of the following compounds with their structures:

A. $CH_3-\overset{\overset{\displaystyle O}{||}}{C}-O-CH_2-CH_3$ **B.** $CH_3-CH_2-CH_2-\overset{\overset{\displaystyle O}{||}}{C}-O^-Na^+$

C. $CH_3-\overset{\overset{\displaystyle O}{||}}{C}-O^-Na^+$ **D.** $CH_3-CH_2-\overset{\overset{\displaystyle CH_2}{|}}{CH}-\overset{\overset{\displaystyle O}{||}}{C}-OH$

E. $CH_3-CH_2-\overset{\overset{\displaystyle O}{||}}{C}-O-CH_3$

6. _____ α-methylbutyric acid

7. _____ methylpropanoate

8. _____ sodium butanoate

9. _____ ethyl acetate

10. _____ sodium acetate

11. An aldehyde can be oxidized to give a(n)

    A. alcohol   **B.** ketone   **C.** carboxylic acid   **D.** ester   **E.** no reaction

12. What is the product when a carboxylic acid reacts with sodium hydroxide?
A. carboxylic acid salt   **B.** alcohol   **C.** ester
D. aldehyde   **E.** no reaction

13. Carboxylic acids are water soluble due to their
A. nonpolar nature   **B.** ionic bonds   **C.** ability to lower pH
D. ability to hydrogen bond   **E.** high melting points

Questions 14–17 refer to the following reactions:

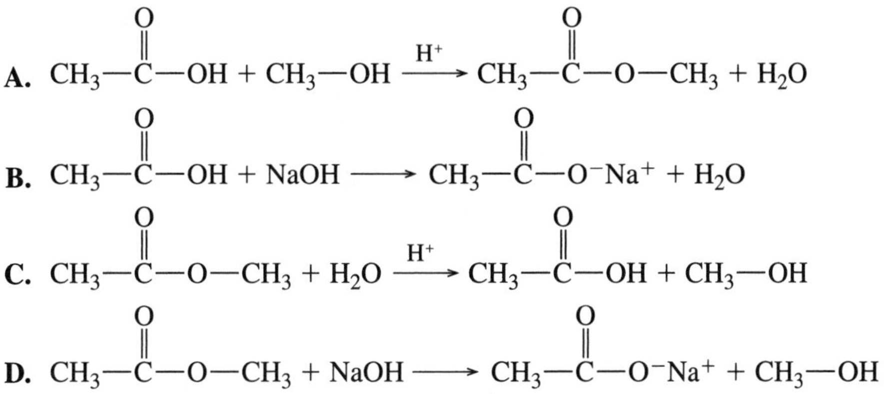

A. $CH_3-\overset{\overset{O}{\|}}{C}-OH + CH_3-OH \xrightarrow{H^+} CH_3-\overset{\overset{O}{\|}}{C}-O-CH_3 + H_2O$

B. $CH_3-\overset{\overset{O}{\|}}{C}-OH + NaOH \longrightarrow CH_3-\overset{\overset{O}{\|}}{C}-O^-Na^+ + H_2O$

C. $CH_3-\overset{\overset{O}{\|}}{C}-O-CH_3 + H_2O \xrightarrow{H^+} CH_3-\overset{\overset{O}{\|}}{C}-OH + CH_3-OH$

D. $CH_3-\overset{\overset{O}{\|}}{C}-O-CH_3 + NaOH \longrightarrow CH_3-\overset{\overset{O}{\|}}{C}-O^-Na^+ + CH_3-OH$

14. _____ is an ester hydrolysis   **15.** _____ is a neutralization

16. _____ is a saponification   **17.** _____ is an esterification

18. What is the name of the organic product of reaction A?
A. methyl acetate   **B.** acetic acid   **C.** methyl alcohol
D. acetaldehyde   **E.** ethyl methanoate

19. The compound with the highest boiling point is
A. formic acid   **B.** acetic acid   **C.** propanol
D. propanoic acid   **E.** ethyl acetate

20. The ester produced from the reactions of 1-butanol and propanoic acid is
A. butyl propanonate   **B.** butyl propanone   **C.** propyl butyrate
D. propyl butanone   **E.** heptanoate

21. The reaction of methyl acetate with NaOH produces
A. ethanol and formic acid
B. ethanol and sodium formate
C. ethanol and sodium ethanoate
D. methanol and acetic acid
E. methanol and sodium acetate

22. Identify the carboxylic acid and alcohol needed to produce

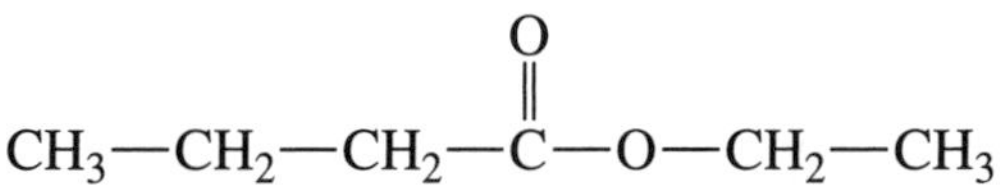

$CH_3-CH_2-CH_2-\overset{\overset{O}{\|}}{C}-O-CH_2-CH_3$

A. propanoic acid and ethanol   **B.** acetic acid and 1-pentanol
C. acetic acid and 1-butanol   **D.** butanoic acid and ethanol
E. hexanoic acid and methanol

23. When butanal is oxidized, the product is
A. butanone   **B.** 1-butanol   **C.** 2-butanol
D. butanoic acid   **E.** butane

24. The name of is $CH_3-CH_2-\overset{\overset{\displaystyle O}{\|}}{C}-O-CH_2-CH_3$ is

    A. ethyl acetate   **B.** ethyl ethanoate   **C.** ethyl propanoate

    D. propyl ethanoate   **E.** ethyl butyrate

25. Soaps are

    A. long-chain fatty acids   **B.** fatty acid salts

    C. esters of acetic acid   **D.** alcohols with 10 carbon atoms

    E. aromatic compounds

26. In a hydrolysis reaction

    A. an acid reacts with an alcohol

    B. an ester reacts with NaOH

    C. an ester reacts with H_2O

    D. an acid neutralizes a base

    E. water is added to an alkene

27. Esters

    A. have pleasant odors

    B. can undergo hydrolysis

    C. are formed from alcohols and carboxylic acids

    D. have a lower boiling point than the corresponding acid

    E. all of the above

28. The products of $H-\overset{\overset{\displaystyle O}{\|}}{C}-OH + H_2O$ are

    A. $H-\overset{\overset{\displaystyle O}{\|}}{C}-O^- + H_3O^+$ **B.** $H-\overset{\overset{\displaystyle O}{\|}}{C}-\overset{+}{O}H_2 + OH^-$

    C. $H-\overset{\overset{\displaystyle O}{\|}}{C}-O-CH_3$ **D.** $CH_3-\overset{\overset{\displaystyle O}{\|}}{C}-OH$

    E. $H-\overset{\overset{\displaystyle O}{\|}}{C}-O^-Na^+ + H_2O$

29. The name of this compound is

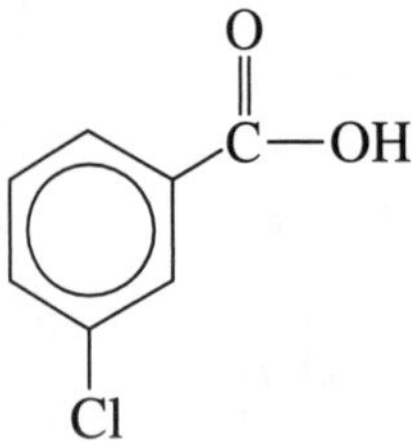

    A. *p*-chlorobenzoic acid   **B.** chlorobenzoic acid

    C. *m*-chlorobenzoic acid   **D.** 4-chlorobenzoic acid

    E. benzoic acid chloride

30. The name of this compound is

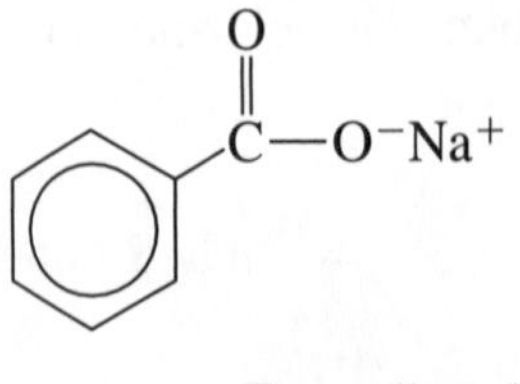

    A. benzene sodium   **B.** sodium benzoate   **C.** *o*-benzoic acid

    D. sodium benzene carboxylate   **E.** benzoic acid

Answers to the Practice Test

1. A	**2.** B	**3.** E	**4.** C	**5.** D
6. D	**7.** E	**8.** B	**9.** A	**10.** C
11. C	**12.** A	**13.** D	**14.** C	**15.** B
16. D	**17.** A	**18.** A	**19.** D	**20.** A
21. E	**22.** D	**23.** D	**24.** C	**25.** B
26. C	**27.** E	**28.** A	**29.** C	**30.** B

Answers and Solutions to Selected Text Problems

16.1 Methanoic acid (formic acid) is the carboxylic acid that is responsible for the pain associated with ant stings.

16.3 Each compound contains three carbon atoms. They differ because propanal, an aldehyde, contains a carbonyl group bonded to a hydrogen. In propanoic acid, the carbonyl group connects to a hydroxyl group.

16.5 **a.** Ethanoic acid (acetic acid) is the carboxylic acid with two carbons.
b. Butanoic acid (butyric acid) is the carboxylic acid with four carbons.
c. 2-chloropropanoic acid (α-chloropropionic acid) is a three-carbon carboxylic acid with a chlorine on the carbon next to the carbonyl.
d. 3-methylhexanoic acid is a six-carbon carboxylic acid with a methyl on carbon 3.
e. 3,4-dihydroxybenzoic acid has a carboxylic acid group on benzene and two hydroxyl groups on carbons 3 and 4.
f. 4-bromopentanoic acid is a five-carbon carboxylic acid with a — Br atom on carbon 4.

16.7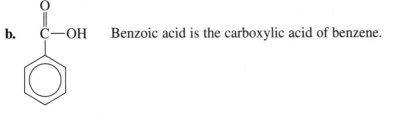

a. $CH_3-CH_2-\overset{\overset{\displaystyle O}{\|}}{C}-OH$ Propionic acid has three carbons.

b. $\overset{\overset{\displaystyle O}{\|}}{C}-OH$ Benzoic acid is the carboxylic acid of benzene.

c. $Cl-CH_2-\overset{\overset{\displaystyle O}{\|}}{C}-OH$ 2-chloroethanoic acid is a carboxylic acid that has a two-carbon chain with a chlorine atom on carbon 2.

d. $HO-CH_2-CH_2-\overset{\overset{\displaystyle O}{\|}}{C}-OH$ 3-hydroxypropanoic acid is a carboxylic acid that has a three-carbon chain with a hydroxyl on carbon 3.

e. $CH_3-CH_2-\overset{\overset{\displaystyle CH_3}{|}}{CH}-\overset{\overset{\displaystyle O}{\|}}{C}-OH$ α-methylbutyric acid is a carboxylic acid that has a four-carbon chain with a methyl on the second (α) carbon.

f. 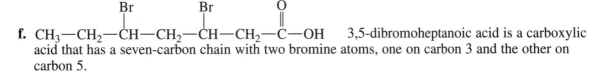 $CH_3-CH_2-\overset{\overset{\displaystyle Br}{|}}{CH}-CH_2-\overset{\overset{\displaystyle Br}{|}}{CH}-CH_2-\overset{\overset{\displaystyle O}{\|}}{C}-OH$ 3,5-dibromoheptanoic acid is a carboxylic acid that has a seven-carbon chain with two bromine atoms, one on carbon 3 and the other on carbon 5.

16.9 Aldehydes and primary alcohols oxidize to produce the corresponding carboxylic acid.

a. $H-\overset{\overset{\displaystyle O}{\|}}{C}-OH$

b. $CH_3-\overset{\overset{\displaystyle O}{\|}}{C}-OH$

c. $CH_3-\overset{\overset{\displaystyle CH_3}{|}}{CH}-CH_2-\overset{\overset{\displaystyle O}{\|}}{C}-OH$

d. (cyclopentyl)$-CH_2-\overset{\overset{\displaystyle O}{\|}}{C}-OH$

16.11 **a.** Butanoic acid has a higher molar mass and would have a higher boiling point.
   b. Propanoic acid can form more hydrogen bonds and would have a higher boiling point.
   c. Butanoic acid can form more hydrogen bonds and would have a higher boiling point.

16.13 **a.** propanoic acid   **b.** propanoic acid

16.15 **a.** $H-\overset{\overset{\displaystyle O}{\|}}{C}-OH + H_2O \rightleftarrows H-\overset{\overset{\displaystyle O}{\|}}{C}-O^- + H_3O^+$

   b. $CH_3-CH_2-\overset{\overset{\displaystyle O}{\|}}{C}-OH + H_2O \rightleftarrows CH_3-CH_2-\overset{\overset{\displaystyle O}{\|}}{C}-O^- + H_3O^+$

   c. $CH_3-\overset{\overset{\displaystyle O}{\|}}{C}-OH + H_2O \rightleftarrows CH_3-\overset{\overset{\displaystyle O}{\|}}{C}-O^- + H_3O^+$

16.17 **a.** $H-\overset{\overset{\displaystyle O}{\|}}{C}-OH + NaOH \rightarrow H-\overset{\overset{\displaystyle O}{\|}}{C}-O^-Na^+ + H_2O$

   b. $CH_3-CH_2-\overset{\overset{\displaystyle O}{\|}}{C}-OH + NaOH \rightarrow CH_3-CH_2-\overset{\overset{\displaystyle O}{\|}}{C}-O^-Na^+ + H_2O$

   c. (benzene ring)$-\overset{\overset{\displaystyle O}{\|}}{C}-OH + NaOH \longrightarrow$ (benzene ring)$-\overset{\overset{\displaystyle O}{\|}}{C}-O^- + H_2O$

16.19 A carboxylic acid salt is named by replacing the *-oic ic* ending of the acid name with *ate*.
   a. The acid is methanoic acid (formic acid). The carboxylic acid salt is sodium methanoate (sodium formate).
   b. The acid is propanoic acid (propionic acid). The carboxylic acid salt is sodium propanoate (sodium propionate).
   c. The acid is benzoic acid. The carboxylic acid salt is sodium benzoate.

16.21 **a.** This is an *aldehyde* since it has a carbonyl bonded to carbon and hydrogen.
   b. This is an *ester* since it has a carbonyl bonded to oxygen that is also bonded to a carbon.
   c. This is a *ketone* since it has a carbonyl bonded to two carbon atoms.
   d. This is a *carboxylic acid* since it has a carboxylic group; a carbonyl bonded to a hydroxyl.

16.23 **a.** $CH_3-\overset{\overset{\displaystyle O}{\|}}{C}-O-CH_3$ The carbonyl portion of the ester has two carbons bonded to a methyl group.

b. $CH_3-CH_2-CH_2-\overset{\overset{\displaystyle O}{\|}}{C}-OCH_3$ The carbonyl portion of the ester is a four-carbon chain bonded to a one-carbon methyl group.

c.

16.25 A carboxylic acid and an alcohol react to give an ester with the elimination of water.

a. $CH_3-CH_2-\overset{\overset{\displaystyle O}{\|}}{C}-O-CH_2-CH_2-CH_3$

b. $CH_3-CH_2-CH_2-CH_2-\overset{\overset{\displaystyle O}{\|}}{C}-O-\overset{\overset{\displaystyle CH_3}{|}}{C}H-CH_3$

16.27 **a.** The carbonyl portion of the ester is derived from methanoic acid (formic acid). The alcohol is methanol (methyl alcohol).
b. The carbonyl portion of the ester is derived from ethanoic acid (acetic acid). The alcohol is methanol (methyl alcohol).
c. The carbonyl portion of the ester is derived from butanoic acid (butyric acid). The alcohol is methanol (methyl alcohol).
d. The carbonyl portion of the ester is derived from 3-methylbutanoic acid (β-methylbutyric acid). The alcohol is ethanol (ethyl alcohol).

16.29 **a.** The name of this ester is methyl methanoate (methyl formate). The carbonyl portion of the ester contains one carbon; the name is derived from methanoic (formic) acid. The alkyl portion has one carbon; it is methyl.
b. The name of this ester is methyl ethanoate (methyl acetate). The carbonyl portion of the ester contains two carbons. The name is derived from ethanoic (acetic) acid. The alkyl portion has one carbon, which is methyl.
c. The name of this ester is methyl butanoate (methyl butyrate). The carbonyl portion of the ester contains four carbons; the name is derived from butanoic (butyric) acid. The alkyl portion has one carbon, which is methyl.
d. The name of this ester is ethyl-3-methyl butanoate (ethyl-β-methyl butyrate). The carbonyl portion of the ester has a four-carbon chain with a methyl group attached to the third (β) carbon, counting the carboxyl carbon as 1. The alkyl portion with two carbons is an ethyl.

16.31 **a.** $CH_3-\overset{\overset{\displaystyle O}{\|}}{C}-O-CH_3$ Acetic acid is the two carbon carboxylic acid. Methanol gives a one-carbon alkyl group.

b. $H-\overset{\overset{\displaystyle O}{\|}}{C}-O-CH_2-CH_2-CH_2-CH_3$ Formic acid is the carboxylic acid bonded to the four-carbon 1-butanol.

c. CH₃—CH₂—CH₂—CH₂—$\overset{\displaystyle O}{\overset{\displaystyle \|}{C}}$—O—CH₂—CH₃   Pentanoic acid is the carboxylic acid bonded to ethanol.

d. CH₃—CH₂—$\overset{\displaystyle O}{\overset{\displaystyle \|}{C}}$—O—CH₂—$\overset{\displaystyle Br}{\overset{\displaystyle |}{CH}}$—CH₃   Propanoic acid is the carboxylic acid bonded to 2-bromo-1-propanol.

16.33 **a.** The flavor and odor of bananas is pentyl ethanoate (pentyl acetate).
   b. The flavor and odor of oranges is octyl ethanoate (octyl acetate).
   c. The flavor and odor of apricots is pentyl butanoate (pentyl butyrate).

16.35 **a.** CH₃—$\overset{\displaystyle O}{\overset{\displaystyle \|}{C}}$—OH   **b.** CH₃—CH₂—CH₂—CH₂—OH

   c. CH₃—$\overset{\displaystyle O}{\overset{\displaystyle \|}{C}}$—O—CH₃

16.37 Acid hydrolysis of an ester adds water in the presence of acid and gives a carboxylic acid and an alcohol.

16.39 Acid hydrolysis of an ester gives the carboxylic acid and the alcohol, which were combined to form the ester; basic hydrolysis of an ester gives the salt of carboxylic acid and the alcohol, which combine to form the ester.

   a. CH₃—CH₂—$\overset{\displaystyle O}{\overset{\displaystyle \|}{C}}$—O⁻Na⁺ and CH₃—OH

   b. CH₃—$\overset{\displaystyle O}{\overset{\displaystyle \|}{C}}$—OH and CH₃—CH₂—CH₂—OH

   c. CH₃—CH₂—CH₂—$\overset{\displaystyle O}{\overset{\displaystyle \|}{C}}$—OH and CH₃—CH₂—C—OH

   d. ⬡—COOH and CH₃CH₂OH

   e. ⬡—COO⁻Na⁺ and CH₃CH₂OH

16.41 **a.** CH₃—$\overset{\displaystyle O}{\overset{\displaystyle \|}{C}}$—O—CH₂—CH₂—CH₃

   b. CH₃—$\overset{\displaystyle O}{\overset{\displaystyle \|}{C}}$—OH + HO—CH₂—CH₂—CH₃ $\xrightarrow{\text{H}^+}$ CH₃—$\overset{\displaystyle O}{\overset{\displaystyle \|}{C}}$—O—CH₂—CH₂—CH₃

   c. CH₃—$\overset{\displaystyle O}{\overset{\displaystyle \|}{C}}$—O—CH₂—CH₂—CH₃ + H₂O $\xrightarrow{\text{H}^+}$ CH₃—$\overset{\displaystyle O}{\overset{\displaystyle \|}{C}}$—OH + HO—CH₂—CH₂—CH₃

d. $CH_3{-}C(=O){-}O{-}CH_2{-}CH_2{-}CH_3 + NaOH \longrightarrow CH_3{-}C(=O){-}O^-Na^+ + HO{-}CH_2{-}CH_2{-}CH_3$

e. $1.58\ \cancel{g} \times \frac{1\ \cancel{mole}}{102\ \cancel{g}} \times \frac{1000\ mL}{0.208\ \cancel{mole}} = 74.5\ mL$

16.43 **a.** 3-methylbutanoic acid; β-methylbutyric acid
b. ethylbenzoate
c. ethyl propanoate; ethylpropionate
d. 2-chlorobenzoic acid; *ortho*chlorobenzoic acid
e. 4-hydroxypentanoic acid
f. 2-propyl ethanoate; isopropyl acetate

16.45

$CH_3{-}CH_2{-}CH_2{-}CH_2{-}C(=O){-}OH$ $\quad CH_3{-}CH_2{-}CH(CH_3){-}C(=O){-}OH$

$CH_3{-}CH(CH_3){-}CH_2{-}C(=O){-}OH$ $\quad CH_3{-}C(CH_3)_2{-}C(=O){-}OH$

16.47 **a.** $CH_3{-}O{-}C(=O){-}CH_3$

b.

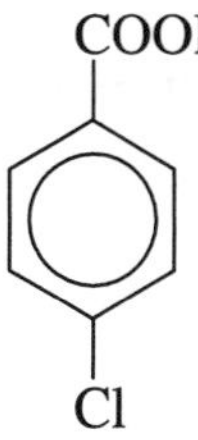

c. $Cl{-}CH_2{-}CH_2{-}C(=O){-}OH$

d. $CH_3{-}CH_2{-}O{-}C(=O){-}CH_2{-}CH_2{-}CH_3$

e. $CH_3{-}CH_2{-}CH(CH_3){-}CH_2{-}C(=O){-}OH$

f.

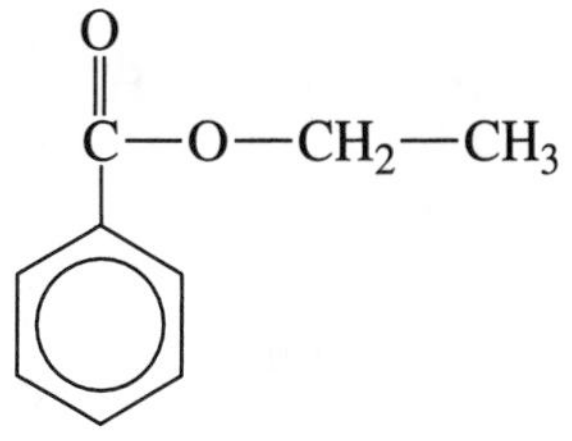

16.49 **a.** $CH_3{-}C(=O){-}OH$

b. $CH_3{-}CH_2{-}C(=O){-}OH$

c. $CH_3{-}CH_2{-}CH_2{-}C(=O){-}OH$

16.51 The presence of two polar groups in the carboxyl group allows hydrogen bonding, including the formation of a dimer that doubles the effective molar mass and requires a higher temperature to form gas.

16.53 Compounds b, c, d, and e are all soluble in water.

16.55 **a.** $CH_3-CH_2-\overset{\displaystyle O}{\overset{\displaystyle \|}{C}}-O^- + H_3O^+$

b. $CH_3-CH_2-\overset{\displaystyle O}{\overset{\displaystyle \|}{C}}-O^-K^+ + H_2O$

c. $CH_3-CH_2-\overset{\displaystyle O}{\overset{\displaystyle \|}{C}}-O-CH_3 + H_2O$

d. $\overset{\displaystyle O}{\overset{\displaystyle \|}{C}}-O-CH_2-CH_3 + H_2O$ (benzene ring attached to C)

16.57 **a.** 3-Methylbutanoic acid is needed to react with methanol (CH_3-OH).
   b. 3-Chlorobenzoic acid is needed to react with ethanol (CH_3-CH_2-OH).
   c. Hexanoic acid is needed to react with methanol (CH_3-OH).

16.59 **a.** $CH_3-CH_2-\overset{\displaystyle O}{\overset{\displaystyle \|}{C}}-OH$ and $HO-\overset{\displaystyle CH_3}{\overset{\displaystyle |}{CH}}-CH_3$

   b. $CH_3-\overset{\displaystyle CH_3}{\overset{\displaystyle |}{CH}}-\overset{\displaystyle O}{\overset{\displaystyle \|}{C}}-O^-Na^+$ and $HO-CH_2-CH_2-CH_3$

16.61 **a.** $CH_2{=}CH_2 + H_2O \xrightarrow{H^+} CH_3-CH_2-OH \xrightarrow{[O]} CH_3-\overset{\displaystyle O}{\overset{\displaystyle \|}{C}}-OH$

   b. $CH_3-CH_2-CH_2-CH_2-OH \xrightarrow{[O]} CH_3-CH_2-CH_2-\overset{\displaystyle O}{\overset{\displaystyle \|}{C}}-OH$

16.63 (benzene)$-\overset{\displaystyle O}{\overset{\displaystyle \|}{C}}-OCH_3 + KOH \longrightarrow$ (benzene)$-\overset{\displaystyle O}{\overset{\displaystyle \|}{C}}-O^-K^+ + CH_3OH$

A soluble salt, potassium benzoate, is formed. When acid is added, the salt is converted to insoluble benzoic acid.

16.65 **a.** hydroxyl and carboxylic acid
   b.

   (structure: benzene ring with $O-\overset{\displaystyle O}{\overset{\displaystyle \|}{C}}-CH_3$ and $\overset{\displaystyle}{\underset{\displaystyle O}{\overset{\displaystyle \|}{C}}}-OH$)

   c.

   (structure: benzene ring with OH and $\overset{\displaystyle}{\underset{\displaystyle O}{\overset{\displaystyle \|}{C}}}-OCH_3$)

Study Goals

- Describe the properties and types of lipids.
- Write the structures of triacylglycerols obtained from glycerol and fatty acids.
- Draw the structure of the product from hydrogenation, hydrolysis, and saponification of triacylglycerols.
- Distinguish between phospholipids, glycolipids, and sphingolipids.
- Describe steroids and their role in bile salts, vitamins, and hormones.
- Describe the lipid bilayer in a cell.

Think About It

1. What are fats used for in the body?

2. What foods are high in fat?

3. What oils are used to produce margarines?

4. What kind of lipid is cholesterol?

Key Terms

Match the key terms with the correct statement shown below.

a. lipid   **b.** fatty acid   **c.** triacylglycerol
d. saponification   **e.** phospholipid   **f.** steroid

1. _____ A lipid consisting of glycerol bonded to two fatty acids and a phosphate group attached to an amino group

2. _____ A type of compound that is not soluble in water but in nonpolar solvents

3. _____ The hydrolysis of a triacylglycerol with a strong base producing salts called soaps and glycerol

4. _____ A lipid consisting of glycerol bonded to three fatty acids

5. _____ A lipid composed of a multicyclic ring system

6. _____ Long-chain carboxylic acid found in triacylglycerols

Answers   **1.** e   **2.** a   **3.** d   **4.** c   **5.** f   **6.** b

17.1 Lipids

- Lipids are nonpolar compounds that are not soluble in water.
- Classes of lipids include waxes, triacylglycerols, glycerophospholipids, and steroids.

◆ **Learning Exercise 17.1**

Match one of the classes of lipids with the composition of lipids below:

    a. wax   **b.** triacylglycerol   **c.** glycerophospholipid
    d. sphingolipid   **e.** glycosphingolipid   **f.** steroid

  1. _____ a fused structure of four cycloalkanes

  2. _____ a long chain alcohol and a fatty acid

  3. _____ glycerol and three fatty acids

  4. _____ glycerol, two fatty acids, phosphate, and choline

  5. _____ sphingosine, fatty acid, and galactose

  6. _____ sphingosine, fatty acid, phosphate, and choline

Answers   **1.** f   **2.** a   **3.** b   **4.** c   **5.** e   **6.** d

17.2 Fatty Acids

- Fatty acids are unbranched carboxylic acids that typically contain an even number (12–18) of carbon atoms.
- Fatty acids may be saturated, monounsaturated with one double bond, or polyunsaturated with two or more double bonds. The double bonds in unsaturated fatty acids are almost always cis.

◆ **Learning Exercise 17.2**

Draw the structural formulas of linoleic acid, stearic acid, and oleic acid.

A. linoleic acid

B. stearic acid

C. oleic acid

Which of these three fatty acids

  1. _____ is the most saturated   **2.** _____ is the most unsaturated

  3. _____ has the lowest melting point   **4.** _____ has the highest melting point

  5. _____ is found in vegetables   **6.** _____ is from animal sources

Answers

linoleic acid $CH_3-(CH_2)_4-CH=CH-CH_2-CH=CH-(CH_2)_7-\overset{\overset{\displaystyle O}{\|}}{C}-OH$

stearic acid $CH_3-(CH_2)_{16}-\overset{\overset{\displaystyle O}{\|}}{C}-OH$

oleic acid $CH_3-(CH_2)_7-CH=CH-(CH_2)_7-\overset{\overset{\displaystyle O}{\|}}{C}-OH$

1. B   **2.** A   **3.** A   **4.** B   **5.** A and C   **6.** B

17.3 Waxes, Fats and Oils

- A wax is an ester of a long-chain fatty acid and a long-chain alcohol.
- The triacylglycerols in fats and oils are esters of glycerol with three long-chain fatty acids.
- Fats from animal sources contain more saturated fatty acids and have higher melting points than fats found in most vegetable oils.

◆ Learning Exercise 17.3A

Write the formula of the wax formed by the reaction of palmitic acid, $CH_3-(CH_2)_{14}-COOH$, and cetyl alcohol, $CH_3-(CH_2)_{14}-CH_2-OH$.

Answer $CH_3-(CH_2)_{14}-\overset{\overset{\displaystyle O}{\|}}{C}-O-CH_2-(CH_2)_{14}-CH_3$

◆ Learning Exercise 17.3B

Consider the following fatty acid called oleic acid:

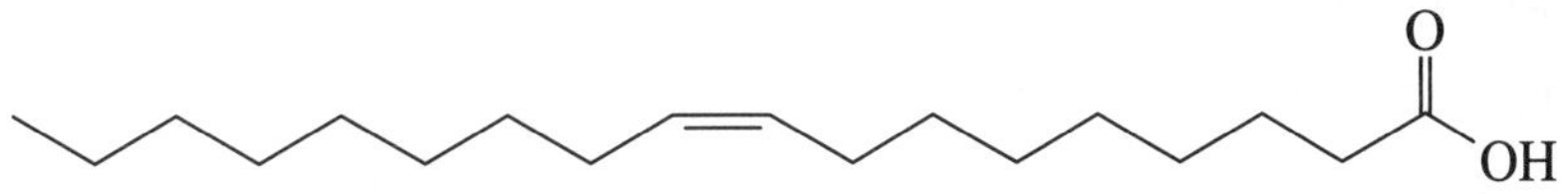

1. Why is the compound an acid?

2. Is it a saturated or unsaturated compound? Why?

3. Is the double bond cis or trans?

4. Is it likely to be a solid or a liquid at room temperature?

5. Why is it not soluble in water?

Answers   **1.** contains a carboxylic acid group   **2.** unsaturated; double bond
        3. cis   **4.** liquid
        5. it has a long hydrocarbon chain

285

◆ **Learning Exercise 17.3C**

Write the structure and name of the triacylglycerol formed from the following:

1. glycerol and three palmitic acids, $CH_3—(CH_2)_{14}—COOH$

2. glycerol and three myristic acids, $CH_3—(CH_2)_{12}—COOH$

Answers

1. 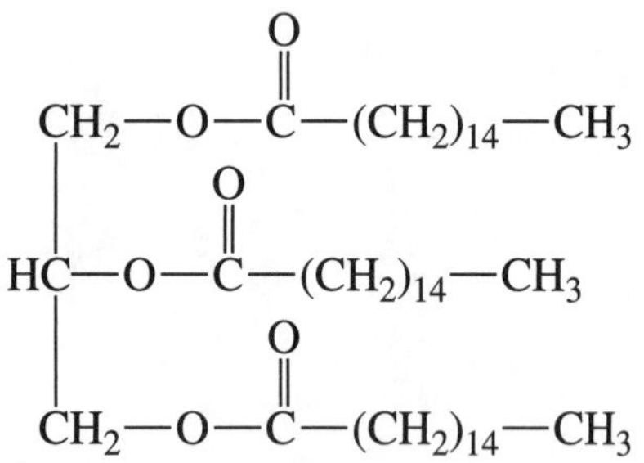
$$CH_2—O—\overset{\overset{\textstyle O}{\|}}{C}—(CH_2)_{14}—CH_3$$
$$HC—O—\overset{\overset{\textstyle O}{\|}}{C}—(CH_2)_{14}—CH_3$$
$$CH_2—O—\overset{\overset{\textstyle O}{\|}}{C}—(CH_2)_{14}—CH_3$$

glyceryl tripalmitate
(tripalmitin)

2. 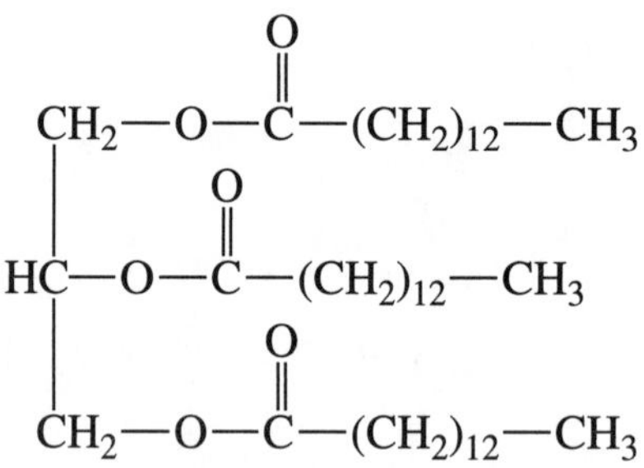
$$CH_2—O—\overset{\overset{\textstyle O}{\|}}{C}—(CH_2)_{12}—CH_3$$
$$HC—O—\overset{\overset{\textstyle O}{\|}}{C}—(CH_2)_{12}—CH_3$$
$$CH_2—O—\overset{\overset{\textstyle O}{\|}}{C}—(CH_2)_{12}—CH_3$$

glyceryl trimyristate
(trimyristin)

◆ **Learning Exercise 17.3D**

Write the structural formulas of the following triacylglycerols:

1. glyceryl tristearate (tristearin)   **2.** glyceryl trioleate (triolein)

Answers

1.

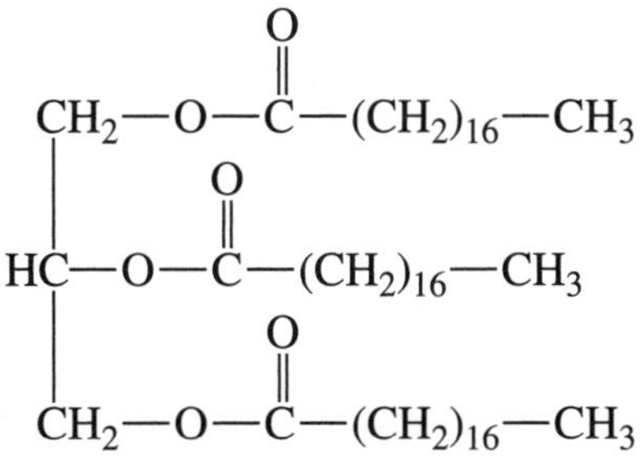

$$CH_2-O-\overset{\displaystyle O}{\overset{\|}{C}}-(CH_2)_{16}-CH_3$$

$$HC-O-\overset{\displaystyle O}{\overset{\|}{C}}-(CH_2)_{16}-CH_3$$

$$CH_2-O-\overset{\displaystyle O}{\overset{\|}{C}}-(CH_2)_{16}-CH_3$$

glyceryl tristearate
(tristearin)

2.

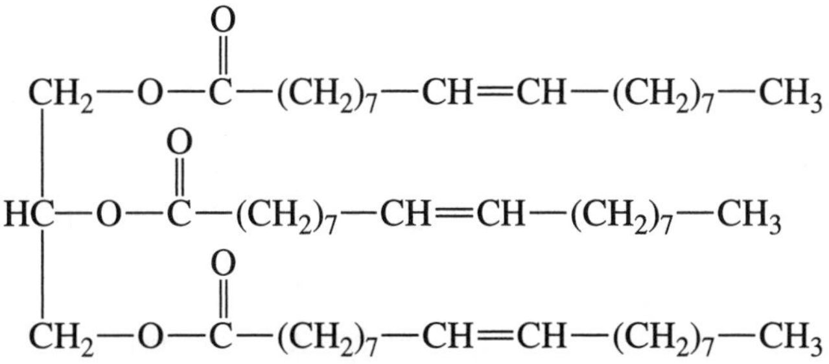

$$CH_2-O-\overset{\displaystyle O}{\overset{\|}{C}}-(CH_2)_7-CH=CH-(CH_2)_7-CH_3$$

$$HC-O-\overset{\displaystyle O}{\overset{\|}{C}}-(CH_2)_7-CH=CH-(CH_2)_7-CH_3$$

$$CH_2-O-\overset{\displaystyle O}{\overset{\|}{C}}-(CH_2)_7-CH=CH-(CH_2)_7-CH_3$$

glyceryl trioleate
(triolein)

17.4 Chemical Properties of Triacylglycerols

- The hydrogenation of unsaturated fatty acids converts double bonds to single bonds.
- The oxidation of unsaturated fatty acids produces short-chain fatty acids with disagreeable odors.
- The hydrolysis of the ester bonds in fats or oils produces glycerol and fatty acids.
- In saponification, a fat heated with a strong base produces glycerol and the salts of the fatty acids or soaps. The dual polarity of soap permits its solubility in both water and oil.

◆ Learning Exercise 17.4

Write the equations for the following reactions of glyceryl trioleate (triolein):

1. hydrogenation with a nickel catalyst

2. acid hydrolysis with HCl

3. saponification with NaOH

Answers

1. 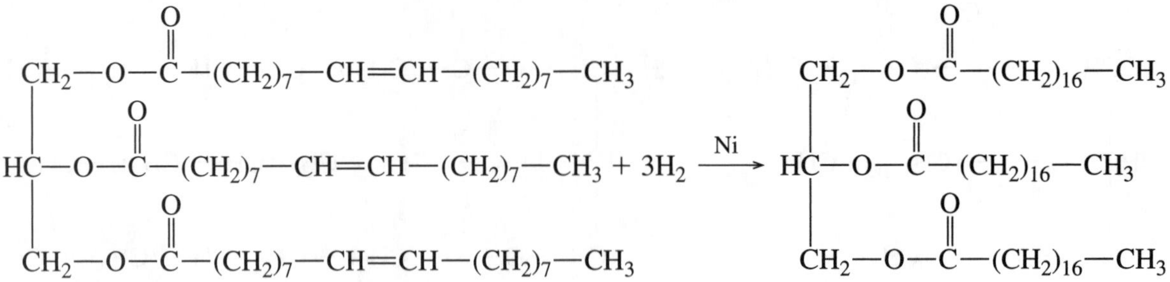 $CH_2-O-\overset{\overset{\displaystyle O}{\|}}{C}-(CH_2)_7-CH=CH-(CH_2)_7-CH_3$

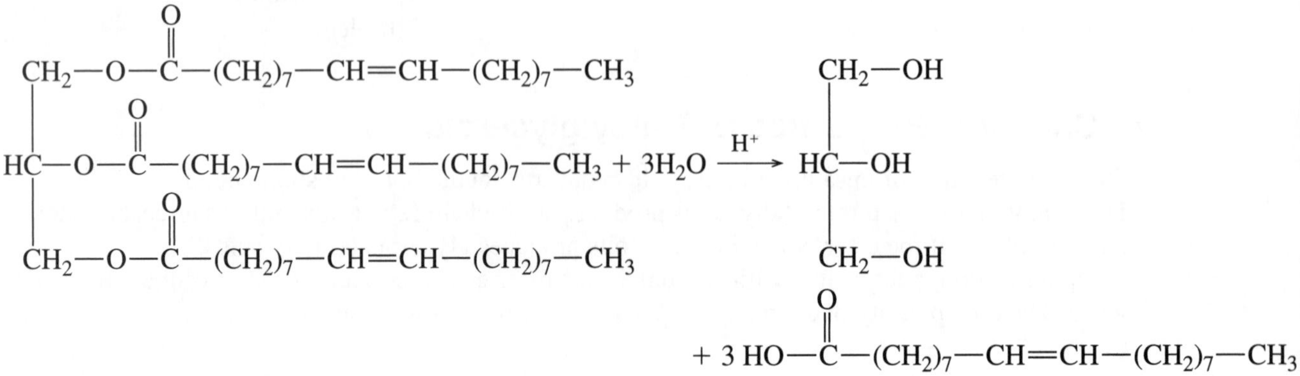

$HC-O-\overset{\overset{\displaystyle O}{\|}}{C}-(CH_2)_7-CH=CH-(CH_2)_7-CH_3 + 3H_2 \xrightarrow{Ni}$

$CH_2-O-\overset{\overset{\displaystyle O}{\|}}{C}-(CH_2)_7-CH=CH-(CH_2)_7-CH_3$

$CH_2-O-\overset{\overset{\displaystyle O}{\|}}{C}-(CH_2)_{16}-CH_3$

$HC-O-\overset{\overset{\displaystyle O}{\|}}{C}-(CH_2)_{16}-CH_3$

$CH_2-O-\overset{\overset{\displaystyle O}{\|}}{C}-(CH_2)_{16}-CH_3$

2. $CH_2-O-\overset{\overset{\displaystyle O}{\|}}{C}-(CH_2)_7-CH=CH-(CH_2)_7-CH_3$

$HC-O-\overset{\overset{\displaystyle O}{\|}}{C}-(CH_2)_7-CH=CH-(CH_2)_7-CH_3 + 3H_2O \xrightarrow{H^+}$

$CH_2-O-\overset{\overset{\displaystyle O}{\|}}{C}-(CH_2)_7-CH=CH-(CH_2)_7-CH_3$

CH_2-OH

$HC-OH$

CH_2-OH

$+ 3\ HO-\overset{\overset{\displaystyle O}{\|}}{C}-(CH_2)_7-CH=CH-(CH_2)_7-CH_3$

3. $CH_2-O-\overset{\overset{\displaystyle O}{\|}}{C}-(CH_2)_7-CH=CH-(CH_2)_7-CH_3$

$HC-O-\overset{\overset{\displaystyle O}{\|}}{C}-(CH_2)_7-CH=CH-(CH_2)_7-CH_3 + 3NaOH \longrightarrow$

$CH_2-O-\overset{\overset{\displaystyle O}{\|}}{C}-(CH_2)_7-CH=CH-(CH_2)_7-CH_3$

CH_2-OH

$HC-OH$

CH_2-OH

$+ 3\ Na^+{}^-O-\overset{\overset{\displaystyle O}{\|}}{C}-(CH_2)_7-CH=CH-(CH_2)_7-CH$

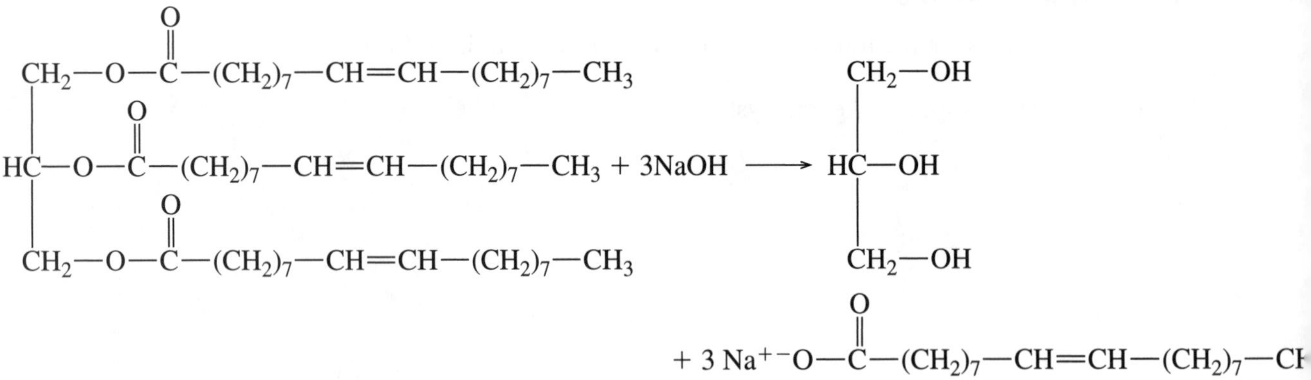

17.5 Glycerophospholipids

- Glycerophospholipids are esters of glycerol with two fatty acids and a phosphate group attached to an amino alcohol.
- The fatty acids are a nonpolar region, whereas the phosphate group and the amino alcohol make up a polar region.

◆ **Learning Exercise 17.5A**

Draw the structure of a glycerophospholipid that is formed from two molecules of palmitic acid and serine, an amino alcohol:

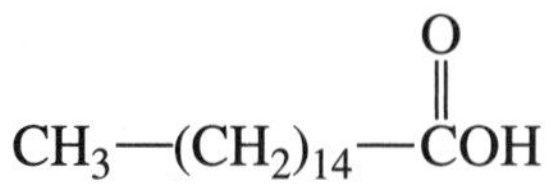

$$CH_3-(CH_2)_{14}-\overset{\overset{O}{\|}}{C}OH$$
palmitic acid

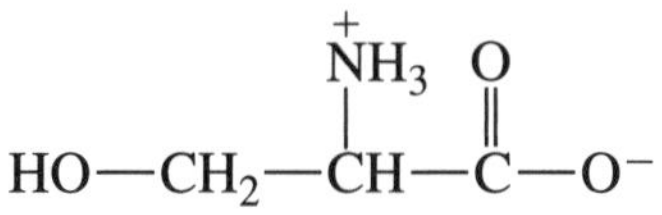

$$HO-CH_2-\overset{\overset{+}{N}H_3}{\underset{|}{C}H}-\overset{\overset{O}{\|}}{C}-O^-$$
serine

Answer

$$CH_2-O-\overset{\overset{O}{\|}}{C}-(CH_2)_{14}-CH_3$$
$$HC-O-\overset{\overset{O}{\|}}{C}-(CH_2)_{14}-CH_3$$
$$CH_2-O-\overset{\overset{O}{\|}}{P}-O-CH_2-\overset{\overset{+}{N}H_3}{\underset{|}{C}H}-\overset{\overset{O}{\|}}{C}-O^-$$
$$\underset{O^-}{|}$$

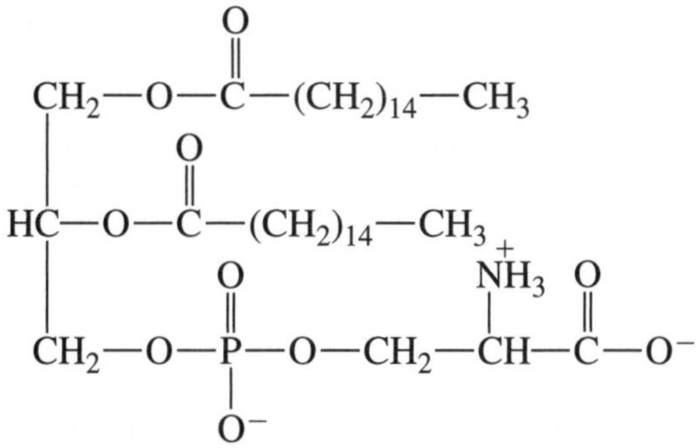

◆ **Learning Exercise 17.5B**

Consider the following glycerophospholipid:

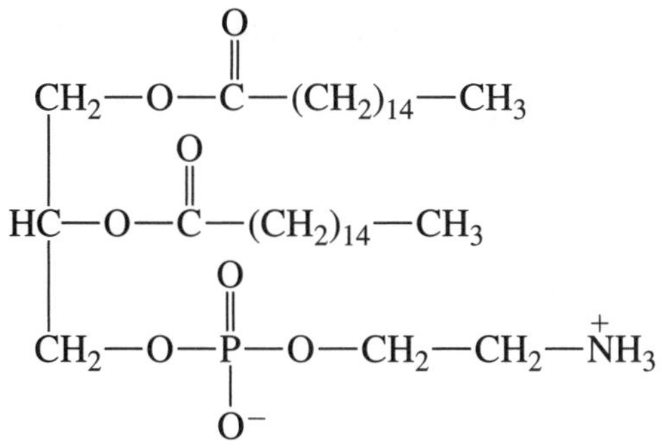

$$CH_2-O-\overset{\overset{O}{\|}}{C}-(CH_2)_{14}-CH_3$$
$$HC-O-\overset{\overset{O}{\|}}{C}-(CH_2)_{14}-CH_3$$
$$CH_2-O-\overset{\overset{O}{\|}}{P}-O-CH_2-CH_2-\overset{+}{N}H_3$$
$$\underset{O^-}{|}$$

On the above structure, indicate the
A. two fatty acids   **B.** part from the glycerol molecule
C. phosphate section   **D.** amino alcohol group
E. nonpolar region   **F.** polar region

1. What is the name of the amino alcohol group? _____

2. What is the name of the phosphoglyceride? _____

3. Why is a phosphoglyceride more soluble in water than most lipids? _____

Answers

1. ethanolamine
2. ethanolamine phosphoglyceride
3. The polar portion of the phosphoglyceride is attracted to water, which makes this type of lipid more soluble in water than other lipids.

17.6 Sphingolipids

- In sphingolipids, the alcohol sphingosine forms an ester bond with one fatty acid and the phosphate-amino alcohol group.
- In glycosphingolipids, sphingosine is bonded to fatty acids and one or more monosaccharides.

◆ Learning Exercise 17.6

Match the following statements with one of the following types of phospholipids:

a. glycerophospholipid   **b.** sphingolipid   **c.** cerebroside   **d.** ganglioside

1. _____ contains sphingosine, a fatty acid and two or more monosaccharides

2. _____ contains sphingosine, a fatty acid, phosphate and an amino alcohol

3. _____ contains sphingosine, a fatty acid, and one monosaccharide

4. _____ contains glycerol, two fatty acids, phosphate, and an amino alcohol

Answers   **1.** d   **2.** b   **3.** c   **4.** a

17.7 Steroids: Cholesterol, Bile Salts, and Steroid Hormones

- Steroids are lipids containing the steroid nucleus, which is a fused structure of four rings.
- Steroids include cholesterol, bile salts, and vitamin D.
- The steroid hormones are closely related in structure to cholesterol and depend on cholesterol for their synthesis. The sex hormones such as estrogen and testosterone are responsible for sexual characteristics and reproduction. The adrenal corticosteroids such as aldosterone and cortisone regulate water balance and glucose levels in the cells.

◆ Learning Exercise 17.7A

1. Write the structure of the steroid nucleus.　　　2. Write the structure of cholesterol.

Answers

1.　

2.　

◆ Learning Exercise 17.7B

Identify one of these compounds with the following statements:

a. estrogen　　　b. testosterone　　　c. cortisone　　　d. aldosterone　　　e. bile salts

1. _____ increases the blood level of glucose
2. _____ increase the reabsorption of Na^+ in the blood
3. _____ stimulates development of secondary sex characteristics in females
4. _____ stimulates reabsorption of water by the kidneys
5. _____ stimulates the secondary sex characteristics in males
6. _____ secreted from the gallbladder into the small intestine to emulsify fats in the diet

Answers　　　1. c　　　2. d　　　3. a
　　　　　　　4. d　　　5. b　　　6. e

17.8 Cell Membranes

- Cell membranes surround all of our cells and separate the cellular contents from the external liquid environment.
- A cell membrane is a lipid bilayer composed of two rows of phospholipids such that the nonpolar hydrocarbon tails are in the center and the polar sections are aligned along the outside.
- The inner portion of the lipid bilayer consists of nonpolar chains of the fatty acids, with the polar heads at the outer and inner surfaces.
- Molecules of cholesterol, proteins, glycolipids, and glycoproteins are embedded in the lipid bilayer.

◆ Learning Exercise 17.8

a. What is the function of the lipid bilayer in cell membranes?

b. What type of lipid makes up the lipid bilayer?

c. What is the general arrangement of the lipids in a lipid bilayer?

d. What are the functions of the proteins embedded in the lipid bilayer?

Answers
a. The lipid bilayer separates the contents of a cell from the surrounding aqueous environment.
b. The lipid bilayer is composed of phospholipids.
c. The nonpolar hydrocarbon tails are in the center of the bilayer, whereas the polar sections are aligned along the outside of the bilayer.
d. Some proteins provide channels for electrolytes and water to flow in and out of the cell. Other proteins act as receptors for chemicals such as hormones, neurotransmitters, and antibiotics.

Checklist for Chapter 17

You are ready to take the practice test for chapter 17. Be sure that you have accomplished the following learning goals for this chapter. If you are not sure, review the section listed at the end of the goal. Then apply your new skills and understanding to the practice test. Good luck.

After studying chapter 17, I can successfully:

_____ Describe the classes of lipids (17.1).

_____ Identify a fatty acid as saturated or unsaturated (17.2).

_____ Write the structural formula of a wax or triacylglycerol produced by the reaction of a fatty acids and an alcohol or glycerol (17.3).

_____ Draw the structure of the product from the reaction of a triacylglycerol with hydrogen, an acid or base, or an oxidizing agent (17.4).

_____ Describe the components of glycerolphospholipids (17.5).

_____ Describe the components of sphingolipids and glycosphingolipids (17.6).

_____ Describe the structure of a steroid and cholesterol (17.7).

_____ Describe the function of the lipid bilayer in cell membranes (17.8).

Practice Test for Chapter 17

1. An ester of a fatty acid is called a
   A. carbohydrate   **B.** lipid   **C.** protein   **D.** oxyacid   **E.** soap

2. A fatty acid that is unsaturated is usually
   A. from animal sources and liquid at room temperature
   B. from animal sources and solid at room temperature
   C. from vegetable sources and liquid at room temperature
   D. from vegetable sources and solid at room temperature
   E. from both vegetable and animal sources and solid at room temperature

3. $CH_3-(CH_2)_{16}-\overset{\overset{\displaystyle O}{\|}}{C}-OH$ is a
   A. unsaturated fatty acid   **B.** saturated fatty acid   **C.** wax
   D. triacylglycerol   **E.** sphingolipid

For questions 4–7, consider the following compound:

$$CH_2-O-\overset{\overset{\displaystyle O}{\|}}{C}-(CH_2)_{16}-CH_3$$
$$HC-O-\overset{\overset{\displaystyle O}{\|}}{C}-(CH_2)_{16}-CH_3$$
$$CH_2-O-\overset{\overset{\displaystyle O}{\|}}{C}-(CH_2)_{16}-CH_3$$

4. This compound belongs in the family called
A. wax B. triacylglycerol C. phosphoglyceride
D. sphingolipid E. steroid

5. The molecule shown above was formed by
A. esterification B. hydrolysis (acid) C. saponification
D. emulsification E. oxidation

6. If this molecule were reacted with strong base such as NaOH, the products would be
A. glycerol and fatty acids B. glycerol and water
C. glycerol and soap D. an ester and salts of fatty acids
E. an ester and fatty acids

7. The compound would be expected to be
A. saturated and a solid at room temperature
B. saturated and a liquid at room temperature
C. unsaturated and a solid at room temperature
D. unsaturated and a liquid at room temperature
E. supersaturated and a liquid at room temperature

8. Which are found in glycerolphospholipids?
A. fatty acids B. glycerol C. a nitrogen compound
D. phosphate E. all of these

For questions 9 and 10, consider the following reaction:

Triacylglycerol + 3NaOH → 3 sodium salts of fatty acids and glycerol

9. The reaction of a triacylglycerol with a strong base such as NaOH is called
A. esterification B. lipogenesis C. hydrolysis
D. saponification E. β-oxidation

10. What is another name for the sodium salts of the fatty acids?
A. margarines B. fat substitutes C. soaps
D. perfumes E. vitamins

For questions 11–16, consider the following phosphoglyceride:

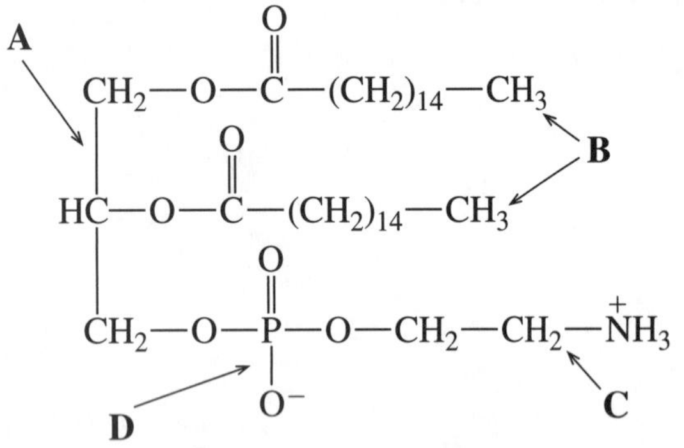

Match the labels with the following:

11. _____ the glycerol portion **12.** _____ the phosphate portion **13.** _____ the amino alcohol

14. _____ the polar region **15.** _____ the nonpolar region

16. Type of phospholipid
  A. choline   **B.** cephalin   **C.** sphingomyelin
  D. glycolipid   **E.** cerebroside

Classify the following lipids as
  A. wax   **B.** triacylglycerol   **C.** phosphoglyceride
  D. steroid   **E.** fatty acid

17. _____ cholesterol

18. _____ $CH_3-(CH_2)_{14}-\overset{\overset{\displaystyle O}{\|}}{C}-OH$

19. _____ $CH_3-(CH_2)_{14}-\overset{\overset{\displaystyle O}{\|}}{C}-O-(CH_2)_{30}-CH_3$

20. _____ an ester of glycerol with three palmitic acids

Select answers from the following:
  A. testosterone   **B.** estrogen   **C.** prednisone
  D. cortisone   **E.** aldosterone

21. _____ stimulates the female sexual characteristics

22. _____ increases the retention of water by the kidneys

23. _____ stimulates the male sexual characteristics

24. _____ increases the blood glucose level

25. _____ used medically to reduce inflammation and treat asthma

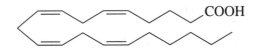

26. This compound is a
  A. cholesterol   **B.** sphingosine   **C.** prostaglandin
  D. glycerosphingolipid **E.** steroid

27. The lipid bilayer of a cell is composed of
  A. cholesterol   **B.** glycerophospholipids **C.** proteins
  D. glycosphingolipids **E.** all of these

28. The type of transport that carries chloride ions through integral proteins in the cell membrane is
  A. passive transport **B.** active transport **C.** diffusion
  D. facilitated transport **E.** all of these

29. The movement of small molecules through a cell membrane from a higher concentration to a lower concentration is
  A. passive transport **B.** active transport **C.** diffusion
  D. facilitated transport **E.** A and C

30. The type of lipoprotein that transport cholesterol to the liver for elimination is called
  A. chylomicron   **B.** high-density lipoprotein   **C.** low-density lipoprotein
  D. very-low-density lipoprotein   **E.** all of these

Answers to the Practice Test

1. B	**2.** C	**3.** B	**4.** B	**5.** A
6. C	**7.** A	**8.** E	**9.** D	**10.** C
11. A	**12.** D	**13.** C	**14.** C, D	**15.** B
16. B	**17.** D	**18.** E	**19.** A	**20.** B
21. B	**22.** E	**23.** A	**24.** D	**25.** C
21. C	**22.** E	**23.** D	**24.** E	**25.** B

Answers and Solutions to Selected Text Problems

17.1 Lipids provide energy, protection, and insulation for the organs in the body. Lipids are also an important component of cell membranes.

17.3 Since lipids are not soluble in water, they are nonpolar molecules.

17.5 All fatty acids contain a long chain of carbon atoms with a carboxylic acid group. Saturated fats contain only carbon-to-carbon single bonds; unsaturated fats contain one or more double bonds.

17.7 **a.** palmitic acid

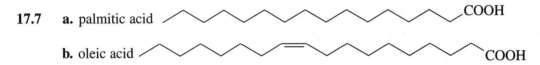

b. oleic acid

17.9 **a.** Lauric acid has only carbon-carbon single bonds; it is saturated.
b. Linolenic has three carbon-carbon double bonds; it is unsaturated.
c. Palmitoleic has one carbon-carbon double bond; it is unsaturated.
d. Stearic acid has only carbon-carbon single bonds; it is saturated.

17.11 In cis double bonds, the alkyl groups are on the same side of the double bond, whereas in trans fatty acids, the alkyl groups are on opposite sides.

17.13 In an omega-3 fatty acid, the first double bond occurs at carbon 3 counting from the methyl. In an omega-6 fatty acid, the first double bond occurs at carbon 6.

17.15 Arachidonic acid contains four double bonds and no side groups. In PGE_2, a part of the chain forms cyclopentane and there are hydroxyl and ketone functional groups.

17.17 Prostaglandins affect blood pressure, stimulate contraction, and relaxation of smooth muscle.

17.19 Palmitic acid is the 16-carbon saturated fatty acid. $CH_3-(CH_2)_{14}-\overset{\displaystyle O}{\overset{\displaystyle \|}{C}}-O-(CH_2)_{29}-CH_3$

17.21 Fats are composed of fatty acids and glycerol. In this case, the fatty acid is stearic acid, an 18-carbon saturated fatty acid.

$$
\begin{array}{l}
CH_2-O-\overset{\displaystyle O}{\overset{\displaystyle \|}{C}}-(CH_2)_{16}-CH_3 \\
\ \ | \qquad\quad \overset{\displaystyle O}{\overset{\displaystyle \|}{}} \\
HC-O-\overset{\displaystyle }{C}-(CH_2)_{16}-CH_3 \\
\ \ | \qquad\quad \overset{\displaystyle O}{\overset{\displaystyle \|}{}} \\
CH_2-O-\overset{\displaystyle }{C}-(CH_2)_{16}-CH_3
\end{array}
$$

17.23 Tripalmitin has three palmitic acids (16 carbon saturated fatty acid) forming ester bonds with glycerol.

$$CH_2-O-\overset{\overset{\displaystyle O}{\|}}{C}-(CH_2)_{14}CH_3$$

$$HC-O-\overset{\overset{\displaystyle O}{\|}}{C}-(CH_2)_{14}-CH_3$$

$$CH_2-O-\overset{\overset{\displaystyle O}{\|}}{C}-(CH_2)_{14}-CH_3$$

17.25 Safflower oil contains fatty acids with two or three double bonds; olive oil contains a large amount of oleic acid, which has a single (monounsaturated) double bond.

17.27 Although coconut oil comes from a vegetable source, it has large amounts of saturated fatty acids and small amounts of unsaturated fatty acids. Since coconut oil contains the same kinds of fatty acids as animal fat, coconut oil has a melting point similar to the melting point of animal fats.

17.29

$$CH_2-O-\overset{\overset{\displaystyle O}{\|}}{C}-(CH_2)_7-CH{=}CH-(CH_2)_7-CH_3$$

$$HC-O-\overset{\overset{\displaystyle O}{\|}}{C}-(CH_2)_7-CH{=}CH-(CH_2)_7-CH_3 + 3H_2 \xrightarrow{Ni}$$

$$CH_2-O-\overset{\overset{\displaystyle O}{\|}}{C}-(CH_2)_7-CH{=}CH-(CH_2)_7-CH_3$$

$$CH_2-O-\overset{\overset{\displaystyle O}{\|}}{C}-(CH_2)_{16}-CH_3$$

$$HC-O-\overset{\overset{\displaystyle O}{\|}}{C}-(CH_2)_{16}-CH_3$$

$$CH_2-O-\overset{\overset{\displaystyle O}{\|}}{C}-(CH_2)_{16}-CH_3$$

17.31 **a.** Partial hydrogenation means that some of the double bonds in the unsaturated fatty acids have been converted to single bonds.
b. Since the margarine has more saturated fatty acids than the original vegetable oil, the fatty acid interact more strongly and remain solid at higher temperatures.

17.33 Acid hydrolysis of a fat gives glycerol and the fatty acids. Basic hydrolysis (saponification) of fat gives glycerol and the salts of the fatty acids.

a.

$$CH_2-O-\overset{\overset{\displaystyle O}{\|}}{C}-(CH_2)_{12}-CH_3$$

$$CH-O-\overset{\overset{\displaystyle O}{\|}}{C}-(CH_2)_{12}-CH_3 \quad 3H_2O \xrightarrow{H^+} \quad CHOH + 3\ HO-\overset{\overset{\displaystyle O}{\|}}{C}-(CH_2)_{12}-CH_3$$

$$CH_2-O-\overset{\overset{\displaystyle O}{\|}}{C}-(CH_2)_{12}-CH_3$$

with CH_2OH above and CH_2OH below the $CHOH$.

b.

$$CH_2-O-\overset{\overset{\displaystyle O}{\|}}{C}-(CH_2)_{12}-CH_3$$

$$CH-O-\overset{\overset{\displaystyle O}{\|}}{C}-(CH_2)_{12}-CH_3 \quad 3NAOH \longrightarrow \quad CHOH + 3Na^{+-}O-\overset{\overset{\displaystyle O}{\|}}{C}-(CH_2)_{12}-CH_3$$

$$CH_2-O-\overset{\overset{\displaystyle O}{\|}}{C}-(CH_2)_{12}-CH_3$$

with CH_2OH above and CH_2OH below the $CHOH$.

17.35 A triacylglycerol is a combination of three fatty acids bonded to glycerol by ester bonds. Olestra is sucrose bonded to six to eight fatty acids by ester bonds. Olestra cannot be digested because digestive enzymes cannot break down the molecule.

17.37

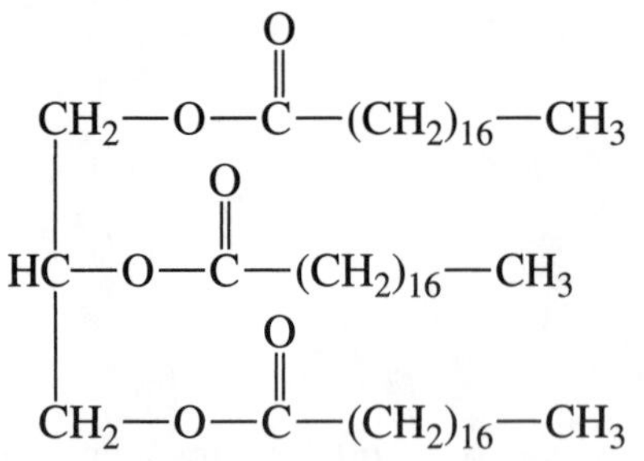

$$CH_2-O-\overset{\overset{\displaystyle O}{\|}}{C}-(CH_2)_{16}-CH_3$$

$$HC-O-\overset{\overset{\displaystyle O}{\|}}{C}-(CH_2)_{16}-CH_3$$

$$CH_2-O-\overset{\overset{\displaystyle O}{\|}}{C}-(CH_2)_{16}-CH_3$$

17.39 A triacylglycerol consists of glycerol and three fatty acids. A glycerophospholipid consists of glycerol, two fatty acids, a phosphate group, and an amino alcohol.

17.41

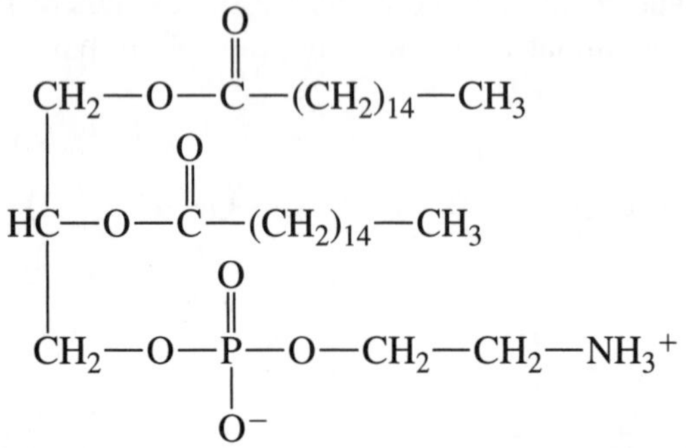

$$CH_2-O-\overset{\overset{\displaystyle O}{\|}}{C}-(CH_2)_{14}-CH_3$$

$$HC-O-\overset{\overset{\displaystyle O}{\|}}{C}-(CH_2)_{14}-CH_3$$

$$CH_2-O-\overset{\overset{\displaystyle O}{\|}}{\underset{\underset{\displaystyle O^-}{|}}{P}}-O-CH_2-CH_2-NH_3^+$$

This is a cephalin.

17.43 This phospholipid is a cephalin. It contains glycerol, oleic acid, stearic acid, phosphate, and ethanolamine.

17.45 A glycerophospholipid consists of glycerol, two fatty acids, a phosphate group, and an amino alcohol. A sphingolipid contains the amino alcohol sphingosine instead of glycerol.

17.47

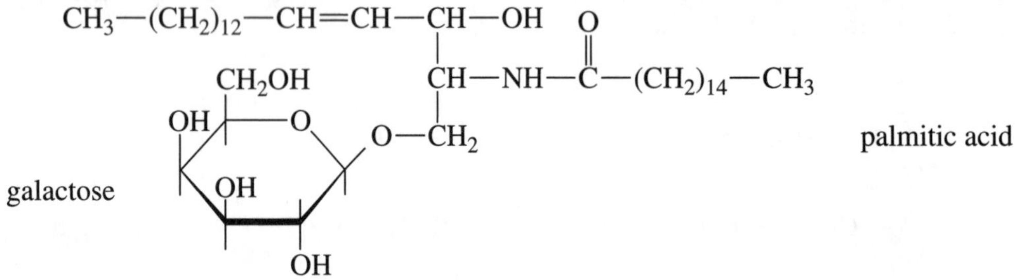

$$CH_3-(CH_2)_{12}-CH=CH-CH-OH$$

galactose — palmitic acid

17.49

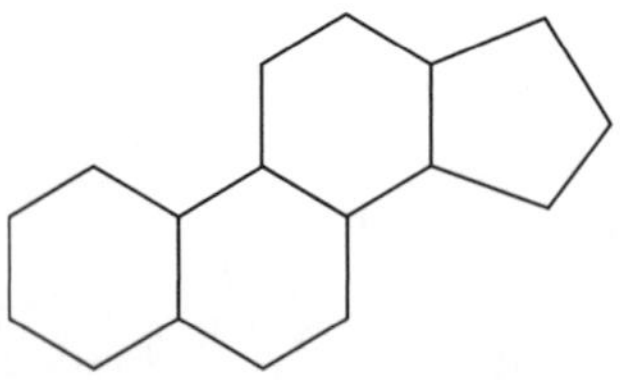

17.51 Bile salts emulsify fat globules, which makes the fat easier to digest by lipases.

17.53 Lipoproteins are large, spherically shaped molecules that transport lipids in the bloodstream. They consist of an outer layer of phospholipids and proteins surrounding an inner core of hundreds of nonpolar lipids and cholesterol esters.

17.55 Chylomicrons have a lower density than VLDLs. They pick up triacylglycerols from the intestine, whereas VLDLs transport triacylglycerols synthesized in the liver.

17.57 "Bad" cholesterol is the cholesterol carried by LDLs to the tissues, where it can form deposits called plaque, which can narrow the arteries.

17.59 Both estradiol and testosterone contain the steroid nucleus and a hydroxyl group, but testosterone has a ketone group, a double bond, and an extra methyl group. Estradiol has a benzene ring and a second hydroxyl group.

17.61 **d.** Testosterone is a male sex hormone.

17.63 Cell membranes contain a number of lipids: phospholipids that contain fatty acids with cis double bonds, glycolipids, which are on the outside of the cell membrane and in animal membranes, and cholesterol.

17.65 The function of the lipid bilayer in the plasma membrane is to keep the cell contents separated from the outside environment and to allow the cell to regulate the movement of substances into and out of the cell.

17.67 The peripheral proteins in the membrane emerge on the inner or outer surface only, whereas the integral proteins extend through the membrane to both surfaces.

17.69 The carbohydrates glycoproteins and glycolipids on the surface of cells act as receptors for cell recognition and chemical messengers such as neurotransmitters.

17.71 Substances move through cell membrane by simple transport, facilitated transport, and active transport.

17.73

$$CH_2-O-\overset{\overset{\displaystyle O}{\|}}{C}-(CH_2)_{14}-CH_3$$
$$H-\overset{|}{\underset{|}{C}}-O-\overset{\overset{\displaystyle O}{\|}}{C}-(CH_2)_{14}-CH_3 \qquad \text{glyceryl tripalmitate}$$
$$CH_2-O-\overset{\overset{\displaystyle O}{\|}}{C}-(CH_2)_{14}-CH_3$$

17.75 a.

$$CH_2-O-\overset{\overset{\displaystyle O}{\|}}{C}-(CH_2)_7-CH{=}CH-CH_2-CH{=}CH-(CH_2)_4-CH_3$$
$$H-\overset{|}{\underset{|}{C}}-O-\overset{\overset{\displaystyle O}{\|}}{C}-(CH_2)_7-CH{=}CH-(CH_2)_7-CH_3$$
$$CH_2-O-\overset{\overset{\displaystyle O}{\|}}{C}-(CH_2)_7-CH{=}CH-CH_2-CH{=}CH-(CH_2)_4-CH_3$$

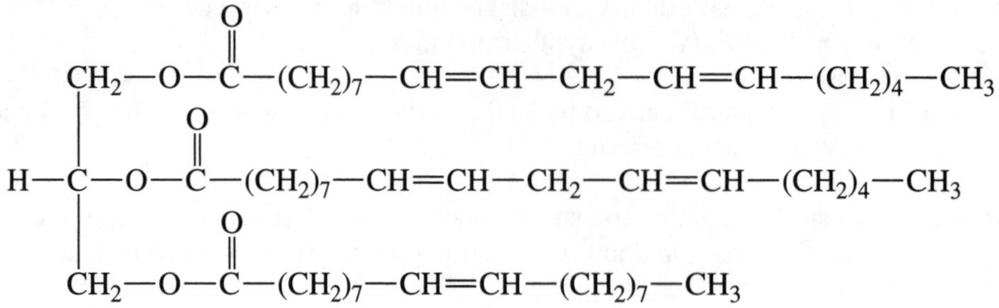

$$CH_2-O-\overset{\overset{\displaystyle O}{\parallel}}{C}-(CH_2)_7-CH=CH-CH_2-CH=CH-(CH_2)_4-CH_3$$

$$H-\overset{|}{C}-O-\overset{\overset{\displaystyle O}{\parallel}}{C}-(CH_2)_7-CH=CH-CH_2-CH=CH-(CH_2)_4-CH_3$$

$$CH_2-O-\overset{\overset{\displaystyle O}{\parallel}}{C}-(CH_2)_7-CH=CH-(CH_2)_7-CH_3$$

b.

$$CH_2-O-\overset{\overset{\displaystyle O}{\parallel}}{C}-(CH_2)_7-CH=CH-CH_2-CH=CH-(CH_2)_4-CH_3$$

$$H-\overset{|}{C}-O-\overset{\overset{\displaystyle O}{\parallel}}{C}-(CH_2)_7-CH=CH-(CH_2)_7-CH_3$$

$$CH_2-O-\overset{\overset{\displaystyle O}{\parallel}}{C}-(CH_2)_7-CH=CH-CH_2-CH=CH-(CH_2)_4-CH_3$$

$$+\ 3H_2 \xrightarrow{\ Ni\ }$$

$$CH_2-O-\overset{\overset{\displaystyle O}{\parallel}}{C}-(CH_2)_{16}-CH_3$$

$$CH-O-\overset{\overset{\displaystyle O}{\parallel}}{C}-(CH_2)_{16}-CH_3$$

$$CH_2-O-\overset{\overset{\displaystyle O}{\parallel}}{C}-(CH_2)_{16}-CH_3$$

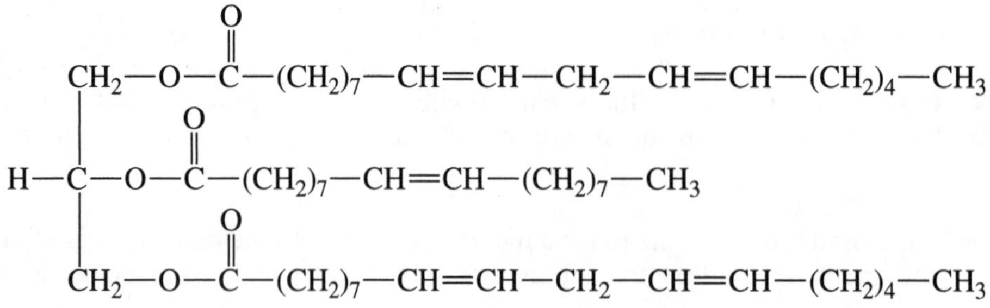

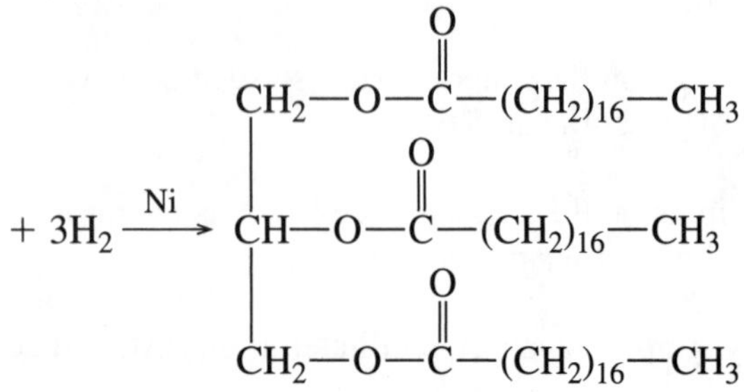

17.77 Beeswax and carnauba are waxes. Vegetable oil and capric triacylglycerol are triacylglycerols.

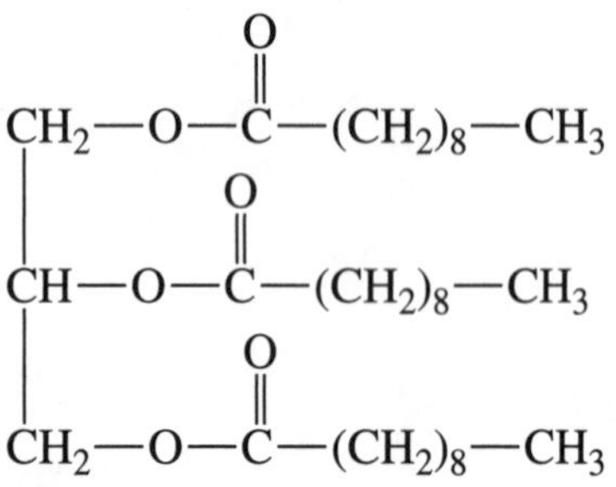

$$CH_2-O-\overset{\overset{\displaystyle O}{\parallel}}{C}-(CH_2)_8-CH_3$$

$$CH-O-\overset{\overset{\displaystyle O}{\parallel}}{C}-(CH_2)_8-CH_3 \qquad \text{capric triacylglycerol}$$

$$CH_2-O-\overset{\overset{\displaystyle O}{\parallel}}{C}-(CH_2)_8-CH_3$$

17.79 **a.** A typical monounsaturated fatty acid has a cis double bond.
  b. A trans fatty acid has a trans double bond with the alkyl groups on opposite sides of the double bond.

  c.

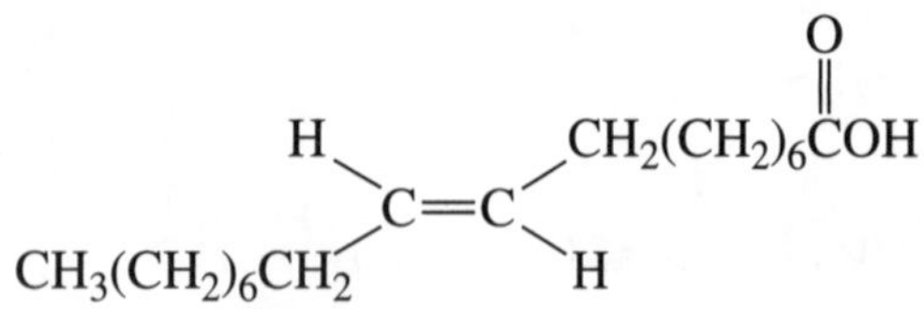

$$\begin{array}{ccc} H & & CH_2(CH_2)_6\overset{\overset{\displaystyle O}{\parallel}}{C}OH \\ \diagdown & & \diagup \\ & C=C & \\ \diagup & & \diagdown \\ CH_3(CH_2)_6CH_2 & & H \end{array}$$

17.81

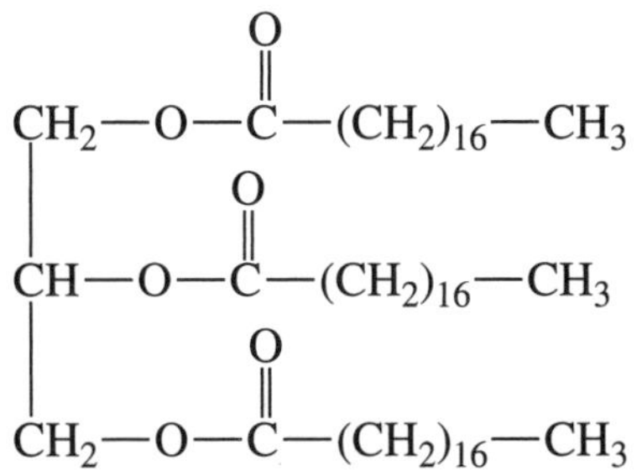

$$CH_2-O-\overset{\overset{\displaystyle O}{\|}}{C}-(CH_2)_{16}-CH_3$$

$$CH-O-\overset{\overset{\displaystyle O}{\|}}{C}-(CH_2)_{16}-CH_3 \qquad \text{glyceryl tristearate}$$

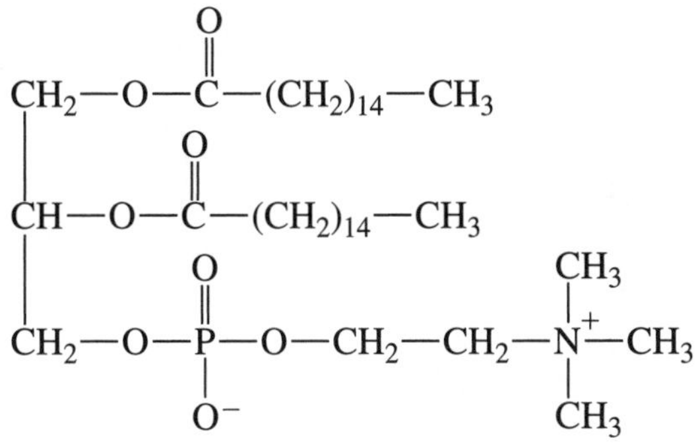

$$CH_2-O-\overset{\overset{\displaystyle O}{\|}}{C}-(CH_2)_{16}-CH_3$$

$$CH_2-O-\overset{\overset{\displaystyle O}{\|}}{C}-(CH_2)_{14}-CH_3$$

$$CH-O-\overset{\overset{\displaystyle O}{\|}}{C}-(CH_2)_{14}-CH_3 \qquad \text{lecithin}$$

$$CH_2-O-\overset{\overset{\displaystyle O}{\|}}{\underset{\underset{\displaystyle O^-}{|}}{P}}-O-CH_2-CH_2-\overset{\overset{\displaystyle CH_3}{|}}{\underset{\underset{\displaystyle CH_3}{|}}{N^+}}-CH_3$$

17.83 Stearic acid (**l**) is a fatty acid. Sodium stearate (**e**) is soap. Glyceryl tripalmitate (**d**), safflower oil (**f**), whale blubber (**h**), and adipose tissue (**i**) are triacylglycerols. Beeswax (**a**) is a wax. Lecithin (**c**) is a glycerophospholipid. Sphingomyelin (**g**) is a sphingolipid. Cholesterol (**b**), progesterone (**j**), and cortisone (**k**) are steroids.

17.85 **a.** 5   **b.** 1, 2, 3, 4   **c.** 2
        d. 1, 2   **e.** 1, 2, 3, 4   **f.** 2, 3, 4, 6

17.87 **a.** 4   **b.** 3   **c.** 1
        d. 4   **e.** 4   **f.** 3
        g. 2   **h.** 1

17.89

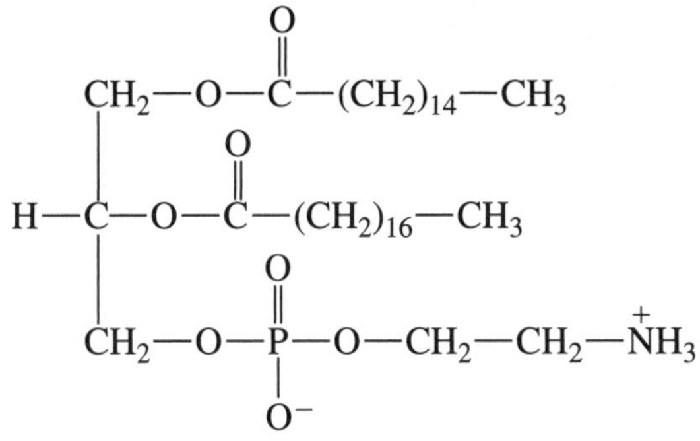

$$CH_2-O-\overset{\overset{\displaystyle O}{\|}}{C}-(CH_2)_{14}-CH_3$$

$$H-\overset{}{C}-O-\overset{\overset{\displaystyle O}{\|}}{C}-(CH_2)_{16}-CH_3$$

$$CH_2-O-\overset{\overset{\displaystyle O}{\|}}{\underset{\underset{\displaystyle O^-}{|}}{P}}-O-CH_2-CH_2-\overset{+}{N}H_3$$

17.91 **a.** Adding NaOH would hydrolyze the tristearate lipid, breaking it up to wash down the drain.

b.

$$CH_2-O-\overset{\overset{\displaystyle O}{\|}}{C}-(CH_2)_{16}-CH_3$$

$$H-\overset{|}{\underset{|}{C}}-O-\overset{\overset{\displaystyle O}{\|}}{C}-(CH_2)_{16}-CH_3 \quad + 3\,NaOH \longrightarrow$$

$$CH_2-O-\overset{\overset{\displaystyle O}{\|}}{C}-(CH_2)_{16}-CH_3$$

$$CH_2-OH$$

$$H-\overset{|}{\underset{|}{C}}-OH \quad + 3Na^{+}{}^{-}O-\overset{\overset{\displaystyle O}{\|}}{C}-(CH_2)_{16}-CH_3$$

$$CH_2-OH$$

glycerol   salts of stearic acid

18

Amines and Amides

Study Goals

- Name and write structural formulas of amines and amides.
- Describe the ionization of amines in water.
- Describe the boiling points of amines and amides compared with alkanes and alcohols.
- Describe the solubility of amines and amides in water.
- Describe the properties of amine salts.
- Write equations for the neutralization and amidation of amines.
- Describe acid and base hydrolysis of amides.

Think About It

1. Fish smell "fishy," but lemon juice removes the "fishy" odor. Why?

2. What functional groups are often found in tranquilizers and hallucinogens?

3. What is indicated by the codes such as 1-PETE on the bottom of plastic bottles and containers?

Key Terms

Match the key term with the correct statement shown below.

a. heterocyclic amine   **b.** amidation   **c.** amine   **d.** amide   **e.** alkaloid

1. _____A nitrogen-containing compound that is active physiologically

2. _____A cyclic organic compound that contains one or more nitrogen atoms

3. _____The reaction of a carboxylic acid and an amine

4. _____The hydrolysis of this compound produces a carboxylic acid and an amine

5. _____An organic compound that contains an amino group

Answers   **1.** e   **2.** a   **3.** b   **4.** d   **5.** c

18.1 Amines

- Amines are derivative of ammonia (NH_3), in which alkyl or aromatic groups replace one or more hydrogen atoms.
- Amines are classified as primary, secondary, or tertiary when the nitrogen atom is bonded to one, two, or three alkyl or aromatic groups.

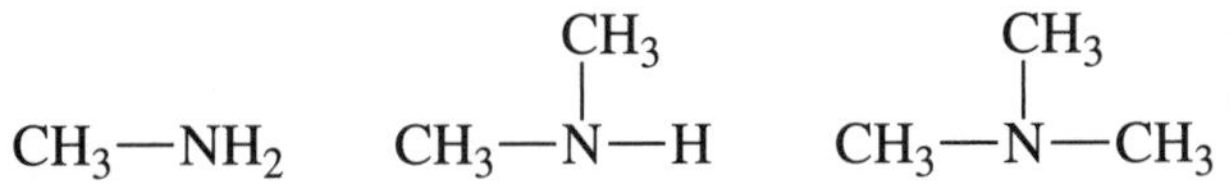

$$CH_3-NH_2 \qquad \underset{\text{secondary (2°)}}{CH_3-\overset{\displaystyle CH_3}{\overset{|}{N}}-H} \qquad \underset{\text{tertiary (3°)}}{CH_3-\overset{\displaystyle CH_3}{\overset{|}{N}}-CH_3}$$
$$\text{primary (1°)}$$

- Amines are usually named by common names in which the names of the alkyl group are listed alphabetically preceding the suffix *amine*.
- In the IUPAC system, the *e* of the alkane name of the main chain is replaced by amine. Alkyl groups attached to the *N* atom are named with the prefix *N*-.
- When another function group takes priority, —NH₂ is named as an amino substituent.
- The amine of benzene is named aniline.

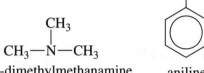

CH₃—NH₂	CH₃—NH—CH₃	CH₃—N—CH₃ with CH₃	aniline
IUPAC: methanamine	*N*-methylmethanamine	*N,N*,-dimethylmethanamine	
Common: methylamine	dimethylamine	trimethylamine	

- Many amines, which are prevalent in synthetic and naturally occurring compounds, have physiological activity.

◆ Learning Exercise 18.1A

Classify each of the following as a primary (1°), secondary (2°), or tertiary (3°) amine:

1. _____ CH₃—N(H)—CH₂CH₃

2. _____ (cyclohexane with NH₂)

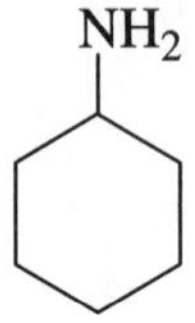

3. _____ CH₃—CH(NH₂)—C(=O)—OH

4. _____ CH₃—CH₂—N(CH₃)—CH₃

5. _____ CH₃—CH₂—CH₂—CH₂—N(H)—CH₂—CH₃

6. _____ (benzene ring with NH₂ and CH₃)

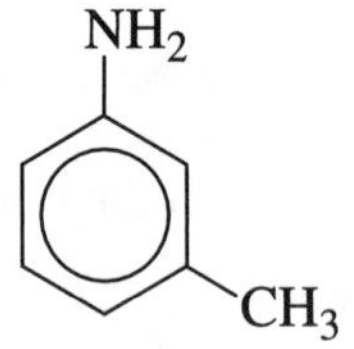

Answers

1. 2°	2. 1°
3. 1°	4. 3°
5. 2°	6. 1°

◆ Learning Exercise 18.1B

Name each of the amines in problem 18.1A.

1. _____   2. _____

3. _____   4. _____

5. _____   6. _____

Answers
1. ethylmethylamine; *N*-methylethanamine
2. cyclohexanamine
3. 2-aminopropanoic acid; β-aminopropionic acid
4. ethyldimethylamine; *N,N*-dimethylethanamine
5. butylethylamine; *N*-ethyl-1-butanamine
6. 3-methylaniline; *m*-methylaniline

◆ Learning Exercise 18.1C

Write the structural formulas of the following amines:

1. 2-propanamine

2. *N*-ethyl-*N*-methyl-1-aminobutane

3. 3-bromoaniline

4. *N*-methylaniline

Answers

1. $CH_3—CH(NH_2)—CH_3$

2. $CH_3—CH_2—N(CH_3)—CH_2—CH_2—CH_2—CH_3$

3. 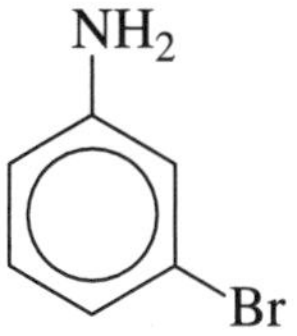

4. 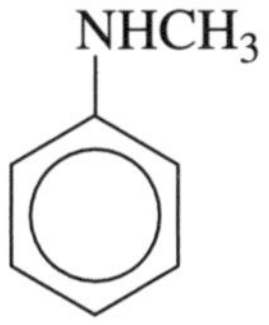

18.2 Properties of Amines

- The N—H bonds in primary and secondary amines form hydrogen bonds.
- Amines have higher boiling points than hydrocarbons but lower than alcohols of similar mass because the N atom is not as electronegative as the O atoms in alcohols.
- Hydrogen bonding allows amines with up to six carbon atoms to be soluble in water.
- In water, amines act as weak bases by accepting protons from water to produce ammonium and hydroxide ions.
- $CH_3—NH_2 + H_2O \rightleftarrows CH_3—NH_3^+ + OH^-$
  methylamine *methylammonium hydroxide*
- Strong acids neutralize amines to yield ammonium salts.
- $CH_3—NH_2 + HCl \rightarrow CH_3—NH_3^+ + Cl^-$
  methylamine *methylammonium chloride*
- When a carboxylic acid reacts with ammonia or an amine, an amide is produced.

$$CH_3—\overset{\overset{O}{\|}}{C}—OH + NH_3 \xrightarrow{\text{Heat}} CH_3—\overset{\overset{O}{\|}}{C}—NH_2 + H_2O$$

$$CH_3—\overset{\overset{O}{\|}}{C}—OH + NH_2—CH_3 \xrightarrow{\text{Heat}} CH_3—\overset{\overset{O}{\|}}{C}—NH—CH_3 + H_2O$$

◆ **Learning Exercise 18.2A**

Indicate the compound in each pair that has the higher boiling point.

1. CH_3-NH_2 and CH_3-OH _____

2. $CH_3-CH_2-CH_2$ and $CH_3-CH_2-NH_2$ _____

3. $CH_3-CH_2-NH_2$ and $CH_3-CH_2-CH_2-NH_2$ _____

4. $CH_3-\overset{\overset{\displaystyle H}{|}}{N}-CH_3$ and $CH_3-CH_2-NH_2$ _____

Answers   **1.** CH_3-OH **2.** $CH_3-CH_2-NH_2$

                 3. $CH_3-CH_2-CH_2-NH_2$ **4.** $CH_3-CH_2-NH_2$

◆ **Learning Exercise 18.2B**

Write the products of the following reactions:

1. $CH_3-CH_2-NH_2 + H_2O \rightleftharpoons$

2. $CH_3-CH_2-CH_2-NH_2 + HCl \rightarrow$

3. $CH_3CH_2-NH-CH_3 + HCl \rightarrow$

4. 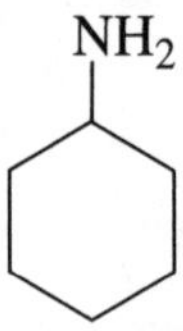
$+ \ HBr \rightarrow$

5. 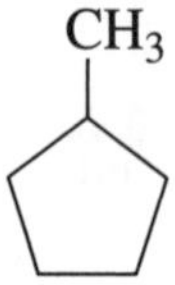
$+ \ H_2O \ \underset{\rightarrow}{\leftarrow}$

6. $CH_3-CH_2-NH_3{}^+Cl^- + NaOH \rightarrow$

Answers

1. $CH_3-CH_2-NH_3{}^+OH^-$ **2.** $CH_3-CH_2-CH_2-NH_3{}^+Cl^-$ **3.** $CH_3-CH_2-\overset{+}{N}H_2-CH_3Cl^-$

4.

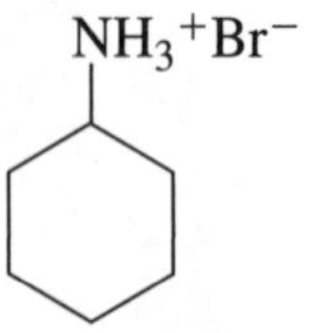

5.

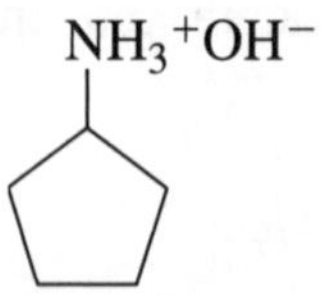

6. $CH_3-CH_2-NH_2 + NaCl + H_2O$

◆ **Learning Exercise 18.2C**

Write the structural formulas of the amides formed in each of the following reactions:

1. $CH_3-CH_2-\overset{\displaystyle O}{\overset{\|}{C}}-OH + NH_3 \xrightarrow{\text{heat}}$

2. 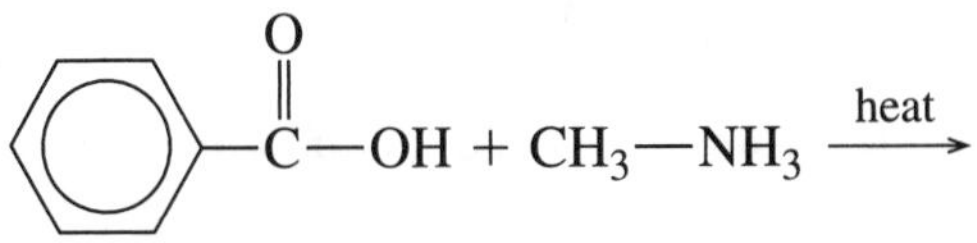 ⟨benzene ring⟩$-\overset{\displaystyle O}{\overset{\|}{C}}-OH + CH_3-NH_3 \xrightarrow{\text{heat}}$

3. $CH_3-\overset{\displaystyle O}{\overset{\|}{C}}-OH + \overset{\displaystyle CH_3}{\overset{|}{NH}}-CH_3 \xrightarrow{\text{heat}}$

Answers   1. $CH_3-CH_2-\overset{\displaystyle O}{\overset{\|}{C}}-NH_2$ 2. 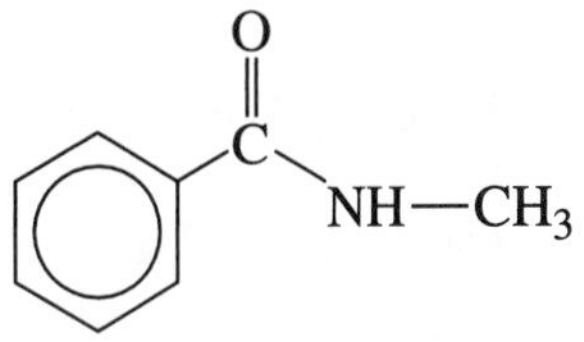 ⟨benzene ring⟩$-\overset{\displaystyle O}{\overset{\|}{C}}-NH-CH_3$

3. $CH_3-\overset{\displaystyle O}{\overset{\|}{C}}-\overset{\displaystyle CH_3}{\overset{|}{N}}-CH_3$

18.3 Heterocyclic Amines and Alkaloids

- A heterocyclic amine is a cyclic compound containing one or more nitrogen atoms in the ring.
- Most heterocyclic amines contain five or six atoms.
- An alkaloid is a physiologically active amine obtained from plants.

pyrrolidine   pyrrole   peperidine   pyridine

◆ **Learning Exercise 18.3**

Match each of the following heterocyclic structures with the correct name.

a. 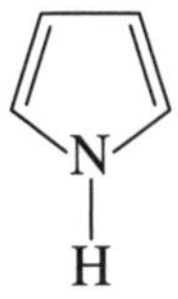   b. 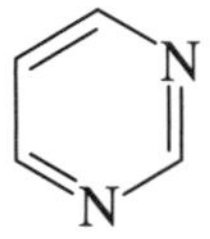   c.

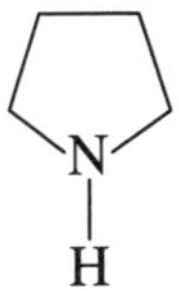

d. 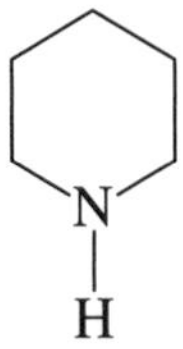   e. 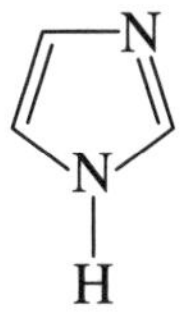   f.

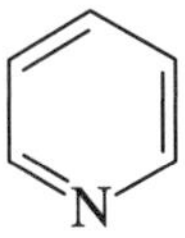

1. ____pyrrolidine   2. ____imidazole   3. ____pyridine

4. ____pyrrole   5. ____pyrimidine   6. ____piperidine

18.4 Amides

- Amides are derivatives of carboxylic acids in which an amine group replaces the —OH group in the acid.
- Amides are named by replacing the *ic acid* or *oic acid* ending by *amide*. When an alkyl group is attached to the *N* atom, it is listed as *N*-alkyl.

$$CH_3-\overset{\displaystyle O}{\overset{\displaystyle \|}{C}}-NH_2 \quad \text{ethanamide (acetamide)}$$

$$CH_3-\overset{\displaystyle O}{\overset{\displaystyle \|}{C}}-NH-CH_3 \quad N\text{-methylethanamide; } (N\text{-methylacetamide})$$

◆ **Learning Exercise 18.4A**

Name the following amides:

1. $CH_3-CH_2-\overset{\displaystyle O}{\overset{\displaystyle \|}{C}}-NH_2$ _____

2.   _____

3. $CH_3-CH_2-CH_2-CH_2-\overset{\displaystyle O}{\overset{\displaystyle \|}{C}}-NH-CH_3$ _____

4. $CH_3-\overset{\displaystyle O}{\overset{\displaystyle \|}{C}}-NH-CH_2-CH_3$ _____

5.   _____

Answers 1. propanamide (propionamide) 2. benzamide
3. *N*-methylpentanamide 4. *N*-ethylethanamide (*N*-ethyl acetamide)
5. *N*-ethylbenzamide

◆ Learning Exercise 18.4B

Write the structural formulas for each of the following amides:

1. propanamide   2. *N*-methylbutanamide

3. *N*-methyl-3-chloropentanamide   4. benzamide

Answers   1. $CH_3-CH_2-\overset{\overset{\displaystyle O}{\|}}{C}-NH_2$ 2. $CH_3-CH_2-CH_2-\overset{\overset{\displaystyle O}{\|}}{C}-NH-CH_3$

3. $CH_3-CH_2-\overset{\overset{\displaystyle Cl}{|}}{CH}-CH_2-\overset{\overset{\displaystyle O}{\|}}{C}-\overset{\overset{\displaystyle CH_3}{|}}{N}-H$ 4.

18.5 Hydrolysis of Amides

● Amides undergo acid and base hydrolysis to produce the carboxylic acid (or carboxylate salt) and the amine (or amine salt).

$CH_3-\overset{\overset{\displaystyle O}{\|}}{C}-NH_2 + HCl + H_2O \rightarrow CH_3-\overset{\overset{\displaystyle O}{\|}}{C}-OH + NH_4^+Cl^-$

$CH_3-\overset{\overset{\displaystyle O}{\|}}{C}-NH_2 + NaOH \rightarrow CH_3-\overset{\overset{\displaystyle O}{\|}}{C}-O^-Na^+ + NH_3$

◆ Learning Exercise 18.5

Write the structural formulas for the hydrolysis of each of the following with HCl and NaOH:

1. $CH_3-CH_2-\overset{\overset{\displaystyle O}{\|}}{C}-NH_2$

2. $CH_3-\overset{\overset{\displaystyle O}{\|}}{C}-NH-CH_2-CH_3$

Answers

1. $(HCl)CH_3-CH_2-\overset{\overset{\displaystyle O}{\|}}{C}-OH + NH_4^+Cl^-$ $\qquad$ $(NaOH)CH_3-CH_2-\overset{\overset{\displaystyle O}{\|}}{C}-O^-Na^+ + NH_3$

2. $(HCl)CH_3-\overset{\overset{\displaystyle O}{\|}}{C}-OH + \overset{+}{N}H_3-CH_2-CH_3Cl^-$ $\qquad$ $(NaOH)CH_3-\overset{\overset{\displaystyle O}{\|}}{C}-O^-Na^+ + NH_2-CH_2-CH_3$

Checklist for Chapter 18

You are ready to take the practice test for chapter 18. Be sure that you have accomplished the following learning goals for this chapter. If you are not sure, review the section listed at the end of the goal. Then apply your new skills and understanding to the practice test. Good luck.

After studying chapter 18, I can successfully:

_____ Classify amines as primary, secondary, or tertiary (18.1).

_____ Write the IUPAC and common names of amines and draw their condensed structural formulas (18.1).

_____ Compare the boiling points and solubility of amines to alkanes and alcohols of similar mass (18.2).

_____ Write equations for the ionization and neutralization of amines (18.2).

_____ Identify heterocyclic amines (18.3).

_____ Write the IUPAC and common names of amides and draw their condensed structural formulas (18.4).

_____ Write equations for the hydrolysis of amines (18.5).

Practice Test for Chapter 18

Classify the amines in questions 1-6 as

A. primary amine $\qquad$ **B.** secondary amine $\qquad$ **C.** tertiary amine

1. _____ $CH_3-\overset{\overset{\displaystyle CH_3}{|}}{CH}-NH_2$ $\qquad\qquad$ 2. _____ $CH_3-CH_2-\overset{\overset{\displaystyle CH_3}{|}}{N}-CH_3$

3. _____ $CH_3-CH_2-\overset{\overset{\displaystyle NH_2}{|}}{CH}-CH_2-CH_3$ $\qquad$ 4. _____ $CH_3-\overset{\overset{\displaystyle H}{|}}{N}-CH_2-CH_3$

5. _____ $CH_3-\overset{\overset{\displaystyle CH_3}{|}}{CH}-CH_2-NH-\overset{\overset{\displaystyle CH_3}{|}}{CH}-CH_3$ $\qquad$ 6. _____ $CH_3-\overset{\overset{\displaystyle CH_3}{|}}{\underset{\underset{\displaystyle CH_3}{|}}{C}}-CH_2-NH_2$

Match the amines and amides in questions 13−16 with the following names:

A. ethyl dimethyl amine   **B.** butanamide   **C.** *N*-methylacetamide

D. benzamide   **E.** *N*-ethylbutyramide

7.
$$CH_3-CH_2-\overset{\overset{\displaystyle CH_3}{|}}{N}-CH_3$$

8.
$$CH_3-CH_2-CH_2-\overset{\overset{\displaystyle O}{\|}}{C}-NH_2$$

9. 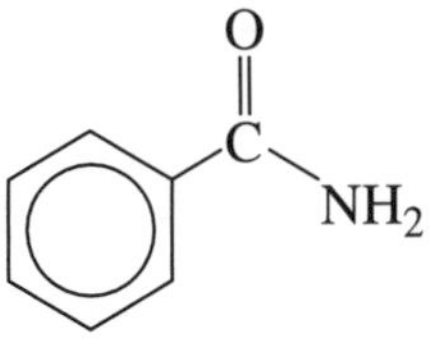
$$\underset{\text{(benzene ring)}}{}\overset{\overset{\displaystyle O}{\|}}{C}-NH_2$$

10.
$$CH_3-CH_2-CH_2-\overset{\overset{\displaystyle O}{\|}}{C}-NH-CH_2-CH_3$$

11.
$$CH_3-\overset{\overset{\displaystyle O}{\|}}{C}-NH-CH_3$$

In questions 12−15, identify the compound with the higher boiling point.

12. A. CH_3-NH_2 or **B.** CH_3-OH

13. A. $CH_3-NH-CH_3$ or **B.** $CH_3-CH_2-NH_2$

14. A. $CH_3-CH_2-CH_3$ or **B.** $CH_3-CH_2-NH_2$

15. A. $CH_3-CH_2-CH_2-OH$ or **B.** $CH_3-CH_2-CH_2-NH_2$

Match the products for the following reactions:

A.
$$CH_3-CH_2-\overset{\overset{\displaystyle O}{\|}}{C}-OH + NH_3$$

B. $CH_3-CH_2-NH_3{}^+Cl^-$

C. $CH_3-CH_2-CH_2-NH_3{}^+OH^-$

D.
$$CH_3-\overset{\overset{\displaystyle O}{\|}}{C}-NH_2$$

16. _____ ionization of 1-propanamine in water

17. _____ hydrolysis of propanamide

18. _____ reaction of ethanamine and hydrochloric acid

19. _____ amidation of acetic acid

20. Amines used in drugs are converted to their amine salt because the salt is

     A. a solid at room temperature   **B.** soluble in water   **C.** odorless

     D. soluble in body fluids   **E.** all of these

21. Heterocyclic amines are organic compounds that
  A. have a ring of five or six atoms   **B.** contain one or more nitrogen atom in a ring
  C. include pyrrolidine and Pyrrole   **D.** include pyridine and pyrinmidine
  E. all of these

22. Alkaloids
  A. are physiologically active nitrogen-containing compounds
  B. are produced by plants
  C. are used in anesthetics, in antidepressants, and as stimulants
  D. are often habit forming
  E. all of these

Match the following alkaloids with their sources
A. caffeine   **B.** nicotine   **C.** morphine   **E.** quinine

23. a painkiller from the Oriental poppy plant

24. obtained from the bark of the cinchona tree and used in the treatment of malaria

25. a stimulant obtained from the leaves of tobacco plants

26. a stimulant obtained from coffee beans and tea

Answers to the Practice Test

1. A	**2.** C	**3.** A	**4.** B	**5.** B
6. A	**7.** A	**8.** B	**9.** D	**10.** E
11. C	**12.** B	**13.** B	**14.** B	**15.** A
16. C	**17.** A	**18.** C	**19.** D	**20.** E
21. E	**22.** E	**23.** C	**24.** E	**25.** B
26. A				

Answers and Solutions to Selected Text Problems

18.1 In a primary amine, there is one alkyl group (and two hydrogen atoms) attached to a nitrogen atom.

18.3 **a.** This is a primary (1°) amine; there is only one alkyl group attached to the nitrogen atom.
  b. This is a secondary (2°) amine; there are two alkyl groups attached to the nitrogen atom.
  c. This is a primary (1°) amine; there is only one alkyl group attached to the nitrogen atom.
  d. This is a tertiary (3°) amine; there are three alkyl groups attached to the nitrogen atom.
  e. This is a tertiary (3°) amine; there are three alkyl groups attached to the nitrogen atom.

18.5 The common name of an amine consists of naming the alkyl groups bonding to the nitrogen atom in alphabetical order. In the IUPAC name, the *e* in the alkane chain is replaced with *amine*.
  a. An ethyl group attached to —NH_2 is ethylamine. In the IUPAC name, the *e* in ethane is replaced by *amine*: ethanamine
  b. Two alkyl groups attach to nitrogen as methyl and propyl for methylpropylamine. The IUPAC name based on the longer chain of propane with a methyl group attached to the nitrogen atoms is *N*-methyl-1-propanamine.
  c. diethylmethylamine; *N*-methyl-*N*-ethylethanamine
  d. isopropylamine; 2-propanamine

18.7 The amine of benzene is called aniline. In amines where a more oxidized functional group takes priority, the —NH_2 group is named as an *amino* group and numbered.
  a. 2-butanamine   **b.** 2-chloroaniline
  c. 3-aminopropanal   **d.** *N*-ethylaniline

18.9   **a.** $CH_3—CH_2—NH_2$

b.

$$\overset{\displaystyle NHCH_3}{\underset{\displaystyle \bigcirc}{|}}$$

c. $CH_3—CH_2—CH_2—CH_2—\overset{\displaystyle H}{\overset{|}{N}}—CH_2—CH_2—CH_3$

d. $CH_3—\overset{\displaystyle NH_2}{\overset{|}{CH}}—CH_2—CH_2—CH_3$

18.11   Amines have higher boiling points than hydrocarbons but lower than alcohols of similar mass.
a. $CH_3—CH_2—OH$ **b.** $CH_3—CH_2—CH_2—NH_2$ **c.** $CH_3—CH_2—CH_2—NH_2$

18.13   Propylamine is a primary amine and forms two hydrogen bonds, which gives it the highest boiling point. Ethylmethylamine, a secondary amine, forms one hydrogen bond, and butane cannot form hydrogen bonds. Thus, butane has the lowest boiling point of the three compounds.

18.15   Amines with one to five carbon atoms are soluble. The solubility in water of amines with longer carbon chains decreases.
a. yes; soluble   **b.** yes; soluble   **c.** no   **d.** yes; soluble

18.17   Amines, which are weak bases, bond with a proton from water to give a hydroxide ion and an ammonium ion.

a. $CH_3—NH_2 + H_2O \rightleftharpoons CH_3—NH_3{}^+ + OH{-}$

b. $CH_3—\overset{\displaystyle CH_3}{\overset{|}{NH}} + H_2O \rightleftharpoons CH_3—\overset{\displaystyle CH_3}{\overset{|}{NH_2{}^+}} + OH^-$

c.

$$\overset{\displaystyle NH_2}{\underset{\displaystyle \bigcirc}{|}} + H_2O \rightleftharpoons \overset{\displaystyle NH_3{}^+}{\underset{\displaystyle \bigcirc}{|}} + OH^-$$

18.19   Amines, which are weak bases, combine with the proton from HCl to yield the ammonium chloride salt.

a. $CH_3—NH_2 + HCl \rightarrow CH_3—NH_3{}^+Cl{-}$

b. $CH_3—\overset{\displaystyle CH_3}{\overset{|}{NH}} + HCl \longrightarrow CH_3—\overset{\displaystyle CH_3}{\overset{|}{NH_2{}^+}} + Cl^-$

c.

$$\overset{\displaystyle NH_2}{\underset{\displaystyle \bigcirc}{|}} + HCl \longrightarrow \overset{\displaystyle NH_3{}^+Cl^-}{\underset{\displaystyle \bigcirc}{|}}$$

18.21   **a.**

$$H_2N—\bigcirc—\overset{\displaystyle O}{\overset{\|}{C}}—O—CH_2—CH_2—\overset{\displaystyle CH_2CH_3}{\underset{\displaystyle CH_2CH_3}{\overset{|+}{\underset{|}{N}}}}—H\ Cl^-$$

b. Amine salts are soluble in body fluids.

18.23 **a.** Aniline is an amine.
  b. an amine with three alkyl groups attached to the nitrogen atom
  c. A nitrogen atom in a ring is a heterocyclic amine.
  d. A nitrogen atom in a ring is a heterocyclic amine.

18.25 **c.** Pyrimidine has two nitrogen atoms in a ring of six atoms.
  d. Pyrrole has one nitrogen atom in a ring of five atoms.

18.27 The five-atom ring with one nitrogen atom and two double bonds is pyrrole.

18.29 Carboxylic acids react with amines to eliminate water and form amides.

  a. $CH_3-\overset{\overset{\displaystyle O}{\|}}{C}-NH_2$

  b. $CH_3-\overset{\overset{\displaystyle O}{\|}}{C}-NH-CH_2-CH_3$

  c. (benzene ring)$-\overset{\overset{\displaystyle O}{\|}}{C}-\overset{\overset{\displaystyle H}{|}}{N}-CH_2CH_2CH_3$

18.31 **a.** *N*-methylethanamide (*N*-methylacetamide). The *N*-methyl means that there is a one-carbon alkyl group attached to the nitrogen. Ethanamide tells us that the carbonyl portion has two carbon atoms.
  b. Butanamide (butyramide) is a chain of four carbon atoms bonded to an amino group.
  c. methanamide (formamide)
  d. *N*-methylbenzamide; the *N*-methyl means that there is a one-carbon alkyl group attached to the nitrogen. Benzamide tells us that this is the amide of benzoic acid.

18.33 **a.** This is an amide of propionic acid, which has three carbon atoms.

  $CH_3-CH_2-\overset{\overset{\displaystyle O}{\|}}{C}-NH_2$

  b. 2-methyl indicates that a methyl is bonded to carbon 2 in an amide chain of five carbon atoms.

  $CH_3-CH_2-CH_2-\overset{\overset{\displaystyle CH_3}{|}}{C}H-\overset{\overset{\displaystyle O}{\|}}{C}-NH_2$

  c. $H-\overset{\overset{\displaystyle O}{\|}}{C}-NH_2$

  d. The nitrogen atom in *N*-ethylbenzamide is bonded to an ethyl group.

  (benzene ring)$-\overset{\overset{\displaystyle O}{\|}}{C}-\overset{\overset{\displaystyle H}{|}}{N}-CH_2-CH_3$

  e. The nitrogen atom is bonded to an ethyl group in *N*-ethylbutyramide.

  $CH_3-CH_2-CH_2-\overset{\overset{\displaystyle O}{\|}}{C}-\overset{\overset{\displaystyle H}{|}}{N}-CH_2-CH_3$

18.35 **a.** Acetamide; primary amines have more hydrogen bonds and higher boiling points.
  b. Propionamide can hydrogen bond, but butane cannot.
  c. *N*-methylpropanamide can hydrogen bond, but *N,N*-dimethylpropanamide cannot.

18.37 Acid hydrolysis of amides gives the carboxylic acid and the amine salt.

a. $CH_3-COOH + NH_4{}^+Cl^-$

b. $CH_3-CH_2-COOH + NH_4{}^+Cl^-$

c. $CH_3-CH_2-CH_2-COOH + CH_3-NH_3{}^+Cl^-$

d.  ⬡—$COOH + NH_4{}^+ Cl^-$

e. $CH_3-CH_2-CH_2-CH_2-COOH + CH_3-CH_2-NH_3{}^+Cl^-$

18.39 carboxylic acid, aromatic, amine, amide, ester

18.41

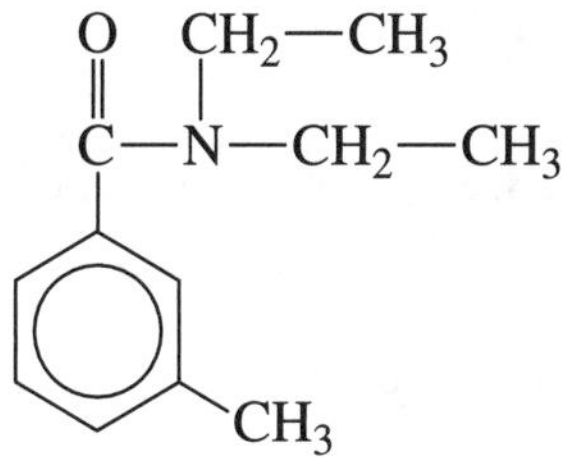

18.43 $CH_3-CH_2-CH_2-NH_2$ $CH_3-CH_2-NH-CH_3$ $CH_3-\overset{\displaystyle CH_3}{\underset{\displaystyle |}{N}}-CH_3$

Propanamine 1°   *N*-methylmethanamine 2°   trimethylamine 3°

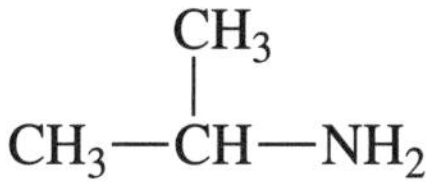

$CH_3-\overset{\displaystyle CH_3}{\underset{\displaystyle |}{CH}}-NH_2$ 2-propanamine 1°

18.45 **a.** 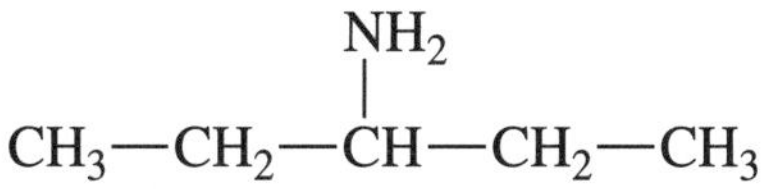 $CH_3-CH_2-\overset{\displaystyle NH_2}{\underset{\displaystyle |}{CH}}-CH_2-CH_3$

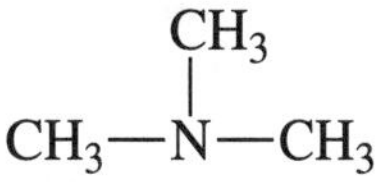

b.

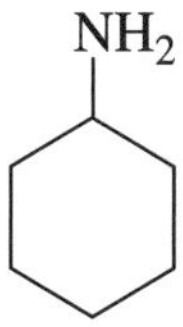

c. This is an ammonium salt with two methyl groups bonded to the nitrogen atom.

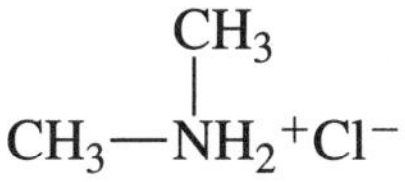

$CH_3-\overset{\displaystyle CH_3}{\underset{\displaystyle |}{NH_2}}{}^+Cl^-$

d. Three ethyl groups are bonded to a nitrogen atom.

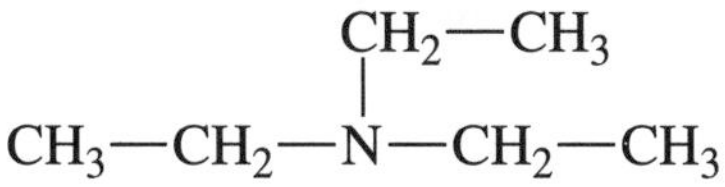

$CH_3-CH_2-\overset{\displaystyle CH_2-CH_3}{\underset{\displaystyle |}{N}}-CH_2-CH_3$

e. This six-carbon chain has a $-NH_2$ group on carbon 3 and an $-OH$ on carbon 2.

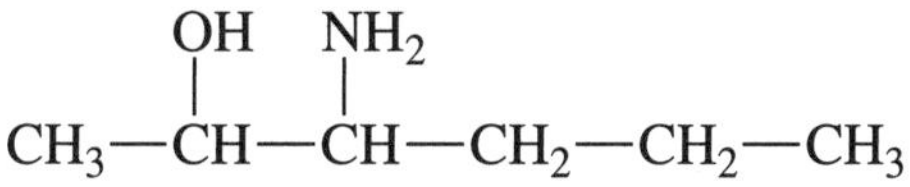

$CH_3-\overset{\displaystyle OH}{\underset{\displaystyle |}{CH}}-\overset{\displaystyle NH_2}{\underset{\displaystyle |}{CH}}-CH_2-CH_2-CH_3$

f. 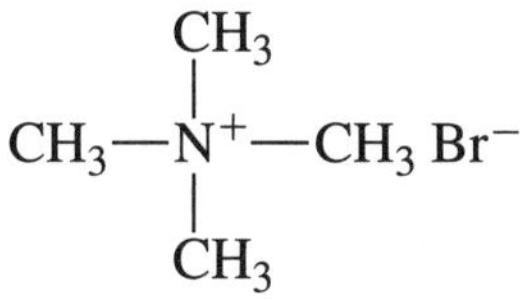 $CH_3-\overset{\displaystyle CH_3}{\underset{\displaystyle \underset{\displaystyle CH_3}{|}}{\overset{\displaystyle |}{N}{}^+}}-CH_3 \ Br^-$

g. Two methyl groups are bonded to the nitrogen of aniline.

18.47 The smaller amines are more soluble in water.
  a. ethylamine   **b.** trimethylamine
  c. butylamine   **d.** $NH_2-CH_2-CH_2-CH_2-CH_2-CH_2-NH_2$

18.49 **a.** Quinine obtained from the bark of the cinchona tree is used in the treatment of malaria.
  b. Nicotine is a stimulant found in cigarettes and cigars.
  c. Caffeine is an alkaloid in coffee, tea, soft drinks, and chocolate.
  d. Morphine and codeine are painkillers obtained from the oriental poppy plant.

18.51 **a.** An amine in water accepts a proton from water, which produces an ammonium ion and OH^-.
  $$CH_3-CH_2-NH_3{}^+ + OH^-$$
  b. The amine accepts a proton to give an ammonium salt: $CH_3-CH_2-NH_3{}^+Cl^-$.

  c. $CH_3-CH_2-\overset{+}{N}H_2-CH_3 + OH^-$

  d. $CH_3-CH_2-\overset{+}{N}H_2-CH_3Cl^-$

  e. An ammonium salt and a strong base produce the amine, a salt, and water.
  $$CH_3-CH_2-CH_2-NH_2 + NaCl + H_2O$$

  f. $CH_3-CH_2-\underset{\underset{H}{|}}{\overset{\overset{CH_3}{|}}{N}} + NaCl + H_2O$

18.53 carboxylic acid salt, aromatic, amine, haloaromatic

18.55 **a.** aromatic, amine, amide, carboxylic acid, cycloalkene
  b. aromatic, ether, alcohol, amine
  c. aromatic, carboxylic acid
  d. phenol, amine, carboxylic acid
  e. aromatic, ether, alcohol, amine, ketone
  f. aromatic, amine

18.57 $CH_3-NH_2 + H_2O \rightarrow CH_3-NH_3{}^+ + OH^-$
  $c = [OH^-]$

  $$K_b = 4.4 \times 10^{-4} = \frac{[CH_3-NH_3{}^+][OH^-]}{[CH_3-NH_2]} = \frac{c^2}{1.0\ M}; \quad c = 2.1 \times 10^{-2} = [OH^-]$$

  $$[H_3O^+] = \frac{1.0 \times 10^{-14}}{[OH^-]} = 4.8 \times 10^{-13} \quad pH = 12.32$$

Amino Acids and Proteins

Study Goals

- Classify proteins by their functions in the cells.
- Draw the structures of amino acids.
- Draw the zwitterion forms of amino acids at the isoelectric point and at pH levels above and below the isoelectric point.
- Write the structural formulas of dipeptides and tripeptides.
- Identify the structural levels of proteins as primary, secondary, tertiary, and quaternary.
- Describe the effects of denaturation on the structure of proteins.

Think About It

1. What are some uses of protein in the body?

2. What are the units that make up a protein?

3. How do you obtain protein in your diet?

Key Terms

Match the following key terms with the correct statement shown below.

a. amino acid   **b.** peptide bond   **c.** denaturation   **d.** primary structure   **e.** isoelectric point

1. _____ The order of amino acids in a protein

2. _____ The pH at which an amino acid has a net charge of zero

3. _____ The bond that connects amino acids in peptides and proteins

4. _____ The loss of secondary and tertiary protein structure caused by agents such as heat and acid

5. _____ The building block of proteins

Answers   **1.** d   **2.** e   **3.** b   **4.** c   **5.** a

19.1 Proteins and Amino Acids

- Some proteins are enzymes or hormones, while others are important in structure, transport, protection, storage, and contraction of muscles.
- A group of 20 amino acids provides the molecular building blocks of proteins.
- In an amino acid, a central (alpha) carbon is attached to an amino group, a carboxyl group, and a side chain or *R* group, which is a characteristic group for each amino acid.
- The particular *R* group makes each amino acid polar, nonpolar, acidic, or basic. Nonpolar amino acids contain hydrocarbon side chains, whereas polar amino acids contain electronegative atoms such as oxygen ($-OH$) or sulfur ($-SH$). Acidic side chains contain a carboxylic acid group, and basic side chains contain an amino group ($-NH_2$).

◆ **Learning Exercise 19.1A**

Match one of the following functions of a protein with the examples below:

    a. structural   **b.** contractile   **c.** storage   **d.** transport
    e. hormonal   **f.** enzyme   **g.** protection

1. _____ hemoglobin carries oxygen in blood   **2.** _____ amylase hydrolyzes starch

3. _____ egg albumin, a protein in egg white   **4.** _____ hormone, which controls growth

5. _____ collagen makes up connective tissue   **6.** _____ immunoglobulin

7. _____ keratin, a major protein of hair   **8.** _____ lipoprotein carries lipids in blood

Answers   **1.** d   **2.** f   **3.** c   **4.** e
                 5. a   **6.** g   **7.** a   **8.** d

◆ **Learning Exercise 19.1B**

Using the appropriate *R* group, complete the structural formula of each of the following amino acids. Indicate whether the amino acid would be polar, nonpolar, acidic, or basic.

glycine ($R = -H$)

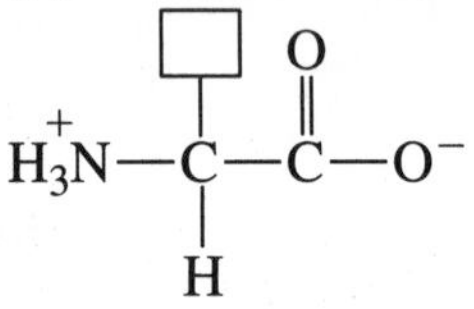

alanine ($R = -CH_3$)

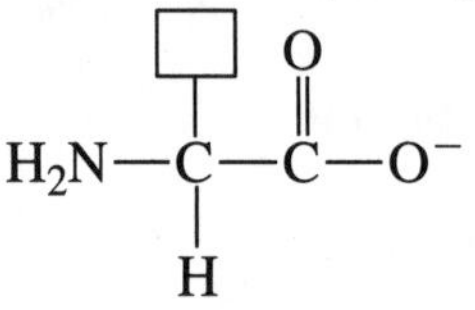

serine ($R = -CH_2-OH$)

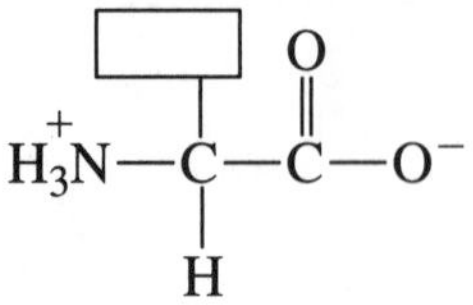

aspartic acid ($R = -CH_2-\overset{\overset{\displaystyle O}{\|}}{C}-OH$)

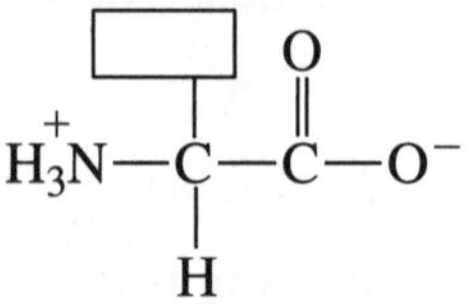

Answers

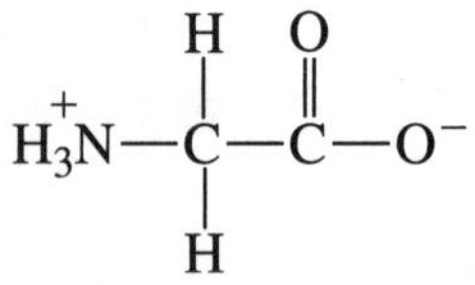

nonpolar

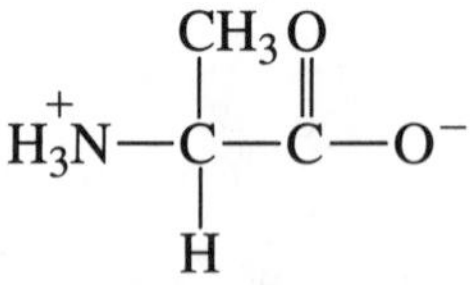

nonpolar

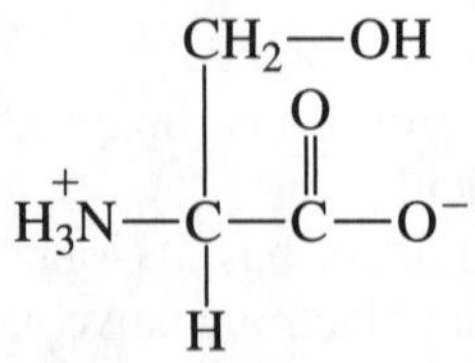

polar

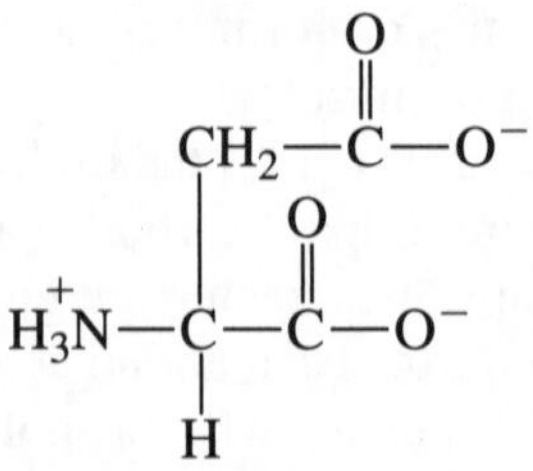

acidic

19.2 Amino Acids as Acids and Bases

- Amino acids exist as dipolar ions called zwitterions, which are neutral at the isoelectric point (pI).
- A zwitterion has a positive charge at pH levels below its pI and a negative charge at pH levels higher than its pI.

Study Note

Example: Glycine has an isoelectric point at a pH of 6.0. Write the zwitterion of glycine at its isoelectric point (pI) and at pH levels above and below its isoelectric point.

Solution: In more acidic solutions, glycine has a net positive charge, and in more basic solutions, a net negative charge.

$$H_3N^+—CH_2—COOH \xleftarrow{H^+} H_3N^+—CH_2—COO^- \xrightarrow{OH^-} H_2N—CH_2—COO^-$$

| *below pI* | *zwitterion of glycine* | *above pI* |

◆ Learning Exercise 19.2

Write the structure of the amino acids under the given conditions:

Zwitterion (pI)	H⁺	OH⁻
Alanine		
Serine		

Answers

Zwitterion (pI)	H⁺	OH⁻
Alanine $\overset{\displaystyle CH_3}{\underset{\displaystyle H_3\overset{+}{N}—CH—COO^-}{\mid}}$	$\overset{\displaystyle CH_3}{\underset{\displaystyle H_3\overset{+}{N}—CH—COOH}{\mid}}$	$\overset{\displaystyle CH_3}{\underset{\displaystyle H_2N—CH—COO^-}{\mid}}$
Serine $\overset{\displaystyle CH_2—OH}{\underset{\displaystyle H_3\overset{+}{N}—CH—COO^-}{\mid}}$	$\overset{\displaystyle CH_2—OH}{\underset{\displaystyle H_3\overset{+}{N}—CH—COOH}{\mid}}$	$\overset{\displaystyle CH_2—OH}{\underset{\displaystyle H_2N—CH—COO^-}{\mid}}$

19.3 Formation of Peptides

• A peptide bond is an amide bond between the carboxyl group of one amino acid and the amino group of the second.

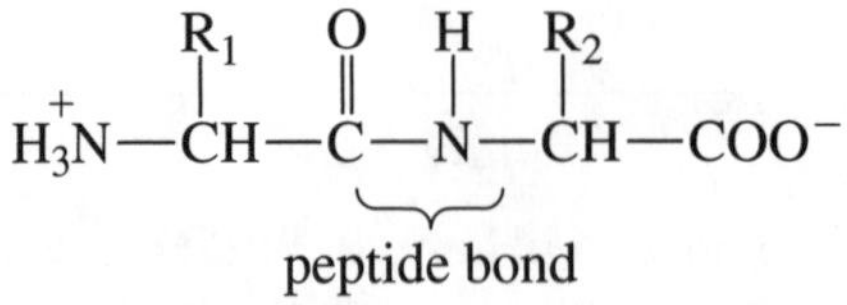

$$\overset{+}{H_3N}-\underset{|}{\overset{R_1}{\underset{|}{CH}}}-\overset{O}{\overset{\|}{C}}-\underset{|}{\overset{H}{\underset{|}{N}}}-\underset{|}{\overset{R_2}{\underset{|}{CH}}}-COO^-$$

peptide bond

• Short chains of amino acids are called peptides. Long chains of amino acids are called proteins.

◆ Learning Exercise 19.3

Draw the structural formulas of the following dipeptides and tripeptides:

1. serylglycine

2. cystylvaline

3. Gly-Ser-Cys

Answers

1. 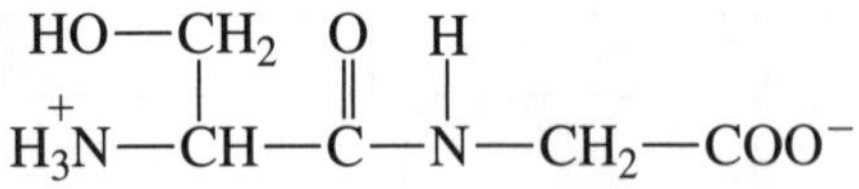 $\overset{+}{H_3N}-\underset{|}{\overset{HO-CH_2}{\underset{|}{CH}}}-\overset{O}{\overset{\|}{C}}-\underset{|}{\overset{H}{\underset{|}{N}}}-CH_2-COO^-$

2. $\overset{+}{H_3N}-\underset{|}{\overset{HS-CH_2}{\underset{|}{CH}}}-\overset{O}{\overset{\|}{C}}-\underset{|}{\overset{H}{\underset{|}{N}}}-\underset{\underset{CH_3}{\overset{|}{CH-CH_3}}}{\overset{|}{CH}}-COO^-$

3. $\overset{+}{H_3N}-CH_2-\overset{O}{\overset{\|}{C}}-\underset{\underset{H}{|}}{N}-\underset{\overset{HO-CH_2}{|}}{CH}-\overset{O}{\overset{\|}{C}}-\underset{\underset{H}{|}}{N}-\underset{\overset{CH_2-SH}{|}}{CH}-COO^-$

320

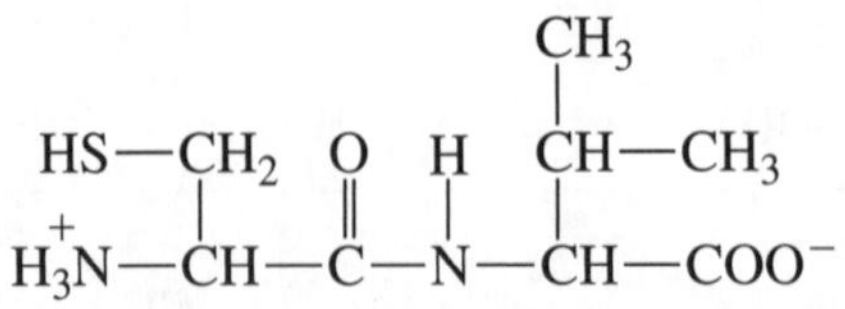

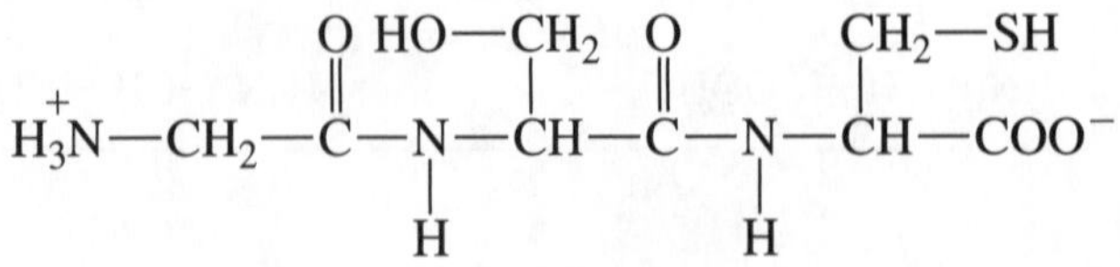

19.4 Protein Structure: Primary and Secondary Levels

- The primary structure of a protein is the sequence of amino acids.
- In the secondary structure, hydrogen bonds between different sections of the peptide produce a characteristic shape such as an α-helix, β-pleated sheet, or a triple helix.
- Certain combinations of vegetables are complementary when the protein from one provides the missing amino acid in the other. For example, garbanzo beans and rice have complementary proteins because tryptophan, which is low in garbanzo beans, is provided by rice, and lysine, which is low in rice, is provided by garbanzo beans.

◆ Learning Exercise 19.4A

Identify the following descriptions of protein structure as primary or secondary structure:

1. _____ Hydrogen bonding forms an alpha (α)-helix.

2. _____ Hydrogen bonding occurs between C═O and N─H within a peptide chain.

3. _____ The order of amino acids, which are linked by peptide bonds.

4. _____ Hydrogen bonds between protein chains form a pleated-sheet structure.

Answers　　1. secondary　　2. secondary　　3. primary　　4. secondary

◆ Learning Exercise 19.4B

Seeds, vegetables, and legumes are typically low in one or more of the essential amino acids, tryptophan, isoleucine, and lysine.

	tryptophan	isoleucine	lysine
sesame seeds	OK	LOW	LOW
sunflower seeds	OK	OK	LOW
garbanzo beans	LOW	OK	OK
rice	OK	OK	LOW
cornmeal	OK	OK	LOW

Indicate whether the following protein combinations are complementary or not:

1. _____ sesame seeds and sunflower seeds

2. _____ sunflower seeds and garbanzo beans

3. _____ sunflower seeds, sesame seeds, and garbanzo beans

4. _____ sesame seeds and garbanzo beans

5. _____ garbanzo beans and rice

6. _____ cornmeal and garbanzo beans

7. _____ rice and cornmeal

Answers　　1. not complementary; both are low in lysine　　2. complementary
　　　　　　　3. complementary　　4. complementary
　　　　　　　5. complementary　　6. complementary
　　　　　　　7. not complementary; both are low in lysine

19.5 Protein Structure: Tertiary and Quaternary Levels

- In globular proteins, the polypeptide chain, including its α-helical and β-pleated sheet regions, folds upon itself to form a tertiary structure.
- In a tertiary structure, hydrophobic R groups are found on the inside and hydrophilic R groups on the outside surface. The tertiary structure is stabilized by interactions between R groups.
- In a quaternary structure, two or more subunits must combine for biological activity. They are held together by the same interactions found in tertiary structures.

◆ Learning Exercise 19.5

Identify the following descriptions of protein structure as tertiary or quaternary:

1. _____ a disulfide bond joining distant parts of a peptide

2. _____ the combination of four protein subunits

3. _____ hydrophilic side groups seeking contact with water

4. _____ a salt bridge forms between two oppositely charged side chains

5. _____ hydrophobic side groups forming a nonpolar center

Answers   **1.** tertiary   **2.** quaternary   **3.** tertiary   **4.** tertiary   **5.** tertiary

19.6 Protein Hydrolysis and Denaturation

- Denaturation of a protein occurs when heat or other denaturing agents destroy the secondary and tertiary structure (but not the primary structure) of the protein until biological activity is lost.
- Denaturing agents include heat, acid, base, organic solvents, agitation, and metal ions.

◆ Learning Exercise 19.6

Indicate the denaturing agent in the following examples:

A. heat or UV light   **B.** pH change   **C.** organic solvent
D. heavy metal ions   **E.** agitation

1. _____ placing surgical instruments in a 120°C autoclave

2. _____ whipping cream to make a dessert topping

3. _____ applying tannic acid to a burn

4. _____ placing $AgNO_3$ drops in the eyes of newborns

5. _____ using alcohol to disinfect a wound

6. _____ using *lactobacillus* bacteria culture to produce acid that converts milk to yogurt

Answers   **1.** A   **2.** E   **3.** B   **4.** D   **5.** C   **6.** B

Checklist for Chapter 19

You are ready to take the practice test for chapter 19. Be sure that you have accomplished the following learning goals for this chapter. If you are not sure, review the section listed at the end of the goal. Good luck.

After studying chapter 19, I can successfully:

_____ Classify proteins by their functions in the cells (19.1).

_____ Draw the structure for an amino acid (19.1).

_____ Draw the zwitterion at the isoelectric point (pI) and above and below the pI (19.2).

_____ Describe a peptide bond; draw the structure for a peptide (19.3).

_____ Distinguish between the primary and secondary structures of a protein (19.4).

_____ Distinguish between the tertiary and quaternary structures of a protein (19.5).

_____ Describe the ways that denaturation affects the structure of a protein (19.6).

Practice Test for Chapter 19

1. Which amino acid is nonpolar?
   A. serine   **B.** aspartic acid   **C.** valine   **D.** cysteine   **E.** glutamine

2. Which amino acid will form disulfide cross-links in a tertiary structure?
   A. serine   **B.** aspartic acid   **C.** valine   **D.** cysteine   **E.** glutamine

3. Which amino acid has a basic side chain?
   A. serine   **B.** aspartic acid   **C.** valine   **D.** cysteine   **E.** glutamine

4. All amino acids
   A. have the same side chains
   B. form zwitterions
   C. have the same isoelectric points
   D. show hydrophobic tendencies
   E. are essential amino acids

5. Essential amino acids
   A. are the amino acids that must be supplied by the diet
   B. are not synthesized by the body
   C. are missing in incomplete proteins
   D. are present in proteins from animal sources
   E. all of the above

Use the following to answer questions for the amino acid alanine in questions 6–9.

A. $H_3\overset{+}{N}-\underset{\underset{\displaystyle CH_3}{|}}{CH}-COO^-$ **B.** $H_2N-\underset{\underset{\displaystyle CH_3}{|}}{CH}-COO^-$ **C.** $H_3\overset{+}{N}-\underset{\underset{\displaystyle CH_3}{|}}{CH}-COOH$

6. _____ alanine in its zwitterion form

7. _____ alanine at a low pH

8. _____ alanine at a high pH

9. _____ alanine at its isoelectric point

10. The sequence Tyr-Ala-Gly
   A. is a tripeptide   **B.** has two peptide bonds
   C. has tyrosine with free $-NH_2$ end
   D. has glycine with the free $-COOH$ end
   E. all of these

11. The type of bonding expected between lysine and aspartic acid is a
   A. ionic bond   **B.** hydrogen bond   **C.** disulfide bond
   D. hydrophobic attraction   **E.** hydrophilic attraction

12. What type of bond is used to form the α-helix structure of a protein?
   A. peptide bond   **B.** hydrogen bond   **C.** ionic bond
   D. disulfide bond   **E.** hydrophobic attraction

13. What type of bonding places portions of the protein chain in the center of a tertiary structure?
  A. peptide bonds   **B.** ionic bonds   **C.** disulfide bonds
  D. hydrophobic attraction   **E.** hydrophilic attraction

In questions 14–18, identify the protein structural levels that each of the following statements describe:
  A. primary   **B.** secondary   **C.** tertiary   **D.** quaternary   **E.** pentenary

14. ____ peptide bonds   **15.** ____ a β-pleated sheet

16. ____ two or more protein subunits   **17.** ____ an α-helix   **18.** ____ disulfide bonds

In questions 19–23, match the function of a protein with each example.

19. ____ enzyme   **A.** myoglobin in the muscles
                                B. α-keratin in skin
20. ____ structural   **C.** peptidase for protein hydrolysis
21. ____ transport   **D.** casein in milk

22. ____ storage

23. Denaturation of a protein
  A. occurs at a pH of 7   **B.** causes a change in protein structure
  C. hydrolyzes a protein   **D.** oxidizes the protein   **E.** adds amino acids to a protein

24. Which of the following will not cause denaturation?
  A. 0°C   **B.** $AgNO_3$ **C.** 80°C   **D.** ethanol   **E.** pH 1

Answers to the Practice Test

1. C	2. D	3. E	4. B	5. E
6. A	7. C	8. B	9. A	10. E
11. A	12. B	13. D	14. A	15. B
16. D	17. B	18. C	19. C	20. B
21. A	22. D	23. B	24. A	

Answers and Solutions to Selected Text Problems

19.1   **a.** Hemoglobin, which carries oxygen in the blood, is a transport protein.
         b. Collagen, which is a major component of tendon and cartilage, is a structural protein.
         c. Keratin, which is found in hair, is a structural protein.
         d. Amylase, which catalyzes the breakdown of starch, is an enzyme.

19.3   All amino acids contain a carboxylic acid group and an amino group on the alpha carbon.

19.5

19.7 **a.** Alanine, which has a methyl (hydrocarbon) side group, is nonpolar.
    b. Threonine has a side group that contains the polar —OH. Threonine is polar.
    c. Glutamic acid has a side group containing a polar carboxylic acid. Glutamic acid is acidic.
    d. Phenylalanine has a side group with a nonpolar benzene ring. Phenylalanine is nonpolar.

19.9 The abbreviations of most amino acids are derived from the first three letters in the name.
    a. alanine   **b.** valine
    c. lysine   **d.** cysteine

19.11 In the L isomer, the —NH_2 is on the left side of the horizontal line of the Fischer projection; in D isomer, the —NH_2 group is on the right.

a.

$$
\begin{array}{c}
\text{COOH} \\
|\\
H_2N\!\!-\!\!\!-\!\!H \\
|\\
\text{CH} \\
H_3C \quad CH_3
\end{array}
$$

b.

$$
\begin{array}{c}
\text{COOH} \\
|\\
H\!\!-\!\!\!-\!\!NH_2 \\
|\\
CH_2SH
\end{array}
$$

19.13 A zwitterion is formed when the H from the acid part of the amino acid is transferred to the amine portion of the amino acid. The resulting dipolar ion has an overall zero charge.

a. $\overset{+}{H_3}N-\overset{\overset{\displaystyle H}{|}}{C}H-\overset{\overset{\displaystyle O}{\|}}{C}O^-$

b. $\overset{+}{H_3}N-\overset{\overset{\displaystyle SH}{|}}{\underset{}{C}}H-\overset{\overset{\displaystyle O}{\|}}{C}O^-$ (with CH$_2$ between SH and CH)

c. $\overset{+}{H_3}N-\overset{\overset{\displaystyle OH}{|}}{\underset{}{C}}H-\overset{\overset{\displaystyle O}{\|}}{C}O^-$ (with CH$_2$ between OH and CH)

d. $\overset{+}{H_3}N-\overset{\overset{\displaystyle CH_3}{|}}{C}H-\overset{\overset{\displaystyle O}{\|}}{C}O^-$

19.15 At low pH (highly acidic), the —COO^- of the zwitterion accepts a proton and the amino acid has a positive charge overall.

a. $\overset{+}{H_3}N-\overset{\overset{\displaystyle H}{|}}{C}H-\overset{\overset{\displaystyle O}{\|}}{C}OH$

b. $\overset{+}{H_3}N-CH-\overset{\overset{\displaystyle O}{\|}}{C}OH$ (with SH—CH$_2$ side chain)

c. $\overset{+}{H_3}N-CH-\overset{\overset{\displaystyle O}{\|}}{C}OH$ (with OH—CH$_2$ side chain)

d. $\overset{+}{H_3}N-\overset{\overset{\displaystyle CH_3}{|}}{C}H-\overset{\overset{\displaystyle O}{\|}}{C}OH$

19.17 **a.** A negative charge means the zwitterion donated a proton from —NH_3^+, which occurs at pH levels above the isoelectric point.
    b. A positive charge means the zwitterion accepted a proton (H^+) from an acidic solution, which occurs at a pH level below the isoelectric point.
    c. A zwitterion with a net charge of zero means that the pH level is equal to the isoelectric point.

19.19 In a peptide, the amino acids are joined by peptide bonds (amide bonds). The first amino acid has a free amine group, and the last one has a free carboxyl group.

a. 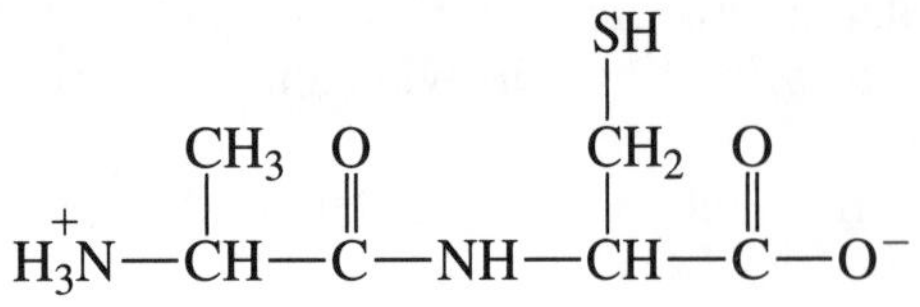 Ala-Cys

b. 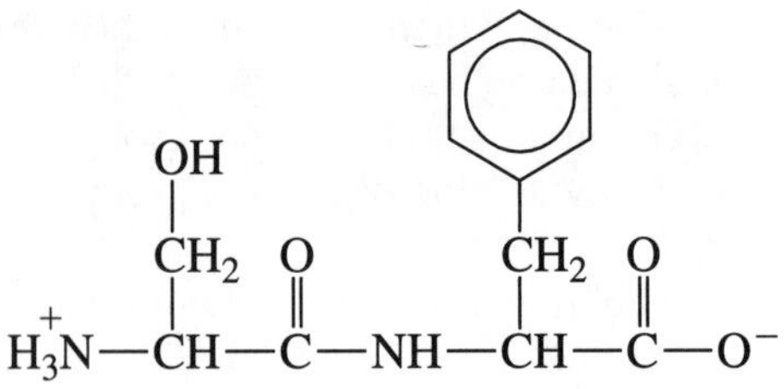 Ser-Phe

c. 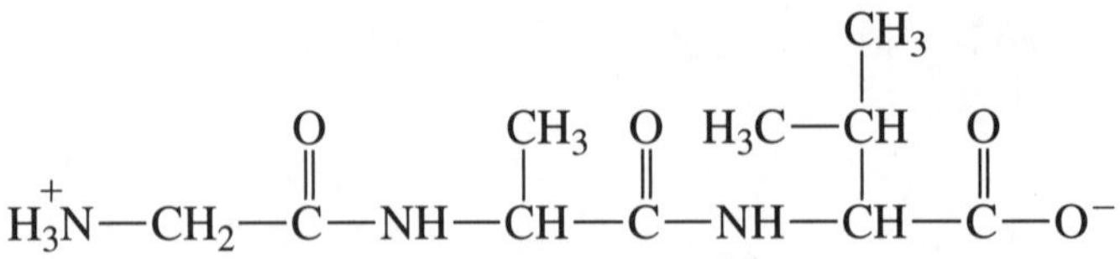 Gly-Ala-Val

d. 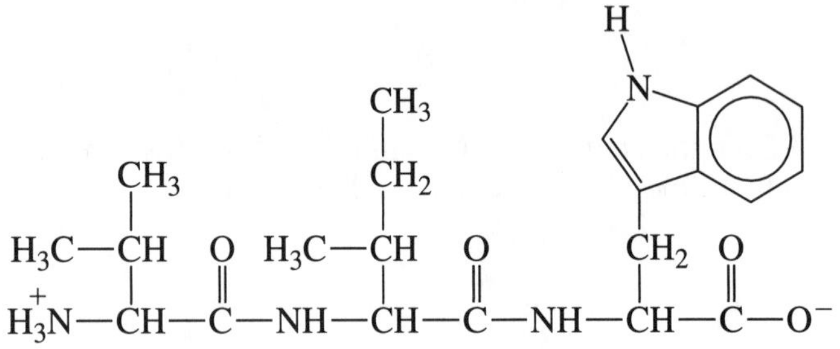 Val-Ile-Trp

19.21 The primary structure of a protein is the order of amino acids; the bonds that hold the amino acids together in a protein are amide or peptide bonds.

19.23 The possible primary structures of a tripeptide of one valine and two serines are Val-Ser-Ser, Ser-Val-Ser, and Ser-Ser-Val.

19.25 When a protein forms a secondary structure, the amino acid chain arranges itself in space. The common secondary structures are the alpha helix, the beta-pleated sheet, and the triple helix.

19.27 In an alpha helix, there are hydrogen bonds between the different turns of the helix, which preserve the helical shape of the protein. In a beta-pleated sheet, the hydrogen bonds occur between two protein chains that are side by side or between different parts of a long protein.

19.29 **a.** The two cysteine residues have —SH groups, which react to form a disulfide bond.
b. Glutamic acid is acidic and lysine is basic; the two groups form an ionic bond, or salt bridge.
c. Serine has a polar —OH group that can form a hydrogen bond with the carboxyl group of aspartic acid.
d. Two leucine residues are hydrocarbon and nonpolar. They would have a hydrophobic interaction.

19.31 **a.** The *R* group of cysteine with the —SH group can form disulfide cross-links.
b. Leucine and valine are found on the inside of the protein since they have nonpolar side groups and are hydrophobic.
c. The cysteine and aspartic acid are on the outside of the protein since they are polar.
d. The order of the amino acid (the primary structure) provides the *R* groups, whose interactions determine the tertiary structure of the protein.

19.33 The complete hydrolysis of the tripeptide Gly-Ala-Ser will give the amino acids glycine (Gly), alanine (Ala), and serine (Ser).

19.35 Partial hydrolysis of the tetrapeptide His-Met-Gly-Val could give the following dipeptides: Met-Gly, His-Met, and Gly-Val.

19.37 The primary level, the sequence of amino acids in the protein, is affected by hydrolysis.

19.39
  a. Placing an egg in boiling water coagulates the protein of the egg by breaking the hydrogen bonds and disrupting the hydrophobic interactions.
  b. Using an alcohol swab coagulates the protein of any bacteria present by forming new hydrogen bonds and disrupting hydrophobic interactions.
  c. The heat from an autoclave will coagulate the protein of any bacteria on the surgical instruments by breaking the hydrogen bonds and disrupting the hydrophobic interactions.
  d. Cauterization (heating) of a wound leads to coagulation of the protein and helps to close the wound by breaking hydrogen bonds and disrupting hydrophobic interactions.

19.41
  a. yes   **b.** yes   **c.** no
  d. yes   **e.** no   **f.** yes

19.43
  a. asparagine and serine; hydrogen bond
  b. aspartic acid and lysine; salt bridge
  c. two cysteines; disulfide bond
  d. valine and alanine; hydrophobic attraction

19.45
  a. α-keratins are fibrous proteins that provide structure to hair, wool, skin, and nails.
  b. α-keratins have a high content of cysteine.

19.47 **a.**

$$\overset{+}{H_3N}-CH-\overset{\overset{\displaystyle O}{\|}}{C}-N-CH-\overset{\overset{\displaystyle O}{\|}}{C}-N-CH-\overset{\overset{\displaystyle O}{\|}}{C}-O^-$$

with side groups CH_2OH, $(CH_2)_4$–NH_2, and CH_2–$COOH$

  b. This segment contains polar *R* groups, which would be found on the surface of globular proteins, where they can hydrogen bond with water.

19.49
  a. The β-pleated sheet is a secondary structure that contains high amount of Val, Pro, and Ser, which have small side groups.
  b. His, Met, and Leu are found predominantly in an α-helix secondary structure.

19.51 Serine is a polar amino acid, whereas valine is nonpolar. Valine would be in the center of the tertiary structure. However, serine would pull that part of the chain to the outside surface of the protein, where valine forms hydrogen bonds with water.

19.53
  a. $\overset{+}{H_3N}-CH(CH_2-OH)-COOH$
  b. $\overset{+}{H_3N}-CH(CH_3)-COOH$
  c. $\overset{+}{H_3N}-CH((CH_2)_4-\overset{+}{NH_3})-COOH$

19.55   **1.** a   **2.** d   **3.** c   **4.** a   **5.** b   **6.** e

19.57 **a.** The secondary structure of a protein depends on hydrogen bonds to form a helix or a pleated sheet. The tertiary structure is determined by the interaction of R groups and determines the three-dimensional structure of the protein.

      b. Nonessential amino acids are synthesized by the body, but essential amino acids must be supplied by the diet.

      c. Polar amino acids have hydrophilic side groups, whereas nonpolar amino acids have hydrophobic side groups.

      d. Dipeptides contain two amino acids, whereas tripeptides contain three.

      e. An ionic bond is an interaction between a basic and acidic side group; a disulfide bond links the sulfides of two cysteines.

      f. Fibrous proteins consist of three to seven alpha helixes coiled like a rope. Globular proteins form a compact spherical shape.

      g. The alpha helix is the secondary shape like a spiral staircase or corkscrew. The beta-pleated sheet is a secondary structure that is formed by many proteins side by side.

      h. The tertiary structure of a protein is its three-dimensional structure. In the quaternary structure, two or more peptide subunits are grouped.

Study Goals

- Classify enzymes according to the type of reaction they catalyze.
- Describe the lock-and-key and induced-fit models of enzyme action.
- Discuss the effect of changes in temperature, pH, and concentration of substrate on enzyme action.
- Describe the competitive, noncompetitive, and irreversible inhibition of enzymes.
- Discuss feedback control and regulation of enzyme action by allosteric enzymes.
- Identify the types of cofactors that are necessary for enzyme action.
- Describe the functions of vitamins and coenzymes.

Think About It

1. What are some functions of enzymes in the cells of the body?

2. Why are enzymes sensitive to high temperatures and low or high pH levels?

3. Why do we need vitamins?

Key Terms

Match the following key terms with the correct statement shown below.

- **a.** lock-and-key theory
- **b.** vitamin
- **c.** inhibitor
- **d.** enzyme
- **e.** active site

1. _____ The portion of an enzyme structure where a substrate undergoes reaction

2. _____ A protein that catalyzes a biological reaction in the cells

3. _____ A model of enzyme action in which the substrate exactly fits the shape of an enzyme like a key fits into a lock

4. _____ A substance that makes an enzyme inactive by interfering with its ability to react with a substrate

5. _____ An organic compound essential for normal health and growth that must be obtained from the diet

Answers   **1.** e   **2.** d   **3.** a   **4.** d   **5.** b

20.1 Enzymes

- Enzymes are globular proteins that act as biological catalysts.
- Enzymes accelerate the rate of biological reactions by lowering the activation energy of a reaction.
- The names of most enzymes are indicated by their *ase* endings.
- Enzymes are classified by the type of reaction they catalyze: oxidoreductase, hydrolase, isomerase, transferase, lyase, or ligase.

◆ Learning Exercise 20.1A

Indicate whether each of the following characteristics of an enzyme is *true* or *false*.

An enzyme

1. _____ is a biological catalyst

2. _____ functions at a low pH

3. _____ usually does not change the equilibrium position of a reaction

4. _____ is obtained from the diet

5. _____ greatly increases the rate of a cellular reaction

6. _____ is needed for every reaction that takes place in the cell

7. _____ catalyzes at a faster rate at higher temperatures

8. _____ functions best at mild conditions of pH 7.4 and 37°C

9. _____ lowers the activation energy of a biological reaction

10. _____ increases the rate of the forward reaction, but not the reverse

Answers	**1.** T	**2.** F	**3.** T	**4.** F	**5.** T
	6. T	**7.** F	**8.** T	**9.** T	**10.** F

◆ Learning Exercise 20.1B

Match the common name of each of the following enzymes with the description of the reaction:

1. dehydrogenase   2. oxidase   3. peptidase
4. decarboxylase   5. esterase   6. transaminase

a. _____ hydrolyzes the ester bonds in triacylglycerols to yield fatty acids and glycerol

b. _____ removes hydrogen from a substrate

c. _____ removes CO_2 from a substrate

d. _____ decomposes hydrogen peroxide to water and oxygen

e. _____ hydrolyzes peptide bonds during the digestion of proteins

f. _____ transfers an amino (NH_2) group from an amino acid to an α-keto acid

Answers	**a.** 5	**b.** 1	**c.** 4
	d. 2	**e.** 3	**f.** 6

◆ Learning Exercise 20.1C

Match the IUPAC classification for enzymes with each of the following types of reactions:

1. oxidoreductase   2. transferase   3. hydrolase
4. lyase   5. isomerase   6. ligase

a. _____ combines small molecules using energy from ATP

b. _____ transfers phosphate groups

c. _____ hydrolyzes a disaccharide into two glucose units

d. _____ converts a substrate to an isomer of the substrate

e. _____ adds hydrogen to a substrate

f. _____ removes H_2O from a substrate

g. _____ adds oxygen to a substrate

h. _____ converts a cis structure to a trans structure.

Answers   **a.** 6   **b.** 2   **c.** 3   **d.** 5

            e. 1   **f.** 4   **g.** 1   **h.** 5

20.2 Enzyme Action

- Within the structure of the enzyme, there is a small pocket called the active site, which has a specific shape that fits a specific substrate.
- In the lock-and-key model or the induced-fit model, an enzyme and substrate form an enzyme-substrate complex so the reaction of the substrate can be catalyzed at the active site.

◆ Learning Exercise 20.2A

Match the terms active site (A), substrate (B), enzyme-substrate complex (C), lock and key (D), and induced fit (E) with the following descriptions:

1. _____ the combination of an enzyme with a substrate

2. _____ a model of enzyme action in which the rigid shape of the active site exactly fits the shape of the substrate

3. _____ has a tertiary structure that fits the structure of the active site

4. _____ a model of enzyme action in which the shape of the active site adjusts to fit the shape of a substrate

5. _____ the portion of an enzyme that binds to the substrate and catalyzes the reaction

Answers   **1.** C   **2.** D   **3.** B   **4.** E   **5.** A

◆ Learning Exercise 20.2B

Write an equation to illustrate the following:

1. the formation of an enzyme-substrate complex   _____

2. the conversion of enzyme-substrate complex to product   _____

Answers   **1.** $E + S \rightleftharpoons ES$ **2.** $ES \rightarrow E + P$

20.3 Factors Affecting Enzyme Activity

- Enzymes are most effective at optimum temperature and pH. The rate of an enzyme reaction decreases considerably at temperatures and pH above or below the optimum.
- An enzyme can be made inactive by changes in pH, temperature, or chemical compounds called inhibitors.
- An increase in substrate concentration increases the reaction rate of an enzyme-catalyzed reaction until all of the enzyme molecules combine with substrate.

◆ Learning Exercise 20.3

Urease, which has an optimum pH of 5, catalyzes the hydrolysis of urea to ammonia and CO_2 in the liver.

$$H_2N-\overset{\overset{\displaystyle O}{\|}}{C}-NH_2 + H_2O \xrightarrow{\text{urease}} 2NH_3 + CO_2$$

Draw a graph to represent the effects of each of the following on enzyme activity. Indicate the optimum pH and optimum temperature.

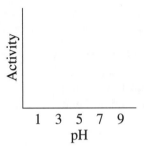 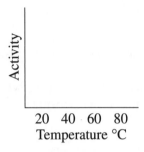 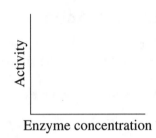

How is the rate of the urease-catalyzed reaction affected by each of the following?

    a. increases   **b.** decreases   **c.** not changed

1. _____ adding more urea when an excess of enzyme is present

2. _____ running the reaction at pH 8

3. _____ lowering the temperature to 0°C

4. _____ running the reaction at 85°C

5. _____ increasing the concentration of urease for a specific amount of urea

6. _____ adjusting pH to the optimum

Answers

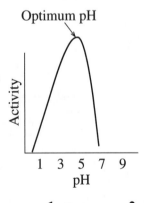 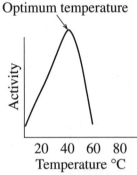 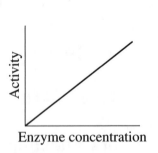

    1. a   **2.** b   **3.** b
    4. b   **5.** a   **6.** a

20.4 Enzyme Inhibition

- A competitive inhibitor has a structure similar to the substrate and competes for the active site. When the active site is occupied by a competitive inhibitor, the enzyme cannot catalyze the reaction of the substrate.
- A noncompetitive inhibitor attaches elsewhere on the enzyme, changing the shape of both the enzyme and the active site. As long as the noncompetitive inhibitor is attached to the enzyme, the altered active site cannot bind with substrate.

◆ **Learning Exercise 20.4**

Identify each of the following as characteristic of competitive inhibition (C), noncompetitive inhibition (N), or irreversible inhibition (I):

1. ____ An inhibitor binds to the surface of the enzyme away from the active site.

2. ____ An inhibitor resembling the substrate molecule blocks the active site on the enzyme.

3. ____ An inhibition causes permanent damage to the enzyme with a total loss of biological activity.

4. ____ The action of this inhibitor can be reversed by adding more substrate.

5. ____ Increasing substrate concentration does not change the effect of this inhibition.

6. ____ Sulfanilamide stops bacterial infections because its structure is similar to PABA (p-aminobenzoic acid), which is essential for bacterial growth.

Answers   **1.** N   **2.** C   **3.** I   **4.** C   **5.** N   **6.** C

20.5 Control of Enzyme Activity

- Many digestive enzymes are produced and stored as inactive forms called zymogens, which are activated at a later time.
- Hormones such as insulin and enzymes that catalyze blood clotting are synthesized as zymogens.
- When allosteric enzymes bind regulator molecules on a different part of the enzyme, there is a change in the shape of the enzyme and the active site. A positive regulator speeds up a reaction, and a negative regulator slows down a reaction.
- In feedback control, the end product of an enzyme-catalyzed sequence acts as a negative regulator and binds to the first enzyme in the sequence, which slows the rate of catalytic activity.

◆ **Learning Exercise 20.5**

Match the following characteristics of types of enzyme of enzyme regulation:
(Z) zymogen   (A) allosteric enzyme   (P) positive regulator
(N) negative regulator   (F) feedback control

1. ____ an enzyme that binds molecules at a site that is not the active site to speed up or slow down the rate of enzyme activity

2. ____ the end product of a reaction sequence binds to the first enzyme in the pathway

3. ____ a molecule that slows down reaction by preventing proper binding to the substrate

4. ____ an inactive form of an enzyme that is activated by removing a peptide section

5. ____ a molecule that binds at a site different than the active site to speed up the reaction

Answers   **1.** A   **2.** F   **3.** N   **4.** Z   **5.** P

20.6 Enzyme Cofactors and Vitamins

- Simple enzymes are biologically active as a protein only, whereas other enzymes require a cofactor.
- A cofactor may be a metal ion, such as Cu^{2+} or Fe^{2+}, or an organic compound called a coenzyme, usually a vitamin.
- Vitamins are organic molecules that are essential for proper health.
- Vitamins must be obtained from the diet because they are not synthesized in the body.
- Vitamins B and C are classified as water-soluble; vitamins A, D, E, and K are fat-soluble vitamins.
- Many water-soluble vitamins function as coenzymes.

◆ **Learning Exercise 20.6A**

Indicate whether each statement describes a simple enzyme or a protein that requires a cofactor.

1. _____ an enzyme consisting only of protein

2. _____ an enzyme requiring magnesium ion for activity

3. _____ an enzyme containing a sugar group

4. _____ an enzyme that gives only amino acids upon hydrolysis

5. _____ an enzyme that requires zinc ions for activity

Answers   **1.** simple   **2.** requires a cofactor   **3.** requires a cofactor
             4. simple   **5.** requires a cofactor

◆ **Learning Exercise 20.6B**

Identify the water-soluble vitamin associated with each of the following:

a. thiamin (B_1)   **b.** riboflavin (B_2)   **c.** niacin (B_3)
d. cobalamin (B_{12})   **e.** ascorbic acid (C)   **f.** pantothenic acid (B_5)

1. _____ collagen formation   2. _____ coenzyme for NAD^+

3. _____ pellagra   4. _____ part of coenzyme A

5. _____ FAD and FMN   6. _____ scurvy

Answers   **1.** e   **2.** c   **3.** c   **4.** f   **5.** b   **6.** e

◆ **Learning Exercise 20.6C**

Identify the fat-soluble vitamin associated with each of the following:

a. vitamin A   **b.** vitamin D   **c.** vitamin E   **d.** vitamin K

1. _____ prevents oxidation of fatty acids   2. _____ blood clotting

3. _____ night vision   4. _____ rickets

5. _____ formed in skin from sunlight   6. _____ derived from cholesterol

Answers   **1.** c   **2.** d   **3.** a
             4. b   **5.** b   **6.** b

Checklist for Chapter 20

You are ready to take the practice test for chapter 20. Be sure that you have accomplished the following learning goals for this chapter. If you are not sure, review the section listed at the end of the goal. Good luck.

After studying chapter 20, I can successfully:

_____ Classify enzymes according to the type of reaction they catalyze (20.1).

_____ Describe the lock-and-key and induced-fit models of enzyme action (20.2).

_____ Discuss the effect of changes in temperature, pH, and concentration of substrate on enzyme action (20.3).

_____ Describe the reversible and irreversible inhibition of enzymes (20.4).

_____ Discuss feedback control and regulation of enzyme action (20.5).

_____ Identify the types of cofactors that are necessary for enzyme action (20.6).

_____ Describe the functions of vitamins as coenzymes (20.7).

Practice Test for Chapter 20

1. Enzymes
  A. are biological catalysts.   **B.** are polysaccharides.
  C. are insoluble in water.   **D.** always contain a cofactor
  E. are named with an *ose* ending

Classify the enzymes described in questions 2–5 as simple (A) or requiring a cofactor (B).

2. _____ an enzyme that yields amino acids and a glucose molecule on analysis

3. _____ an enzyme consisting of protein only

4. _____ an enzyme requiring zinc ion for activation

5. _____ an enzyme containing vitamin K

For problems 6–10, select answers from the following (**E** = enzyme; **S** = substrate; **P** = product):
  A. $S \rightarrow P$ **B.** $EP \rightarrow E + P$ **C.** $E + S \rightarrow ES$
  D. $ES \rightarrow EP$ **E.** $EP \rightarrow ES$

6. _____ the enzymatic reaction occurring at the active site

7. _____ the release of product from the enzyme

8. _____ the first step in the lock-and-key theory of enzyme action

9. _____ the formation of the enzyme-substrate complex

10. _____ the final step in the lock-and-key theory of enzyme action

In problems 11–15, match the names of enzymes with a reaction they each catalyze.
  A. decarboxylase   **B.** isomerase   **C.** dehydrogenase
  D. lipase   **E.** sucrase

11. _____ $CH_3-\overset{OH}{\underset{|}{C}H}-COOH \rightarrow CH_3-\overset{O}{\underset{\|}{C}}-COOH$

12. _____ sucrose $+ H_2O \rightarrow$ glucose and fructose

13. _____ $CH_3-\overset{O}{\underset{\|}{C}}-COOH \rightarrow CH_3COOH + CO_2$

14. _____ fructose $\rightarrow$ glucose

15. _____ triglyceride $+ 3H_2O \rightarrow$ fatty acids and glycerol

For problems 16–20, select your answers from the following:
  A. increases the rate of reaction   **B.** decreases the rate of reaction
  C. denatures the enzyme, and no reaction occurs

16. _____ setting the reaction tube in a beaker of water at 100°C

17. _____ adding substrate to the reaction vessel

18. _____ running the reaction at 10°C

19. _____ adding ethanol to the reaction system

20. _____ adjusting the pH to optimum pH

335

For problems 21–25, identify each description of inhibition as one of the following:
  A. competitive   **B.** noncompetitive

21. _____ an alteration in the conformation of the enzyme

22. _____ A molecule closely resembling the substrate interferes with activity.

23. _____ The inhibition can be reversed by increasing substrate concentration.

24. _____ The heavy metal ion, Pb^{2+}, bonds with an —SH side group.

25. _____ The inhibition is not affected by increased substrate concentration.

26. _____ The presence of zinc in the enzyme called alcohol dehydrogenase classifies a protein as
  A. simple   **B.** requiring a cofactor   **C.** hormonal
  D. structural   **E.** secondary

Answers to the Practice Test

1. A	**2.** B	**3.** A	**4.** B	**5.** B
6. D	**7.** B	**8.** C	**9.** C	**10.** B
11. C	**12.** E	**13.** A	**14.** B	**15.** D
16. C	**17.** A	**18.** B	**19.** C	**20.** A
21. B	**22.** A	**23.** A	**24.** B	**25.** B
26. B				

Answers and Solutions to Selected Text Problems

20.1   The chemical reactions can occur without enzymes, but the rates are too slow. Catalyzed reactions, which are many times faster, provide the amounts of products needed by the cell at a particular time.

20.3   **a.** Oxidoreductases catalyze oxidation and reduction.
   b. Transferases move groups such as amino or phosphate groups from one substance to another.
   c. Hydrolases use water to split bonds in molecules such as carbohydrates, peptides, and lipids.

20.5   **a.** A hydrolase enzyme would catalyze the hydrolysis of sucrose.
   b. An oxidoreductase enzyme would catalyze the addition of oxygen (oxidation).
   c. An isomerase enzyme would catalyze converting glucose to fructose.
   d. A transferase enzyme would catalyze moving an amino group.

20.7   **a.** A lyase such as a decarboxylase removes CO_2 from a molecule.
   b. The transfer of an amino group to another molecule would be catalyzed by a transferase.

20.9   **a.** Succinate oxidase catalyzes the oxidation of succinate.
   b. Fumarate hydrase catalyzes the addition of water to fumarate.
   c. Alcohol dehydrogenase removes 2H from an alcohol.

20.11   **a.** An enzyme has a tertiary structure that recognized the substrate.
   b. The combination of the enzyme and substrate is the enzyme-substrate complex.
   c. The substrate has a structure that complements the structure of the enzyme.

20.13   **a.** The equation for an enzyme-catalyzed reaction is:

$$E + S \rightleftarrows ES \rightarrow E + P$$

   E = enzyme, S = substrate, ES = enzyme-substrate complex, P = products
   b. The active site is a region or pocket within the tertiary structure of an enzyme that accepts the substrate, aligns the substrate for reaction, and catalyzes the reaction.

20.15 Isoenzymes are slightly different forms of an enzyme that catalyze the same reaction in different organs and tissues of the body.

20.17 A doctor might run tests for the enzymes CK, LDH, and AST to determine if the patient had a heart attack.

20.19 **a.** Decreasing the substrate concentration decreases the rate of reaction.
b. Running the reaction at a pH below optimum pH will decrease the rate of reaction.
c. Temperature above 37°C (optimum pH) will denature the enzymes and decrease the rate of reaction.
d. Increasing the enzyme concentration would increase the rate of reaction.

20.21 pepsin, pH 2; urease, pH 5; trypsin; pH 8

20.23 **a.** If the inhibitor has a structure similar to the structure of the substrate, the inhibitor is competitive
b. If adding more substrate cannot reverse the effect of the inhibitor, the inhibitor is noncompetitive.
c. If the inhibitor competes with the substrate for the active site, it is a competitive inhibitor.
d. If the structure of the inhibitor is not similar to the structure of the substrate, the inhibitor is noncompetitive.
e. If adding more substrate reverses inhibition, the inhibitor is competitive.

20.25 **a.** Methanol has the structural formula $CH_3—OH$, whereas ethanol is $CH_3—CH_2—OH$.
b. Ethanol has a structure similar to methanol and could compete for the active site.
c. Ethanol is a competitive inhibitor of methanol oxidation.

20.27 Enzymes that act on proteins are proteases and would digest the proteins of the organ where they are produced if they were active immediately upon synthesis.

20.29 In feedback inhibition, the product binds to the first enzyme in a series, changing the shape of the active site. If the active site can no longer bind the substrate effectively, the reaction stops.

20.31 When a regulator molecule binds to an allosteric site, the shape of the enzyme is altered, which makes the active site more or less reactive and thereby increases or decreases the rate of the reaction.

20.33 **a.** 3; A negative regulator binds to the allosteric site and slows down the reaction.
b. 4; Typically, the first enzyme in a reaction sequence is an allosteric enzyme, which regulates the flow of substrates through the sequence to yield end product.
c. 1; A zymogen is an inactive form of an enzyme.

20.35 **a.** The active form of this enzyme requires a cofactor.
b. The active form of this enzyme requires a cofactor.
c. A simple enzyme is active as a protein.

20.37 **a.** THF   **b.** NAD^+

20.39 **a.** Pantothenic acid (vitamin B_5) is part of coenzyme A.
b. Tetrahydrofolate (THF) is a reduced form of folic acid.
c. Niacin (vitamin B_3) is a component of NAD^+.

20.41 **a.** A deficiency of vitamin D or cholecalciferol can lead to rickets.
b. A deficiency of ascorbic acid or vitamin C can lead to scurvy.
c. A deficiency of niacin or vitamin B_3 can lead to pellagra.

20.43 Vitamin B_6 is a water-soluble vitamin, which means that each day any excess of vitamin B_6 is eliminated from the body.

20.45 The side chain —CH_2OH on the ring is oxidized to —CHO, and the other —CH_2OH forms a phosphate ester.

20.47 **a.** The oxidation of glycol to an aldehyde and carboxylic acid is catalyzed by an oxidoreductase.
b. Ethanol would act as a competitive inhibitor of ethylene glycol, saturate the enzyme, and allow ethylene glycol to be removed from the body without producing oxalic acid.

20.49 **a.** Fresh pineapple contains an enzyme that breaks down protein, which means that Jello would not turn solid. The high temperatures used to prepare canned pineapple will denature the enzyme so it no longer can break down protein.
b. The enzyme in fresh pineapple juice can be used to tenderize tough meat because the enzyme breaks down proteins.

20.51 The many different reactions that take place in cells require different enzymes because enzymes react with only a certain type of substrate.

20.53 Enzymes are catalysts that are proteins and function only at mild temperature and pH. Catalysts used in chemistry laboratories are usually inorganic materials that can function at high temperatures and in strongly acidic or basic conditions.

20.55 **a.** The disaccharide lactose is a substrate.
b. The -*ase* in lactase indicates that it is an enzyme.
c. The -*ase* in urease indicates that it is an enzyme.
d. Trypsin is an enzyme, which hydrolyzes polypeptides.
e. Pyruvate is a substrate.
f. The -*ase* in transaminase indicates that it is an enzyme.

20.57 **a.** Urea is the substrate of urease.
b. Lactose is the substrate of lactase.
c. Aspartate is the substrate of aspartate transaminase.
d. Phenylalanine is the substrate of phenylalanine hydroxylase.

20.59 **a.** The transfer of an acyl group is catalyzed by a transferase.
b. Oxidases are classified as oxidoreductases.
c. A lipase, which splits esters bonds in lipids with water, is a hydrolase.
d. A decarboxylase is classified as a lyase.

20.61 Sucrose fits the shape of the active site in sucrase, but lactose does not.

20.63 A heart attack may be the cause. Normally, the enzymes LDH and CK are present only in low levels in the blood.

20.65 **a.** An enzyme is saturated if adding more substrate does not increase the rate.
b. An enzyme is unsaturated when increasing the substrate increases the rate.

20.67 In a reversible inhibition, the inhibitor can dissociate from the enzyme, whereas in irreversible inhibition, the inhibitor forms a strong covalent bond with the enzyme and does not dissociate. Irreversible inhibitors act as poisons to enzymes.

20.69 **a.** Antibiotics such as amoxicillin are irreversible inhibitors.
b. Antibiotics inhibit enzymes needed to form cell walls in bacteria, not humans.

20.71 **a.** When pepsinogen enters the stomach, the low pH cleaves a peptide from its protein chain to form pepsin.
b. An active protease would digest the proteins of the pancreas rather than the proteins in the foods entering the stomach.

20.73 An allosteric enzyme contains sites for regulators that alter the enzyme and speed up or slow down the rate of the catalyzed reaction.

20.75 The end product of the reaction pathway is a negative regulator that binds to the enzyme to decrease or stop the first reaction in the reaction pathway.

20.77 **a.** The Mg^{2+} is a cofactor that is required by this enzyme.
b. A protein that is catalytically active is a simple enzyme.
c. Folic acid is a coenzyme that is required by this enzyme.

20.79 **a.** Coenzyme A requires pantothenic acid (B_5).
b. NAD^+ requires niacin (B_3).
c. TPP needs thiamin (B_1).

20.81 A vitamin combines with an enzyme only when the enzyme and coenzyme are needed to catalyze a reaction. When the enzyme is not needed, the vitamin dissociates for use by other enzymes in the cell.

20.83 **a.** A deficiency of niacin can lead to pellagra.
b. A deficiency of vitamin A can lead to night blindness.
c. A deficiency of vitamin D can weaken bone structure.

20.85 **a.** The reactant is lactose, and the products are glucose and galactose.

b.

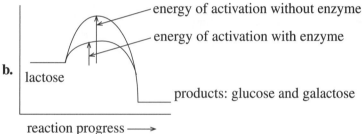

c. By lowering the energy of activation, the enzyme furnishes a lower energy pathway by which the reaction can take place.

20.87 **a.** In this reaction, oxygen is added to an aldehyde. The enzyme that catalyzes this reaction would be an oxidoreductase.
b. In this reaction, a dipeptide is hydrolyzed. The enzyme that catalyzes this reaction would be a hydrolase.
c. In this reaction, water is added to a double bond. The enzyme that catalyzes this reaction would be a lyase.

Nucleic Acids and Protein Synthesis

Study Goals

- Draw the structures of the nitrogen bases, sugars, and nucleotides in DNA and RNA.
- Describe the structures of DNA and RNA.
- Explain the process of DNA replication.
- Describe the preparation of recombinant DNA.
- Describe the transcription process during the synthesis of mRNA.
- Use the codons in the genetic code to describe protein synthesis.
- Explain how an alteration in the DNA sequence can lead to mutations in proteins.
- Describe the regulation of protein synthesis in the cells.

Think About It

1. Where is DNA in your cells?

2. How does DNA determine your height or the color of your hair or eyes?

3. What is the genetic code?

4. How does a mutation occur?

5. What is recombinant DNA?

Key Terms

Match the following key terms with the correct statement shown below.

    a. DNA   **b.** RNA   **c.** double helix   **d.** mutation   **e.** transcription

1. _____ The formation of mRNA to carry genetic information from DNA to protein synthesis

2. _____ The genetic material containing nucleotides and nitrogenous bases adenine, cytosine, guanine, and thymine

3. _____ The shape of DNA with a sugar-phosphate backbone and base pairs linked in the center

4. _____ A change in the DNA base sequence that may alter the shape and function of a protein

5. _____ A type of nucleic acid with a single strand of nucleotides of adenine, cytosine, guanine, and uracil

Answers   **1.** e   **2.** a   **3.** c   **4.** d   **5.** b

21.1 Components of Nucleic Acids

- Nucleic acids are composed of four nitrogenous bases, five-carbon sugars, and a phosphate group.
- In DNA, the nitrogen bases are adenine, thymine, guanine, or cytosine. In RNA, uracil replaces thymine.
- In DNA, the sugar is deoxyribose; in RNA, the sugar is ribose.
- A nucleoside is composed of a nitrogen base and a sugar.
- A nucleotide is composed of three parts: a nitrogen base, a sugar, and a phosphate group.
- Deoxyribonucleic acid (DNA) and ribonucleic acid (RNA) are polymers of nucleotides.

◆ Learning Exercise 21.1A

1. Write the names and abbreviations for the nitrogen bases in each of the following:

DNA _____

RNA _____

2. Write the name of the sugar in each of the following nucleotides:

DNA _____

RNA _____

Answers   **1.** DNA: adenine (A), thymine (T), guanine (G), cytosine (C)
                    RNA: adenine (A), uracil (U), guanine (G), cytosine (C)
    2. DNA: deoxyribose
                    RNA: ribose

◆ Learning Exercise 21.1B

Name each of the following and classify it as a purine or a pyrimidine:

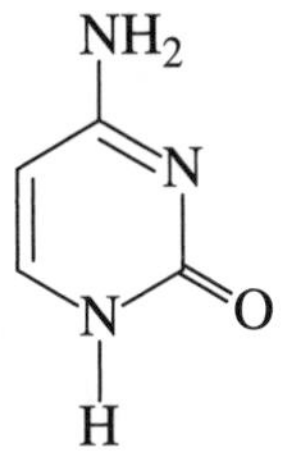

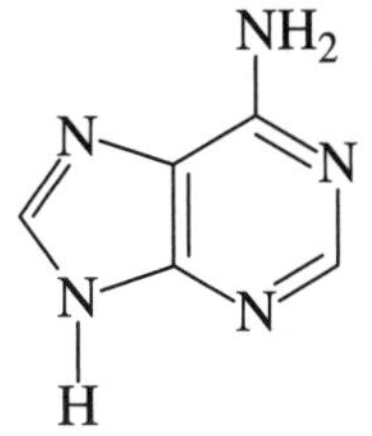

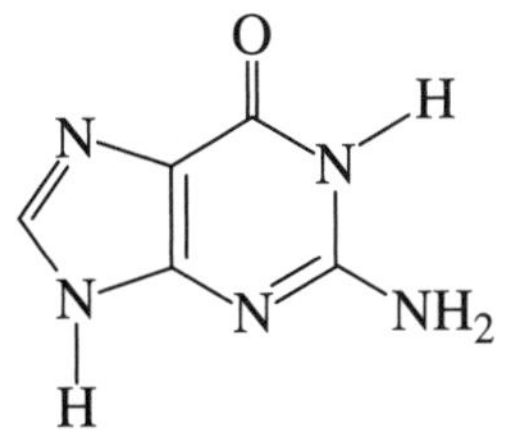

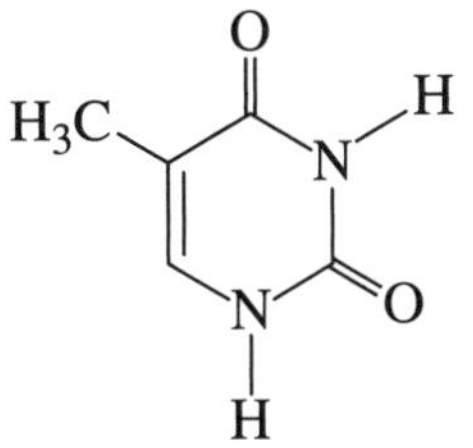

1. cytosine, pyrimidine   **2.** adenine; purine
                3. guanine, purine   **4.** thymine, pyrimidine

◆ Learning Exercise 21.1C

Identify the nucleic acid (DNA or RNA) in which each of the following are found:

1. ____ adenosine-5′-monophosphate   **2.** ____ dCMP

3. ____ deoxythymidine-5′-monophosphate   **4.** ____ dGMP

5. ____ guanosine-5′-monophosphate   **6.** ____ cytidine-5′-monophosphate

7. ____ UMP   **8.** ____ deoxyadenosine-5′-monophosphate

Answers   **1.** RNA   **2.** DNA   **3.** DNA   **4.** DNA
          5. RNA   **6.** RNA   **7.** RNA   **8.** DNA

◆ Learning Exercise 21.1D

Write the structural formula for deoxyadenosine-5′-monophosphate. Indicate the 5′- and the 3′-carbon atoms on the sugar.

Answer

Deoxyadenosine 5′-monophosphate (dAMP)

21.2 Primary Structures of Nucleic Acids

- Nucleic acids are polymers of nucleotides in which the —OH group on the 3′-carbon of a sugar in one nucleotide bonds to the phosphate group attached to the 5′-carbon of a sugar in the adjacent nucleotide.

◆ Learning Exercise 21.2A

In the following dinucleotide, identify each nucleotide, the phosphodiester bond, the 5′-free phosphate group, and the free 3′-hydroxyl group.

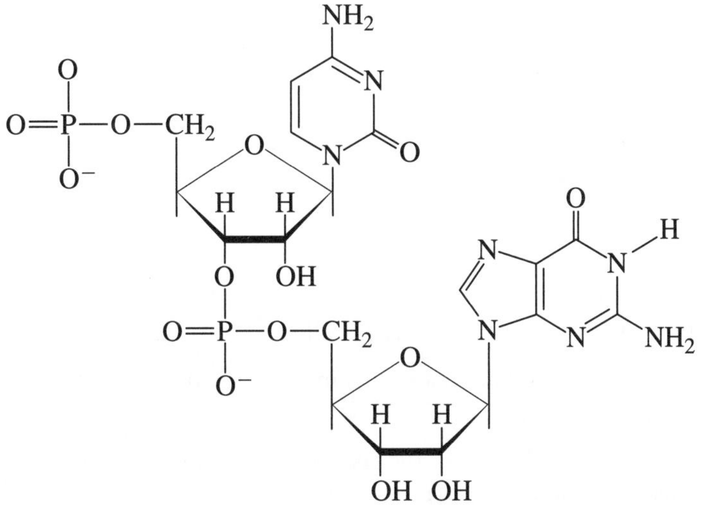

Answer

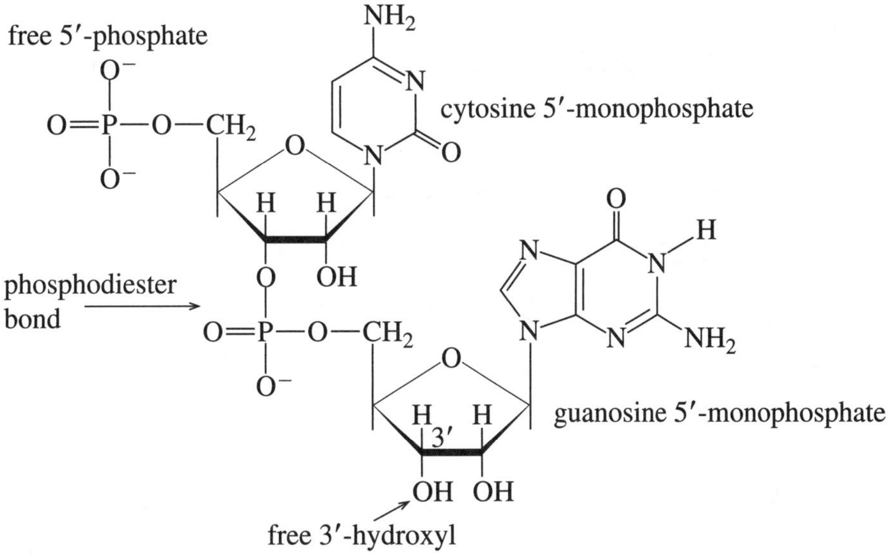

free 5′-phosphate

cytosine 5′-monophosphate

phosphodiester bond →

guanosine 5′-monophosphate

free 3′-hydroxyl

◆ Learning Exercise 21.2B

Consider the following sequence of nucleotides in RNA: —A—G—U—C—

1. What are the names of the nucleotides in this sequence?

2. Which nucleotide has the free 5′-phosphate group? _____

3. Which nucleotide has the free 3′-hydroxyl group? _____

Answer

    1. adenosine 5′-monophosphate, guanosine 5′-monophosphate, uridine 5′-monophosphate, cytosine 5′-monophosphate

    2. adenosine 5′-monophosphate (AMP) read as 5′—A—G—C—T—3′

    3. cytosine 5′-monophosphate (CMP)

21.3 DNA Double Helix

- The two strands in DNA are held together by hydrogen bonds between complementary base pairs, A with T and G with C.
- One DNA strand runs in the 5′-3′ direction with a free 5′ phosphate, and the other strand runs in the 3′-5′ direction with a free 3′ phosphate.

◆ Learning Exercise 21.3A

Complete the following statements:

1. The structure of the two strands of nucleotides in DNA is called a _____ .

2. In one strand of DNA, the sugar-phosphate backbone runs in the 5′-3′ direction, whereas the opposite strand goes in the _____ direction.

3. On the DNA strand that runs in the 5′-3′ direction, the free phosphate group is at the _____ end and the free hydroxyl group is at the _____ end.

4. The only combinations of base pairs that connect the two DNA strands are _____ and _____ .

5. The base pairs along one DNA strand are _____ to the base pairs on the opposite strand.

Answers   **1.** double helix   **2.** 3′-5′   **3.** 5′-, 3′
             4. A—T; G—C   **5.** complementary

◆ Learning Exercise 21.3B

Complete each DNA section by writing the complementary strand.

1. 5′—ATGCTTGGCTCC—3′   2. 5′—AAATTTCCCGGG—3′

3. 5′—GCGCTCAAATGC—3′

Answers   **1.** 3′—TACGAACCGAGG—5′   **2.** 3′—TTTAAAGGGCCC—5′
             3. 3′—CGCGAGTTTACG—5′

21.4 DNA Replication

- During DNA replication, DNA polymerase makes new DNA strands along each of the original DNA strands that serve as templates.
- Complementary base pairing ensures the correct pairing of bases to give identical copies of the original DNA.

◆ Learning Exercise 21.4A

How does the replication of DNA produce identical copies of the DNA?

Answer   In the replication process, the bases on each strand of the separated parent DNA are paired with their complementary bases. Because each complementary base is specific for a base in DNA, the new DNA strands exactly duplicate the original strands of DNA.

◆ **Learning Exercise 21.4B**

Match each of the following terms with components or events in DNA replication:

a. replication fork   **b.** Okazaki fragment   **c.** DNA polymerase
d. helicase   **e.** leading strand   **f.** lagging strand

1. _____ the enzyme that catalyzes the unwinding of a section of the DNA double helix

2. _____ the points in open sections of DNA where replication begins

3. _____ the enzyme that catalyzes the formation of phosphodiester bonds between nucleotides

4. _____ short segments produced in the formation of the 3'-5' DNA daughter strand

5. _____ the new DNA strand that grows in the 5' to 3' direction during the formation of daughter DNA

6. _____ the new DNA strand that is synthesized in the 3' to 5' direction.

Answers   **1.** d   **2.** a   **3.** c
                 4. b   **5.** e   **6.** f

21.5 RNA and Transcription

- The three types of RNA differ by function in the cell: ribosomal RNA makes up most of the structure of the ribosomes, messenger RNA carries genetic information from the DNA to the ribosomes, and transfer RNA places the correct amino acids in the protein.
- Transcription is the process by which RNA polymerase produces mRNA from one strand of DNA.
- The bases in the mRNA are complementary to the DNA, except U is paired with A in DNA.
- The polymerase enzyme moves along an unwound section of DNA in a 3' to 5' direction.
- In eukaryotes, initial RNA includes noncoding sections, which are removed before the RNA leaves the nucleus.
- The production of mRNA occurs when certain proteins are needed in the cell.
- In enzyme induction, the appearance of a substrate in a cell removes a repressor, which allows RNA polymerase to produce mRNA at the structural genes.

◆ **Learning Exercise 21.5A**

Match each of the following characteristics with a specific type of RNA: mRNA, tRNA, or rRNA.

1. the most abundant type of RNA in a cell _____

2. the RNA that has the shortest chain of nucleotides _____

3. the RNA that carries information from DNA to the ribosomes for protein synthesis _____

4. the RNA that is the major component of ribosomes _____

5. the RNA that carries specific amino acids to the ribosome for protein synthesis _____

6. the RNA that consists of a large and a small subunit _____

Answers   **1.** rRNA   **2.** tRNA   **3.** mRNA
                 4. rRNA   **5.** tRNA   **6.** rRNA

◆ **Learning Exercise 21.5B**

Fill in the blanks with a word or phrase that answers each of the following questions:

1. Where in the cell does transcription take place? _____

2. How many strands of the DNA molecules are involved? _____

3. sections in genes that code for proteins _____

4. sections in genes that do not code for proteins _____

5. the abbreviations for the four nucleotides in mRNA _____

6. Write the corresponding section of a mRNA produced from each of the following:

   A. 3′—C—A—T—T—C—G—G—T—A—5′

   B. 3′—G—T—A—C—C—T—A—A—C—G—T—C—C—G—5′

Answers   **1.** nucleus   **2.** one   **3.** exons   **4.** introns   **5.** A, U, G, C
6 A. 5′—G—U—A—A—G—C—C—A—U—3′
B. 5′—C—A—U—G—G—A—U—U—G—C—A—G—G—C—3′

◆ **Learning Exercise 21.5C**

Match the following descriptions of cellular control with the terms:

A. repressor   **B.** operon   **C.** structural gene
D. enzyme repression   **E.** enzyme induction

_____ **1.** the production of an enzyme caused by the appearance of a substrate

_____ **2.** a unit formed by a structural gene and an operator gene

_____ **3.** high levels of an end product stop the production of the enzymes in that pathway

_____ **4.** a protein that attaches to the operator gene and blocks the synthesis of protein

_____ **5.** the portion of DNA that produces the mRNA for protein synthesis

Answers   **1.** E   **2.** B   **3.** D   **4.** A   **5.** C

21.6 The Genetic Code

- The genetic code consists of a sequence of three bases (triplet) that specifies the order for the amino acids in a protein.
- There are 64 codons for the 20 amino acids, which means there are several codons for most amino acids.
- The codon AUG signals the start of transcription, and codons UAG, UGA, and UAA signal the stop.

◆ **Learning Exercise 21.6**

Indicate the amino acid coded for by the following mRNA codons:

1. UUU _____   2. GCG _____

3. AGC _____   4. CCA _____

5. GGA _____   6. ACA _____

7. AUG _____   8. CUC _____

9. CAU _____   10. GUU _____

Answers   1. Phe   2. Ala   3. Ser   4. Pro   5. Gly
            6. Thr   7. Start/Met   8. Leu   9. His   10. Val

21.7 Protein Synthesis: Translation

- Proteins are synthesized at the ribosomes in a translation process that includes three steps: initiation, elongation, and termination.
- During translation, the different tRNA molecules bring the appropriate amino acids to the ribosome, where the amino acid is bonded by a peptide bond to the growing peptide chain.
- When the polypeptide is released, it takes on its secondary and tertiary structures to become a functional protein in the cell.

◆ **Learning Exercise 21.7A**

Match the following components of the translation process with the following:

a. initiation   **b.** activation   **c.** anticodon   **d.** translocation   **e.** termination

1. _____ the three bases in each tRNA that complement a codon on the mRNA

2. _____ the combining of an amino acid with a specific tRNA

3. _____ the placement of methionine on the large ribosome

4. _____ the shift of the ribosome from one codon on mRNA to the next

5. _____ the process that occurs when the ribosome reaches a UAA or UGA codon on mRNA

Answers   1. c   2. b   3. a   4. d   5. e

◆ **Learning Exercise 21.7B**

Write the mRNA that would form for the following section of DNA. For each codon in the mRNA, write the amino acid that would be placed in the protein by a tRNA.

1. DNA strand: 3′ — CCC — TCA — GGG — CGC — 5′

mRNA: _____ — _____ — _____ — _____

amino acid order: _____ — _____ — _____ — _____

2. DNA: 3′ — ATA — GCC — TTT — GGC — AAC — 5′

mRNA: _____ — _____ — _____ — _____ — _____

amino acid order: _____ — _____ — _____ — _____ — _____

Answers   **1.** mRNA: 5′ — GGG — AGU — CCC — GCG — 3′
                       — Gly — Ser — Pro — Ala —
                2. mRNA: 5′ — UAU — CGG — AAA — CCG — UUG — 3′
                       — Tyr — Arg — Lys — Pro — Leu —

◆ Learning Exercise 21.7C

A segment of DNA that codes for a protein contains 270 nucleic acids. How many amino acids would be present in the protein for this DNA segment?

Answer   Assuming that the entire segment codes for a protein, there would be 90 (270 ÷ 3) amino acids in the protein produced.

21.8 Genetic Mutations

- A genetic mutation is a change of one or more bases in the DNA sequence that may alter the structure and ability of the resulting protein to function properly.
- In a substitution, one base is altered, which codes for a different amino acid.
- In a frame shift mutation, the insertion or deletion of one base alters all of the codons following the base change, which affects the amino acid sequence that follows the mutation.

◆ Learning Exercise 21.8

Consider the DNA template of 3′ — AAT — CCC — GGG — 5′.

1. Write the mRNA produced.

_____ — _____ — _____

2. Write the amino acid order for the mRNA codons.

_____ — _____ — _____

3. Suppose a point mutation replaces the thymine in the DNA template with a guanine. Write the mRNA it produces.

_____ — _____ — _____

4. What is the new amino acid order?

_____ — _____ — _____

5. Why is this effect referred to as a point mutation?

6. How is a point mutation different from an insertion or deletion mutation?

7. What are some possible causes of genetic mutations?

Answers   **1.** 5′—UUA—GGG—CCC—3′   **2.** Leu-Gly-Pro
    3. 5′—UUC—GGG—CCC—3′   **4.** Phe-Gly-Pro
    5. In a point mutation, only one codon is affected, and one amino acid substituted.
    6. In an insertion or deletion mutation, the triplet codes that follow the mutation point are shifted by one base, which changes the amino acid order.
    7. X rays, UV light, chemical called mutagens, and some viruses are possible causes of mutations.

21.9 Recombinant DNA

* Recombinant DNA is DNA that has been synthesized by opening a piece of DNA and inserting a DNA section from another source.
* Much of the work in recombinant DNA is done with the small circular DNA molecules called *plasmids* found in *Escherichia coli* bacteria.
* Recombinant DNA is used to produce large numbers of copies of foreign DNA that is useful in genetic engineering techniques.

◆ Learning Exercise 21.9

Match the statements shown below with the following terms:

A. plasmids   **B.** restriction enzymes   **C.** polymerase chain reaction
D. recombinant DNA   **E.** Human Genome Project

1. _____ a synthetic form of DNA that contains a piece of foreign DNA

2. _____ research that is mapping the DNA sequences for all the genes in a human cell

3. _____ small, circular, DNA molecules found in *E. coli* bacteria

4. _____ a process that makes multiple copies of DNA in a short amount of time

5. _____ enzymes that cut open the DNA strands in the plasmids

Answers   **1.** D   **2.** E   **3.** A   **4.** C   **5.** B

21.10 Viruses

- Viruses are small particles of 3–200 genes that cannot replicate unless they invade a host cell.
- A viral infection involves using the host cell machinery to replicate the viral DNA.
- A retrovirus contains RNA and a reverse transcriptase enzyme that synthesizes a viral DNA in a host cell.

◆ Learning Exercise 21.10

Match the key terms with the statements shown below:

A. host cell   **B.** retrovirus   **C.** vaccine   **D.** protease   **E.** virus

1. _____ The enzyme inhibited by drugs that prevent the synthesis of viral proteins.
2. _____ A small, disease-causing particle that contains either DNA or RNA as its genetic material.
3. _____ A type of virus that must use reverse transcriptase to make a viral DNA.
4. _____ Required by viruses to replicate.
5. _____ Inactive form of viruses that boosts the immune response by causing the body to produce antibodies.

Answers   **1.** D   **2.** E   **3.** B   **4.** A   **5.** C

Checklist for Chapter 21

You are ready to take the practice test for chapter 21. Be sure that you have accomplished the following learning goals for this chapter. If you are not sure, review the section listed at the end of the goal. Then apply your new skills and understanding to the practice test. Good luck.

After studying chapter 21, I can successfully:

_____ Identify the components of nucleic acids RNA and DNA (21.1).

_____ Describe the nucleotides contained in DNA and RNA (21.1).

_____ Describe the primary structure of nucleic acids (21.2).

_____ Describe the structures of RNA and DNA; show the relationship between the bases in the double helix (21.3).

_____ Explain the process of DNA replication (21.4).

_____ Describe the structures and characteristics of the three types of RNA (21.5).

_____ Describe the synthesis of mRNA (transcription) (21.5).

_____ Describe the function of the codons in the genetic code (21.6).

_____ Describe the role of translation in protein synthesis (21.7).

_____ Describe some ways in which DNA is altered to cause mutations (21.8).

_____ Describe the process used to prepare recombinant DNA (21.9).

_____ Explain how retroviruses use reverse transcription to synthesize DNA (21.10).

Practice Test for Chapter 21

1. A nucleotide contains
  A. a nitrogen base
  B. a nitrogen base and a sugar
  C. a phosphate and a sugar
  D. a nitrogen base and a deoxyribose
  E. a nitrogen base, a sugar, and a phosphate

2. The double helix in DNA is held together by
  A. hydrogen bonds
  B. ester linkages
  C. peptide bonds
  D. salt bridges
  E. disulfide bonds

3. The process of producing DNA in the nucleus is called
  A. complementation
  B. replication
  C. translation
  D. transcription
  E. mutation

4. Which occurs in RNA but **NOT** in DNA?
  A. thymine
  B. cytosine
  C. adenine
  D. phosphate
  E. uracil

5. Which molecule determines protein structure in protein synthesis?
  A. DNA   **B.** mRNA   **C.** tRNA   **D.** rRNA   **E.** ribosomes

6. Which type of molecule carries amino acids to the ribosomes?
  A. DNA   **B.** mRNA   **C.** tRNA   **D.** rRNA   **E.** protein

For questions 7–15, select answers from the following nucleic acids:
  A. DNA   **B.** mRNA   **C.** tRNA   **D.** rRNA

7. _____ Along with protein, it is a major component of the ribosomes.

8. _____ A double helix consisting of two chains of nucleotides held together by hydrogen bonds between nitrogen bases.

9. _____ A nucleic acid that uses deoxyribose as the sugar

10. _____ A nucleic acid produced in the nucleus that migrates to the ribosomes to direct the formation of a protein.

11. _____ It can place the proper amino acid into the peptide chain.

12. _____ It has nitrogen bases of adenine, cytosine, guanine, and thymine.

13. _____ It contains the codons for the amino acid order.

14. _____ It contains a triplet called an anticodon loop.

15. _____ This nucleic acid is replicated during cellular division.

For questions 16–20, select answers from the following:

  A. —A—G—C—C—T—A—   **B.** —A—U—U—G—C—U—C—
           | | | | | |
          —T—C—G—G—A—T—

  C. —A—G—T—U—G—U—   **D.** —G—U—A—   **E.** —A—T—G—T—A—T—
           | | | | | |
          —T—C—A—A—C—A—

16. _____ a section of an mRNA   **17.** _____ an impossible section of DNA

18. _____ a codon   **19.** _____ a section from a DNA molecule

20. _____ a single strand that would not be possible for mRNA

Read the following statements:
  A. tRNA assembles the amino acids at the ribosomes.
  B. DNA forms a complementary copy of itself called mRNA.
  C. Protein is formed and breaks away.
  D. tRNA picks up specific amino acids.
  E. mRNA goes to the ribosomes.

Of the statements above, select the order in which they occur during protein synthesis.

21. ____ first step   **22.** ____ second step   **23.** ____ third step

24. ____ fourth step   **25.** ____ fifth step

For questions, 26–30, select your answers from the following:
  A. mutation   **B.** enzyme induction   **C.** inducer
  D. operon   **E.** repressor

26. ____ a unit attaches to the operator gene and blocks the synthesis of a protein

27. ____ an error in the transmission of the base sequence of DNA

28. ____ a portion of a gene composed of the operating gene and the structural genes

29. ____ a substrate that promote the synthesis of the enzymes necessary for its metabolism

30. ____ the level of end product regulates the synthesis of the enzymes in that metabolic pathway

Answers to the Practice Test

1. E	**2.** A	**3.** B	**4.** E	**5.** A
6. C	**7.** D	**8.** A	**9.** A	**10.** B
11. C	**12.** A	**13.** B	**14.** C	**15.** A
16. B, D	**17.** C	**18.** D	**19.** A	**20.** E
21. B	**22.** E	**23.** D	**24.** A	**25.** C
26. E	**27.** A	**28.** D	**29.** B	**30.** C

Answers and Solutions to Selected Text Problems

21.1 DNA contains two purines, adenine (A) and guanine (G), and two pyrimidines, cytosine (C) and thymine (T). RNA contains the same bases, except thymine (T) is replaced by the pyrimidine uracil (U).
  a. pyrimidine   **b.** pyrimidine

21.3 DNA contains two purines, adenine (A) and guanine (G), and two pyrimidines, cytosine (C) and thymine (T). RNA contains the same bases, except thymine (T) is replaced by the pyrimidine uracil (U).
  a. DNA   **b.** both DNA and RNA

21.5 Nucleotides contain a base, a sugar, and a phosphate group. The nucleotides found in DNA would all contain the sugar deoxyribose. The four nucleotides are deoxyadenosine $5'$-monophosphate (dAMP), deoxythymidine $5'$-monophosphate (dTMP), deoxycytidine $5'$-monophosphate (dCMP), and deoxyguanosine $5'$-monophosphate (dGMP).

21.7 **a.** Adenosine is a nucleoside found in RNA.
  b. Deoxycytidine is a nucleoside found in DNA.
  c. Uridine is a nucleoside found in RNA.
  d. Cytidine $5'$-monophosphate is a nucleotide found in RNA.

21.9

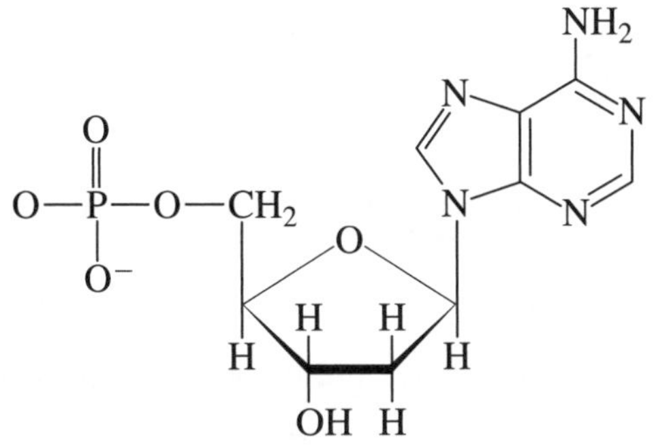

21.11 The nucleotides in nucleic acids are held together by phosphodiester bonds between the 3′-OH of a sugar (ribose or deoxyribose) and the 5′-carbon H of another sugar.

21.13

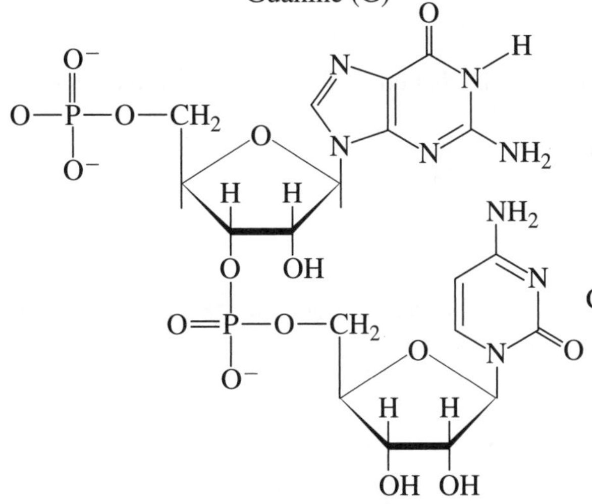

21.15 The two DNA strands are held together by hydrogen bonds between the bases in each strand.

21.17 **a.** Since T pairs with A, if one strand of DNA has the sequence 5′ — AAAAAA — 3′, the second strand would be 3′ — TTTTTT — 5′.
b. Since C pairs with G, if one strand of DNA has the sequence 5′ — GGGGGG — 3′, the second strand would be 3′ — CCCCCC — 5′.
c. Since T pairs with A and C pairs with G, if one strand of DNA has the sequence 5′ — AGTCCAGGT — 3′, the second strand would be 3′ — TCAGGTCCA — 5′.
d. Since T pairs with A and C pairs with G, if one strand of DNA has the sequence 5′ — CTGTATACGTTA, the second strand would be 3′ — GACATATGCAAT — 5′.

21.19 The enzyme helicase unwinds the DNA helix to prepare the parent DNA strand for the synthesis of daughter DNA strands.

21.21 First, the two DNA strands separate in a way that is similar to the unzipping of a zipper. Then the enzyme DNA polymerase begins to copy each strand by pairing each of the bases in the strands with its complementary base: A pairs with T and C with G. Finally, a phosphodiester bond joins the base to the new, growing strand.

21.23 The three types of RNA are the messenger RNA (mRNA), ribosomal RNA (rRNA), and transfer RNA (tRNA).

21.25 A ribosome, which is about 65% rRNA and 35% protein, consists of a small subunit and a large subunit.

353

21.27 In transcription, the sequence of nucleotides on a DNA template (one strand) is used to produce the base sequences of a messenger RNA. The DNA unwinds, and one strand is copied as complementary bases are placed in the mRNA molecule. In RNA, U (uracil) is paired with A in DNA.

21.29 In mRNA, C, G, and A pair with G, C, and T in DNA. However, in mRNA, U will pair with A in DNA. The strand of mRNA would have the following sequence: 5′—GGC—UUC—CAA—GUG—3′.

21.31 In eukaryotic cells, genes contain sections called exons that code for protein and sections called introns that do not code for protein.

21.33 An operon is a section of DNA that regulates the synthesis of one or more proteins.

21.35 When the lactose level is low in *E. coli*, a repressor produced by the mRNA from the regulatory gene binds to the operator, blocking the synthesis of mRNA from the genes and preventing the synthesis of protein.

21.37 A codon is the three-base sequence (triplet) in mRNA that codes for a specific amino acid in a protein.

21.39 **a.** The codon CUU in mRNA codes for the amino acid leucine.
b. The codon UCA in mRNA codes for the amino acid serine.
c. The codon GGU in mRNA codes for the amino acid glycine.
d. The codon AGG in mRNA codes for the amino acid arginine.

21.41 When AUG is the first codon, it signals the start of protein synthesis and incorporates methionine as the first amino acid in the peptide. Eventually the initial methionine is removed as the protein forms its secondary and tertiary protein structure. In the middle of an mRNA sequence, AUG codes for methionine.

21.43 A codon is a base triplet in the mRNA template. An anticodon is the complementary triplet on a tRNA for a specific amino acid.

21.45 The three steps in translation are initiation, translocation, and termination.

21.47 The mRNA must be divided into triplets and the amino acid coded for by each triplet read from the table.
a. The codon AAA in mRNA codes for lysine: —Lys—Lys—Lys—.
b. The codon UUU codes for phenylalanine and CCC for proline: —Phe—Pro—Phe—Pro—.
c. —Tyr—Gly—Arg—Cys—

21.49 After a tRNA attaches to the first binding site on the ribosome, its amino acid forms a peptide bond with the amino acid on the tRNA attached to the second binding site. The ribosome moves along the mRNA, and a new tRNA with its amino acid occupies the open binding site.

21.51 **a.** The mRNA sequence would be: 5′—CGA—AAA—GUU—UUU—3′.
b. The tRNA triplet anticodons would be: GCU, UUU, CAA, AAA.
c. From the table of mRNA codons, the amino acids would be: —Arg—Lys—Val—Phe—.

21.53 In a substitution mutation, an incorrect base replaces a base in DNA.

21.55 If the resulting codon still codes for the same amino acid, there is no effect. If the new codon codes for a different amino acid, there is a change in the order of amino acids in the polypeptide.

21.57 The normal triplet TTT in DNA transcribes to AAA in mRNA. AAA codes for lysine. The mutation TTC in DNA transcribes to AAG in mRNA, which also codes for lysine. Thus, there is no effect on protein synthesis.

21.59 **a.** —Thr—Ser—Arg—Val— is the amino acid sequence produced by normal DNA.

b. —Thr—Thr—Arg—Val— is the amino acid sequence produced by a mutation.

c. —Thr—Ser—Gly—Val— is the amino acid sequence produced by a mutation.

d. —Thr—STOP Protein synthesis would terminate early. If this mutation occurs early in the formation of the polypeptide, the resulting protein will probably be nonfunctional.

e. The new protein will contain the sequence —Asp—Ile—Thr—Gly—.

f. The new protein will contain the sequence —His—His—Gly—.

21.61 **a.** Both codons GCC and GCA code for alanine.

b. A vital ionic cross-link in the tertiary structure of hemoglobin cannot be formed when the polar glutamine is replaced by valine, which is nonpolar. The resulting hemoglobin is malformed and less capable of carrying oxygen.

21.63 *E. coli* are used in recombinant DNA work because they are easy, fast and inexpensive to grow. They contain plasmids, the portion of the cell into which the foreign DNA can be inserted. Then the plasmids are replicated to make copies of the foreign DNA.

21.65 The cells of the *E. coli* are soaked in a detergent solution, which dissolves the plasma membrane and frees the plasmids, which can then be collected.

21.67 A gene for a specific protein is inserted into plasmids by using a restriction enzyme that cuts the DNA in the plasmids in specific places. The same enzyme is used to cut a piece from the DNA to be inserted. The cut-out genes and the cut plasmids are mixed, and DNA ligase, an enzyme that catalyzes the joining of DNA, is added. After the foreign gene is inserted into the plasmids, *E. coli* take up the plasmids and replication begins.

21.69 In DNA fingerprinting, restriction enzymes cut a DNA sample into fragments. These fragments are sorted by size on a gel and tagged with a radioactive material. A piece of film is placed over the gel, and the exposed film gives a unique pattern known as a DNA fingerprint.

21.71 A virus contains either DNA or RNA, but not both, inside a protein coating.

21.73 **a.** An RNA-containing virus must make viral DNA from the RNA to produce a protein coat, allowing the virus to replicate and leave the cell to infect new cells.

b. A virus that uses reverse transcription is a retrovirus.

21.75 Nucleoside analogs like AZT or ddI mimic the structures of nucleosides that the HIV virus uses for DNA synthesis. These analogs are incorporated into the new viral DNA chain, but the lack of a hydroxyl group in position 3′ of the sugar stops the chain from growing any longer and prevents replication of the virus.

21.77 **a.**

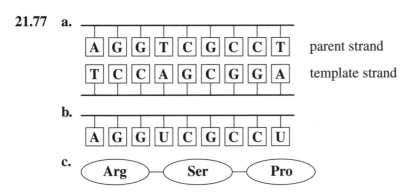

355

21.79 **a.** pyrimidine   **b.** purine   **c.** pyrimidine
          d. pyrimidine   **e.** purine

21.81 **a.** thymine and deoxyribose   **b.** adenine and ribose
          c. cytosine and ribose   **d.** guanine and deoxyribose

22.83 They are both pyrimidines, but thymine has a methyl group.

21.85

21.87 They are both polymers of nucleotides connected through phosphodiester bonds between alternating sugar and phosphate groups, with bases extending out from each sugar.

21.89 28% T, 22% G, and 22% C

21.91 **a.** There are two hydrogen bonds between A and T in DNA.
          b. There are three hydrogen bonds between G and C in DNA.

21.93 **a.** 3′—CTGAATCCG—5′
          b. 5′—ACGTTTGATCGT—3′
          c. 3′—TAGCTAGCTAGC—5′

21.95 DNA polymerase synthesizes the leading strand continuously in the 5′ to 3′ direction. The lagging strand is synthesized in small segments called Okazaki fragments because it must grow in the 3′ to 5′ direction.

21.97 One strand of the parent DNA is found in each of the two copies of the daughter DNA molecule.

21.99 **a.** tRNA   **b.** rRNA   **c.** mRNA

21.101 **a.** ACU, ACC, ACA, and ACG   **b.** UAU, UCC, UCA, and UCG
          c. UGU and UGC

21.103 **a.** AAG codes for lysine   **b.** AUU codes for isoleucine   **c.** CGG codes for arginine

21.105 Using the genetic code the codons indicate the following:
         start(methionine)—Tyr—Gly—Gly—Phe—Leu—stop

21.107 The anticodon consists of the three complementary bases to the codon.
         a. UCG   **b.** AUA   **c.** GGU

21.109 Three nucleotides are needed for each amino acid, plus a start and stop triplet, which makes a minimum total of 33 nucleotides.

21.111 A DNA virus attaches to a cell and injects viral DNA that uses the host cell to produce copies of DNA to make viral RNA. A retrovirus injects viral RNA, from which complementary DNA is produced by reverse transcription.

Metabolic Pathways for Carbohydrates

Study Goals

- Explain the role of ATP in anabolic and catabolic reactions.
- Compare the structures and function of the coenzymes NAD^+, FAD, and coenzyme A.
- Give the sites, enzymes, and products for the digestion of carbohydrates.
- Describe the key reactions in the degradation of glucose in glycolysis.
- Describe the three possible pathways for pyruvate.
- Discuss the impact of ATP levels on glycogen metabolism.
- Describe gluconeogenesis and the Cori cycle.

Think About It

1. Why do you need ATP in your cells?

2. What monosaccharides are produced when carbohydrates undergo digestion?

3. What is meant by *aerobic* and *anaerobic* conditions in the cells?

4. How does glycogen help maintain blood glucose level?

Key Terms

Match the following key terms with the correct statement shown below.

a. ATP   **b.** glycogen   **c.** glycolysis
d. catabolic reaction   **e.** mitochondria

1. _____The storage form of glucose in the muscle and liver

2. _____A metabolic reaction that produces energy for the cell by degrading large molecules

3. _____A high-energy compound produced from energy-releasing processes that provides energy for energy-producing reactions

4. _____The degradation reactions of glucose that yield two pyruvate molecules

5. _____The organelles in the cells where energy-producing reactions take place

Answers   **1.** b   **2.** d   **3.** a   **4.** c   **5.** e

22.1 Metabolism and Cell Structure

- Metabolism is all of the chemical reactions that provide energy and substances for cell growth.
- Catabolic reactions degrade large molecules to produce energy.
- Anabolic reactions utilize energy in the cell to build large molecules for the cells.
- In cells, different organelles contain the enzymes and coenzymes for the various catabolic and anabolic reactions.

◆ Learning Exercise 22.1A

Match each of the following organelles with their description or cellular function:

a. lysosomes   b. ribosomes   c. mitochondria
d. Golgi apparatus   e. cytoplasm   f. plasma membrane

1. _____ separates the contents of a cell from the external environment

2. _____ contain enzymes that catalyze energy-producing reactions

3. _____ the cellular material between the plasma membrane and the nucleus

4. _____ modifies proteins from the endoplasmic reticulum for cell membranes

5. _____ protein synthesis

6. _____ hydrolytic enzymes digest old cell structures

Answers   1. f   2. c   3. e   4. d   5. b   6. a

◆ Learning Exercise 22.1B

Identify the stages of metabolism for each of the following processes:

a. stage 1   b. stage 2   c. stage 3

1. _____ oxidation of two-carbon acetyl CoA enters a series of reactions that provide most of the energy for ATP synthesis

2. _____ polysaccharides undergo digestion to monosaccharides, such as glucose

3. _____ digestion products such as glucose are degraded to two- or three-carbon compounds

Answers   1. c   2. a   3. b

22.2 ATP and Energy

- Energy is stored in ATP, a high-energy compound that is hydrolyzed when energy is required for the anabolic reactions that do work in the cells.
- The hydrolysis of ATP, which releases energy, is linked with many anabolic reactions in the cell.

◆ Learning Exercise 22.2

Complete the following statements for ATP:

The ATP molecule is composed of a nitrogen base (1)_____, a (2) _____ sugar, and three (3) _____. ATP undergoes (4)_____, which cleaves a (5) _____ and releases (6) _____. For this reason, ATP is called a (7)_____ compound. The resulting phosphate group called inorganic phosphate is abbreviated as (8) _____. This equation can be written as (9)_____.
The energy from ATP is linked to cellular reactions that are (10)_____.

Answers   1. adenine   2. ribose   3. phosphate groups   4. hydrolysis
               5. phosphate   6. energy   7. high-energy   8. P_i
               9. $ATP + H_2O \rightarrow ADP + Pi + Energy$ (7.3 kcal/mole)   10. energy requiring

22.3 Important Coenzymes in Metabolic Pathways

- Coenzymes such as FAD and NAD^+ pick up hydrogen and electrons during oxidative processes.
- Coenzyme A is a coenzyme that carries acetyl (two-carbon) groups produced when glucose, fatty acids, and amino acids are degraded.

Select the coenzyme that matches each of the following descriptions of coenzymes:

    a. NAD^+ **b.** NADH   **c.** FAD   **d.** $FADH_2$ **e.** coenzyme A

  1. ____participates in reactions that convert a hydroxyl group to a $C{=}O$ group

  2. ____contains riboflavin (vitamin B_2)

  3. ____reduced form of nicotinamide adenine dinucleotide

  4. ____contains the vitamin niacin

  5. ____oxidized form of flavin adenine dinucleotide

  6. ____contains the vitamin pantothenic acid ADP and an aminoethanethiol

  7. ____participates in oxidation reactions that produce a carbon–carbon double bond ($C{=}C$)

  8. ____transfers acyl groups such as the two-carbon acetyl group

  9. ____reduced form of flavin adenine dinucleotide

Answers   **1.** a   **2.** c, d   **3.** b   **4.** a, b   **5.** c
               6. e   **7.** c   **8.** e   **9.** d

22.4 Digestion of Carbohydrates

- Digestion is a series of reactions that break down large food molecules of carbohydrates, lipids, and proteins into smaller molecules that can be absorbed and used by the cells.
- The end products of digestion of polysaccharides are monosaccharides glucose, fructose, and galactose.

◆ Learning Exercise 22.4

Complete the table to describe sites, enzymes, and products for the digestion of carbohydrates.

Food	Digestion Site(s)	Enzyme	Products
1. amylose			
2. amylopectin			
3. maltose			
4. lactose			
5. sucrose			

Answers

Food	Digestion Site(s)	Enzyme	Products
1. amylose	**a.** mouth **b.** small intestine (mucosa)	**a.** salivary amylase **b.** pancreatic amylase	**a.** smaller polysaccharides (dextrins), some maltose and glucose **b.** maltose, glucose
2. amylopectin	**a.** mouth **b.** small intestine (mucosa)	**a.** salivary amylase **b.** pancreatic amylase, branching enzyme	**a.** smaller polysaccharides (dextrins), some maltose and glucose **b.** maltose, glucose
3. maltose	small intestine	maltase	glucose and glucose
4. lactose	small intestine	lactase	glucose and galactose
5. sucrose	small intestine	sucrase	glucose and fructose

22.5 Glycolysis: Oxidation of Glucose

- Glycolysis is the primary anaerobic pathway for the degradation of glucose to yield pyruvic acid. Glucose is converted to fructose-1,6-diphosphate that is split into two triose phosphate molecules.
- The oxidation of the three-carbon sugars yields the reduced coenzyme 2 NADH and 2 ATP.

◆ Learning Exercise 22.5

Match each of the following terms of glycolysis with the best description:

a. 2 NADH   **b.** anaerobic   **c.** glucose   **d.** two pyruvate
e. energy invested   **f.** energy generated   **g.** 2 ATP   **h.** 4 ATP

1. _____ the starting material for glycolysis   **2.** _____ steps 1−5 of glycolysis

3. _____ operates without oxygen   **4.** _____ net ATP energy produced

5. _____ number of reduced coenzymes produced   **6.** _____ steps 6−10 of glycolysis

7. _____ end product of glycolysis   **8.** _____ number of ATP required

Answers   **1.** c   **2.** e   **3.** b   **4.** g   **5.** a
                 6. f   **7.** d, a   **8.** g

22.6 Pathways for Pyruvate

- In the absence of oxygen, pyruvate is reduced to lactate and NAD^+ is regenerated for the continuation of glycolysis.
- Under aerobic conditions, pyruvate is oxidized in the mitochondria to acetyl CoA, which enters the citric acid cycle.

◆ Learning Exercise 22.6A

Fill in the blanks with the following terms:

lactate NAD$^+$ fermentation
NADH aerobic anaerobic acetyl CoA

When oxygen is available during glycolysis, the three-carbon pyruvate may be oxidized to form

(1) _____ + CO$_2$. The coenzyme (2) _____ is reduced to (3) _____ .

Under (4) _____ conditions, pyruvate is reduced to (5) _____ . In yeast, pyruvate

forms ethanol in a process known as (6) _____ .

Answers   **1.** acetyl CoA   **2.** NAD$^+$ **3.** NADH
         4. anaerobic   **5.** lactate   **6.** fermentation

◆ Learning Exercise 22.6B

Essay: Explain how the formation of lactate from pyruvate during anaerobic conditions allows glycolysis to continue.

Answer Under anaerobic conditions, the oxidation of pyruvate to acetyl CoA to regenerate NAD$^+$ cannot take place. Then pyruvate is reduced to lactate using NADH in the cytoplasm and regenerating NAD$^+$.

22.7 Glycogen Metabolism

◆ Learning Exercise 22.7

Associate each of the following descriptions with pathways in glycogen metabolism:

a. glycogenesis   **b.** glycogenolysis

1. _____ break down of glycogen to glucose   **2.** _____ activated by glucagon

3. _____ starting material is glucose-6-phosphate   **4.** _____ synthesis of glycogen from glucose

5. _____ activated by insulin   **6.** _____ UDP activates glucose

Answers   **1.** b   **2.** b   **3.** a   **4.** a   **5.** a   **6.** a

22.8 Gluconeogenesis: Glucose Synthesis

◆ Learning Exercise 22.7

Associate each of the following descriptions:

a. gluconeogenesis   **b.** pyruvate   **c.** pyruvate kinase
d. pyruvate carboxylase   **e.** Cori cycle

1. _____ an enzyme in glycolysis that cannot be used in gluconeogenesis

2. _____ a typical noncarbohydrate source of carbon atoms for glucose synthesis

3. _____ a process whereby lactate produced in muscle is used for glucose synthesis in the liver and used again by the muscle

4. _____ the metabolic pathway that converts noncarbohydrate sources to glucose

5. _____ an enzyme used in gluconeogenesis that is not used in glycolysis

6. _____ a metabolic pathway that is activated when glycogen reserves are depleted

Answers   **1.** c   **2.** b   **3.** e   **4.** a   **5.** d   **6.** a

Checklist for Chapter 22

You are ready to take the practice test for chapter 22. Be sure that you have accomplished the following learning goals for this chapter. If you are not sure, review the section listed at the end of the goal. Then apply your new skills and understanding to the practice test. Good luck.

After studying chapter 22, I can successfully:

_____ Associate catabolic and anabolic reactions with organelles in the cell (22.1).

_____ Describe the role of ATP in catabolic and anabolic reactions (22.2).

_____ Describe the coenzymes NAD^+, FAD, and coenzyme A (22.3).

_____ Describe the sites, enzymes, and products of digestion for carbohydrates (22.4).

_____ Describe the conversion of glucose to pyruvate in glycolysis (22.5).

_____ Give the conditions for the conversion of pyruvate to lactate, ethanol, and acetyl coenzyme A (22.6).

_____ Describe the formation and breakdown of glycogen (22.7).

_____ Describe the reactions in which noncarbohydrate sources are used to synthesize glucose (22.8).

Practice Test for Chapter 22

1. The main function of the mitochondria is
   A. energy production   **B.** protein synthesis   **C.** glycolysis
   D. genetic instructions   **E.** waste disposal

2. ATP is a(n)
   A. nucleotide unit in RNA and DNA
   B. end product of glycogenolysis
   C. end product of transamination
   D. enzyme
   E. energy storage molecule

Use one or more of the following enzymes and end products for the digestion of each of the following:
A. maltase   **B.** glucose   **C.** fructose   **D.** sucrase
E. galactose   **F.** lactase   **G.** pancreatic amylase

3. sucrose_____   4. lactose _____

5. small polysaccharides _____   6. maltose _____

Match the parts of the cell with each of the following descriptions:
   A. mitochondria   **B.** lyosomes   **C.** cytosol
   D. ribosomes   **E.** plasma membrane

7. ____ protein synthesis   8. ____ fluid part of the cytoplasm

9. ____ separates cell contents from external fluids   10. ____ energy-producing reactions

11. ____ hydrolytic enzymes degrade old cell structures

12. Glycolysis
   A. requires oxygen for the catabolism of glucose
   B. represents the aerobic sequence for glucose anabolism and ATP production
   C. represents the splitting off of glucose residues from glycogen
   D. represents the anaerobic catabolism of glucose to pyruvate
   E. produces acetyl units and ATP as end products

13. Which does *not* appear in the glycolysis pathway?
   A. dihydroxyacetone phosphate   **B.** pyruvate   **C.** NAD$^+$
   D. acetyl CoA   **E.** lactate

Match each of the following with the correct metabolic pathway:
   A. glycolysis   **B.** glycogenolysis   **C.** gluconeogenesis
   D. glycogenesis   **E.** fermentation

14. ____ conversion of pyruvate to alcohol   15. ____ breakdown of glucose to pyruvate

16. ____ formation of glycogen   17. ____ synthesis of glucose

18. ____ break down of glycogen to glucose

Associate each of the following coenzymes with the correct description:
A. NAD$^+$ **B.** NADH   **C.** FAD   **D.** FADH$_2$ **E.** coenzyme A

19. ____ converts a hydroxyl group to a C$=$O group

20. ____ reduced form of nicotinamide adenine dinucleotide

21. ____ oxidized form of flavin adenine dinucleotide

22. ____ contains the vitamin pantothenic acid ADP and an aminoethanethiol

23. ____ participates in oxidation reactions that produce a carbon–carbon double bond (C$=$C)

24. ____ transfers acyl groups, such as the two-carbon acetyl group

25. ____ reduced form of flavin adenine dinucleotide

Answer the following questions for glycolysis:

26. ____ number of ATP invested to oxidation of one glucose molecule

27. ____ number of ATP (net) produced from one glucose molecule

28. ____ number of NADH produced from the degradation of one glucose molecule

Answers to the Practice Test

1. A	**2.** E	**3.** B, C, D	**4.** B, E, F	**5.** G, B
6. A, B	**7.** D	**8.** C	**9.** E	**10.** A
11. B	**12.** D	**13.** D	**14.** E	**15.** A
16. D	**17.** C	**18.** B	**19.** A	**20.** B
21. C	**22.** E	**23.** C	**24.** E	**25.** D
26. 2	**27.** 2	**28.** 2		

Answers and Solution to Selected Text Problems

22.1   The digestion of polysaccharides takes place in stage 1.

22.3   A catabolic reaction breaks down larger molecules to smaller molecules accompanied by the release of energy.

22.5   **a.** (3) Smooth endoplasmic reticulum is the site for the synthesis of fats and steroids.
   b. (1) Lysosomes contain hydrolytic enzymes.
   c. (2) The Golgi complex modifies products from the rough endoplasmic reticulum.

22.7   The phosphoric anhydride bonds (P—O—P) in ATP release energy that is sufficient for energy-requiring processes in the cell.

22.9   **a.** PEP + H_2O → pyruvate + P_i + 14.8 kcal/mole
   b. ADP + P_i + 7.3 kcal/mole → ATP + H_2O
   c. Coupled: PEP + ADP → ATP + pyruvate + 7.5 kcal/mole

22.11   **a.** Pantothenic acid is a component in coenzyme A.
   b. Niacin is the vitamin component of NAD^+.
   c. Ribitol is the alcohol sugar that makes up riboflavin in FAD.

22.13   In biochemical systems, oxidation is usually accompanied by gain of oxygen or loss of hydrogen. Loss of oxygen or gain of hydrogen usually accompanies reduction.
   a. The reduced form of NAD^+ is abbreviated NADH.
   b. The oxidized form of $FADH_2$ is abbreviated FAD.

22.15   The coenzyme FAD accepts hydrogen when a dehydrogenase forms a carbon-carbon double bond.

22.17   Digestion breaks down the large molecules in food into smaller compounds that can be absorbed by the body. Hydrolysis is the main reaction involved in the digestion of carbohydrates.

22.19   **a.** The disaccharide lactose is digested in the small intestine to yield galactose and glucose.
   b. The disaccharide sucrose is digested in the small intestine to yield glucose and fructose.
   c. The disaccharide maltose is digested in the small intestine to yield two glucose molecules.

22.21   Glucose is the starting reactant for glycolysis.

22.23   In the initial reactions of glycolysis, ATP molecules are required to add phosphate groups to glucose.

22.25   When fructose-1, 6-bisphosphate splits, glyceraldehyde-3-phosphate and dihydroxyacetone phosphate are formed. The dihydroxyacetone phosphate is converted to glyceraldehyde-3-phosphate for subsequent reactions.

22.27   ATP is produced directly in glycolysis in two places. In reaction 7, phosphate from 1,3-bisphospho-glycerate is transferred to ADP and yields ATP. In reaction 10, phosphate from phosphoenolpyruvate is transferred directly to ADP.

22.29   **a.** In glycolysis, phosphorylation is catalyzed by the enzyme hexokinase.
   b. In glycolysis, direct transfer of a phosphate group is catalyzed by the enzyme phosphokinase.

22.31   **a.** In the phosphorylation of glucose to glucose-6-phosphate 1, ATP is required.
   b. One ATP is required for the conversion of glyceraldehyde-3-phosphate to 1,3-bisphosphoglycerate.
   c. When glucose is converted to pyruvate, two ATP and two NADH are produced.

22.33 **a.** The first ATP is hydrolyzed in the first reaction in glycolysis; the change of glucose to glucose-6-phosphate.
   b. Direct substrate phosphorylation occurs in reaction 7 of glycolysis when the transfer of phosphate from 1,3-bisphosphoglycerate to ADP generates ATP. In reaction 10 of glycolysis, phosphate is transferred from phosphoenolpyruvate directly to ADP.
   c. In reaction 4 of glycolysis, the six-carbon fructose-1, 6-bisphosphate is converted to two three-carbon molecules.

22.35 Galactose reacts with ATP to yield galactose-1-phosphate, which is converted to glucose phosphate, an intermediate in glycolysis. Fructose reacts with ATP to yield fructose-1-phosphate, which is cleaved to give dihydroxyacetone phosphate and glyceraldehyde. Dihydroxyacetone phosphate isomerizes to glyceraldehyde-3-phosphate, and glyceraldehyde is phosphorylated to glyceraldehyde-3-phosphate, which is an intermediate in glycolysis.

22.37 **a.** Low levels of ATP activate phosphofructokinase to increase the rate of glycolysis.
   b. When ATP levels are high, ATP inhibits phosphofructokinase and slows or prevents glycolysis.

22.39 A cell converts pyruvate to acetyl CoA only under aerobic conditions; there must be sufficient oxygen available.

22.41 The overall reaction for the conversion of pyruvate to acetyl CoA is:

$$\underset{pyruvate}{CH_3-\overset{\overset{O}{\|}}{C}-COO^-} + NAD^+ + HS-CoA \longrightarrow \underset{acetyl\ CoA}{CH_3-\overset{\overset{O}{\|}}{C}-S-CoA} + CO_2 + NADH + H^+$$

22.43 The reduction of pyruvate to lactate regenerates NAD^+, which allows glycolysis to proceed and produce two ATPs.

22.45 During fermentation, the three-carbon compound pyruvate is reduced to ethanol while decarboxylation removes one carbon as CO_2.

22.47 In glycogenesis, glycogen is synthesized from glucose molecules.

22.49 Muscle cells break down glycogen to glucose 6-phosphate, which enters glycolysis.

22.51 Glycogen phosphorylase cleaves the glycosidic bonds at the ends of glycogen chains to remove glucose monomers as glucose 1-phosphate.

22.53 When there are no glycogen stores remaining in the liver, gluconeogenesis synthesizes glucose from noncarbohydrate compounds such as pyruvate and lactate.

22.55 The enzymes in glycolysis that are also used in their reverse directions for gluconeogenesis are phosphoglucoisomerase, aldolase, triosephosphate isomerase, glyceraldehyde 3-phosphate dehydrogenase, phosphoglycerokinase, phosphoglyceromutase, and enolase.

22.57 **a.** Low glucose levels activate glucose synthesis.
   b. Glucagon produced when glucose levels are low activates gluconeogenesis.
   c. Insulin produced when glucose levels are high inhibits gluconeogenesis.

22.59 $2.5 \ \text{hr} \times \dfrac{350 \ \text{kcal}}{\text{hr}} \times \dfrac{1 \ \text{mole ATP}}{7.3 \ \text{kcal}} = 120$ moles ATP

22.61 Metabolism includes all the reactions in cells that provide energy and material for cell growth.

22.63 Stage 1 involves the digestion of large molecules, such as polysaccharides.

22.65 A eukaryotic cell has a nucleus, whereas a prokaryotic cell does not.

22.67 ATP is the abbreviation for adenosine triphosphate.

22.69 $ATP + H_2O \rightarrow ADP + P_i + 7.3$ kcal (31 kJ)/mole

22.71 FAD is the abbreviation for flavin adenine dinucleotide.

22.73 NAD^+ is the abbreviation for nicotinamide adenine dinucleotide.

22.75 The reduced forms of these coenzymes include hydrogen obtained from an oxidation reaction.
    a. $FADH_2$ **b.** $NADH + H^+$

22.77 Lactose undergoes digestion in the mucosal cells of the small intestine to yield galactose and glucose.

22.79 Galactose and fructose are converted in the liver to glucose phosphate compounds that can enter the glycolysis pathway.

22.81 Glucose is the reactant and pyruvate is the product of glycolysis.

22.83 Reactions 1 and 3 involve phosphorylation of hexoses with ATP, and reactions 7 and 10 involve direct substrate phosphorylation that generates ATP.

22.85 Reaction 4 catalyzed by aldolase converts fructose 1,6-bisphosphate into two triose phosphates.

22.87 Phosphoglucoisomerase converts glucose-6-phosphate to the isomer fructose-6-phosphate.

22.89 Pyruvate is converted to lactate when oxygen is not present in the cell (anaerobic) to regenerate NAD^+ for glycolysis.

22.91 Phosphofructokinase is an allosteric enzyme that is activated by high levels of AMP and ADP because the cell needs to produce more ATP. When ATP levels are high, ATP inhibits phosphofruc-tokinase, which reduces its catalysis of fructose-6-phosphate.

22.93 The rate of glycogenolysis increases when blood glucose levels are low and glucagon has been secreted, which accelerate the breakdown of glycogen.

23.95 The breakdown of glycogen in the liver produces glucose.

22.97   **a.** Low glucose increases the breakdown of glycogen.
     b. Insulin produced when glucose levels are high decreases the rate of glycogenolysis in the liver.
     c. Glucagon secreted when glucose levels are low increases the breakdown of glycogen.
     d. High levels of ATP decrease the breakdown of glycogen.

22.99   **a.** High glucose levels decrease the synthesis of glucose (gluconeogenesis).
     b. Insulin produced when glucose levels are high decreases glucose synthesis.
     c. Glucagon secreted when glucose levels are low increases glucose synthesis.
     d. High levels of ATP decrease glucose synthesis (gluconeogenesis).

22.101 The cells in the liver, but not skeletal muscle, contain a phosphatase enzyme needed to convert glucose-phosphate to free glucose that can diffuse through cell membranes into the blood stream. Glucose-6-phosphate, which is the end product of glycogenolysis in muscle cells, cannot diffuse easily across cell membranes.

22.103 Insulin increases the rate of glycogenolysis and glycolysis and decreases the rate of glycogenesis. Glucagon decreases the rate of glycogenolysis and glycolysis and increases the rate of glycogenesis.

22.105 The Cori cycle is a cyclic process that involves the transfer of lactate from muscle to the liver where glucose is synthesized, which can be used again by the muscle.

22.107 a. $1 \text{ day} \times \dfrac{24 \text{ hr}}{1 \text{ day}} \times \dfrac{3600 \text{ s}}{1 \text{ hr}} \times \dfrac{2 \times 10^6 \text{ ATP}}{1 \text{ s} \cdot \text{cell}} \times 10^{13} \text{ cells}$

$\times \dfrac{7.3 \text{ kcal}}{1 \text{ mole ATP}} \times \dfrac{1 \text{ mole ATP}}{6.02 \times 10^{23} \text{ ATP}} = 21 \text{ kcal}$

b. 1500 g ATP

Metabolism and Energy Production

Study Goals

- Describe the reactions in the citric acid cycle that oxidize acetyl CoA.
- Explain how electrons from NADH and H^+ and FAD move along the electron transport chain to form H_2O.
- Describe the role of oxidative phosphorylation in ATP synthesis.
- Calculate the ATP produced by the complete combustion of glucose.

Think About It

1. Why is the citric acid cycle considered a central pathway in metabolism?

2. How is the citric acid cycle connected to electron transport?

3. Which stage of metabolism produces most of the ATP for the cells?

Key Words

Match the following key terms with the correct statement shown below.

  a. citric acid cycle   **b.** oxidative phosphorylation   **c.** coenyzme Q
  d. cytochromes   **e.** proton pump   **f.** tricarboxylic acid cycle

1. _____ A mobile carrier that passes electrons from NADH and $FADH_2$ to cytochrome b in complex III

2. _____ Proteins containing iron as Fe^{3+} or Fe^{2+} that transfer electrons from QH_2 to oxygen

3. _____ A function of complexes I, II, and III whereby protons move from the matrix into the intermembrane space to create a proton gradient

4. _____ The synthesis of ATP from ADP and P_i using energy generated from electron transport

5. _____ Oxidation reactions that convert acetyl CoA to CO_2, producing reduced coenzymes for energy production via the electron chain transport system

6. _____ Another name for the citric acid cycle

Answers   **1.** c   **2.** d   **3.** e   **4.** b   **5.** a   **6.** f

23.1 The Citric Acid Cycle

- Under aerobic conditions, pyruvate is oxidized in the mitochondria to acetyl CoA, which enters the citric acid cycle.
- In a sequence of reactions called the citric acid cycle, acetyl CoA combines with oxaloacetate to yield citrate.
- In one turn of the citric acid cycle, the oxidation of acetyl CoA yields two CO_2, GTP, three NADH, and $FADH_2$. The phosphorylation of ADP by GTP yields ATP.

◆ Learning Exercise 23.1A

Match the name of the enzymes with the following steps in the citric acid cycle:

a. isocitrate dehydrogenase   **b.** α-ketoglutarate dehydrogenase
c. fumarase   **d.** succinate dehydrogenase
e. malate dehydrogenase   **f.** aconitase
g. succinyl CoA synthetase   **h.** citrate synthase

1. _____ acetyl CoA + oxaloacetate $\rightarrow$ citrate   **2.** _____ citrate $\rightarrow$ isocitrate

3. _____ isocitrate $\rightarrow$ α-ketoglutarate acid   **4.** _____ α-ketoglutarate $\rightarrow$ succinyl CoA

5. _____ succinyl CoA $\rightarrow$ succinate   **6.** _____ succinate $\rightarrow$ fumarate

7. _____ fumarate $\rightarrow$ malate   **8.** _____ malate $\rightarrow$ oxaloacetate

9. _____ allosteric enzymes that regulate the citric acid cycle

Answers   **1.** h   **2.** f   **3.** a   **4.** b   **5.** g
             6. d   **7.** c   **8.** e   **9.** a, b

◆ Learning Exercise 23.1B

In each of the following steps of the citric acid cycle, indicate if oxidation occurs (yes or no) and any coenzyme or direct phosphorylation product produced (NADH + H$^+$, FADH$_2$, GTP).

Step in citric acid cycle	Oxidation	Coenzyme
1. acetyl CoA + oxaloacetate $\rightarrow$ citrate	_____	_____
2. citrate $\rightarrow$ isocitrate	_____	_____
3. isocitrate $\rightarrow$ α-ketoglutarate acid	_____	_____
4. α-ketoglutarate $\rightarrow$ succinyl CoA	_____	_____
5. succinyl CoA $\rightarrow$ succinate	_____	_____
6. succinate $\rightarrow$ fumarate	_____	_____
7. fumarate $\rightarrow$ malate	_____	_____
8. malate $\rightarrow$ oxaloacetate	_____	_____

Answer   **1.** no   **2.** no   **3.** yes, NADH + H$^+$ **4.** yes, NADH + H$^+$
         5. no, GTP   **6.** yes, FADH$_2$ **7.** no   **8.** yes, NADH + H$^+$

23.2 Electron Carriers

- The reduced coenzymes from glycolysis and the citric acid cycle are oxidized to NAD$^+$ and FAD by transferring protons and electrons to the electron transport chain.

◆ Learning Exercise 23.2

Write the oxidized and reduced forms of each of the following electron carriers:

1. flavin mononucleotide   oxidized _____   reduced _____

2. coenzyme Q   oxidized _____   reduced _____

3. iron-protein clusters   oxidized _____   reduced _____

4. cytochrome *b*   oxidized _____   reduced _____

Answers   **1.** oxidized: FMN   reduced: $FMNH_2$
                       2. oxidized: Q   reduced: QH_2
                       3. oxidized: Fe^{3+} S cluster   reduced Fe^{2+} S cluster
                       4. oxidized: Cyt *b* (Fe^{3+})   reduced: Cyt *b* (Fe^{2+})

23.3 Electron Transport

- In the electron transport system or respiratory chain, electrons are transferred to electron carriers, including flavins, coenzyme Q, iron-sulfur proteins, and cytochromes with Fe^{3+}/Fe^{2+}.
- The final acceptor, O_2, combines with protons and electrons to yield H_2O.

◆ Learning Exercise 23.3A

Identify the protein complexes and mobile carriers in the electron transport chain.

a. cytochrome *c* oxidase (IV)   **b.** NADH dehydrogenase (I)
c. cytochrome *c*   **d.** coenzyme Q-cytochrome *c* reductase (III)
e. succinate dehydrogenase (II)   **f.** Q

1. _____ FMN and Fe-S clusters

2. _____ $FADH_2 + Q \rightarrow FAD + QH_2$

3. _____ mobile carrier from complex I or complex II to complex III

4. _____ electrons are passed from cyt *a* and a_3 to O_2 and $4H^+$ to yield $2H_2O$.

5. _____ mobile carrier between complex III and IV

6. _____ cyt *b* and Fe-S clusters

Answers   **1.** b   **2.** e   **3.** f   **4.** a   **5.** c   **6.** d

◆ Learning Exercise 23.3B

1. Write an equation for the transfer of hydrogen from $FMNH_2$ to Q.

2. What is the function of coenzyme Q in the electron transport chain?

3. What are the end products of the electron transport chain?

Answers   1. $FMNH_2 + Q \rightarrow FMN + QH_2$
2. Q accepts hydrogen atoms from $FMNH_2$ or $FADH_2$. From QH_2, the hydrogen atoms are separated into protons and electrons, with the electrons being passed on to the cytochromes, the electron acceptors in the chain.
3. $CO_2 + H_2O$

23.4 Oxidative Phosphorylation and ATP

- The flow of electrons along the electron chain pumps protons across the inner membrane, which produces a high-energy proton gradient that provides energy for the synthesis of ATP.
- The process of using the energy of the electron transport chain to synthesize ATP is called oxidative phosphorylation.

◆ Learning Exercise 23.4

Match the following terms with the correct description below:
a. oxidative phosphorylation   **b.** tight (T) site   **c.** ATP synthase
d. proton pumps   **e.** loose (L) site   **f.** open (O) site
g. proton gradient

1. _____ the complexes I, III, and IV, through which H^+ ions move out of the matrix into the inner membrane space.

2. _____ the protein tunnel where proton flow from the intermembrane space back to the matrix generates energy for ATP synthesis

3. _____ energy from electron transport is used to form a proton gradient that drives ATP synthesis

4. _____ the conformation on the F_1 section of ATP synthase that binds ADP and P_i

5. _____ the accumulation of protons in the intermembrane space that lowers pH

6. _____ the conformation on the F_1 section of ATP synthase that releases ATP

7. _____ the conformation on the F_1 section of ATP synthase where ATP forms

Answers   **1.** d   **2.** c   **3.** a   **4.** e   **5.** g   **6.** f   **7.** b

23.5 ATP Energy from Glucose

- The oxidation of NADH yields three ATP molecules, and $FADH_2$ yields two ATP molecules.
- The complete oxidation of glucose yields a total of 36 ATP from direct phosphorylation and the oxidation of the reduced coenzymes NADH and $FADH_2$ by the electron transport chain and oxidative phosphorylation.

◆ Learning Exercise 23.5

Complete the following:

Substrate	Reaction	Products	Amount of ATP
1. glucose	glycolysis (aerobic)		
2. pyruvate	oxidation		
3. acetyl CoA	citric acid cycle		
4. glucose	glycolysis (anaerobic)		
5. glucose	complete oxidation		

Answers

Substrate	Reaction	Products	Amount of ATP
1. glucose	glycolysis (aerobic)	2 pyruvate acid	6 ATP
2. pyruvate acid	oxidation	acetyl CoA + CO_2	3 ATP
3. acetyl CoA	citric acid cycle	$2CO_2$	12 ATP
4. glucose	glycolysis (anaerobic)	2 lactate	2 ATP
5. glucose	complete oxidation	$6CO_2 + 6H_2O$	36 ATP

Checklist for Chapter 23

You are ready to take the practice test for chapter 23. Be sure that you have accomplished the following learning goals for this chapter. If you are not sure, review the section listed at the end of the goal. Then apply your new skills and understanding to the practice test. Good luck.

After studying chapter 23, I can successfully:

_____ Describe the oxidation of acetyl CoA in the citric acid cycle (23.1).

_____ Identify the electron carriers in the electron transport system (23.2).

_____ Describe the process of electron transport (23.3).

_____ Explain the chemiosmotic theory whereby ATP synthesis is linked to the energy of the electron transport chain and a proton gradient (23.4).

_____ Account for the ATP produced by the complete oxidation of glucose (23.5).

Practice Test for Chapter 23

1. Which is true of the citric acid cycle?
  A. Acetyl CoA is converted to CO_2 and H_2O.
  B. Oxaloacetate combines with acetyl units to form citric acid.
  C. The coenzymes are NAD^+ and FAD.
  D. ATP is produced by direct phosphorylation.
  E. All of the above.

Match the types of reactions with each of the following:
  A. malate   **B.** fumarate   **C.** succinate
  D. citrate   **E.** oxaloacetate

2. _____ formed when oxaloacetate combines with acetyl CoA

3. _____ H_2O adds to its double bond to form malate

4. _____ FAD removes hydrogen to form a double bond

5. _____ formed when the hydroxyl group in malate is oxidized

6. _____ the compound that is regenerated in the citric acid cycle

7. One turn of the citric acid cycle produces
  A. 3 NADH   **B.** 3 NADH, 1 $FADH_2$ **C.** 3 $FADH_2$, 1 NADH, 1 ATP
  D. 3 NADH, 1 $FADH_2$, 1 ATP   **E.** 1 NADH, 1 $FADH_2$, 1 ATP

8. The citric acid cycle is activated by
  A. high ATP levels   **B.** NADH   **C.** high ADP levels
  D. low ATP levels   **E.** succinyl CoA

9. The end products of the electron transport chain are
  A. H_2O + ATP   **B.** CO_2 + H_2O **C.** NH_3 + CO_2 + H_2O
  D. H_2 + O_2 **E.** urea (NH_2CONH_2)

10. How many electron transfers in the electron transport chain provide sufficient energy for ATP synthesis?
  A. none   **B.** 1   **C.** 2   **D.** 3   **E.** 4

11. The electron transport chain
  A. produces most of the ATP in the body
  B. carries oxygen to the cells
  C. produces CO_2 + H_2O
  D. is only involved in the citric acid cycle
  E. operates during fermentation

In questions 12–20, match the components of the electron transport system with the following activities:
A. NAD^+ **B.** FMN   **C.** FAD   **D.** Q   **E.** cytochromes

12. _____ a mobile carrier that transfers electrons from FMN and $FADH_2$ to cytochromes

13. _____ the coenzyme that accepts hydrogen atoms from NADH

14. _____ coenzyme derived from niacin

15. _____ the coenzyme used to remove hydrogen atoms from two adjacent carbon atoms to form carbon–carbon double bonds.

16. _____ the electron acceptors containing iron

17. _____ a coenzyme derived from quinone

18. _____ coenzymes that contain flavin

19. _____ the reduced form of this coenzyme generates three molecules of ATP

20. _____ the reduced form of this coenzyme generates two molecules of ATP

Match the components of ATP synthase with each of the following descriptions:
A. F_0 **B.** F_1 **C.** loose (L) site   **D.** tight (T) site   **E.** open (O) site

21. _____ consists of the channel for the return of protons to the matrix

22. _____ binds ADP + P_i

23. _____ consists of a center subunit and three subunits that change conformations

24. _____ ADP + $P_i \rightarrow$ ATP

25. _____ releases ATP from ATP synthase

Indicate the number of ATPs for the equations in questions 21–25. Select answers from below.

A. 2 ATP **B.** 3 ATP **C.** 6 ATP **D.** 12 ATP **E.** 24 ATP **F.** 36 ATP

26. one turn of the citric acid cycle   (acetyl CoA $\rightarrow$ $2CO_2$)

27. complete combustion of glucose (glucose $+ 6O_2 \rightarrow 6H_2O + 6CO_2$)

28. produced when NADH enters electron transport

29. glycolysis (glucose $+ O_2 \rightarrow$ 2 pyruvate $+ 2H_2O$)

30. oxidation of 2 pyruvate (2 pyruvate $\rightarrow$ 2 acetyl CoA $+ 2CO_2$)

Answers to the Practice Test

1. E	2. D	3. B	4. C	5. E
6. E	7. D	8. D	9. B	10. D
11. A	12. D	13. B	14. A	15. C
16. E	17. D	18. B, C	19. A	20. C
21. A	22. C	23. B	24. D	25. E
26. D	27. F	28. B	29. C	30. C

Answers and Solution to Selected Text Problems

23.1 Other names for the citric acid cycle are the Krebs cycle and tricarboxylic acid cycle.

23.3 One turn of the citric acid cycle converts 1 acetyl CoA to $2CO_2$, $3NADH + 3H^+$, $FADH_2$, GTP (ATP), and HS—CoA.

23.5 The reactions in steps 3 and 4 involve oxidative decarboxylation, which reduces the length of the carbon chain by one carbon in each reaction.

23.7 NAD^+ is reduced by the oxidation reactions 3, 4, and 8 of the citric acid cycle.

23.9 In reaction 5, GDP undergoes a direct substrate phosphorylation to yield GTP, which converts ADP to ATP and regenerates GDP for the citric acid cycle.

23.11 **a.** The six-carbon compounds in the citric acid cycle are citrate and isocitrate.
  b. Decarboxylation reactions remove carbon atoms as CO_2, which reduces the number of carbon atoms in a chain (reactions 3 and 4).
  c. The one five-carbon compound is α-ketoglutarate.
  d. Several reactions are oxidation reactions; isocitrate $\rightarrow$ α-ketoglutarate; α-ketoglutarate $\rightarrow$ succinyl CoA; succinate $\rightarrow$ fumarate; malate $\rightarrow$ oxaloacetate
  e. Secondary alcohols are oxidized in reactions 3 and 8.

23.13 **a.** Citrate synthase combines oxaloacetate with acetyl CoA.
  b. Succinate dehydrogenase and aconitase converts a carbon–carbon single bond to a double bond.
  c. Fumarase adds water to the double bond in fumarate; aconitase adds water to the double bond in aconitate from citrate.

23.15 **a.** NAD^+ accepts 2H from the oxidative decarboxylation of isocitrate.
  b. GDP is phosphorylated in the formation of succinate.

23.17 Isocitrate dehydrogenase and α-ketoglutarate dehydrogenase are allosteric enzymes, which increase or decrease the flow of materials through the citric acid cycle.

23.19 High levels of ADP means there are low levels of ATP. To provide more ATP for the cell, the reaction rate of the citric acid cycle increases.

23.21 The Fe^{3+} is the oxidized form of the iron in cytochrome *c*.

23.23 **a.** The loss of $2H^+$ and $2e^-$ is oxidation. **b.** The gain of $2H^+ + 2e^-$ is reduction.

23.25 NADH and $FADH_2$ produced in glycolysis, oxidation of pyruvate, and the citric acid cycle provide the electrons for electron transport.

23.27 FAD is reduced to $FADH_2$, which provides $2H^+$ and $2e^-$ for coenzyme Q, then cytochrome *b*, and then cytochrome *c*.

23.29 The mobile carrier coenzyme Q (or Q) transfers electrons from complex I to III.

23.31 When NADH transfers electrons to FMN in complex I, NAD^+ is produced.

23.33 **a.** $NADH + H^+ + \underline{FMN} \rightarrow \underline{NAD^+} + FMNH_2$
b. $QH_2 + 2\,cyt\,b\,(Fe^{3+}) \rightarrow \underline{Q} + \underline{2\,cyt\,b\,(Fe^{2+})} + 2H^+$

23.35 In oxidative phosphorylation, the energy from the oxidation reactions in the electron transport chain is used to drive ATP synthesis.

23.37 Protons must pass through F_0 channel of ATP synthase to return to the matrix. During the process, energy is released to drive the synthesis of ATP in F_1.

23.39 The oxidation of the reduced coenzymes NADH and $FADH_2$ by the electron transport chain generates energy to drive the synthesis of ATP.

23.41 ATP synthase consists of two protein complexes known as F_0 and F_1.

23.43 The loose (L) site in ATP synthase begins the synthesis of ATP by binding ADP and P_i.

23.45 Glycolysis takes place in the cytoplasm, not in the mitochondria. Because NADH cannot cross the mitochondrial membrane, one ATP is hydrolyzed to transport the electrons from NADH to FAD. The resulting $FADH_2$ produces only 2 ATP for each NADH produced in glycolysis.

23.47 **a.** Three ATP are produced by the oxidation of NADH in electron transport.
b. Two ATP are produced in glycolysis when glucose degrades to 2 pyruvate.
c. Six ATP are produced when 2 pyruvate are oxidized to 2 acetyl CoA and 2 CO_2.

23.49 **a.** citric acid cycle **b.** electron transport **c.** both
d. electron transport **e.** electron transport **f.** both
g. citric acid cycle **h.** both

23.51 **f.** $FMNH_2$ **e.** QH_2 **h.** cyt *b* **g.** cyt c_1 **d.** cyt *c*
c. cyt *a* **a.** cyt a_3 **b.** O_2

23.53 **a.** aconitase H_2O **b.** succinate dehydrogenase FAD
c. fumarase H_2O **d.** isocitrate dehydrogenase NAD^+
e. succinyl CoA synthase GDP **f.** malate dehydrogenase NAD^+

23.55 The oxidation reactions of the citric acid cycle produce a source of reduced coenzymes for the electron transport chain and ATP synthesis.

23.57 The electron transport chain regenerates the oxidized forms of the coenzymes NAD^+ and FAD for use again by the citric acid cycle.

23.59 **a.** Citrate and isocitrate are six-carbon compounds in the citric acid cycle.
     b. α-Ketoglutarate is a five-carbon compound.
     c. The compounds α-ketoglutarate, succinyl-CoA, and oxaloacetate have keto groups.

23.61 **a.** In reaction 4, α-ketoglutarate, a five-carbon keto acid, is decarboxylated.
     b. In reactions 1 and 7, double bonds in aconitate and fumarate are hydrated.
     c. NAD^+ is reduced in reactions 3, 4, and 8.
     d. In reactions 3 and 8, a secondary hydroxyl group in isocitrate and malate is oxidized.

23.63 **a.** NAD^+ is the coenzyme for the oxidation of a secondary hydroxyl group in isocitrate to a keto group in α-ketoglutarate.
     b. NAD^+ and CoA are needed in the oxidative decarboxylation of α-ketoglutarate to succinyl CoA.

23.65 **a.** High levels of NADH inhibit isocitrate dehydrogenase and α-ketoglutarate dehydrogenase to slow the rate of the citric acid cycle.
     b. High levels of ATP inhibit the citric acid cycle.

23.67 **a.** A heme group is found in all the cytochromes (4).
     b. FMN (1) contains a ribitol group.

23.69 **a.** CoQ is a mobile carrier.
     b. Fe-S clusters are found in complexes I, III, and IV.
     c. Cyt a_3 is part of complex IV.

23.71 **a.** $FADH_2$ is oxidized in complex II: $FADH_2 + Q \rightarrow FAD + QH_2$
     b. Cyt a (Fe^{2+}) is oxidized in complex IV:
     Cyt a (Fe^{2+}) + Cyt a_3 (Fe^{3+}) $\rightarrow$ Cyt a (Fe^{3+}) + Cyt a_3 (Fe^{2+})

23.73 **a.**

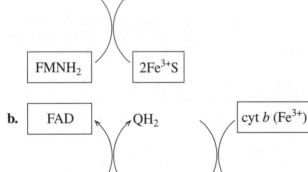

23.75 The transfer of electrons by complexes I, III, and IV generates energy to pump protons out of the matrix into the inner membrane space.

23.77 In the chemiosmotic model, energy released by the flow of protons through the ATP synthase is utilized for the synthesis ATP.

23.79 In the inner membrane space, there is a higher concentration of protons, which reduces the pH and forms an electrochemical gradient. As a result, protons flow into the matrix, where the proton concentration is lower and the pH is higher.

23.81 Two ATP molecules are produced from the energy generated by the electrons from $FADH_2$ moving through electron transport to oxygen.

23.83 **a.** Amytal and rotenone inhibit the transfer of electrons in NADH dehydrogenase (complex I).
  b. Antimycin inhibits electron flow from cyt b to cyt c_1 in complex III.
  c. Cyanide and carbon monoxide inhibit the flow of electron through cytochrome c oxidase (complex IV).

23.85 The oxidation of glucose to pyruvate by glycolysis produces 6 ATP. Two ATPs are formed by direct phosphorylation along with 2 NADH. Because the 2 NADH are produced in the cytosol, the electrons are transferred to form 2 $FADH_2$, which produces an additional 4 ATP. The oxidation of glucose to CO_2 and H_2O produces 36 ATP.

23.87 The ATP synthase extends through the inner mitochondrial membrane with the F_0 part in contact with the proton gradient in the intermembrane space, whereas the F_1 complex is in the matrix.

23.89 As protons from the proton gradient move through the ATP synthase to return to the matrix, energy is released and used to drive ATP synthesis at F_1.

23.91 A hibernating bear has stored fat as brown fat, which can be used during the winter for heat rather than ATP energy.

23.93 **a.** 6 moles ATP $\times$ 7.3 kcal/mole = 44 kcal
  b. 6 moles ATP $\times$ 7.3 kcal/mole = 44 kcal (2 pyruvate to 2 acetyl CoA)
  c. 24 moles ATP $\times$ 7.3 kcal/mole = 175 kcal (2 acetyl CoA citric acid cycle)
  d. 36 moles ATP $\times$ 7.3 kcal/mole = 263 kcal (complete oxidation of glucose to CO_2 and H_2O)

23.95 In a calorimeter, the complete combustion of glucose gives 687 kcal. The efficiency of ATP synthesis is determined by comparing the total kcal in 36 ATP (36 $\cancel{ATP}$ $\times$ 7.3 kcal/$\cancel{ATP}$ = 263 kcal) to the energy obtained from glucose in a calorimeter.

263/687 $\times$ 100 = 38.0% efficient

23.97 $1.0 \, \cancel{\mu g} \times \dfrac{1 \, \cancel{g}}{10^6 \, \cancel{\mu g}} \times \dfrac{1 \, \cancel{mole}}{809 \, \cancel{g}} \times \dfrac{12 \text{ moles ATP}}{1 \, \cancel{\text{mole acetyl CoA}}} = 1.5 \times 10^{-8}$ mole ATP

Metabolic Pathways for Lipids and Amino Acids

Study Goals

- Describe the sites, enzymes, and products for the digestion of triacylglycerols.
- Describe the oxidation of fatty acids via β-oxidation.
- Calculate the ATP produced by the complete oxidation of a fatty acid.
- Explain ketogenesis and the conditions in the cell that form ketone bodies.
- Describe the biosynthesis of fatty acids from acetyl CoA.
- Describe the sites, enzymes, and products of the digestion of dietary proteins.
- Explain the role of transamination and oxidative deamination in the degradation of amino acids.
- Describe the formation of urea from ammonium ion.
- Explain how carbon atoms from amino acids are prepared to enter the citric acid cycle or other pathways.
- Show how nonessential amino acids are synthesized from substances used in the citric acid cycle and other pathways.

Think About It

1. What are the products from the digestion of triacylalcohols and proteins?

2. What is the purpose of adding the enzyme lactase to milk products?

3. When do you utilize fats and proteins for energy?

Key Words

Match the following key terms with the correct statement shown below.
a. essential amino acid   **b.** transamination   **c.** lipogenesis
d. ketosis   **e.** beta (β)-oxidation

1. _____ A reaction cycle that oxidizes fatty acids by removing acetyl CoA units

2. _____ The synthesis of fatty acids by linking two-carbon acetyl units

3. _____ A condition in which high levels of ketone bodies lower blood pH

4. _____ An amino acid that must be obtained from the diet

5. _____ The transfer of an amino group from an amino acid to an α-keto acid

Answers   **1.** e   **2.** c   **3.** d   **4.** a   **5.** b

24.1 Digestion of Triacylglycerols

- Dietary fats begin digestion in the small intestine, where they are emulsified by bile salts.
- Pancreatic lipases hydrolyze the triacylglycerols to yield monoacylglycerols and free fatty acids.

- The triacylglycerols reformed in the intestinal lining combine with proteins to form chylomicrons for transport through the lymph system and bloodstream.
- In the cells, triacylglycerols hydrolyze to glycerol and fatty acids, which can be used for energy.

◆ Learning Exercise 24.1

a. chylomicrons   **b.** lipases   **c.** fat mobilization
d. monoacylglycerols and fatty acids   **e.** emulsification

1. _____ the hydrolysis of triacylglycerols in adipose tissues to produce energy

2. _____ lipoproteins formed when triacylglycerols are coated with proteins

3. _____ the breakup of fat globules in the small intestine by bile salts

4. _____ enzymes released from the pancreas that hydrolyze triacylglycerols

5 _____ the products of lipase hydrolysis of triacylglycerols in the small intestine

Answers   **1.** c   **2.** a   **3.** e   **4.** b   **5.** d

24.2 Oxidation of Fatty Acids

- When needed for energy, fatty acids link to coenzyme A for transport to the mitochondria, where they undergo β-oxidation.
- In β-oxidation, a fatty acyl chain is oxidized to yield a shortened fatty acid, acetyl CoA, and the reduced coenzymes NADH and $FADH_2$.

◆ Learning Exercise 24.2A

Match each of the following terms with the descriptions that follow:
a. activation   **b.** fatty acyl carnitine   **c.** β-oxidation
d. NAD^+ and FAD   **e.** mitochondria

1. _____ coenzymes needed for β-oxidation

2. _____ site in the cell where β-oxidation of fatty acids takes place

3. _____ a fatty acid combines with SH—CoA to form fatty acyl CoA

4. _____ carries the fatty acyl group into the mitochondria matrix

5. _____ the sequential removal of two-carbon sections from fatty acids

Answers   **1.** d   **2.** e   **3.** a   **4.** b   **5.** c

◆ Learning Exercise 24.2B

1. Write an equation for the activation of myristic (C_{14}) acid: $CH_3-(CH_2)_{12}-\overset{\overset{\displaystyle O}{\|}}{C}-OH$

2. Write an equation for the first oxidation of myristyl CoA.

3. Write an equation for the hydration of the double bond.

4. Write the overall equation for the complete oxidation of myristyl CoA.

5. a. How many cycles of β-oxidation will be required?
   b. How many acetyl CoA units will be produced?

Answers

1. $CH_3-(CH_2)_{12}-\overset{\overset{O}{\|}}{C}-OH + HS-CoA + ATP \xrightarrow{\overset{acyl\ CoA}{synthetase}} CH_3-(CH_2)_{12}-\overset{\overset{O}{\|}}{C}-S-CoA + AMP + 2P_i$

2. $CH_3-(CH_2)_{12}-\overset{\overset{O}{\|}}{C}-S-CoA + FAD \xrightarrow{\overset{acyl\ CoA}{dehydrogenase}} CH_3-(CH_2)_{10}-CH{=}CH-\overset{\overset{O}{\|}}{C}-S-CoA + FADH_2$

3. $CH_3-(CH_2)_{10}-CH{=}CH-\overset{\overset{O}{\|}}{C}-S-CoA + H_2O \xrightarrow{thiolase} CH_3-(CH_2)_{10}-\overset{\overset{OH}{|}}{C}H-CH_2-\overset{\overset{O}{\|}}{C}-S-CoA$

4. myristyl $(C_{14})-CoA + 6\,CoA + 6\,FAD + 6\,NAD^+ + 6\,H_2O \rightarrow$
$\qquad\qquad\qquad\qquad\qquad 7$ acetyl $CoA + 6\,FADH_2 + 6\,NADH + 6H^+$

5. a. 6 cycles   **b.** 7 acetyl CoA units are produced

24.3 ATP and Fatty Acid Oxidation

- The energy obtained from a particular fatty acid depends on the number of carbon atoms.
- Two ATP are required for activation. Then each acetyl CoA produces 12 ATP via citric acid cycle, and the electron transport chain converts each NADH to 3 ATP and each FADH to 2 ATP.

◆ Learning Exercise 24.3

Lauric acid is a 12-carbon fatty acid: $CH_3(CH_2)_{10}COOH$

1. How much ATP is needed for activation?

2. How many cycles of β-oxidation are required?

3. How many NADH and $FADH_2$ are produced during β-oxidation?

4. How many acetyl CoA units are produced?

5. What is the total ATP produced from the electron transport chain and the citric acid cycle?

Answers
1. 2 ATP   **2.** 5 cycles
3. 5 cycles produce 5 NADH and 5 $FADH_2$ **4.** 6 acetyl CoA
5. 5 NADH $\times$ 3 ATP = 15 ATP; 5 $FADH_2$ $\times$ 2 ATP = 10 ATP;
        6 acetyl CoA $\times$ 12 ATP = 72 = ATP;
                total ATP = 15 ATP + 10 ATP + 72 ATP $-$ 2 ATP (for activation) = 95 ATP

24.4 Ketogenesis and Ketone Bodies

- When the oxidation of large amounts of fatty acids cause high levels of acetyl CoA, the acetyl CoA undergo ketogenesis.
- Two molecules of acetyl CoA form acetoacetyl CoA, which is converted to acetoacetate, β-hydroxybutyrate, and acetone.

◆ Learning Exercise 24.4

Match each of the following terms with the correct description:
a. ketone bodies   **b.** ketogenesis   **c.** ketosis
d. liver   **e.** acidosis

1. ____ high levels of ketone bodies in the blood

2. ____ a metabolic pathway that produces ketone bodies

3. ____ β-hydroxybutyrate, acetoacetate, and acetone

4. ____ the condition whereby ketone bodies lower the blood pH below 7.4

5. ____ site where ketone bodies form

Answers   **1.** c   **2.** b   **3.** a   **4.** e   **5.** d

24.5 Fatty Acid Synthesis

- When there is an excess of acetyl CoA in the cell, the two-carbon units link together to synthesize fatty acids that are stored in the adipose tissue.
- Two-carbon acetyl CoA units link together to give palmitic (C_{16}) acid and other fatty acids.

◆ **Learning Exercise 24.5**

Indicate if each of the following is characteristic of lipogenesis (L) or β-oxidation (O).

1. _____ occurs in the matrix of mitochondria   2. _____ occurs in the cytosol of mitochondria

3. _____ activated by insulin   4. _____ activated by glucagon

5. _____ starts with fatty acids   6. _____ starts with acetyl CoA units

7. _____ produces fatty acids   8. _____ produces acetyl CoA units

9. _____ requires NADPH coenzyme   10. _____ requires FAD and NAD$^+$ coenzymes

11. _____ activated with CoA   12. _____ activated by ACP

Answers   1. O   2. L   3. L   4. O
              5. O   6. L   7. L   8. O
              9. L   10. O   11. O   12. L

24.6 Digestion of Proteins

- Proteins begin digestion in the stomach, where HCl denatures proteins and activates peptidases that hydrolyze peptide bonds.
- In the small intestine, trypsin and chymotrypsin complete the hydrolysis of peptides to amino acids.

◆ **Learning Exercise 24.6**

Match each of the following terms with the correct description:
a. nitrogen-containing compounds   **b.** protein turnover   **c.** stomach
d. nitrogen balance   **e.** small intestine

1. _____ HCl activates enzymes that hydrolyzes peptide bonds in proteins

2. _____ trypsin and chymotrypsin convert peptides to amino acids

3. _____ include amino acids, amino alcohols, protein hormones, and nucleic acids

4. _____ the process of synthesizing protein and breaking them down

5. _____ the amount of protein hydrolyzed is equal to the amount of protein used in the body

Answers   1. c   2. e   3. a   4. b   5. d

24.7 Degradation of Amino Acids

- Amino acids are normally used for protein synthesis.
- Amino acids are degraded by transferring an amino group from an amino acid to an α-keto acid to yield a different amino acid and α-keto acid.
- In oxidative deamination, the amino group in glutamate is removed as an ammonium ion, NH_4^+.

◆ **Learning Exercise 24.7A**

Match each of the following descriptions with transamination (T) or oxidative deamination (D):

1. _____ produces an ammonium ion, NH_4^+

2. _____ transfers an amino group to an α-keto acid

3. _____ usually involves the degradation of glutamate

4. _____ requires NAD^+ or $NADP^+$

5. _____ produces another amino acid and α-keto acid

6. _____ usually produces α-ketoglutarate

Answers   **1.** D   **2.** T   **3.** D
             4. T   **5.** T   **6.** D

◆ **Learning Exercise 24.7B**

1. Write an equation for the transamination reaction of serine and oxaloacetate.

2. Write an equation for the oxidation deamination of glutamate.

Answers

1. $$HO-CH_2-\underset{\underset{NH_3^+}{|}}{CH}-COO^- + {}^-OOC-\underset{\overset{O}{\|}}{C}-CH_2-COO^- \longrightarrow$$

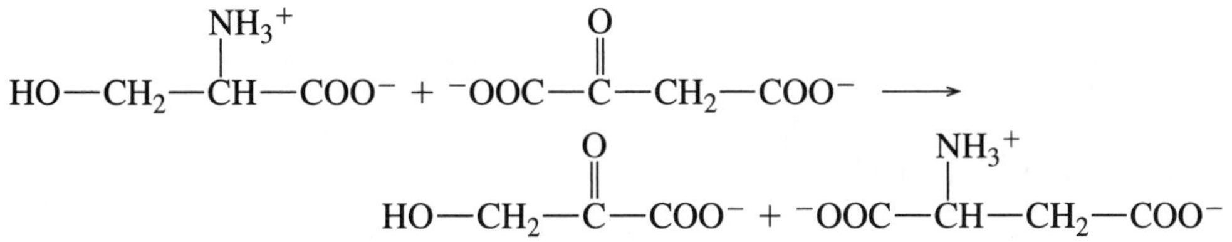

$$HO-CH_2-\underset{\overset{O}{\|}}{C}-COO^- + {}^-OOC-\underset{\underset{NH_3^+}{|}}{CH}-CH_2-COO^-$$

2. $${}^-OOC-\underset{\underset{NH_3^+}{|}}{CH}-CH_2-CH_2-COO^- + NAD^+ \text{ (or } NADP^+\text{)} + H_2O \longrightarrow$$

$${}^-OOC-\underset{\overset{O}{\|}}{C}-CH_2-CH_2-COO^- + NH_4^+ + NADH \text{ (or NADPH)} + H^+$$

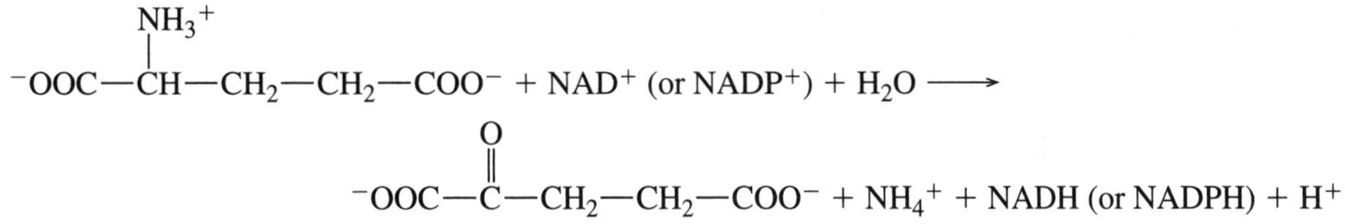

24.8 Urea Cycle

- The ammonium ion, NH_4^+, from amino acid degradation is toxic if allowed to accumulate.
- The urea cycle converts ammonium ion to urea, which forms urine in the kidneys.

◆ **Learning Exercise 24.8**

Arrange the following reactions in the order they occur in the urea cycle:
  a. argininosuccinate is split to yield arginine and fumarate
  b. aspartate condenses with citrulline to yield argininosuccinate
  c. arginine is hydrolyzed to yield urea and regenerates ornithine
  d. ornithine combines with the carbamoyl group from carbamoyl phosphate

Answers   **1.** d   **2.** b   **3.** a   **4.** c

24.9 Fates of the Carbon Atoms from Amino Acids

• α-Keto acids resulting from transamination can be used as intermediates in the citric acid cycle or in the synthesis of lipids or glucose or oxidized for energy.

◆ **Learning Exercise 24.9**

Match each of the following terms with the correct description:
a. glucogenic   **b.** ketogenic   **c.** oxaloacetate
d. acetyl CoA   **e.** α-ketoglutarate   **f.** pyruvate

  1. _____ amino acids that generate pyruvate or oxaloacetate, which can be used to synthesize glucose

  2. _____ keto acid obtained from carbon atom of alanine and serine

  3. _____ keto acid obtained from carbon atom of glutamine and glutamate

  4. _____ keto acid obtained from carbon atoms from aspartate and asparagine

  5. _____ amino acids that generate compounds that can produce ketone bodies

  6. _____ compound obtained from carbon atoms of leucine and tryptophan

Answers   **1.** a   **2.** f   **3.** e   **4.** c   **5.** b   **6.** d

24.10 Synthesis of Amino Acids

• Humans synthesize only 10 amino acids. The other 10, called essential amino acids, must be obtained from the diet.

◆ **Learning Exercise 24.10**

Match each of the following terms with the correct description:
  a. essential amino acids   **b.** nonessential amino acids
  c. transamination   **d.** phenylketonuria (PKU)

  1. _____ amino acids synthesized in humans

  2. _____ a genetic condition when phenylalanine is not converted to tyrosine

  3. _____ amino acids that must be supplied by the diet

  4. _____ reaction that produces some nonessential amino acids

Answers   **1.** b   **2.** d   **3.** a   **4.** c

Checklist for Chapter 24

You are ready to take the practice test for chapter 24. Be sure that you have accomplished the following learning goals for this chapter. If you are not sure, review the section listed at the end of the goal. Then apply your new skills and understanding to the practice test.

After studying chapter 24, I can successfully:

_____ Describe the sites, enzymes, and products for the digestion of triacylglycerols (24.1).

_____ Describe the oxidation of fatty acids via β-oxidation (24.2).

_____ Calculate the ATP produced by the complete oxidation of a fatty acid (24.3).

_____ Explain ketogenesis and the conditions in the cell that form ketone bodies (24.4).

_____ Describe the biosynthesis of fatty acids from acetyl CoA (24.5).

_____ Describe the sites, enzymes, and products of the digestion of dietary proteins (24.6).

_____ Explain the role of transamination and oxidative deamination in degrading amino acids (24.7).

_____ Describe the formation of urea from ammonium ion (24.8).

_____ Explain how carbon atoms from amino acids are prepared to enter the citric acid cycle or other pathways (24.9).

_____ Show how nonessential amino acids are synthesized from substances used in the citric acid cycle and other pathways (24.10).

Practice Test for Chapter 24

1. The digestion of triacylglycerols takes place in the _____ by enzymes called _____.
 A. small intestine; peptidases **B.** stomach; lipases **C.** stomach; peptidases
 D. small intestine; lipases **E.** all of these

2. The products of the digestion of triacylglycerols are
 A. fatty acids **B.** monoacylglycerols **C.** glycerol
 D. diacylglycerols **E.** all of these

3. The function of the bile salts in the digestion of fats is
 A. emulsification **B.** hydration **C.** dehydration
 D. oxidation **E.** reduction

4. Chylomicrons formed in the intestinal lining
 A. are lipoproteins
 B. are triacylglycerols coated with proteins
 C. transport fats into the lymph system and blood stream
 D. carry triacylglycerols to the cells of the heart, muscle, and adipose tissues
 E. all of these

5. Glycerol obtained from the hydrolysis enters glycolysis when converted to
 A. glucose **B.** fatty acids **C.** dihydroxyacetone phosphate
 D. pyruvate **E.** glycerol-3-phosphate

6. Fatty acids are prepared for β-oxidation by forming
 A. carnitine **B.** fatty acyl carnitine **C.** acetyl CoA
 D. fatty acyl CoA **E.** pyruvate

7. The reactions in the β-oxidation cycle do *not* involve
 A. reduction **B.** hydration **C.** dehydrogenation
 D. oxidation **E.** cleavage of acetyl CoA

Consider the β-oxidation of palmitic (C_{16}) acid for questions 8-11.

8. The number of β-oxidation cycles required for palmitic (C_{16}) acid is
    A. 16   **B.** 9   **C.** 8   **D.** 7   **E.** 6

9. The number of acetyl CoA groups produced by the β-oxidation of palmitic (C_{16}) acid is
    A. 16   **B.** 9   **C.** 8   **D.** 7   **E.** 6

10. The number of NADH and $FADH_2$ produced by the β-oxidation of palmitic (C_{16}) acid is
    A. 16   **B.** 9   **C.** 8   **D.** 7   **E.** 6

11. The total ATP produced by the β-oxidation of palmitic (C_{16}) acid is
    A. 96   **B.** 129   **C.** 131   **D.** 134   **E.** 136

12. The oxidation of large amounts of fatty acids can produce
    A. ketone bodies   **B.** glucose   **C.** low pH level in the blood
    D. acetone   **E.** pyruvate

13. The metabolic pathway of lipogenesis requires
    A. fatty acids   **B.** acetyl CoA   **C.** FAD and NAD^+
    D. glucagon   **E.** ketone bodies

14. The digestion of proteins takes place in the _____ by enzymes called _____.
    A. small intestine; peptidases   **B.** stomach; lipases   **C.** stomach; peptidases
    D. small intestine; lipases   **E.** stomach and small intestine; proteases and peptidases

15. The process of transamination
    A. is part of the citric acid cycle   **B.** converts α-amino acids to β-keto acids
    C. produces new amino acids   **D.** is not used in the metabolism of amino acids
    E. is part of the β-oxidation of fats

16. The oxidative deamination of glutamate produces
    A. a new amino acid   **B.** a new α-keto acid
    C. ammonia, NH_3 **D.** ammonium ion, NH_4^+
    E. urea

17. The purpose of the urea cycle in the liver is to
    A. synthesize urea
    B. convert urea to ammonium ion, NH_4^+
    C. convert ammonium ion NH_4^+ to urea
    D. synthesize new amino acids
    E. take part in the β-oxidation of fats

18. The urea cycle begins with the conversion of NH_4^+ to
    A. aspartate   **B.** carbamoyl phosphate
    C. citrulline   **D.** argininosuccinate
    E. urea

19. The carbon atoms from a ketogenic amino acid can be used to
    A. synthesize ketone bodies   **B.** convert urea to ammonium ion, NH_4^+
    C. synthesize fatty acids   **D.** produce energy
    E. synthesize proteins

20. The carbon atoms from various amino acids can be used in several ways, such as
    A. intermediates of the citric acid cycle   **B.** formation of pyruvate
    C. synthesis of glucose   **D.** formation of ketone bodies
    E. all of these

21. Essential amino acids
    A. are not synthesized by humans   **B.** are required in the diet
    C. are excreted if in excess   **D.** include leucine, lysine, and valine
    E. all of these

22. When the quantity of amino acids in the diet exceeds the needs of the cells, the excess amino acids
    A. are stored for use at a later time   **B.** are used to synthesize glycogen
    C. excreted   **D.** are converted to fat
    E. are used to make more protein

23. Phenylketonuria is a condition
    A. abbreviated as PKU   **B.** where a person does not synthesize tyrosine
    C. that can be detected at birth   **D.** that causes severe mental retardation
    E. all of these

Answers to the Practice Test

1. D	**2.** E	**3.** A	**4.** E	**5.** C
6. D	**7.** A	**8.** D	**9.** C	**10.** D
11. B	**12.** A	**13.** A	**14.** E	**15.** C
16. D	**17.** C	**18.** B	**19.** A	**20.** E
21. E	**22.** C	**23.** E		

Answers and Solutions to Selected Text Problems

24.1 The bile salts emulsify fat to give small fat globules for lipase hydrolysis.

24.3 Fats are mobilized when blood glucose and glycogen stores are depleted.

24.5 Glycerol is converted to glycerol-3-phosphate and then to dihydroxyacetone phosphate, which is an intermediate of glycolysis.

24.7 Fatty acids are activated in the cytosol of the mitochondria.

24.9 The coenzymes FAD, NAD^+, and HS-CoA are required for β-oxidation.

24.11 The designation β carbon is based on the common names of carboxylic acids, where the α carbon and the β carbons are adjacent to the carboxyl group.

    a. $CH_3-CH_2-CH_2-CH_2-CH_2-\overset{\beta}{C}H_2-CH_2-\overset{\overset{\displaystyle O}{\|}}{C}-S-CoA$

    b. $CH_3-(CH_2)_{14}-\overset{\beta}{C}H_2-CH_2-\overset{\overset{\displaystyle O}{\|}}{C}-S-CoA$

    c. $CH_3-CH_2-CH=CH-CH_2-CH_2-CH_2-\overset{\beta}{C}H_2-CH_2-\overset{\overset{\displaystyle O}{\|}}{C}-S-CoA$

24.13 **a., b.** $CH_3-(CH_2)_6-\underset{\beta}{C}H_2-\underset{\alpha}{C}H_2-\overset{\overset{\displaystyle O}{\|}}{C}-S-CoA$

    c. $CH_3-(CH_2)_8-\overset{\overset{\displaystyle O}{\|}}{C}-S-CoA + NAD^+ + FAD + H_2O + SH-CoA \longrightarrow$

        $CH_3-(CH_2)_6-\overset{\overset{\displaystyle O}{\|}}{C}-S-CoA + CH_2-\overset{\overset{\displaystyle O}{\|}}{C}-S-CoA + NADH + H^+ FADH_2$

    d. $CH_3-(CH_2)_8-COOH + 4 HS\text{-}CoA + 4FAD + 4NAD^+ + 4H_2O \rightarrow$
                                      5 acetyl CoA + $4FADH_2$ + 4NADH + $4H^+$

24.15 The hydrolysis of ATP to AMP hydrolyzes ATP to ADP and ADP to AMP, which provides the same amount of energy as the hydrolysis of 2 ATP to 2 ADP.

24.17 **a.** The β-oxidation of a chain of 10 carbon atoms produces 5 acetyl CoA units.
 b. A C_{10} fatty acid will go through four β-oxidation cycles.
 c. 60 ATP from 5 acetyl CoA (citric acid cycle) + 12 ATP from 4 NADH + 8 ATP from 4 $FADH_2$ − 2 ATP (activation) = 80 − 2 = 78 ATP

24.19 Ketogenesis is the synthesis of ketone bodies from excess acetyl CoA from fatty acid oxidation, which occurs when glucose is not available for energy. This occurs in starvation, fasting, low-carbohydrate diets, and diabetes.

24.21 Acetoacetate undergoes reduction using NADH + H^+ to yield β-hydroxybutyrate.

24.23 High levels of ketone bodies lead to ketosis, a condition characterized by acidosis (a drop in blood pH values), by excessive urination, and by strong thirst.

24.25 Fatty acid synthesis takes place in the cytosol of cells in liver and adipose tissue.

24.27 Fatty acid synthesis starts when acetyl CoA, HCO_3^-, and ATP produce malonyl CoA.

24.29 **a.** (3) Malonyl CoA transacylase converts malonyl CoA to malonyl ACP.
 b. (1) Acetyl CoA carboxylase combines acetyl CoA with bicarbonate to yield malonyl CoA.
 c. (2) Acetyl CoA transacylase converts acetyl CoA to acetyl ACP.

24.31 Capric acid is a fatty acid with 10 carbon atoms, $C_{10}H_{20}O_2$. How are each of the following involved in the synthesis of a molecule of capric acid?
 a. A C_{10} fatty acid requires the formation of 4 malonyl ACP, which uses 4 HCO_3^-.
 b. 4 ATP are required to produce 4 malonyl CoA.
 c. 5 acetyl CoA are needed to make 1 acetyl ACP and 4 malonyl ACP.
 d. A C_{10} fatty acid requires 4 malonyl ACP and 1 acetyl ACP.
 e. A C_{10} fatty acid chain requires 4 cycles with 2 NADPH per cycle or a total of 8 NADPH.
 f. The four cycles remove a total of 4 CO_2.

24.33 The digestion of proteins begins in the stomach and is completed in the small intestine.

24.35 Nitrogen-containing compounds in the cells include hormones, heme, purines, and pyrimidines for nucleotides, proteins, nonessential amino acids, amino alcohols, and neurotransmitters.

24.37 The reactants are an amino acid and an α-keto acid, and the products are a new amino acid and a new α-keto acid.

24.39 In transamination, an amino group replaces a keto group in the corresponding α-keto acid.

a. $H-\overset{\overset{\displaystyle O}{\|}}{C}-COO^-$ **b.** $CH_3-\overset{\overset{\displaystyle O}{\|}}{C}-COO^-$ **c.** $CH_3-\overset{\overset{\displaystyle CH_3}{|}}{CH}-\overset{\overset{\displaystyle O}{\|}}{C}-COO^-$

24.41 In an oxidative deamination, the amino group in an amino acid such as glutamate is removed as an ammonium ion. The reaction requires NAD^+ or $NADP^+$.

$$^-OOC-\overset{\overset{\displaystyle \overset{+}{N}H_3}{|}}{CH}-CH_2-CH_2-COO^- + H_2O + NAD^+ (NADP^+) \xrightarrow{\text{glutamate dehydrogenase}}$$

glutamate

$$^-OOC-\overset{\overset{\displaystyle O}{\|}}{C}-CH_2-CH_2-COO^- + NH_4^+ + NADH (NADPH) + H^+$$

α-ketoglutarate

24.43 NH_4^+ is toxic if allowed to accumulate in the liver.

24.45 $$H_2N-\overset{\overset{\displaystyle O}{\|}}{C}-NH_2$$

24.47 The carbon atom in urea is obtained from the CO_2 produced by the citric acid cycle.

24.49 Glucogenic amino acids can be used to produce intermediates for glucogenesis, which is glucose synthesis.

24.51 **a.** The three-carbon atom structure of alanine is converted to pyruvate.
b. The four-carbon structure of aspartate is converted to fumarate or oxaloacetate.
c. Valine is converted to succinyl CoA.
d. The five-carbon structure from glutamine can be converted to α-ketoglutarate.

24.53 Humans can synthesize only nonessential amino acids.

24.55 Glutamine synthetase catalyzes the addition of an amino group to glutamate using energy from the hydrolysis of ATP.

24.57 **phenylketonurnia**

24.59 Lauric acid, $CH_3-(CH_2)_{10}-COOH$, is a C_{12} fatty acid. $(C_{12}H_{24}O_2)$

a., b. $$CH_3-(CH_2)_8-\underset{\beta}{CH_2}-\underset{\alpha}{CH_2}-\overset{\overset{\displaystyle O}{\|}}{C}-S-CoA$$

c. lauryl-CoA + 5 CoA + 5 FAD + 5 NAD^+ + 5 $H_2O \rightarrow$
$\qquad\qquad\qquad\qquad\qquad$ 6 acetyl CoA + 5 $FADH_2$ + 5 NADH + $5H^+$
d. Six acetyl CoA units are produced.
e. Five cycles of β oxidation are needed.
f.

activation	$\rightarrow$ -2 ATP
6 acetyl CoA $\times$ 12 ATP/1 acetyl CoA	$\rightarrow$ 72 ATP
5 $FADH_2$ $\times$ 2 ATP/1 $FADH_2$	$\rightarrow$ 10 ATP
5 NADH $\times$ 3 ATP/1 NADH	$\rightarrow$ 15 ATP
Total	95 ATP

24.61 Triacylglycerols are hydrolyzed to monoacylglycerols and fatty acids in the small intestine, which are reformed into triacylglycerols in the intestinal lining for transport as lipoproteins to the tissues.

24.63 Fats can be stored in unlimited amounts in adipose tissue compared with the limited storage of carbohydrates as glycogen.

24.65 The fatty acids cannot diffuse across the blood-brain barrier.

24.67 **a.** Glycerol is converted to glycerol-3-phosphate and to dihydroxyacetone phosphate, which can enter glycolysis or gluconeogenesis.
b. Activation of fatty acids occurs on the outer mitochondrial membrane.
c. The energy cost is equal to 2 ATP.
d. Only fatty acyl CoA can move into the intermembrane space for transport by carnitine into the matrix.

24.69 **a.** β oxidation **b.** β oxidation
c. fatty acid synthesis **d.** β oxidation
e. fatty acid synthesis **f.** fatty acid synthesis

24.71 **a.** (1) fatty acid oxidation **b.** (2) the synthesis of fatty acids

24.73 Ammonium ion is toxic if allowed to accumulate in the liver.

24.75 **a.** citrulline **b.** carbamoyl phosphate

24.77 **a.** The carbon atom structure of valine is converted to pyruvate.
b. Lysine, a ketogenic amino acid, is converted to acetoacetyl CoA.
c. The degradation of methionine produces succinyl-CoA.
d. Glutamate can be converted to five-carbon α-ketoglutarate.

24.79 Serine is degraded to pyruvate, which is oxidized to acetyl CoA. The oxidation produces NADH + H^+, which provides 3 ATP. In one turn of the citric acid cycle, the acetyl CoA provides 12 ATP. Thus, serine can provide a total of 15 ATP.

24.81 **a.** 14 kg fat × 1000 g/kg × 0.49 moles ATP/g fat = 6900 moles ATP

b. 6900 moles ATP × $\dfrac{7.3 \text{ kcal}}{1 \text{ mole ATP}}$ = 5.0 × 10^4 kcal

24.83 **a.**

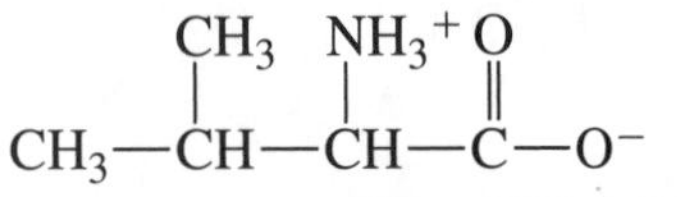

$$CH_3-\overset{\overset{\displaystyle CH_3}{|}}{CH}-\overset{\overset{\displaystyle NH_3^+}{|}}{CH}-\overset{\overset{\displaystyle O}{\|}}{C}-O^-$$ valine

b.

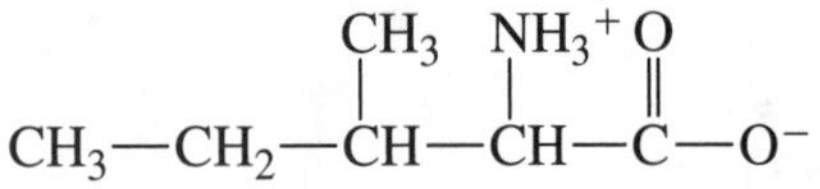

$$CH_3-CH_2-\overset{\overset{\displaystyle CH_3}{|}}{CH}-\overset{\overset{\displaystyle NH_3^+}{|}}{CH}-\overset{\overset{\displaystyle O}{\|}}{C}-O^-$$ isoleucine

c.

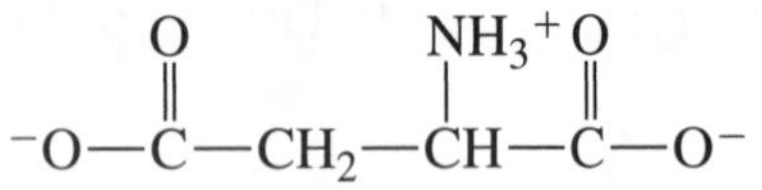

$$^-O-\overset{\overset{\displaystyle O}{\|}}{C}-CH_2-\overset{\overset{\displaystyle NH_3^+}{|}}{CH}-\overset{\overset{\displaystyle O}{\|}}{C}-O^-$$ aspartic acid